The Geological Society of America

Memoir 71

UPPER CRETACEOUS
OF THE
PACIFIC COAST

BY

F. M. ANDERSON

June 6, 1958

Made in United States of America

PRINTED BY WILLIAM BYRD PRESS, INC.

RICHMOND, VIRGINIA

PUBLISHED BY THE GEOLOGICAL SOCIETY OF AMERICA

ADDRESS ALL COMMUNICATIONS TO

THE GEOLOGICAL SOCIETY OF AMERICA
419 WEST 117 STREET, NEW YORK 27, N. Y.

The Memoir Series

of

The Geological Society of America

made possible

through the bequest of

Richard Alexander Fullerton Penrose, Jr.

EDITORIAL PREFACE

This paper, in one sense at least, is the culmination of the first and the last efforts of F. M. Anderson in the fields of geology and paleontology. Born and raised in the Rogue River Valley of southern Oregon in the midst of numerous exposures of marine Upper Cretaceous rocks, he was early attracted to ammonites and other fossils. His first published paper, "Some Cretaceous beds of Rogue River Valley, Oregon" (Jour. Geol., vol. 3, p. 455–468, 1895), was on the geology of that region. During much of his professional career, geological assignments and duties led him away from his early interests, but during the latter years of his life he returned to the study of the Upper Mesozoic of California and Oregon. The present paper is the result of his study and observation on the Upper Cretaceous of this region. At his insistence, as if by premonition, the manuscript was mailed to the Geological Society of America by his wife one evening in September 1945; that night his last illness began.

The manuscript as received by the Geological Society of America was not fully collated or complete. Having expressed an interest in the paper, I was asked if I would undertake the final preparation of it for the editors. Most of the actual work of editing and co-ordinating the manuscript was carried out by Mahlon V. Kirk under my direction. Additionally, Dr. L. G. Hertlein has greatly aided in the task. Dr. Robert M. Kleinpell has also advised on many of the editorial problems.

The editorial work undertaken has included: collation of various parts of the manuscript; deletion of certain *nomina nuda;* correction of parts of the stratigraphic nomenclature to agree with published data; and deletion of certain new stratigraphic names that were not adequately described or proposed. The balance of the paper is essentially as completed by Dr. Anderson; no new data have been added to it.

J. WYATT DURHAM

Museum of Paleontology, University
of California, Berkeley, California
April 17, 1950.

ACKNOWLEDGMENTS

First it is important to record the interest and co-operative spirit shown by the many friends and students of geology who have contributed to the final results of this study. The author desires to express here his indebtedness to the various institutions, operating oil companies, active geologists and many individuals who have given time, labor, funds and needed materials for the work; to The Geological Society of America for needed grants of money, and for encouragement and advice; to the California Academy of Sciences for storage, use of its library and many other facilities, and for the cooperation of its personnel; to the University of California, to Leland Stanford Junior University, the universities of Oregon and Washington, the California Institute of Technology, to the geological departments of each, and to their personnel, the author is greatly indebted.

CONTENTS

ILLUSTRATIONS

PLATES

FIGURES

Figure

TABLES

Table

ABSTRACT

Rocks of Late Cretaceous age occur on the Pacific Coast of North America from Baja California, Mexico, to the Queen Charlotte Islands of British Columbia. The standard term Upper Cretaceous series is adopted for these deposits instead of the often widely and variously misused term Chico series (or "group" or "formation"), and Chico is applied only to those sediments on the east side of the Sacramento valley from whose occurrence on Chico Creek the term was derived. The series is best represented in the Sacramento and San Joaquin valleys of California where rocks of Cenomanian to Maestrichtian ages are recognized and thicknesses of as much as 28,000 feet have been reported. South of the Transverse Ranges of California only post-Cenomanian ages are represented, and over much of the area only Campanian-Maestrichtian. The Oregon-Washington-British Columbia sequences are similar in age to those of Baja California, but the Campanian-Maestrichtian is comparatively restricted in distribution. In neither the northern nor southern areas are the thicknesses comparable to those of the central area, but the sediments in all three consist primarily of sandstones, shales, and conglomerates, with limestone present only as concretions or local lenses.

Throughout the Pacific Coast region the Upper Cretaceous appears to rest unconformably on various Lower Cretaceous or older rocks. The series is subdivided into the lower Pacheco group and the overlying Asuncion group, in many places separated by an unconformity. Subdivisions of these groups, and particularly the upper, are recognized over wide areas.

Five hundred and four species of invertebrates are recorded. These include: 1 coral; 2 (1 new) crinoids (2 genera); 7 (2 new) echinoid species (4 genera); 7 brachiopod species (5 genera); 151 (45 new) pelecypod species (45 genera); 109 (28 new) gastropod species (40 genera); 223 (118 new) ammonite species (53 genera); 3 (2 new) nautiloid species (one genus); and 1 belemnite. The occurrence of 2 mosasaurs, 1 tylosaur, and 2 dinosaurs is also recorded.

The following new genera and subgenera are proposed: Crinoidea, *Pachecocrinus;* Ammonidea, *Neocyrtochilus, Exicrioceras, Neokotôceras, Joaquinites, Oregoniceras, Butticeras,* and *Eocanadoceras* (subgenus).

INTRODUCTION
RECORD OF SEDIMENTATION

The major published accounts of the Upper Cretaceous series in the Joaquin embayment have essentially ended with that of the U. S. Geological Survey (Anderson and Pack, 1915). These authors placed all strata of the Upper Cretaceous in the "Chico Group," divided into the "Panoche" and the "Moreno" formations, which they tentatively defined. The formal description of the "Moreno" formation (p. 46) limits this unit to an average thickness of 2000 feet. The remainder of the "Group" was termed the "Panoche formation," for its prominence in the Panoche Hills, western Fresno County. The upper division as thus limited is very useful in the present discussions, but the larger division is subject to stratigraphic analysis and revision in important respects. In the Joaquin embayment, the Upper Cretaceous deposits range in age from Cenomanian to Upper Maestrichtian, including the "Moreno" at the top.

The entire Upper Cretaceous succession consists of detritus brought into the embayment by streams arising in the mountains of Salinia and includes the usual sedimentary types carried by streams whose gradients vary greatly at geologic intervals because of diastrophic events. These events have been accompanied by positive movements on land surfaces, owing to denudation and to subsidences in areas of sedimentation due to accumulating load.

In addition to the broader and more continuous belts of sandy shales and sandstones in the Upper Cretaceous series on the west border of the Joaquin embayment, there are thick and sometimes extensive belts of boulder conglomerates. These provide data about various aspects of the series, including the direction from which the materials came, the extent of their source areas, the gradients of the streams that carried them, the character of the terrains from which the sediments were derived, and even the volumes of the transporting streams themselves. In some areas, these conglomerates carry marine shells. The conglomerates occur near or at the base of the series as well as at intervals through it; they aggregate about 3000 feet. Not all the lenses of conglomerate have equal importance in the sedimentary column, though certain of them occur in such alignment and continuity in the general strike of the beds as to arouse greater interest and attention.

The fact that the Upper Cretaceous sediments in the Joaquin embayment came from the west fixes their source as within the area of Salinia which, in post-Upper Cretaceous times, suffered greatly from thrusts and later tectonic movements. This foreland has lost much in area and in altitude, and it seems probable that a major part is now beneath the sea. If we regard Salinia during Upper Cretaceous times as comparable in area to Klamathonia, as it appears to have been, it evidently suffered a greater loss in both area and altitude than the latter. This would be in accord with the relative instability of the area in modern times, as compared to Klamathonia. This is also testified to by the highly folded Tertiary strata in its environs. The reversal of the modern drainage direction from that which had brought these sediments into the Joaquin embayment,

3

differs in no essential respect from that described for the Shasta series in the Sacramento embayment.

In the northern foothills of Mount Hamilton, the San Leandro and Berkeley hills, and farther north, traces of a western land area are seen. That this site formed part of a land area during later Cretaceous time, is shown by the present attitude of the Cretaceous deposits in these hills. That the western limits of this land area were probably west of the longitude of the Farallone Islands is indicated by the submarine topography of the region, and by the geologic relations of these islands to neighboring coastal points.

East of the present bay, two somewhat parallel belts of Upper Cretaceous sediments of considerable extent are well known. The older, on the north and east flanks of Mount Diablo, contains strata of early, middle, and later Upper Cretaceous age dipping steeply to the east and northeast. Between these belts is situated the Tertiary "synclinorium" mentioned by Lawson (1914). For these Upper Cretaceous sediments no adequate source areas have been shown, although it may be assumed that all their materials came from the west, as did those in the major embayments to the north and to the south. Only land areas now submerged, lying west of the present coastline, could have been large enough to supply the sediments of the Upper Cretaceous in this region.

Most of the Upper Cretaceous strata in these belts stand at a high angle (40°–80°), dipping northeast, as the result of post-Upper Cretaceous thrusting which greatly shortened the transverse sections of the land areas of Upper Cretaceous times, and developed many local tectonic features.

During Late Cretaceous time the Great Valley trough was land-locked at the north and isolated from any northern extensions of the "Pacific Geosyncline." The closure of the trough at the north in the region of Pitt River was shown by the writer (1938b), and evidence of a direct connection between the Great Valley of California and any Cretaceous basin to the north is lacking. This has been shown by a study of the Upper Cretaceous faunas as well as those of the older Cretaceous in northern California and southern Oregon. Indirect connections between the Great Valley and that of the Rogue River are indicated in part by analogous molluscan species. Furthermore, the structural conditions in the Great Valley are not continued to the north of it in California or Oregon.

In both embayments of the Great Valley, the highly inclined or folded structures of its west borders are not duplicated on the east, and, although a synclinal condition is seen in a greatly modified form, it is by no means symmetrical. Briefly, the thick strata exposed on the west side of the valley do not appear on the east, and, contrariwise, strata exposed on the east side of the Valley are not found, or are greatly modified on the west. In both embayments the Upper Cretaceous deposits on the west are more than 10 times thicker than those on the east or than those found in deep wells. These stratigraphic contrasts are more strongly marked in the Joaquin embayment than in the Sacramento, though this may be due in part to climatic contrasts in the two regions.

South of the Great Valley there is little or no evidence that the structural conditions found at any place resemble those in the Great Valley, and the Upper

Cretaceous column is nowhere so complete. Only the later part of the Upper Cretaceous (Turonian and younger) has been found south of the Great Valley.

The stratigraphic features and the faunas of the Upper Cretaceous deposits in southern California resemble those found in northernmost California and southern Oregon. This is probably due to similarity in the tectonic records of these regions. The "Pacific Geosyncline" described by Schuchert (1935), if it existed during later Cretaceous time, can hardly have reached these areas. In western Oregon and Washington, the present Willamette and Cowlitz valleys may be assumed to lie within the locus of this "Geosyncline," but in neither of them has erosion cut through the cover of younger sediments.

STRATIGRAPHIC RELATIONSHIPS

On the west border of the Great Valley the Upper Cretaceous is related unconformably to the Shasta series, since it follows a depositional hiatus in late Albian or early Cenomanian time. In some areas the oldest beds of the series rest directly upon pre-Cretaceous terrains. This unconformity is evidenced by the following:

(1) Local differences in strike and dip of the respective strata below and above the line of contact;

(2) The presence of boulder conglomerates at the base of the Upper Cretaceous series, with boulders or blocks containing fossils derived from pre-Upper Cretaceous terrains;

(3) The wide overlapping of older formations by the lower beds of the Upper Cretaceous series in depositional contact;

(4) Important faunal changes in passing from basal beds of the Upper Cretaceous series down to the underlying rocks, Cretaceous or older.

In the Cottonwood district, western Shasta County, near Hulen Creek, the lowest beds of the Upper Cretaceous series, with *Pervinquieria inflata* (Sowerby) and *P. tehamaensis* (Reagan) and other types, mark a probably uppermost Albian horizon, resting directly upon the upper beds of the Shasta series with *Douvilleiceras* aff. *D. mammillatum* (Schlotheim), and other species. Farther south on Dry Creek, northern Tehama County, the basal beds of the Upper Cretaceous series are somewhat later (Lower Cenomanian), with *Turrilites* aff. *T. bergeri* Stoliczka, and *Cyrtochilus stylus* n. sp., and species of *Acanthoceras,* and other Cenomanian types. Near Sites, western Colusa County, a still higher horizon of Cenomanian age with *Mantelliceras* sp., and *Beudanticeras alamoense* n. sp. mark the base of the Upper Cretaceous series, showing a gradual transgression of the Upper Cretaceous beds upon older rocks.

In the Joaquin embayment similar stratigraphic conditions are found, with the lowest beds of the Upper Cretaceous series marked by *Cyrtochilus stylus* n. sp. and *Lyelliceras stanislausense* n. sp., and other Cenomanian types, these beds rest directly upon pre-Cretaceous terrains, including serpentine or other rocks of Franciscan age.

In the Pioneer district west of Phoenix, southern Oregon, similar basal Upper Cretaceous beds containing *Nautilus charlottensis* Whiteaves, *Beudanticeras* aff. *B. breweri* Gabb, *Brancoceras parvum* (Anderson) occur at "Dark Hollow." In the Illinois Valley, Josephine County, and east of Riddle, Douglas County, beds of lower Upper Cretaceous age are found resting directly upon basement rocks (peridotites, greenstones and shales), and contain diagnostic invertebrate fossils. These facts show widespread diastrophism, regional subsidence, and marine transgression into intermontane valleys in northern California and southern Oregon during early Upper Cretaceous times. The occurrence of some of these species on the Queen Charlotte Islands is recorded by Whiteaves (1876, p. 14–22; 1900, p. 269, 273, 284). These wide regional overlaps near the beginning of Cenomanian time in California, Oregon, British Columbia and the Queen Charlotte Islands are an important feature of West Coast geologic history.

In brief, evidence of unconformity between the Upper Cretaceous series and the Shasta are clearly seen throughout the Great Valley. On the west border of the San Joaquin Valley, in the Pacheco Pass quadrangle, the basal relations of the Upper Cretaceous series are shown in thick beds of boulder conglomerates which are readily traced for many miles. These beds rest directly upon pre-Cretaceous terrains. Although continuity of these conditions in the Sacramento Valley is not traceable on the surface; it can be proved by wholly satisfactory paleontologic evidence. Invertebrate fossils that mark this unconformity on Dry Creek, northern Tehama County, have been found in the basal conglomerates resting upon peridotites and metamorphic rocks by McCoy, Bennison and the author on an upper branch of Garzas Creek, at Loc. 29,096 (California Academy of Sciences), where specimens of *Lyelliceras* sp., and of *Cyrtochilus* aff. *C. stylus* n. sp. occur.

The following representative localities affording similar evidence are from the records of the California Academy of Sciences:

Locality 27,812 (C. A. S.) on Hospital Creek, by Taff, Hanna, and Cross, from which examples of *Sonneratia* sp. were collected from the lowest beds of the Upper Cretaceous series.

Locality 31,127 (C. A. S.) on Ingram Creek, Stanislaus County, where McCoy and the writer collected examples of *Syncyclonema* and *Parapuzosia* from a basal conglomerate of the Upper Cretaceous series, resting upon older beds of the Shasta series.

South of the Great Valley few, if any, exposures of the older part (Cenomanian) of the Upper Cretaceous are known. In the San Rafael and Santa Ynez mountains, lower Upper Cretaceous beds have not been recognized, and may not be present. In Orange County, on the west flank of the Santa Ana Mountains, older Upper Cretaceous deposits have been recognized by Fairbanks, Anderson, Packard, Popenoe, and others, and many fossils have been described from them, although no species yet found indicates an age older than middle Turonian. Farther south, no Cretaceous strata older than Turonian have been recorded within California.

THICKNESS OF THE UPPER CRETACEOUS

In the Great Valley of California, the stratigraphic thickness of the Upper Cretaceous series varies greatly in the major embayments, and in the several sections studied in each embayment.

On the eastern border of the Sacramento Valley the beds are largely hidden by late Tertiary volcanics, and exposures are found only where stream erosion has reached these beds. North of the south Shasta County line some sections expose only lower Upper Cretaceous beds (Pacheco group), as to the north of Oak Run, whereas south of this line only the higher parts of the series (Lower Asuncion) are definitely known. On the northeast border of the Valley, near Frazier Corners, lower Upper Cretaceous beds do not exceed a thickness of 3000 feet; south of the County line, incomplete exposures of later Upper Cretaceous beds nowhere exceed 2500 feet in thickness. As traced southward on the east border of the valley, the outcrops show successively thinner sections as far as the American River, beyond which they are not exposed. The total aggregate thickness of the Upper Cretaceous series on the north and east borders of the valley is probably not more than 5000 feet.

On the west border of the Sacramento Valley, the Upper Cretaceous is largely concealed by late Tertiary volcanics, the Tehama formation, but thicker sections are exposed here than on its east border. On the west, the exposed sections vary in thickness from less than 3000 feet on the North fork of Cottonwood Creek, to 6200 feet on Dry Creek, and 13,000 feet on Cache Creek and on Putah Creek. In the thickest sections of the series north of Fairfield, the lower Upper Cretaceous exhibits only a reduced thickness, whereas the later Upper Cretaceous beds assume a much greater proportion as a result of overlapping and some duplication.

In the vicinity of Mount Diablo the series reaches a thickness of nearly 22,000 feet, although smaller estimates have been made. On the west border of the San Joaquin Valley the series attains its greatest development, where its stratigraphic thickness probably exceeds 28,000 feet. For sections across the sequence south of Hospital Creek, Brewer (1866) gives an estimate for Puerto Creek of 23,700 feet, although the section is not complete. West of the section that was probably embraced in his estimate, are earlier beds of the series, detached from its principal areas. If these beds were added to the latter, the total would greatly exceed this estimate. For Orestimba Creek, Brewer gives the basis for an estimate of 17,300 feet of strata, but here also the section appears to be incomplete.

The thickest sections of the series are found in the Pacheco Pass area, and southward to the Panoche Hills. However, the maximum thickness is not found in any single section, because of disconformities, strike faulting, or both.

If the thickness of its several portions were combined, the total would probably greatly exceed the thickness of any single section. Exact estimates for many sections are difficult to obtain, and have not been attempted. For the district west of Coalinga, between the Los Gatos and Waltham Creeks, Pack and English (1914) sketched a section passing through Sherman Peak; a continuation of this section to the northeast would include higher beds near Los Gatos Creek. Statements made by these writers supports an estimate of 20,000 feet in this area, to which could be added 2000 feet or more. The thickness here is comparable to that on Orestimba Creek and Puerto Creek and at Mount Diablo, and in intervening areas, where estimates have varied from 23,000 feet to near a maximum of 28,000 feet for the Panoche Hills.

The most rapid sedimentation, and the thickest sections are near Los Banos Creek, where the thickest beds of conglomerate and sandstone are found, indicating the entrance of large streams into the basin of deposition. The lack of molluscan remains in these deposits conforms to this view.

Beyond the limits of the Great Valley toward the south, little information is found in the literature as to the thickness of the series and the source areas of its sediments, and no places are known in which complete sections exist. According to Reed (Reed and Hollister, 1936, p. 1636):

> "The Upper Cretaceous is well developed in the San Rafael Mountains . . . and along the North flank of the Santa Ynez Mountains. . . ."

For these areas he gives (Reed and Hollister, 1936, p. 1642) only indirect statements, from which an estimate of 14,000 for the entire section may be made.

For the Upper Cretaceous deposits on the west flank of the Santa Ana Mountains, Popenoe (personal account) has estimated a total thickness of more than 2500 feet, and the maximum according to his published account (1942) is about the same.

For the Upper Cretaceous beds on the flanks of the Santa Monica Mountains, Waring (1917) gives data for the following estimates, possibly conservative: north slope, 8200 feet; south slope, 6000 feet or more. It cannot be assumed, however, that either section is complete, and thicker sections are possible.

In the San Luis quadrangle and to the northwest, Fairbanks (1904) has estimated a thickness of 3000 to 4000 feet for the Atascadero formation.

In northern California and southern Oregon, the beds are covered on their east border by volcanic tuffs, or alluvium, as in the Rogue River Valley. Near the Klamath River, east and west of Henley, an estimated thickness exceeds 4000 feet. South of the river it may be less.

On the south border of Bear Creek on the old Pioneer road west of Phoenix, the equivalent of the Pacheco group have an exposed thickness of 3500 feet, but toward the northeast they are overlain by shales at least 2500 feet thick. The total thickness of the section should be as much as 6200 feet, and maybe more. Toward the northeast these beds are covered by nonmarine formations of great thickness.

In the basin of the John Day River, Upper Cretaceous beds, as shown by Merriam (1901), may have a thickness of 3000 feet to 4000 feet. The fauna of these beds shows them to be correlative with a part of the Pacheco group, but the complete section is not known, and appears to be thicker.

For the "Nanaimo series" of Vancouver Island, C. H. Clapp (1912a), gave a total thickness of 6785 feet.

For the "Queen Charlotte Series," of the Queen Charlotte Islands, MacKenzie (1916, p. 54–62) gives summary figures for its several members, from which an aggregate thickness of 9000 feet may be computed. From the lists of invertebrate species it may be inferred that these beds may be correlated with the Pacheco group, although neither its lowest nor its highest beds appears to be represented. No evidence is known that any beds equivalent to the Lower Asuncion group have been described from these islands, nor have any beds correlative with the "Nanaimo series" been definitely recognized there.

To the Standard Oil Company of California, the Shell Oil Company, and the Texas Company we are indebted for assistance and many courtesies during the progress of this work. Especially to the Tidewater-Associated Oil Company and its geological staff, under the lead of Joseph A. Taff, much is owed for their interest, cooperation, observational notes, carefully kept records of fossil localities, and the use of their collections. Their explorations have extended to all parts of the Great Valley, and to areas outside of it. Their extensive fossil collections, from all parts of the Upper Cretaceous succession, have been donated to the California Academy of Sciences, and have been made available for the present work.

Among the institutions and their personnel to whom credit is due is the State Division of Mines, and to its Chief Geologist, Olaf P. Jenkins, and to the State Mineralogist, W. M. Bradley. Among individuals who have contributed time, labor and materials for the success of the project may be mentioned B. L. Clark and his students, S. W. Müller, A. S. Huey, R. Dana Russell, Chas. V. Averill, Max Birkhauser, Donald Birch, J. M. Kirby, Theo. H. Crook, S. G. Clark, C. C. Church, W. P. Popenoe, H. L. Dobbins, Allan P. Bennison, and Stanley McCoy; and in Oregon, E. L. Packard and his students.

PREVIOUS WORK
PIONEER EXPLORATIONS

The earliest proof of Cretaceous formations in California was given by John B. Trask, first State Geologist (1856b), who described a few invertebrate fossils found in Shasta and Butte counties in the northern part of the Great Valley. He gave no stratigraphic data concerning them or the formation in which they occurred. He seemed content to show that Cretaceous formations existed in this region, a fact then new and important.

The systematic study of the geology, including these and other formations, was begun by the Second State Geological Survey under the direction of J. D. Whitney (1860–1869). The field explorations were placed under the leadership of Wm. H. Brewer, first Assistant to Whitney. This preliminary work was essentially a topographical and geological reconnaissance, and was begun in the Coast Ranges, which offered convenient starting points for a systematic study of the geological constitution and history of the state. There were no maps upon which observational data of any sort could be recorded, and a major interest of Whitney and Brewer was to provide such maps, although other phases of the work were not overlooked. Ores and mineral deposits, geological formations and structures, topography, routes of travel, all came within the scope of essential information. Many fossils, all new, were collected as a basis for historical determinations. Most of the fossils in the areas first traversed were from Cretaceous and Tertiary terrains. Others were obtained from the older Mesozoic and Paleozoic strata outcropping in the northern part of the State.

Cretaceous formations were soon found to cover large areas on the West Coast, extending from the Islands of British Columbia southward into Washington, Oregon and California, and to areas far beyond in Mexico. In many places these were overlain by Tertiary deposits.

The interpretation of the Cretaceous and Tertiary formations and their fossils were given to Wm. M. Gabb, paleontologist of the Survey. At first no stratigraphic data were known upon which the geological succession could be based. Only gradually could the meaning and value of this work become known.

After more than 6 years of exploratory work in the field and in the laboratory, Gabb attempted a formal classification of the Cretaceous deposits of California and Oregon, which he thought might apply to the entire West Coast. The older portion of the Cretaceous succession he termed the "Shasta Group," and except for the later use of the term series, it is still so known. For the later portion of the succession the term "Chico Group" was first proposed and defined by Gabb (1868) in an unpublished paper read before the National Academy of Sciences at Northampton Massachusetts. The Chico Group followed the Shasta, and for its definition Whitney gave full credit to Gabb (1869, p. xiii–xiv). In adopting this definition Whitney states;

"The Chico Group is one of the most extensive and important members of the Pacific Coast Cretaceous. Its exact relations with the formation in Europe have not yet been fully determined, though it is on the horizon of either the Upper or Lower Chalk, and may probably prove to be the equivalent of both. It is extensively represented in Shasta and Butte Counties, and in the foothills of the Sierra Nevada as far south as Folsom, occurring also on the eastern face of the Coast Ranges bordering the Sacramento Valley, at Martinez, and again in Orestimba Canyon, in Stanislaus County. It includes all the known Cretaceous of Oregon, and of the extreme northern portion of California, and is the coal-bearing formation of Vancouver Island."

The chronological span of the "Chico Group" as indicated in this definition shows that Gabb and Whitney had been well advised, although its complete stratigraphic range at bottom and top was not definitely known. As fixed by diastrophic events, not recognized by either Gabb or Whitney, it began somewhat earlier, and closed somewhat later than is indicated in the definition. It opened in late Albian time, and as since shown, it may continue to the close of Danian time. Both diastrophic and faunal data found within the Great Valley, extend the span of the "Chico series" from the unconformity at its base to the final close of the Cretaceous period as known in Europe and in other parts of the world. Its beginning coincided with a widespread subsidence, marked by a broad sedimentary overlap of Upper Cretaceous strata, and by a corresponding abrupt change in the Cretaceous faunal succession, which in the Great Valley of California, as in the "Pacific geosyncline" began in latest Albian time. This subsidence immediately introduced the succession of sedimentation that was correctly thought by Gabb and Whitney to be correlative with the "Lower Chalk" (Cenomanian) of western Europe, although its beginning was slightly earlier in parts of the Great Valley. Thus, the Chico "Series" or " group," as the term has been variously used since its proposal, is synonomous with Upper Cretaceous Series of other regions.

LATER EXPLORATIONS

During the last 4 decades much exploratory work has been done in the Upper Cretaceous areas in the Great Valley and in other parts of California and the West Coast. Not all of the work can be given proper recognition here. Many of the explorations made on the peninsula of Lower California were recorded by Anderson and Hanna (1935) in brief notes.

Whiteaves (1876–1903) has given much information on the exploration of the Canadian West Coast by geologists of the Canadian Geological Survey, notably on Vancouver and neighboring islands, and on Queen Charlotte Islands prior to these dates.

Within California and Oregon, explorations have been carried on by the U. S. Geological Survey and by private geologists, not all of whom have had due recognition. Near the turn of the century H. W. Fairbanks (1896–1903) did much work, notably in areas near San Luis Obispo; some of the results were included in the San Luis Folio (Fairbanks, 1904). The Atascadero formation was described and mapped as belonging to the "Chico Group," though few fossils were mentioned as the basis for this assignment. Stephen Bowers collected many Upper Cretaceous invertebrate fossils in the Santa Monica and Santa Ana Mountains; some were described by Cooper (1894), and others were later collected and are in the Collections of the California Academy of Sciences.

Bruce Martin (1912–1913) visited western Washington and islands in the Strait of Georgia, and collected numerous fossils for the California Academy of Sciences.

C. H. Clapp (1911–1912) reworked the Upper Cretaceous on parts of Vancouver Island, revised the section, giving the name "Nanaimo series" to the succession. He divided it into 10 or more units, having an aggregate thickness of 6785 feet of conglomerates, sandstones, and shales. The basal conglomerates rest directly upon crystalline or other metamorphic rocks. No fossils were mentioned, although many had already been described, showing the series to be Senonian or younger.

The writer (1900–1942) with various assistants made many excursions in California and Oregon, greatly enlarging the existing fossil collections and gathering geologic data. All fossils collected were donated to the California Academy of Sciences.

Work in the prospective oil areas of the Great Valley and of the West Coast was begun for the U. S. Geological Survey by Arnold and Johnson, and later by Arnold and R. Anderson (1907–1910), followed by that of Arnold and Anderson (1909–1910), R. Anderson and R. W. Pack (1914–1915), Pack and English (1914). We are indebted to Anderson and Pack (1915) for a map giving the formational boundaries, the structures, strikes and dips, and for important notes covering the same. The study and analysis of their statements, and of their map data have been of great aid.

Pack and English (1914) described the geologic sequence in the Waltham Creek district, western Fresno County, giving in general the following section:

	Thickness Feet
Upper Cretaceous—conglomerates, sandstones, and shales	4,800
Lower Cretaceous—Paskenta and later	11,400
Upper Jurassic—Knoxville	3,500
Aggregate thickness of strata	19,700

Taliaferro (1941) in his valuable paper on the Central Coast Range of California, proposed the two group names, Pacheco and Asuncion, which are adopted in this paper as subdivisions of the Upper Cretaceous Series of the Great Valley and Coast Ranges areas.

SUBDIVISIONS OF THE PACIFIC COAST
UPPER CRETACEOUS
GENERAL STATEMENT

The marine Upper Cretaceous deposits on the west American coast have been widely known as the Chico series. This name was introduced into California geologic literature as early as 1869 by W. M. Gabb and J. D. Whitney to include the whole of the Upper Cretaceous (upper Albian to Maestrichtian).[1]

A conglomerate of unusual character was first recognized by B. L. Clark and the writer in 1913 in the district south of Livermore, Alameda County, a mile west of the Arroyo del Valle. The bed has a general thickness of 40 to 60 feet and contains large pebbles of quartzite, porphyrite, and various types of ancient rocks not outcropping in the vicinity. With these a large block of sandstone containing early Upper Cretaceous (Turonian) fossils was included. This conglomerate follows the general strike of the beds, and forms the basal part of an overlying sequence of sandy beds that outcrop on the Arroyo del Valle about 4000 feet to the east.

A later collection of fossils from the Isabel Jordan ranch, previously listed in part by Smith (1898, p. 138), proved these exposures to be of lower Senonian age, rather than older, and correlative with other outcrops in the Great Valley and in Siskiyou County.

R. Anderson and R. W. Pack (1915, Pl. IVB) figure a similar but broader exposure of conglomerate crossing Ortigalita Creek, in southwest Merced County. It has a thickness of about 1000 feet and dips to the northeast. J. A. Taff and C. M. Cross recognized its continuity northward to Los Banos Creek and further. Later Allan Bennison discovered on Quinto Creek, in northern Merced County, a large *Peroniceras* in shales immediately overlying beds of conglomerate. These beds rest upon sandy shales that contain the Turonian species *Prionotropis bakeri* Anderson, and other prionotropids.

Further investigation by Bennison and the writer disclosed a clear unconformity traceable along the strike of the beds to Los Banos Creek. This unconformity has since been traced, or otherwise identified throughout the extent of the Upper Cretaceous Series from the Santiago district, Orange County, California, north to the Rogue River Valley, north of Grants Pass, Oregon. It divides the Upper Cretaceous beds into distinct groups of strata much more clearly than was thought possible by the writer in his earlier work (1902a).

The increase in both stratigraphic and faunal data available requires a com-

---

[1] The use of the term "Chico Group" as a formational name began with W. M. Gabb in 1868. As used (1869), the name was intended to cover all Upper Cretaceous strata in California and Oregon and on the West Coast. As defined by Whitney, the "Chico Group" included: "all the known Cretaceous of Oregon and of the extreme northern portion of California, and the coal-bearing formation of Vancouver Island." Gabb continually employed the term "Chico Group" in an inclusive sense in all his stratigraphical references. Taff, Hanna, and Cross (1940) used the term Chico formation to include only those beds exposed on Chico Creek. The type area was described and a measured section given. This restricted usage of the term Chico is followed in this work.

plete revision of the Upper Cretaceous series, and its division into at least two distinct groups, the Pacheco and Asuncion, after the usage of these terms by Taliaferro (1941, p. 130), and these into units which can be directly correlated with the European section.

The boundary between the Pacheco group and the Lower Asuncion is for the most part readily traceable, but overlap by the Upper Asuncion group renders the contact between it and the Lower Asuncion less easily recognizeable. The faunal difference between them is distinctive, however. Besides the segregation of the major groups of the series, it is also possible to differentiate a number of subdivisions of each group based partly upon diastrophism as shown by overlaps and evidences of disconformities, and in part by faunal changes.

On the west border of the Sacramento Valley, north of Colusa County, the Pacheco group is widely exposed. Exposures of the Upper Asuncion group are known in a small area west of Hunters but this group is mostly covered by the Pliocene Tehama formation. Similar outcrops extend around the north end of the Sacramento Valley to Little Cow Creek, east of Frazier Corners, and southward on the east border of the valley to Oak Run, or a little further south. A small area of Turonian strata is also exposed on Bear Creek, north of the Lassen highway.

South of the Shasta County line no exposures of the Pacheco group are known on the east side of the valley, although in the deep canyons parts of the Lower Asuncion are exposed by erosion, as at Tuscan Springs, Chico Creek, the American River, and at other scattered localities.

During deposition of the Pacheco group, differential subsidence resulted in progressive overlaps in many areas, bringing Turonian rocks into contact with basement rocks at Henley, Siskiyou County, and farther north in Oregon, and as far south as the Santa Ana Mountains in Orange County, California. On the west border of the San Joaquin Valley, between Orestimba Creek and the Panoche Hills, a large area of the Pacheco group is exposed but it is overlapped to the north and to the south by the Lower Asuncion group, which also border it on the east. On the other hand, the "Nanaimo series," correlative with a part of the Asuncion group, occupies large areas on eastern Vancouver Island, where no strata of the Pacheco group have been reported. Similarly there are many regions in California and Oregon where beds of the Lower Asuncion group occupy large areas to the exclusion of the Pacheco group, as between New Idria and Los Gatos Creek, near Coalinga, and to the south of Antelope Valley in northern Kern County.

Beds equivalent in age to the Lower Asuncion group, as indicated by their faunas, are present in southern Alaska, in the Japanese Islands, in southern India, and on other borders of the Pacific Ocean.

Similar conditions exist with respect to the Upper Asuncion group, which is rarely exposed in the Sacramento Valley, except at Marysville Buttes, although it is found in deep wells in Colusa County. West and south of the Great Valley, in the Coast Ranges and in the coastal areas south of Point Arena, few exposures, if any, of Upper Cretaceous beds older than Upper Asuncion are known, whereas strata of this group exclusively outcrop over large areas as far south as Santa Catarina in Lower California.

This widespread discrepancy in the surficial distribution of the major groups of the Upper Cretaceous series is evidence of regional disastrophism on the West Coast, and of more or less local differential vertical movements, positive or negative, at various intervals. In areas of uplift, erosion acted upon the older sediments, and in areas of subsidence overlaps by strata of the younger groups are found. These facts do not indicate violent disastrophism; the movements may have been slow, though no less effective. More pronounced movements may be indicated by sudden changes in lithologic types, as from shales to sandstone, or to conglomerate, or vice versa. Thick lenses of conglomerate in the Lower Asuncion group in the Joaquin embayment may be evidence of uplift in the land areas of Salinia, with shifting of the strand lines and stimulation of stream activity.

PACHECO GROUP

Introduction.—The name Pacheco Group[2] was proposed by Taliaferro (1941, p. 131) to include "those deposits which are thought to be equivalent to the Upper Albian, the Cenomanian, and the Turonian."

The Pacheco Group is extensively exposed on the west side of the San Joaquin and Sacramento Valleys. Strata of this group also occupy much of the mining districts on Cottonwood Creek, Shasta County, California.

In Oregon, the valley of Rogue River about Medford unites with that of the Illinois River near Grants Pass, and although the latter is said to contain Horsetown (Shasta) strata, they are not known near Medford or Jacksonville. In this valley the lower beds of Pacheco age rest directly upon basement rocks (granite, greenstone, limestone, and slate), as do correlative beds in the Cottonwood district, Shasta County, California.

For these reasons the deposits in both basins are believed to show a landward invasion by marine waters following the diastrophism that closed the Shasta epoch in California and in Oregon. The abundant fossils include many cephalopods, which make possible the dating of the subsidence and marine invasion, and a correlation with similar events in western Canada and in Alaska.

In California, the Pacheco group covers large areas in the Cottonwood district and southward, and eastward to old Horsetown and Texas Springs, as first described by Stanton (*in* Merriam, 1901, p. 283). When traced southward from the north fork of Cottonwood Creek, rocks of this age are found on the Middle fork, on Dry Creek, west of Rosewood, on Elder Creek, 2 miles east of Lowry's, north of Sites, at Venado, on Cache Creek above Rumsey, and on Putah Creek at the Napa-Yolo county line. Farther south, the group occurs east of Mount Diablo, at Curry Creek, and on the west border of the San Joaquin Valley. The thickness of the group varies greatly in some exposures that are not continuous and in some that are overlapped by later beds, or have suffered erosion. In the

---

[2] The term group is used as a subdivision of the Upper Cretaceous Series as indicated by Ashley (1939, p. 1080, Article 12).

Cottonwood district and in other areas in the Sacramento Valley the group may have an exposed thickness of less than 3000 feet; on the west borders of the Sacramento and San Joaquin valleys it attains a thickness of 7000 to 9000 feet, or more.

In the Sacramento Valley, the thickest sections are exposed in western Tehama and Colusa counties. On Dry Creek, 20 miles west of Red Bluff, it has an exposed thickness of 6200 feet west of Rosewood, whereas, on Putah Creek, a partial exposure aggregates more than 7700 feet. This latter thickness is exceptional, since the greater part of it is referable to the Turonian.

Under somewhat similar conditions an even greater thickness of the Pacheco group was developed in the Pacheco Pass quadrangle where an aggregate thickness of 9000 feet largely referable to the early part of the group (late Albian to Cenomanian) had accumulated.

Lithologically the Pacheco group varies from thick aggregates of coarse stream-borne boulder conglomerates, especially near its base, to sandstones and sandy shales, and to fine silt in the upper part. These sediments are the normal result of the accumulation of detrital materials derived from land areas toward the west, and their distribution in the basin of deposition under the influence of moderate currents.

In age the Pacheco group ranges from latest Albian, with species of *Beudanticeras, Pervinquieria,* and even *Brancoceras,* to the close of Turonian time, with species of *Fagesia, Vascoceras,* and numerous prionotropids.

Divisions of the Pacheco Group.—During deposition differential movements caused local disconformity between beds which resulted in separate development of the lower and upper parts. These movements were also responsible for the overlap of the younger across the older, and the final occupation by the younger of distinct areas in which the older is not present.

UPPER ALBIAN—CENOMANIAN DEPOSITS: This part of the Pacheco is most typically exposed about Gaines Flat near the mouth of Hulen Creek, Shasta County, where it was first studied. The outcrops are largely Cenomanian, correlative with the "Lower Chalk" of England and western Europe, although in some places the lowest beds contain fossils that have been regarded as indicative of upper Albian. In the typical area on the North fork of Cottonwood Creek, near the mouth of Hulen Creek, are found species of *Pervinquieria* and *Beudanticeras,* and the rare pelecypod, *Remondia.* The Upper Albian and Cenomanian deposits are readily traced from Hulen Creek southward along the border of the valley, and eastward for a short distance to the site of old Horsetown, and to Texas Flat, whence the fauna was first partly described by T. W. Stanton. These deposits are recognizable on all the larger streams that cross the outcrop as far south as Elder Creek, beyond which exposures are not continuous, although they form a conspicuous front ridge from Logan Creek, south of Willows, to Venado, northwest of Williams, Colusa County. Farther south beds of this age are exposed about Mount Diablo, beyond which they outcrop at intervals in the Diablo Range. Upper Albian and Cenomanian deposits have not been found south of Antelope Valley, in northwest Kern County. Gabb (1864; 1869) described many invertebrate species from these beds in California and Oregon referring them to the "Chico group." Representative invertebrates from the Upper Albian and Cenomanian include the following:

Beudanticeras haydeni (Gabb)
Desmoceras diabloense Anderson
Puzosia (Parapuzosia) colusaënsis
  (Anderson)
Sonneratia stantoni Anderson
Pervinquieria inflata (Sowerby) var.
Pervinquieria tehamaensis (Reagan)
Mantelliceras sp.

Durania ? californica n. sp.
Rhynchonella densleonis Anderson
Rhynchonella whiteana Anderson
Syncyclonema operculiformis (Gabb)
Remondia shastensis n. sp.
Trigonia aequicostata Gabb
Neohibolites fontinalis Anderson

From near Mount Diablo has come *Calycoceras (Eucalycoceras) turneri* White, and also a related form *Calyoceras (Eucalycoceras) diabloense* n. sp.

Upper Albian and Cenomanian outcrops occur at the old mining camp site at Horsetown, at Texas Springs, and in small areas farther east. T. W. Stanton (*in* Merriam, 1901) referred to beds outcropping here and at Texas Springs, assigning them to a lower Upper Cretaceous age. With little exception, this assignment is accepted, although it may be pointed out that at old Horsetown the highest beds of the Shasta series also outcrop in a small easily overlooked area.

The approximately 600 feet of the beds exposed here includes about 60 feet of thin-bedded sandy shale of the older series (Shasta), dipping to the southeast or south. In the early history of the camp these beds were penetrated by a drainage tunnel, and from it came most of the fossils that have been recorded from this locality. The tunnel has long been closed and hidden by its caving walls. It was open and accessible as late as 1894, and the writer obtained many fossils from it, some later (Anderson, 1902a, 1938b) described as belonging to the Shasta series. These beds are overlapped by massive pebbly buff sandstone exposed about 600 feet west of the tunnel site, and from it the writer obtained a large fragment of *Nautilus charlottensis* Whiteaves.

The overlying buff sandstone extends eastward, though not continuously, to Texas Springs, where it has been quarried for building stone. Here a considerable fauna has been collected, by Diller, Stanton, and the writer. These fossils were obtained partly from concretions and partly from flat or rounded blocks that appear to have been transported from other points and lodged in the sandstone. Many of the species that have been recorded from this place were obtained from these inclusions, namely, *Sonneratia stantoni* Anderson, *Rhynchonella densleonis* Anderson, and *Beudanticeras breweri* (Gabb). All of these have also been collected from the lowest beds at old Horsetown.

Other species found at Texas Springs, but not from these inclusions, include *Neohibolites fontinalis* Anderson, *Trigonia perrinsmithi* n. sp., and *Beudanticeras haydeni* (Gabb.). These may be regarded as representing the lowest beds of the Upper Cretaceous series, and probably the horizon which at Hulen Creek contains *Pervinquieria tehamaensis* (Reagan) and *P. inflata* (Sowerby), var.

From a horizon about 400 feet higher near the mouth of Hulen Creek was obtained the holotype of *Desmoceras barryae* n. sp. and *Cucullaea (Indonearca) alamoensis* n. sp.

This appears to be the interval that on Dry Creek, northern Tehama County, has yielded the following, collected by McCoy, Bennison, and the writer.

Desmoceras (*Latidorsella*) *inane* (Stoliczka)
Cyrtochilus stylus n. sp.
Turrilites bergeri Brongniart
Acanthoceras sp. indet.

All of these are regarded as of Cenomanian age, though higher in the column than any of the species just previously cited from Hulen Creek.

In southern Oregon, as in northern California, the lowest beds of the correlatives of the Pacheco group exposed 5 miles east of Jacksonville contain invertebrates of lower Cenomanian or upper Albian types, as in the district about "Dark Hollow," where the following species have been collected:

Beudanticeras aff. *B. haydeni* (Gabb)   *Nautilus charlottensis* Whiteaves
Pervinquieria sp.   *Remondia oregonensis* n. sp. (?)
Brancoceras parvum (Anderson)   *Trigonia jacksonensis* n. sp.
Mantelliceras oregonense n. sp.   *Syncyclonema latum* n. sp.

During the course of long-continued subsidence and transgression of the marine seaways, later deposits often mark the local base of the series, with corresponding faunal types ranging up to lower Turonian in age. In northern Tehama County, on Dry Creek, west of Rosewood, the base of the series is somewhat younger than on the north fork of Cottonwood Creek. On Dry Creek, as on many streams that cross the outcrop of the Pacheco group, one finds a succession of faunal zones. The section here begins later than on the Middle fork of Cottonwood Creek a few miles to the north, where fragments of *Pervinquieria* sp. have been found. Fifteen miles south, on Elder Creek, east of Lowrey's, the older beds of the Upper Cretaceous series yielded an example of *Beudanticeras* sp., indicating a low horizon, above which occurs the succession described by Diller and Stanton (1894). This section on Dry Creek covers the span of the Pacheco group, whereas that on Elder Creek includes only the lower part of this group, being overlapped on the east by beds of the Lower Asuncion group with *Canadoceras* aff. *C. newberryanum* (Meek), and *Inoceramus whitneyi* Gabb.

On the west side of the San Joaquin Valley, in western Merced and Stanislaus counties, portions of the Pacheco group are exposed between Ortigalita Creek at the south, and Puerto Creek at the north, where beds of Turonian age have been proved by species of *Scaphites* and *Inoceramus*. Immediately north of Los Banos Creek, and on Quinto and Garzas creeks, the occurrence of older beds of the Pacheco group has already been noted. Furthermore, evidence of the existence of part of the Shasta series has been found in boulders in conglomerates and by a few fossils found in this area. Bennison obtained from Garzas Creek an imperfect example of *Neocraspedites,* and from Romero Creek a fragment of *Hemibaculites* both evidence of the former existence of beds of late Shasta age.

TURONIAN DEPOSITS: The upper part of the Pacheco group is distinct from the lower in its geographic distribution and faunal characteristics. It occupies large areas on the West Coast in which no Upper Albian or Cenomanian beds out-crop. Its most characteristic development is in the northern part of the Sacramento Valley, in the Cow Creek district on its eastern border, extending south to Swede Creek, and the west side of the valley from the North fork of Cottonwood Creek to Mount Diablo and the Diablo Range.

The most characteristic feature of the Turonian deposits, well illustrated on the east side of the valley in the Cow Creek region north and east of Frazier Corners, is a sudden expansion of the seaways. This expansion near the beginning of Turonian time is seen in many parts of the Great Valley, and outside of it, extending south to Orange County or farther, and north to Redding, to the valley of the Klamath River, to southern Oregon (upper Rogue River Valley), to British Columbia (Queen Charlotte Islands), and to southern Alaska.

The physical aspects of the deposits in the Cow Creek area have been described by Popenoe (1943 p. 308) whose account contains the basis for an estimate of 1800 feet. The north border of the deposit outcrops about 2.5 miles north of Frazier Corners, extends easterly for a few miles, and westerly (under cover) to Sand Flat, north of Redding, to Stillwater and Buckeye creeks and other localities. The north border of the deposit curves roundly to the east and to the south, as shown on Popenoe's sketch map, but its east border can be traced southward by exposures in the stream valleys only to Sweede Creek, beyond which it is overlain by later Cretaceous beds, volcanic ejecta, or by rubble. It outcrops still farther south on Bear Creek, about the Aldrich home, where thick basal conglomerates are clearly exposed, with fossils indicating a Turonian age in the overlying sandstones. Popenoe (1943, p. 307–311) divides the Cretaceous sequence in the Cow Creek area into members I–VI which appear to be well characterized lithologically and faunally. The lower three divisions seem referable to the Turonian and appear to outcrop only as far south as Sweede Creek. No exposure of this age has been found in Oak Run Valley, where the lowest-exposed Cretaceous beds contain *Peroniceras* and *Prionocyclus,* both representing lower Coniacian (Emscherian) horizons.

In the Cow Creek district, strata of Turonian age dip gently to the southwest and are overlain on the west by the upper Tertiary Tehama formation.

The upper portion of the Turonian is not as well exposed here, as on the North fork of Cottonwood Creek near Gas Point and about the mouth of Roaring River, where it has an exposed thickness of more than 400 feet, although it is partly overlapped by the Tehama formation. To the thickness of these strata exposed on the east border of the valley, we may now add more than 400 feet that outcrop on the west border, making a total thickness of 2200 feet, with *Prionotropis bakeri* Anderson and other associated types that mark a high horizon in the Turonian succession.

Near Redding, the lowest beds of the Turonian outcrop on the highway near the north end of the Redding bridge, where Charles V. Averill discovered a very large but imperfect example of *Austiniceras,* with a diameter of 20 inches, septate throughout. This species, a Turonian index, occurs low in the section here, as it does also on the Middle fork of Cottonwood Creek, a mile west of the old Foster homestead, on the west side of the valley, and on Dry Creek, northern Tehama County.

In the Cow Creek district, a section beginning near Locality 27831 (C. A. S.) in the SE ¼ of sec. 31, T. 33 N., R. 3 W., M. D. B. and M., and ending at Little Cow Creek, a mile east of Frazier Corners, is well exposed. Its lowest fossil-bearing horizon is about 60 feet thick, beneath which are conglomerates.

At this locality Taff, Hanna, and Cross collected the following species:

Acteonella oviformis (Gabb)	*Gyrodes expansus* Gabb
"*Aphrodina*" *varians* (Gabb)	*Nerinea* sp. indet.
	Glycymeris shastensis n. sp.

At a second fossil horizon, about 450 feet higher in the section, and half a mile up stream, there are hard sandstone outcrops containing *Pugnellus manubriatus* Gabb and *Ostrea* sp.

This horizon is found also at Sand Flat, 4.5 miles north of Redding, at Loc. 1284 (C. A. S.) where the writer collected the following:

Pachydiscus aff. *P. ashlandicus* (Anderson)	*Trigonia leana* Gabb
Pugnellus manubriatus Gabb	*Trigonia* aff. *T. evansana* Meek
Acteonina californica Gabb	*Trigonia fitchi* Packard
Gyrodes expansa Gabb	*Glycymeris shastensis* n. sp.
Pleuromya sp.	*Cyprimeria moorei* Popenoe

About 500 feet above this horizon, a mile north of Frazier Corners, on the same stream, at Locality 1293A (C. A. S.) the writer, and later Taff, Hanna, and Cross collected the following:

Nautilus sp. indet.	*Anchura condoniana* Anderson
Puzosia (*Parapuzosia*) *klamathonrae* n. sp.	*Anchura californica* (Gabb)
Scaphites pittensis n. sp.	*Gyrodes dowelli* White
Hyphantoceras ceratopse (Anderson)	*Inoceramus glennensis* n. sp.
Scaphites aff. *S. inermis* Anderson	*Inoceramus aduncus* Anderson
Bostrychoceras occidentale n. sp.	*Glycymeris shastensis* n. sp.

As determined by stratigraphic and faunal evidence, the strata at this horizon should be regarded as middle Turonian. Some of the above species, including *Puzosia* (*Parapuzosia*) *klamathonia, Inoceramus aduncus,* and *Anchura californica* Gabb, have been collected from correlative deposits on Roaring River, on the west border of the valley, south of Ono, Shasta County.

About 500 feet above the preceding horizon, the fourth horizon was found by Bennison and the writer on the Alturas highway, 1.5 miles east of Frazier Corners. It represents an upper Turonian horizon that has been found at many places in Oregon and California. From this interval were collected the following species, regarded as diagnostic of it:

Oregoniceras aff. *O. knighteni* (Anderson)	*Inoceramus jacksonensis* n. sp.
Oregoniceras sp. indet.	

On the west side of the valley, the thickness of the Turonian varies greatly, the maximum thickness outcropping on the Middle fork of Cottonwood Creek and on Dry Creek, excluding 480 feet not found on the east side, is about 3000 feet, or 1.6 times that in the Little Cow Creek district. On Roaring River, it is similar;

in other areas the ratios are somewhat less. On the North fork of Cottonwood above Gas point, and on the lower 2 miles of Roaring River, the faunal sequence in the upper 480 feet is about as follows, in descending order:

top—

Prionotropis bakeri (Anderson)
Lytoceras (Gaudryceras) aff. *L. tenuiliratum*
  Yabe
Fagesia californica Anderson
Puzosia (Parapuzosia) sp.
Scaphites sp.
Oregoniceras oregonense (Anderson)
Inoceramus aduncus Anderson
Puzosia (Austiniceras) giganteum
  Anderson, n. sp.

Acanthoceras sp. indet.
Nerinea stewarti n. sp.
Pecten (Propeamusium) cowperi Waring
Eriphyla umbonata Gabb
Inoceramus aff. *I. klamathensis* Anderson
Baculites buttensis n. sp.
Acanthoceras aff. *A. roguense* Anderson
Vascoceras shastense (Anderson)
Pedalion sp. (large, thick-shelled form)
?Vascoceras shastense (Anderson)

In the valley of the Klamath River and northward to Hilt, and on the north slope of the Siskiyou Mountains, south of Ashland, and in the Pioneer district south of Medford, the faunal sequence is about the same. In these areas the latest Turonian beds are characterized by prionotropids. About 1200 feet south of the Fitch home, and in the ravine to the west, the latest beds of Turonian age outcrop with the following species:

Prionotropis bakeri (Anderson)
Prionotropis casperi n. sp.

Prionotropis branneri Anderson
Prionotropis sp.

and somewhat higher in the sequence *Fagesia siskiyouensis* Anderson and *Inoceramus* sp. indet. were found.

In the Little Cow Creek district, about 500 feet above the position of the *Oregoniceras* beds on Little Cow Creek, 1.5 miles east of Frazier Corners, Popenoe and Scharf collected:

Phylloceras vaculae n. sp.
Kotôceras frazierense n. sp.

Ostrea sp. indet.

None of these species have previously been described, and their horizon may therefore be regarded as somewhat doubtful, although it is near the upper boundary of the Turonian.

Sections of the Pacheco Group.—In northern California (Siskiyou Mountains area) the Turonian occurs in the Shasta Valley near Montague, in areas near the Klamath River, whence it extends north to the State line. Southward the formation is not complete, though it is well stocked with littoral molluscan fossils. Thicker sections outcrop north of the river, near Hornbrook and Henley, where the thickness is about 2430 feet.

In these areas the formation rests directly upon Paleozoic cherts, greenstones, and granite, both extending north into southern Oregon.

The Turonian is usually fossiliferous and is overlain by later Upper Cretaceous beds referable to the lower Asuncion group. These beds are readily traced to the north slope of the Siskiyou Mountains, to Ashland, and westward to Griffin Creek, Jacksonville, and farther west; and northward to Rogue River, and west to the Illinois Valley, southwest of Grants Pass.

The Pacheco group in this area is at least 3200 feet thick, the larger part referable to the Turonian. The beds are well exposed east and north of Jacksonville, and, according to Diller (1903b), they occur on Grave Creek, 12 miles north of Grants Pass, and have been reported on Evans Creek farther south.

At the old "Forty-nine" mine, 2 miles southwest of Phoenix, numerous fossils have been collected and partly described by the writer (1902a and in the present work). On the north slope of a spur from this ridge, placer mining disclosed a bed of conglomerate, beneath the Lower Asuncion beds, dipping steeply north, with an easterly strike. The conglomerate contains numerous sandstone blocks and concretions, with invertebrate fossils from the Pacheco group, derived from both the Upper Albian-Cenomanian and the Turonian. These included species of *Lytoceras, Parapuzosia, Brancoceras, Mantelliceras,* and many Cenomanian types, as well as many from the Turonian (*Scaphites, Acanthoceras, Oregoniceras,* and others). Overlying the conglomerates are sandstones containing invertebrates of the Lower Asuncion group, including *Metaplacenticeras, Diplomoceras, Gryphaea, Inoceramus,* and other types. To the west and southwest are the outcropping strata from which these blocks and concretions may have been derived. At "Dark Hollow," 2 miles west, and on the Shutte ranch, to the southwest on the east branch of Coleman Creek, the lower beds are exposed.

From these beds and from overlying strata, fossils similar to those from the old mine are still obtainable. The conglomerate and the overlying sandstone are still exposed at the mine site and on the Fitch (formerly Smith) ranch, west of the "Forty-nine" mine. The conglomerate marks an unconformity between the equivalents of the Pacheco group and the equivalents of the overlying Lower Asuncion group, as in many places in the Great Valley of California.

North fork of Cottonwood Creek.—Diller and Stanton (1894) described and illustrated the section exposed on the North fork of Cottonwood Creek, assigning a large part of it to the "Chico" (Upper Cretaceous) sequence, listing many species that occurr in it. This work afforded a needed starting point for the present faunal study. However, they placed the base of the Upper Cretaceous Series at the second conglomerate rather than the first, thereby omitting about 450 feet from the lower part.

Pervinquieria inflata var. was assigned (1894, p. 442) to the "Upper Horsetown" group, showing that they regarded the second (thicker) conglomerate bed in this area as the base of the Upper Cretaceous Series. However, the more important diastrophic, stratigraphic, and faunal change in the Cretaceous began with the first conglomerate, rather than the second. In the lowest conglomerate, east of Hulen Creek, are found large fragments of the rudistid *Durania* (?) *californica* n. sp. which seems to have been regarded (p. 444) as a "characteristic Chico fossil," here, on the Cold Ford, and on Elder Creek, in the belief that it was *Coralliochama orcutti* White, which its fragments somewhat resemble. This latter species is now known to be characteristic of the Upper Asuncion group, in the southern coastal areas of California; it has no place in the older faunas of the series.

Between the first and second conglomerates on Hulen Creek the writer has collected examples of *Pervinquieria inflata* var., *Lytoceras (Tetragonites)* aff. *L.*

timotheanum (Mayor), and *Lytoceras* aff. *L. sacya* Forbes, and other forms that characterize the Ootatoor group in southern India, as noted earlier (Anderson 1902a, p. 63).

In the second conglomerate on the North fork of Cottonwood Creek transported blocks containing *Pervinquieria inflata* var., *Durania* (?) *californica* n. sp., and other forms, were found showing their origin from older strata. This area seems to be among the first affected by the diastrophism that initiated the regional subsidence and the spread of the Upper Cretaceous sediments westward and southward in the Sacramento Valley, and probably in the San Joaquin Valley. No older Upper Cretaceous beds outcrop on the borders of the Great Valley, although beds of about the same age occur on the west border of the San Joaquin Valley and in the Pioneer district in southern Oregon.

The highest beds of the Upper Cretaceous Series on the North fork of Cottonwood Creek outcrop half a mile above Gas Point, where they contain *Prionotropis bakeri* Anderson, found also on Roaring River, and on Quinto Creek on the west border of the San Joaquin Valley, marking the top of the Turonian and of the Pacheco group.

Dry Creek, Tehama County.—In northern Tehama County an excellent section of the Pacheco group is exposed on the Redbluff—Beegum road west of Rosewood (Figs. 1, 2).

The same stratigraphic and faunal succession is also found on the Middle fork of Cottonwood Creek, a few miles north.

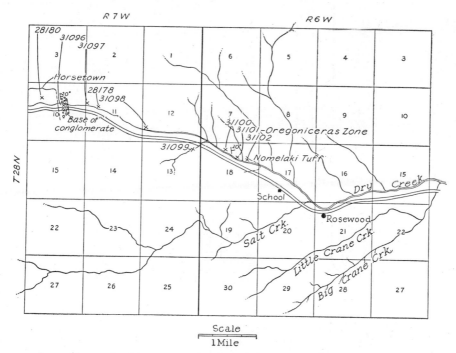

FIGURE 1.—*Map of Dry Creek area, Tehama County, California*

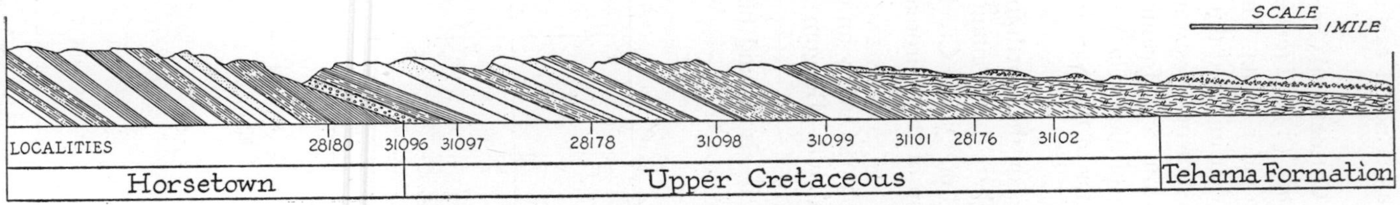

FIGURE 2.—*Section along Dry Creek, Tehama County, California*

Loc. 28180:
  Lytoceras whitneyi (Gabb)
  Pervinquieria sp.
  Parahoplites aff. *P. sjogreni* Anthula
  Desmoceras voyi Anderson
Loc. 31096:
  Basal U. K. conglomerate
  Tellina (Arcopagia) tehama Anderson
  Cucullaea aff. *C. alamoensis* n. sp.
Loc. 31097:
  Phylloceras velledae Michelin
  Turrilites aff. *T. bergeri* Brongniart
  Turrilites aff. *T. pachecoensis* n. sp.

Cyrtochilus stylus n. sp.
  Rudistids
Loc. 28178:
  Baculites aff. *B. chicoensis* (Trask)
  Inoceramus sp. indet.
Loc. 31098:
  Puzosia (Parapuzosia) sp.
  Acanthoceras aff. *A. rhotomagense*
    Defrance
  Cunningtoniceras aff. *C. meridionale*
    (Stoliczka)
Loc. 31099:
  Acanthoceras sp. indet

Loc. 31101:
  Oregoniceras aff. *O. oregonense*
    (Anderson)
  Prionotropis bakeri (Anderson)
Loc. 31101a:
  Exiteloceras sp.
  Oregoniceras sp. indet.
Loc. 31101b:
  Oregoniceras sp. indet.
Loc. 28176:
  Oregoniceras sp. indet.
Loc. 31102:
  Pachydiscus rosewoodensis n. sp.

On both these streams the thickness of the Turonian greatly exceeds that of the Upper Albian and Cenomanian, just as in both California and Oregon its surface outcrop covers many times the area of the latter, due to the overlap by the Turonian.

Elder Creek.—For the foothill belt crossed by Elder Creek, southern Tehama County, Diller and Stanton (1894, p. 439) have given a stratigraphic and faunal column. Most of the named fossils (at least 90 per cent) were obtained from beds below the conglomerate 2500 feet above the base of their column.

Two species given in their list within the upper 1200 feet of the column are representative of the Coniacian, namely, *Canadoceras newberryanum* (Meek), and *Inoceramus whitneyi* Gabb.

Nearly all others specifically named are referable to the Pacheco group, as here defined. In view of the known thickness of the Lower Asuncion group in the lower Cache Creek area this conglomerate and the overlying sandstones and shales probably should be referred to the Lower Asuncion group, and the underlying 1500 feet of coarser sediments should be referable to the Pacheco group.

Stanton's lists of fossils for this section show a great majority of species indicative of the Turonian. Characteristic are the following:

Gyrodes expansa Gabb	"*Aphrodina*" *varians* (Gabb)
Anchura californica Gabb	*Trigonia leana* Gabb
Cucullaea truncata (Gabb)	*Trigonocallista nitida* (Gabb)

Few of the species in these lists definitely represent the Upper Albian and Cenomanian, although the following species often occur in it:

Lunatia avellana Gabb	*Syncyclonema operculiformis* (Gabb)
"*Thetis*" *annulata* Gabb	*Trigonia aequicostata* Gabb

South of Elder Creek, the Pacheco group is overlapped near McCarthy Creek by the Tehama formation, but the Turonian is well exposed and richly fossiliferous farther south.

Glenn—Colusa syncline.—West of Orland, Willows, and Maxwell, and farther south, the Pacheco group occupies a broad foothill belt. It is folded for more than 30 miles into a broad syncline, whose axial belt is occupied by Turonian deposits, with older beds appearing only at intervals on its borders. The axis of this belt lies east of Fruto, Glenn County, with a northerly strike. The west flank of the structure is well exposed a few miles south of Fruto on the west border of the Willow Creek Valley, where its basal beds include lenses of conglomerate. In a lens 15 feet thick near the Stonyford road a large sandstone boulder containing Upper Albian or Cenomanian fossils was found. A large fragment of *Acanthoceras shastense* Reagan was obtained from the upper part of the underlying Cenomanian. The fossiliferous sandstone boulder is evidence of unconformity between the basal beds of the Turonian and the upper beds of the Cenomanian, and accords with the fact that the Turonian occupies large areas in which the Cenomanian does not appear in outcrop. On the east half of sec. 29, T. 20 N., R. 5 W., the Turonian shales contain *Inoceramus glennensis* n. sp., and farther south characteristic ammonites.

This syncline has been traced southward into Colusa County, although a few miles south of Sites it becomes lost in a broad homoclinal belt in which the strata dip uniformly eastward. Four miles north of Sites, near the Petersen ranch, the strata of the Pacheco group are folded into an anticline. The eastern limb is faulted up, disclosing about 800 feet in an escarpment facing the west. Many diagnostic invertebrates have been collected here, including the following:

Puzosia (Parapuzosia) colusaënsis (Anderson)
Beudanticeras haydeni (Gabb)
Beudanticeras alamoense n. sp.
Mantelliceras sp.

Turrilites petersoni n. sp.
Durania (?) *californica* n. sp.
Trigonia aequicostata Gabb
Nautilus charlottensis Whiteaves

These species clearly indicate a Cenomanian age. Kirby and Crook collected numerous fossils, now in the California Academy of Science Collections, from this belt farther south.

The beds on the Petersen ranch are traceable northward for some miles but are overlain on the east by the Turonian outcrops near Logan Creek, Glenn County, and southward toward Venádo, Colusa County.

From a locality north of Logan Creek, on the north border of the NE ¼ of sec. 20, T. 19 N., R. 4 W., W. E. Kennett collected the following species:

Acteonina californica Gabb
Drepanochilus transversus Gabb
Volutoderma aff. *V. averillii* (Gabb)
Scobinella dilleri White

Trigonarca excavata Packard
Trigonarca aff. *T. californica* Packard
Glycymeris aff. *G. shastensis* n. sp.

Most of the above species are also abundant in the Turonian on Little Cow Creek.

At the head of Cortina Creek, probably on the SW ¼ of sec. 23, T. 13 N., R. 4 W., Bennison found the holotype of *Hyphantoceras laqueum* n. sp., in the upper part of the Turonian.

The basal conglomerate of the Pacheco group in this region outcrops on Bear Creek, Colusa County, about 2 miles above its mouth, whence it has been traced south to Cache Creek, and west to Fiske Creek, along the county line southward to Putah Creek, and to the Vaca Mountain area west of Pleasants Valley. North of Putah Creek, near the county line, McCoy and the writer obtained from the second conglomerate, at the base of the Turonian, the following species:

Puzosia (Austiniceras) cf. *P. (A.) giganteum* n. sp.
Trigonia aff. *T. inezana* Packard
Paleotractus crassus Gabb
Glycymeris shastensis n. sp.

Trophon condoni White
Inoceramus cf. *I. steinmanni* Wilkins
Acteon politus Gabb
Cucullaea (Idonearca) gravida (Gabb)

From about the same zone, W. E. Kennett obtained a block with similar lithology, containing the following invertebrates:

Durania(?)aff. *D.*(?)*californica* n. sp.
Acteonina californica Gabb
Cypraea berryessae n. sp.

Trigonia sp., indet.
Anchura californica Gabb
Gyrodes expansa Gabb

In the canyon of Thompson Creek, at a point about 2100 feet above the base of the Pacheco group, Kennett discovered a stratum a little higher than the preceding, from which he collected:

Acteonina berryessensis n. sp.
Gyrodes expansa Gabb

Trignoarca aff. *T. excavata* Packard
Trigonocallista nitida (Gabb)

All these species are of Turonian aspect. The beds are referable to the lower Turonian.

South of Vaca Mountain, the Pacheco group is not exposed continuously, though it has been recognized at intervals about Carquinez Strait and east of Mount Diablo in Curry Canyon, where Turner obtained *"Acanthoceras" turneri* White, a recognized Cenomanian form. Nearby the writer found the holotype of *Calycoceras (Eucalycoceras) diabloensis* n. sp. Gabb (1864, p. 220–236) lists the following species from somewhat higher beds:

Eriphyla umbonata Gabb
Cucullaea (Idonearca) truncata (Gabb)
Cardium annulatum Gabb

Trigonia evansana Meek
"Aphrodina" varians Gabb

Pacheco Pass Quadrangle.—On the west border of the San Joaquin Valley, in Pacheco Pass quadrangle and farther south, the Pacheco group outcrops in a broad belt extending for many miles, with a maximum thickness of about 9000 feet. Its lower beds include boulder conglomerate, which on Quinto Creek attain a thickness of 3000 feet or more. In these beds was found the holotype of *Turrilites pachecoensis* n. sp.; higher in the section Bennison found *Puzosia waringi* n. sp. Farther north on Garzas Creek, the basal conglomerate is less than 25 feet thick, and is overlain by sandstones. From the basal conglomerate, McCoy, Bennison, and the writer collected the following species:

Desmoceras aff. *D. inane* Stoliczka
Cyrtochilus aff. *C. stylus* n. sp.
Puzosia (Parapuzosia) waringi n. name

Durania (?) fragments
Lyelliceras stanislausense n. sp.

None of these species seem younger than Cenomanian, though the last-named form may be older, since some species of the genus are of Albian age.

Overlying these conglomerates on Quinto Creek are Turonian sandstones with a thickness of 3900 feet. From the upper part Taff, Hanna, and Cross collected *Prionotropis bakeri* Anderson, and other Upper Turonian cephalopods. Later Bennison collected from the same or slightly higher beds, *Prionotropis casperi* n. sp. and *Scaphites* sp.; from a bed a little higher in the section, he obtained examples of other prionotropids (*Oregoniceras* aff. *O. oregonense, O. knighteni,* and a form resembling *Hyphantoceras*).

On the southwest slope of the Panoche Hills, near the center of sec. 8, T. 15 S., R. 11 E., Taff and Cross collected the following Turonian species from a reworked block of sandstone in a basal conglomerate of Early Asuncion age:

Leda translucida Gabb
Tornatella impressa Gabb
Turritella aff. *T. peterseni* Anderson

Cardium (Protocardium) translucidum Gabb
Acteon politus Gabb

This block of sandstone from conglomerate is the only evidence of the one-time existence of the Turonian in this area.

Similar and convincing proof of the former presence of the Cenomanian just west of the Panoche Hills was found by Taff and Cross, at Locality 28326 (C. A. S.), in the SW ¼ of sec. 13, T. 14 S., R. 10 E., where they collected the following species from a boulder in a conglomerate.

Puzosia (Parapuzosia) waringi n. name   *Syncyclonema* aff. *S. operculiformis* (Gabb)
"Callista" aff. *C. pseudoplana*   *Amauropsis pseudoalveata* Packard
     Yabe and Nagao   *Margarites* aff. *M. inornatus* Gabb
Thetironia annulata (Gabb)

All but one of these species occur in Cenomanian beds in the Pacheco group farther north in the Great Valley, on its western border.

Southern California.—South of the Great Valley, no beds of Turonian age are known in the Coast Ranges north of the Santa Ana Mountains, Orange County, where deposits similar to, and probably contemporaneous with, those of the Klamath River and parts of the Rogue River Valley in Oregon occur, resting directly upon basement rocks, with no evidence of the Cenomanian intervening. In this area, the Turonian is incomplete and has a thickness less than half that found in the San Joaquin and Sacramento Valleys. In the Orange County area (Popenoe 1942), the Baker member contains Turonian faunas, but lacks many important cephalopod and other faunal elements found in the Sacramento Valley and farther north. In thickness, the Turonian in the Santa Ana Mountains compares more closely with that of the Klamath River area, aggregating less than 2200 feet. The faunal content (Table 1) is like that of the Turonian in the areas near the Klamath River, and in parts of the Rogue River Valley, Oregon.

Faunal contrasts.—In all areas that contain both Upper Albian-Cenomanian and Turonian strata, their faunal contrasts are striking. This is shown in representative lists of species from each from California, Oregon, and British Colombia. Each of these regions is rich in the principal classes of Mollusca—pelecypods, gastropods, and cephalopods—that are known in other Indo-Pacific regions, though they lack the elements common in Atlantic and Mediterranean areas. Few of the cephalopods in the West Coast Turonian seem to have descended from any known in the West Coast Cenomanian. In great measure this is true of other classes of invertebrates, although some exceptional stocks have persisted.

Among the Turonian cephalopods, neither acanthoceratids, pachydiscids, nor prionotropids can be traced to sources in the Cenomanian, just as the desmoceratids, the puzosids, and the acanthoceratids in the Upper Albian-Cenomanian are not traceable to any occurring in the Shasta series.

Passing of Pacheco time.—The changes that took place on the West Coast during Turonian time cannot be completely given here. The extensive diastrophism that succeeded Turonian deposition began with uplifts in many places, followed by erosion and denudation. These post-Turonian disturbances appear to have been differential, with progressive uplifts in some areas and subsidences in others. In areas of uplift, the event led to erosion or denudation; in other areas, there was continued sedimentation and no important biological changes.

The time occupied by the successive phases of transition—uplift, or withdrawal of the sea from great areas, erosion or denudation on land surfaces, and

Table 1.—*Stratigraphic and faunal succession in the Pacheco group*

	Southern Oregon ("Forty-nine" Mine)	Northern California (North of Red Bluff)
	Prionotropis bakeri (Anderson) *Prionotropis branneri* Anderson *Pachydiscus oregonensis* n. sp.	*Prionotropis hiltensis* n. sp. *Fagesia klamathensis* n. sp. *Fagesia siskiyouensis* Anderson
	Scaphites roguensis Anderson *Scaphites condoni* Anderson *Oregoniceras oregonense* (Anderson) *Trigonia leana* Gabb *Anchura californica* Gabb	*Modiolus siskiyouensis* Gabb *Oregoniceras siskiyouense* (Anderson) *Oregoniceras jillsoni* n. sp. *Anchura condoniana* Anderson *Trigonia* aff. *T. evansana* Meek
Turonian	*Pachydiscus ashlandicus* (Anderson) *Pachydiscus oregonensis* n. sp. *Nautilus modestus* n. sp. *Gyrodes dowelli* White *Acteonella oviformis* Gabb *Acteonella frazierensis* n. sp.	*Pachydiscus* aff. *P. ashlandicus* (Anderson) *Pachydiscus* sp. indet. *Nautilus* sp. *Gyrodes dowelli* White *Acteonella oviformis* Gabb *Acteonella packardi* n. name *Durania* sp. *Trigonarca* aff. *T. excavata* Packard
		Puzosia (*Austiniceras*) *giganteum* n. sp.
Cenomanian	*Acanthoceras* sp. indet.	*Calycoceras* (*Eucalycoceras*) *turneri* White *Calycoceras* (*Eucalycoceras*) aff. *C. diabloense*, n. sp. *Acanthoceras* aff. *A. shastensae* Reagan *Calycoceras* (*Eucalycoceras*) *diabloense* n. sp.
	Syncyclonema latum n. sp. *Nautilus charlottensis* Whiteaves *Beudanticeras alamoense* n. sp. *Beudanticeras haydenii* (Gabb)	*Phylloceras* aff. *P. velledae* Kossmat *Syncyclonema latum* n. sp. *Nautilus charlottensis* Whiteaves *Beudanticeras alamoense* n. sp. *Pervinquieria* aff. *P. inflata* (Sowerby)
Albian	*Brancoceras? parvum* (Anderson) *Remondia oregonensis* n. sp.	*Neohibolites fontinalis* Anderson *Remondia shastensis* n. sp.

the removal of vast masses of sediment to be deposited elsewhere—could not have been short. These events were followed by differential subsidences under remote control by the land surface itself. This acted as an agent in the redistribution of material and initiated a new cycle of sedimentation in many areas where the sea had withdrawn. The time interval between the withdrawal of the sea at the close of Turonian time, and its return to areas it formerly occupied, could not have been short. This interval is probably best estimated in terms of biologic changes, which include not only the disappearance of large and varied faunas (genera and families), but also the later invasion of other races not previously present. Such faunal changes afford evidence of great paleogeographic changes and also of the duration of the transition period between the close of Pacheco time and the Senonian invertebrate invasions. In this interval, new genera and new families of invertebrates were introduced into West Coast areas from remote regions, including both the Atlantic and Mediterranean, as well as the Pacific basin, India, Australia, and southeast Africa.

In early Senonian time, the Turonian desmoceratids, pachydiscids, priono-tropids, and other ammonoid types, and *Inoceramus* of the *I. labiatus* group disappeared. They were replaced by species of *Peroniceras, Prionocyclus, Meta-placenticeras, Nowakites, Prionocycloceras, Desmophyllites,* and even *Para-pachydiscus,* and by *Inoceramus* of the group of *I. digitatus* Sowerby and of *I. undulatoplicatus* Roemer, and later by *Mortoniceras,* of the group of *M. dela-warense* Morton, and *Submortoniceras* of the group of *S. woodsi* Spath and *Canadoceras.* These all illustrate the character and extent of the faunal changes introduced on the West Coast following early Senonian time, especially when contrasted with the faunas of the Turonian. The most conspicuous lithological changes were in degree of lithification and induration of the strata, rather than in the materials.

ASUNCION GROUP

The Asuncion group was described by Taliaferro (1941, p. 132) as including all the Upper Cretaceous strata above the Pacheco group. In this work it has been found convenient to include all strata definitely referable to the Senonian in the "Lower Asuncion group" and strata of probable Maestrichtian age in the "Upper Asuncion group."

Lower Asuncion group.—Evidence of a two-fold division of the series was first pointed out by the writer (1902a) in the faunas and in the areal distribution of the lower and upper portions of the sequence, but definite proofs of uncon-formity were first discovered by B. L. Clark and the writer in 1913, in a thick body of boulder conglomerates outcropping 8 miles south of Livermore, and west of the Arroyo del Valle (*See* Taff, 1935). One of the blocks in this conglomerate from older beds that outcrop immediately to the west contained the following Turonian fossils:

Glycymeris shastensis n. sp.   *Trigonia* sp.
Inoceramus (thick-shelled)   *Tellina whitneyi* Gabb
Parallelodon brewerianus (Gabb)

Later A. S. Huey, in mapping the upper branches of Arroyo del Valle along the strike of this conglomerate, collected from a single boulder in a conglomerate probably identical in age with the above, the following species:

Baculites fairbanksi Anderson   *Beudanticeras* aff. *B. brewerii* (Gabb)
Trigonocallista nitida (Gabb)   *Turritella* aff. *T. peterseni* Anderson

On the west border of the San Joaquin Valley, in the foothills of the Diablo Range, strata of the Pacheco group are frequently overlapped by younger beds with a basal conglomerate similar to those described above. Anderson and Pack (1915, p. 43) described "lenses of conglomerate" that "locally form a large part of the section." These conglomerates cross Ortigalita Creek where they are said to have a thickness of "nearly 1000 feet, composed almost wholly of boulders and cobbles." It is not now difficult to correlate these lenses with those west of Arroyo del Valle, and to show that both initiate a new sequence of strata of early Senonian age. According to Anderson and Pack (1915, p. 43):

"These lentils of coarse material first appear prominently at the south in the Panoche Hills, and increasing rapidly in size northward reach their maximum development just north of Pacheco Pass."

On Quinto Creek, Taff, Hanna and Cross first discovered the uppermost beds referable to the Turonian, with *Prionotropis bakeri* Anderson, and species of *Oregoniceras*. This zone is overlain by a moderately thick conglomerate, followed by beds of shale. In the lower part of these shales on Quinto Creek, Bennison discovered a large example of *Peroniceras,* the holotype of *P. quintoense* n. sp. The genus is usually regarded as marking the early part of Senonian time. Here, then, at Locality 29596 (C. A. S.) in the NW ¼ of sec. 7, T. 9 S., R. 8 E., is found stratigraphic and faunal evidence of the closing stage of the Turonian, and the beginning of the Lower Asuncion group and of the Senonian.

The strata composing the Lower Asuncion group contrast with those of the Pacheco group. They are younger, less indurated, and less resistant to erosion and denudation. This has resulted in the rounded hills and ridges in a belt of low relief, as contrasted to the relief exhibited by the Pacheco group. In many areas in the San Joaquin Valley, however, the harder sandstones of the uppermost Lower Asuncion group rise in relief. When traced along the west border of the Great Valley, the thickness of the Lower Asuncion group varies locally, due in part to overlapped exposures, to volume of stream discharge, or to other causes. Brewer (1866) gave an estimate of 23,700 feet for the section traversed by his party along Puerto Creek, although its upper part includes strata belonging to latest Cretaceous beds not well segregated from Tertiary deposits. The base has been faulted or otherwise disturbed. On other stream crossings farther south, his estimates were greater, covering more than the Panoche formation alone. Conservative estimates of the thickness as exposed in five sections on the west border of the valley are given below:

	Thickness Feet
Panoche Hills, Fresno County (Birkhauser)	17,500
Quinto Creek, Merced County (Bennison)	13,717
Puerto Creek, Stanislaus County, the writer,	13,546
East and north of Mount Diablo, the writer	12,850
Cache Creek, northern Yolo County,	16,200
Average 14,762 feet	

The Lower Asuncion group followed the diastrophism and uplift that interrupted sedimentation at the close of Turonian time. This uplift was followed by erosion and waste. Locally, thick beds of pebble and boulder conglomerate make up the lower part of the group, and may be regarded as evidence of a gradual uplift.

The earliest fossil-bearing beds in the Lower Asuncion group contain species of *Peroniceras, Prionocyclus, Desmophyllites,* and some unidentified ammonoids.

In both the San Joaquin and Sacramento valleys, species of *Peroniceras* mark the earliest fossil-bearing beds of the Asuncion group above its basal conglomerate. In the Sacramento Valley, the horizon is marked by *Peroniceras tehamaense*

(Gabb), and by *Peroniceras shastense* n. sp., which is soon followed by *Priono-cyclus*, and in other districts by *Mortoniceras* aff. *M. soutoni* Baily, as found on Cache Creek.

The closing stage of the Lower Asuncion group is marked by a horizon containing few fossils other than *Inoceramus*. This horizon is overlain by the lower beds of the Upper Asuncion group, in which diagnostic types of Mollusca are abundant. It may be concluded that the Lower Asuncion group conforms fairly well to the limits of Senonian time, and is marked at both bottom and top by diastrophism, emphasized by an abrupt change in the faunal succession. Numerous fossils collected from intervening levels give strong support to these deductions and assignments.

The faunal aspects of the Lower Asuncion group contrast strongly with those of the Pacheco. Few Turonian species or genera have been recorded from the Lower Asuncion group. Also to an important extent, each of the units in the Lower Asuncion group is marked by diastrophic changes and possesses characteristic faunas or faunal elements.

By these faunas rather than by lithologic changes, the Lower Asuncion group and its divisions are traceable without difficulty from the west side of the San Joaquin Valley northward to Puerto Creek, to near Mount Diablo, to the border of the Sacramento Valley, and in part far beyond its border. From the Great Valley, various faunal elements are traceable into the coastal areas of southern California or farther, although much of the evidence has been lost as a result of later diastrophism.

Many of these fossils belong to types or genera, whose chronological positions are known in other Pacific border regions or in Europe, and thus serve here as indices of age. These zones and horizons are often traceable or recognizable in other sections, and thus serve as beginning points for the determination of other horizons. Such, for example, is locality 25730 (C. A. S.) on Sand Creek, Colusa County, locality 28323 (C. A. S.) on Puerto Creek, and many others. From Sand Creek, many excellent and diagnostic ammonite species have been reported, including *Eupachydiscus, Nowakites,* and *Parapuzosia,* and a number of species of *Inoceramus* including *Inoceramus undulatoplicatus* Roemer. This horizon has also been recognized on Puerto Creek.

In the Chico formation on Chico Creek, Butte County, types of *Mortoniceras,* closely allied to *M. delawarensis* Morton and *M. campaniense* Grossouvre, determine the chronological position of the central part of the section, and help to approximate that of other zones below and above it.

Outside the Great Valley in California and Oregon, equivalents of the Lower Asuncion group have been recognized by both diastrophic features and by faunal evidence in many West Coast areas between Lower California and southern Alaska. At no localities can the equivalents be shown to have the thickness of the section exposed in the Panoche Hills. Only in the San Rafael Mountains, Santa Barbara County, are comparably thick Cretaceous deposits known. Fairbanks (1894) estimated the Upper Cretaceous strata in this region as 6000 to 10000 feet thick; Reed and Hollister (1936) gave a thickness of 14000 feet for the same.

A hint as to the age of this sequence was given by Fairbanks (1898, p. 450) in a list of invertebrate fossils found in the area. This list of species as here emended includes:

Baculites aff. *B. chicoensis* (Trask)	*Glycymeris veatchii* (Gabb)
Inoceramus sp. indet.	*Meekia sella* Gabb
"Venus" lenticularis Gabb	*Oligoptycha obliqua* (Gabb)
Tellina ashburnerii Gabb	*Dentalium* cf. *D. stramineum* Gabb

All these forms occur in the Lower Asuncion group, and may represent some part of the Coniacian, but the evidence is not conclusive.

Most if not all the Upper Cretaceous strata known on Vancouver Island, and on other islands in the Strait of Georgia, are correlative with the Asuncion group. The Upper Cretaceous deposits on the Alaskan peninsula about Chignik Bay and in the Matanuska Valley, western Alaska, correlate with the upper part of the Lower Asuncion group.

Divisions of the Lower Asuncion group.—The Lower Asuncion group has a maximum thickness of 17500 feet, which spans at least two important episodes of diastrophism, by which it is divided into three important units, each recognizable in most parts of the West Coast by its appropriate faunal assemblage. These subdivisions are better developed in the San Joaquin Valley, whereas only the lower two are exposed, though faunally better characterized, in the Sacramento Valley and in southern Oregon.

CONIACIAN DEPOSITS: In the Great Valley, the lowest unit of the Lower Asuncion group is best developed, most fossiliferous, and best known in western Yolo County whence it extends north into Colusa County, and south into Solano County. Its thickest sections are crossed by Putah and Cache creeks. The source areas of these sediments probably included the present sources of Putah Creek, the streams of Clear Lake Valley, Russian River, and other drainage areas leading into them. The long-continued action of Cretaceous streams built up exceptionally thick accumulations of Upper Cretaceous sediments, belonging in part to the highest portion of the Pacheco group and in part to the Coniacian, the earliest sediments of Coniacian Age overlapping those of the Pacheco group unconformably upon its eastern border. In these areas, the Coniacian has a general thickness of about 13000 feet, and distinctive lithological and faunal characters. As in many other areas in the Great Valley, the lowest Coniacian beds include conglomerate lenses and thick beds of sandstone and shale.

In the Putah-Cache Creek areas, the Coniacian, including the Funks, Guinda and Forbes formations (Kirby, 1943) occupies a belt 2—3 miles wide, extending more than 40 miles along its strike, in which the beds near the base, standing at high angles and dipping northeast, constitute a homocline. The Coniacian in this area may for convenience be divided into two parts, chiefly upon the basis of faunal differences.

As exposed along the larger streams, the lower portion contains lenses of conglomerate at its base and heavy beds of sandstone interspersed with thinner belts of shale. Shales form a large part of the upper portion, above which beds of sandstone and shale alternate in more nearly equal parts. At the top this division

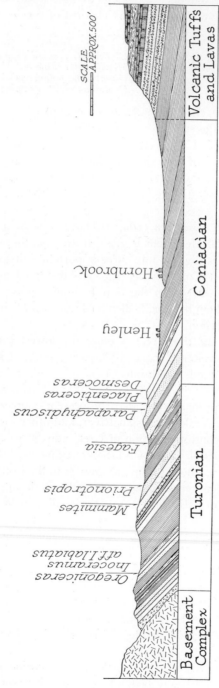

FIGURE 3.—*Section along south side of Rancheria Creek, near Henley, Siskiyou County, California*

is overlain by the lower beds of the Guinda formation (Kirby, 1943), but without evidence of disconformity or interruption in sedimentation. The lenses of conglomerate at the base are not known to be continuous.

In the lower part of the Funks formation, few fossils have been found, but its upper portion includes a belt of fossiliferous shale traceable from the north end of Pleasants Valley northward for many miles. This shale belt forms the upper part of the lower division of the Coniacian and is well exposed at the north end of Pleasants Valley, Solano County. From Pleasants Valley it has been traced northward to the west border of Capay Valley, where it is overlain by Eocene deposits and lost from view for some miles. In its exposed areas in Pleasants Valley its thickness is not constant because of overlapping of later deposits on its eastern margin. Its thickness varies from a thin belt at the south to a body of dark clay shale 1800 feet or more in thickness. In the lower part of this shale are found lentils of limestone 2 to 10 feet or more in thickness, often highly fossiliferous. At locality 1343 (C. A. S.), in the E ½ of sec. 11, T. 7 N., R. 2 W., the writer collected from a large lentil of limestone the following species, among many others:

Echinocorys yoloensis n. sp.
Lytoceras (Gaudryceras) alamedense (Smith)
Desmophyllites yoloensis n. sp.

Thyasira cretacea Whiteaves
Cyprina aff. *C. denmanensis* Whiteaves
"*Cyprina*" *anthracocola* Whiteaves

These limestones lentils are traceable northward to Enos Canyon, where the Funks shale is well exposed, and lentils of limestone outcrop at frequent intervals in its lower part. The shale belt has here a thickness of 1640 feet or more, and is underlain on the west by a thick succession of sandstone and shale probably referable to the Turonian.

Half a mile north of Enos Creek, the lentils of limestone are broken and fractured, and are not continuous. The limestone of these lentils is hard and compact, weathering into large or small mottled gray blocks, having a somewhat reef like appearance, as if formed off shore in quiet water. The calcareous rock shows numerous remains of marine invertebrates, including echinoids, and probably marine algae.

From Enos Canyon, the belt of limestone has been traced northward for some miles, and its horizon appears to have been found near the north end of the Capay Valley.

At locality 1467 (C. A. S.) on the south side of Enos Canyon, McCoy and the writer collected from limestone lentils in the midst of the Funks shale, the following:

Echinocorys sp.
Phylloceras ramosum Meek
Desmophyllites yoloensis n. sp.
Metaplacenticeras pacificum (Smith)
Metaplacenticeras californicum (Anderson)
Parapuzosia sp.
Oxyбеloceras sp.

Baculites aff. *B. fairbanksi* Anderson
Tessarolax distorta Gabb
Bullina yoloensis n. sp.
Oligoptycha obliqua (Gabb)
Elimia aff. *E. veatchii* (Gabb)
Anisomyon meekii (Gabb)
Dentalium (Entalis) whiteavesi Anderson and Hanna

Exogyra parasitica Gabb
Thyasira cretacea Whiteaves
Acila demessa Finlay
Pecten (Propeamuseum) cowperi Waring

Pecten (Camptonectes) cf. P. curvatus
Geinitz
Inoceramus aff. I. whitneyi Gabb

A local facies of the Funks formation is exposed on Cache Creek at its southward bend 2 miles above Rumsey. Here the higher part of the formation consists of thick beds of sandstone interspersed with thinner beds of shale. Some are sparingly fossilferous, and some are rich, though all are not well preserved. At locality 31209 (C. A. S.) on the west border of the Valley, McCoy and the writer collected the following species:

Peroniceras aff. P. leei Reeside
Lytoceras (Gaudryceras) alamedense
(Smith)
Lytoceras (Gaudryceras) sp.
Scaphites (Discoscaphites?) sp.
Scaphites (Yesoites) sp.
Scaphites aff. S. hippocrepis DeKay

Desmophyllites aff. D. yoloensis n. sp.
Eupachydiscus sp.
Hauericeras sp.
Diplomoceras sp. indet.
Cerithidea (2 species)
Cerithium sp.
Tessarolax aff. T. distorta Gabb
Inoceramus aff. I. vancouverensis Shumard

This locality is about on the strike of the beds in Enos Canyon, or it may be somewhat lower in the column. The presence of Eupachydiscus sp. and Inoceramus aff. I. vancouverensis Shumard relate the horizon to the Dobbins horizon described below. The presence of this fauna with Scaphites hippocrepis Dekay and Peroniceras aff. P. leei Reeside is of special interest, being about 600 feet below the horizon of Inoceramus undulatoplicatus Roemer and of an Inoceramus closely akin to Inoceramus digitatus Sowerby.

On the Arroyo del Valle 8 miles southeast of Livermore, Alameda County, a correlative horizon has been recognized on the former Isabel Jordan ranch, 1 mile north of the line of the Aqueduct tunnel. From this district, a considerable collection of invertebrate fossils had once been obtained by Dr. L. G. Yates, and had been loaned to the Geological Department at Stanford University, where it was studied by the writer (1895). Later J. P. Smith added to the collection, and published lists (1898, p. 138; 1900, p. 209), in the belief that all of the Yates collection had come from the same locality, namely, on the east side of the creek opposite the Jordan homesite. Later investigations by the writer, indicated that the Yates collection contained a number of species that were from an older horizon. The species collected by Smith, and a few found by the writer, undoubtedly came from the above named point. It is probable, however, that some of the specimens of the Yates collection had been found farther south on the Arroyo del Valle, where fossils have since been collected by Huey. From the Jordan locality, the species that are important, and which correctly represent the Smith collection are the following:

Phylloceras ramosum Meek
Lytoceras cala (Forbes)
Lytoceras (Gaudryceras) alamedense Smith
Lytoceras (Gaudryceras) delvallense n. sp.
Metaplacenticeras pacificum (Smith)
Metaplacenticeras californicum (Anderson)

Desmophyllites aff. D. selwynianus
Whiteaves
Baculites aff. B. chicoensis Trask
Oligoptycha obliqua (Gabb)
Inoceramus aff. I. vancouverensis Shumard
Inoceramus subundatus Meek
Acila demessa Finlay

From Hospital Creek, McCoy obtained an example of *Metaplacenticeras pacificum* (Smith) indicating the occurrence of correlative beds in this area.

In the Cache Creek district, the lowest division of the Coniacian is overlain on the east by younger beds which form the summit and northeast slope of the Rumsey Hills. This upper division has a maximum thickness of about 3950 feet, divided into two or more units, as exposed in the stream valleys.

According to Kirby (1943) the lowest part of the upper division, the Guinda formation, is exposed on the upper branches of Salt Creek, in the central and north-central part of T. 12 N., R. 3 W., Yolo County, and on the faulted west slope of Rumsey Hills. The strata of this unit consists chiefly of massive, well bedded, sometimes concretionary sandstone, said to be 1400 feet thick in surface exposures and well sections.

Overlying this formation is the Forbes shale, consisting of clay shale and silty or sandy shale, given a thickness of 1300 feet by Kirby, although in some areas it may be thicker. This formation is well exposed on most of the larger streams on the east slope of the Rumsey Hills, as on Sand Creek, Salt Creek and others. Its lower beds appear on the summit of the hills at the head of Buckeye Creek, and farther north. In the sandy shale at the base of this formation, on the southeast border of "Nigger Heaven dome," Dobbins and Johnson collected the following invertebrate species:

Canadoceras celeste n. sp.   *Parapuzosia* sp.
Eupachydiscus sp. indet.   *Inoceramus vancouverensis* Shumard

These beds are well exposed on Salt Creek west of the south fork, in section 34, whence came another specimen of the same species of *Parapuzosia*. Overlying the lower beds of the Forbes shale is the Dobbins horizon with numerous characteristic species. From near the center of section 34, on Salt Creek were obtained the following:

Eupachydiscus arbucklensis n. sp.   *Nowakites* aff. *N. dobbinsi* n. sp.
Desmophyllites sp. indet.   *Inoceramus* aff. *I. digitatus* Sowerby
Oxybeloceras aff. *O. petrolense* n. sp.   *Inoceramus vancouverensis* Shumard
Baculites sp.   *Inoceramus subundatus* Meek.

On Sand Creek, near the Dobbins ranchhouse, at locality 25730 (C. A. S.) on the E ½ sec. 7, T. 13 N., R. 3 W., Dobbins and the writer collected:

Eupachydiscus arbucklensis n. sp.   *Nautilus campbelli* Meek
Parapachydiscus cortinaensis n. sp.   *Pseudomelania colusaensis* n. sp.
Puzosia (Parapuzosia) arenaica n. sp.   *Inoceramus* aff. *I. klamathensis* Anderson
Nowakites rumseyensis n. sp.   *Inoceramus* aff. *I. digitatus* Sowerby
Nowakites dobbinsi n. sp.   *Inoceramus undulatoplicatus* Roemer
Baculites aff. *B. inornatus* Meek   *Inoceramus subundatus* Meek

This locality is believed to be somewhat older than the locality on Salt Creek, although some of the species are found at both localities and indicate a nearly similar age.

In the Forbes shale on the lower reaches of Buckeye Creek, and more clearly on Petroleum Creek, fossil-bearing beds overlying the Dobbins horizon are exposed. From these Bennison collected many invertebrate species not found lower in the section, including the following:

Baculites chicoensis Trask
Baculites inornatus Meek
Haueticeras sp.
Desmophyllites aff. *D. siskiyouensis* n. sp.
Canadoceras sp. indet.
Oxybeloceras petrolense n. sp.
Cypraea aff. *C. kayei* (Forbes)
Oligoptycha obliqua (Gabb)
Volutoderma californica Dall

Pseudomelania colusaensis n. sp.
Tessarolax distorta Gabb
Dentalium (Entalis) whiteavesi Anderson
    and Hanna
Inoceramus aff. *I. whitneyi* Gabb
Inoceramus aff. *I. chicoensis* n. sp.
Glycymeris veatchii (Gabb)
Parallelodon brewerianus (Gabb)

On the east side of Sacramento Valley, the lowest known beds of Senonian age, belonging to the Coniacian, are found at a few places only. On Oak Run Creek, eastern Shasta County, strata outcrop that may be regarded as representing the lowest part of the Coniacian. Here beds containing *Peroniceras shastense* n. sp., and *Prionocyclus californicus* n. sp., were discovered by Popenoe and Findlay near the Hathaway home, a fourth of a mile west of the basement. The thickness of the exposed section on Oak Run Creek is not known, although it can hardly exceed 1300 feet, in part exposed toward the west, where a fragment of *Placenticeras* was found by the writer.

On Battle Creek, some miles to the south, Gabb obtained the holotype of *Peroniceras tehamaense*. No other example of the species has since been found.

If these lower Senonian beds extend south of Battle Creek they are concealed by volcanic formations that cover the region west of Mount Lassen. Whether these lower Senonian beds of the east side of the Valley may be closely correlated with any part of the section on the west, is uncertain, although it is probable.

Higher in the column on the south fork of Cow Creek, half a mile below the Waggoner home, Dobbins and the writer collected a few species from the shales, including:

Lytoceras (Gaudryceras) alamedense (Smith)
Baculites sp. indet.

Baculites inornatus Meek
Inoceramus subundatus Meek

Lower in the section, half a mile above the small power plant, was found a recognizable fragment of *Metaplacenticeras* sp., and *Inoceramus* aff. *I. vancouverensis* Shumard.

South of Battle Creek no Coniacian exposures are known for a distance of nearly 100 miles to the vicinity of Folsom. Here the beds are widely overlapped by the younger Coniacian; farther south no exposures of this age are known.

As illustrated by Whitney (1865, p. 207), the small area of upper Chico beds at Tuscan Springs were brought to the surface by an anticline with steep dips to the northeast and southwest. A fossil assemblage, collected chiefly by Gabb, consists of more than 30 species of marine Mollusca. The locality is situated about 6 miles east of the axis of the trough and is probably about 30 miles from the eastern shore line of its epoch, as indicated by the outcrops of Lower Asuncion beds. In its position near the axis of the trough, and in its faunal aspects, the area resembles that exposed on Petroleum Creek more than any other known to the writer. A near-shore facies of the same age may exist on Rock Creek, near Folsom.

The assemblage in Gabb's synopsis (1864, p. 220-236) includes many gastropod and pelecypod species, but only two cephalopod forms, indicating a shallow-water habitat. As partly emended and enlarged by more recent collections, the Tuscan Springs assemblage includes the following marine invertebrates:

Ammonites peruvianus Gabb (not v. Buch)
Baculites chicoensis Trask
Eripachla ponderosa (Gabb)
Haydenia impressa Gabb
Margarites inornatus (Gabb)
Margarites ornatissima (Gabb)
Elimia veatchii (Gabb)
Scaphander costatus (Gabb)
Perissitys brevirostris (Gabb)
Tessarolax distorta Gabb
Anchura falciformis (Gabb)
Volutoderma californica Dall
Volutoderma gabbi White
Volutoderma averillii (Gabb)
Volutoderma dilleri (White)
Pugnellus hamulus Gabb

Trigonia tryoniana Gabb
Mytilus quadratus Gabb
Astarte tuscana Gabb
"Aphrodina" varians (Gabb)
Tellina quadrata Gabb
Cymbophora ashburnerii Gabb
Corbula traskii Gabb
?Loripes dubia Gabb
Cucullaea truncata Gabb
Martesia clausa Gabb
Meekia sella Gabb
Glycymeris veatchii (Gabb)
Glycymeris shastensis n. sp.
Inoceramus aff. *I. subundatus* Meek
Modiolus cylindricus (Gabb)
Acila demessa Finlay

"Ammonites peruvianus" Gabb is based upon a fragment of shell showing neither the periphery nor umbilical margin, and only a limited number of sinuous, branching ribs. In general aspect it somewhat resembles *Kossmaticeras* of the type of *K.* (*Madrasites*) *bhavani* (Stoliczka), from the Trichinopoli district (Senonian) of southern India. Some of the species in this assemblage have been found in the lower portion of the Coniacian.

For a more definite age determination of the fauna at Tuscan Springs a short list of the more diagnostic species with notes as to their occurrence in other places, is as shown in Table 2.

Others could be added but all indicate that the horizon at Tuscan Springs is not younger than that at Petroleum Creek, and a critical comparison of the fauna seems to indicate that both are referable to Lower Senonian.

Gabb records (1864, pp. 220–236) from "Texas Flat" (Rock Creek) 34 species, including 15 common to Tuscan Springs. This collection was obtained from a shaft 40 feet deep. The shaft and its precise locality are no longer known. The strata now exposed on Rock Creek, said by the local residents to have been the locality of "Texas Flat," do not exceed 200 feet in thickness and rest directly on granite.

The species common to both Tuscan Springs and "Texas Flat" includes the following; many of them also occur at Petroleum Creek:

Baculites chicoensis Trask
Gyrodes expansa Gabb
Oligoptycha obliqua (Gabb)
Margarites ornatissima (Gabb)
Anchura falciformis (Gabb)
Scaphander costatus (Gabb)
?Loripes dubia Gabb
Glycymeris veatchii (Gabb)

Martesia clausa Gabb
Cymbophora ashburnerii Gabb
Corbula traski Gabb
Cucullaea truncata Gabb
Trigonia evansana Meek
"Aphrodina" varians (Gabb)
Astarte conradiana Gabb

According to Stewart (1926) terrestrial gastropods found here associated with the marine Mollusca include *Ventridens lens* (Gabb), *?Straparollus paucivolva* Gabb, *Discohelix leana* Gabb.

To these may be added an inflated form related to the land snail *Helix* Linné, found by the writer in a block of sandstone associated with various marine invertebrates, now in the collections at the California Academy of Sciences. These terrestrial species may be taken as evidence of the proximity of this locality to the shoreline.

A comparison of the species from Petroleum Creek with those from Tuscan Springs shows 37 per cent in common. The Petroleum Creek fauna indicates somewhat deeper water than at Tuscan Springs. The Rock Creek fauna indicates a near-shore position, and a shallow-water facies. All however may be regarded as essentially synchronous, and referable to a Santonian or slightly older horizon.

Oregon Basin.—This basin was partially described by the writer (1902a, p. 17) as including all the Cretaceous deposits known in southern Oregon (Jackson

TABLE 2.—*Diagnostic species of the fauna at Tuscan Springs*

Tuscan Springs	Other localities	Recognized stage
Tessarolax distorta Gabb	Enos Canyon, Yolo County,	Coniacian (Lr. ?)
Volutoderma dilleri White	Little Cow Creek, Shasta Co.	Coniacian ?
Margarites ornatissima Gabb	Sucia Island, Strait of Georgia	Lower Senonian
Elimia veatchii (Gabb)	Sucia Island, ” ” ”	Lower Senonian
Inoceramus subundatus Meek	Sucia Island, ” ” ”	Lower Senonian

and Josephine counties), and extending into northern California (Siskiyou County) in later Cretaceous time. It was stated (p. 18) that:

"These Oregon deposits, especially their lower strata, appear to belong to an embayment distinct from that of the Sacramento Valley; but they show a similar transgression of later members of the series, only in this case, the expansions were toward the southeast."

In early Cretaceous (Shasta time) this basin did not receive marine waters or sediments, and it was probably occupied by a river system draining toward the west, not unlike that of the present. Beginning with later Cretaceous (late Albian time), widespread subsidence in coastal areas was initiated, and with it the sea entered the river valley and progressively spread east and southeast, as evidenced by marine Upper Cretaceous (late Albian) deposits.

In early Senonian time, this invasion by the sea had reached the Shasta Valley in northern California. Near Henley, Siskiyou County, the writer (1895) collected the following species:

Metaplacenticeras pacificum (Smith)   *Parapachydiscus henleyensis* (Anderson)
Metaplacenticeras californicum (Anderson)   *Kotôceras* aff. *K. richardsoni* n. sp.
Lytoceras (Tetragonites) henleyense n. sp.   *Inoceramus subundatus* Meek
Anisoceras draconum n. name   *Inoceramus* aff. *I. pembertoni* Waring

This assemblage was found near the local base of the Senonian and about 350 feet above the upper Turonian which contains *Fagesia siskiyouensis* Anderson and *Fagesia klamathensis* n. sp., and other Turonian species (Fig. 3).

On the Richardson ranch, 2 miles or more south of the river, a correlative horizon of the Coniacian is found in the same stratigraphic position as that at Henley. From the shales on the Richardson ranch, the writer collected the following species:

Kotôceras richardsoni n. sp.
Kotôceras subsugatum n. name
Lytoceras (Tetragonites) cala (Forbes)
Volutoderma gabbi (White)

?Desmophyllites aff. *D. pyrenaicum* (Grossouvre)
Desmophyllites siskiyouensis n. sp.
Prionocycloceras crenulatum (Anderson)
Inoceramus klamathensis Anderson

From underlying concretionary sandstones, probably the lowest beds of the Coniacian, were obtained: *Puzosia (Parapuzosia) hearni* n. sp. and *Nowakites klamathonis* n. sp. The thickness of the Coniacian in these areas probably nowhere exceeds 2500 feet and south of the river it is limited to 2000 feet.

In southern Oregon equivalents of the Coniacian have been proved by the finding of *Metaplacenticeras pacificum* (Smith), *Metaplacenticeras californicum* (Anderson), *Phylloceras ramosum* Meek, and *Gaudryceras* aff. *G. newberryanum* Meek, southwest of Phoenix (F. M. Anderson, 1902, p. 27). The thickness in this area does not equal that in northern California, probably because of an overlap by later beds referable to the Asuncion.

San Joaquin Valley.—In the southern embayment of the trough, data concerning the Coniacian are confined to its west border, since no Upper Cretaceous deposits outcrop on its eastern side. On the west side of the Valley the sequence is usually incomplete. Younger deposits which widely overlap the Coniacian on the east border of the Sacramento Valley do the same on the west border of the San Joaquin Valley, as between New Idria and the north border of McLure Valley, where few outcrops of Coniacian strata are known. In the Pacheco Pass quadrangle, only the early beds, with *Peroniceras quintoense* n. sp., are known, though higher beds may be found. Only on Puerto Creek have fossils been collected that show the presence of the Upper Coniacian, though the faulted condition of the area renders stratigraphic work difficult. At locality 28323 (C. A. S.), on the SW ¼ of sec. 35, T. 5 S., R. 6 E., beds correlative with the upper portion of the Coniacian as exposed on the west side of the Sacramento Valley occur, with a thickness not exceeding 2600 feet. At this locality, Taff, Hanna, and Cross collected the following diagnostic species:

Canadoceras aff. *C. multicostatum* Whiteaves
Baculites inornatus Meck
Pseudomelania colusaensis n. sp.

Anchura falciformis (Gabb)
Inoceramus cf. *I. undulatoplicatus* Roemer
Inoceramus aff. *I. pembertoni* Waring

The strata yielding this fauna undoubtedly represent the Dobbins horizon of the Forbes formation, here cut off from older beds by a north-south fault. West of the fault, though not adjoining it, Turonian strata outcrop over a large area.

In the Panoche Hills, strata regarded as correlative with the Coniacian of the west side of the Sacramento Valley by reason of their stratigraphic position have a thickness of about 6600 feet. Near the base of the unit is a succession of boulder conglomerates well exposed on Ortigalita Creek (Anderson and Pack, 1915, Pl. IV, B).

A small area of the Coniacian is found at locality 1552 (C. A. S.) on sec. 28, T. 26 N., R. 18 E., on the south border of Antelope Valley, in northwest Kern

County, from which Hanna and Henny collected the fauna listed below, at a point 800 feet west of the center of the section:

Parapachydiscus (large species)
Desmophyllites selwynianus (Whiteaves),
Desmophyllites sp. indet.
Lytoceras (Gaudryceras) aff. *L. (G.) cinctum* (Spath)
Lytoceras (Gaudryceras) aff. *L. (G.) alamedense* (Smith)
Baculites inornatus Meek
Baculites aff. *B. inornatus* Meek

Paleotractus crassus Gabb
Glauconia sp.
Bulimulus sp.
Glycymeris sp.
Inoceramus sp.
Inoceramus subundatus Meek
Inoceramus klamathensis Anderson
Acila (Truncacila) demessa Finlay

A correlative horizon later found by Hanna on Avenal Creek, west of McLure Valley, 18 miles northwest of the above locality, contained *Desmophyllites selwynianus* Whiteaves, and a stout species of *Cerithium*. This locality is on the northwest border of a poorly known large Cretaceous area. Arnold and Johnson (1910) were unable to devote sufficient time for a complete exploration of the area, and did not indicate what part of it might be referable to Upper Cretaceous; some part of it may be of Shasta age. The structural and other features of the region as depicted on their map show a prevailing northeast dip, with the younger beds on its northeast border. On the basis of fossils found by Hanna and Huett, and of the stratigraphic relations known in this area, these beds seem to be a continuation of those on the border of Antelope Valley, and probably are referable to the upper part of the Coniacian.

Southern California.—West and south of the Great Valley, no deposits of the Coniacian are known north of the Santa Ynez Range. In the Santa Monica and the Santa Ana mountains, strata of this age were indicated by Waring (1917), and later by Popenoe (1942). Waring (p. 56, 57) gave a list of 36 or more invertebrate fossils collected from strata exposed near Santa Monica, and farther north, including the following:

Metaplacenticeras pacificum (Smith)
Metaplacenticeras californicum (Anderson)
Metaplacenticeras transitionale (Waring)

Pugnellus rotundus Waring
Pholadomya subelongata Meek
Crassatellites triangulata Waring

No species in the above list represent beds older than Coniacian. These strata represent an overlap synchronous with that in southern Oregon, and in northern California, near Henley.

Popenoe (1942, Fig. 4) has given a list of species from an outcrop in the Simi Hills, farther to the north, in Dayton Canyon, Calabasas Quadrangle. Among the species he recorded are:

Metaplacenticeras pacificum (Smith)
Metaplacenticeras californicum (Anderson)
Margarites ornatissima (Gabb)

Lysis californica Packard
Trigonocallista bowersiana (Cooper)
Cucullaea youngi Waring

The species listed by Popenoe from the Simi Hills include some that occur in higher beds, but none that range down to horizons below the Coniacian. In his Figure 4, he shows a similar column and list of species collected from the west slope of the Santa Ana Mountains, Orange County, and from the beds to which he first attached the name Pleasants member.

Lower California.—Whether Coniacian deposits occur as a whole, or in part, on the peninsula of Lower California is not known, although they may be represented among the older beds of the "Two principal series . . . both of late Cretaceous age," noted by Darton (1921, p. 725).

No species of either *Peroniceras, Prionocyclus,* or *Desmophyllites* have been recorded south of the Great Valley, and at no point south of this Valley does the great thickness of Coniacian deposits occur. Its maximum thickness is found near the southern border of Klamathonia.

Alaska.—In parts of western Alaska, Upper Cretaceous deposits occur that are faunally related to those in the upper division of the Coniacian in the Great Valley of California, and in part with those in the "Nanaimo series" on Vancouver Island, although the Alaskan faunas are not always specifically determined.

On the Alaskan peninsula, in the Chignik formation, according to Stanton and others who have worked there, as seen in G. C. Martin's summary account (1926), the following species have been collected, *Glycymeris veatchi* (Gabb), *Trigonocallista nitida* (Gabb), *Inoceramus undulatoplicatus* Roemer.

The formation is comparatively thin, is of Upper Cretaceous age, and rests unconformably upon Upper Jurassic and Lower Cretaceous. In the Matanuska Valley strata of both ages occur. The Upper Cretaceous, 4000 feet or more thick, is said to rest unconformably upon the older Cretaceous. In some places, the Matanuska formation (Upper Cretaceous) contains conglomerate in its lower part, though not in thick or numerous beds.

According to Martin (1926, p. 321): "Marine molluscan remains are fairly abundant in the shale that constitutes the Matanuska formation" (on Boulder Creek).

Concerning the marine fossils, Martin includes a note by Stanton, wherein the Upper Cretaceous faunas of this region are said to be "a part of the general Indo-Pacific faunas found in the Chico formation of California, on Vancouver Island, in Japan, and in India." Among the Upper Cretaceous fossils from the Matanuska formation, Martin lists (p. 324, 325) the following species:

Phylloceras ramosum Meek	*Gaudryceras kayei* Forbes
"*Anisoceras*" *subcompressum* Whiteaves	*Inoceramus undulatoplicatus* Roemer

At least two of these species, and analogues of others, have been found in the Guinda and Forbes formations in the Great Valley of California, and in correlative beds in the "Nanaimo series" on Vancouver Island, here regarded as being of lower Senonian age.

In the Chitina Valley, from the Upper Cretaceous shale of Chititu and Young Creeks, Martin (p. 366, 367) records the following invertebrate species:

Phylloceras (?) *ramosum* Meek	*Cyprina occidentalis* Whiteaves
Tessarolax sp.	*Thyasira* sp.

All these species occur in the Coniacian of California in the Great Valley. Although most of the invertebrate species listed by Martin from the Upper Cretaceous of Alaska were only generically determined, the foregoing lists contain enough specifically named to afford some evidence that the diastrophism on the

West Coast during early Senonian time, as recorded in the Great Valley, and in Oregon, was not wholly local, but had to some extent operated along the West Coast from Alaska south to Mexico and Chile.

DIASTROPHIC RELATIONSHIPS OF THE CONIACIAN: Within the environs of the Great Valley, the altitudinal relations between its floor and its border areas were slowly changing during Coniacian time, with progressive uplift on its borders, and a narrowing of the Valley floor in both embayments.

In the Sacramento embayment, in which the evidence is clearer, as seen in the northern and western parts, the Coniacian has a thickness of at least 7240 feet, in which older beds lie farther west, and the younger farther east. All present a neritic, or a somewhat littoral aspect, as if during this part of Senonian time the areas of Klamathonia were slowly rising, with a gradual retreat of the strand line eastward. On the eastern border of the trough similar movements are recognizable, though in the reverse direction, and they are less pronounced. The results, measured in cumulative thickness, are much less on the east than on the west, and it may be assumed that the belts of withdrawal on opposite sides of the trough corresponded in like manner. As seen on the South fork of Cow Creek, the Coniacian can hardly exceed 3000 feet, or less than half that exposed on the west side.

At Tuscan Springs, Tehama County, a small area of Upper Coniacian includes about 500 feet of strata. The fauna contains many species of gastropods and pelecypods of neritic aspect. On the east side of the valley, the belt of withdrawal is not less than 15 miles, whereas on the west side, the corresponding belt is about half this width. The width of the marine belt between that of Tuscan Springs, and its nearest counterpart on the west along the strike of the Petroleum Creek horizon, indicates a definite narrowing of the intervening marine areas during Coniacian time to little more than half their former width. The marine faunas on both sides of the trough at the close of Coniacian time were almost wholly gastropods and pelecypods of near-shore habitat from protected, quiet waters. During the following Santonian many important changes are readily recognized, beginning with an almost sudden expansion of marine waters, especially on the east border of the trough, and in its northern portion. In its southern embayments similar expansion took place toward the west, where equivalents of the Chico formation are also found. These facts constitute an important contrast between the northern and southern embayments of the Great Valley trough.

SANTONIAN AND CAMPANIAN DEPOSITS: The Chico formation in its type areas on Chico and Butte creeks apparently represents deposition through the Santonian and Campanian. These beds are characterized by species of *Canadoceras* and *Mortoniceras*. Correlative deposits have been found on the west side of the San Joaquin Valley from Mount Diablo southward at intervals to the Panoche Hills, south of Coalinga, and as far south as Orange County.

The second important unit of the Lower Asuncion group, the Chico formation, so named from its occurrence in Butte County, was first described by Trask (1855). Its sedimentary history began with a subsidence on the borders of the trough following an interval of gradual uplift and marine retreat during Coniacian time. The outcrop of the Chico can be traced sporadically on the east border of the Valley, from near the north end of Butte County, southward to Pentz, a distance of about 40 miles. It then passes under cover of later deposits.

In its type areas in Butte County, the Chico is overlain by thick deposits of volcanic agglomerates, lava flows, and rubble, and is exposed only where streams have trenched its cover deeply enough to reach the gently inclined beds. Where so exposed the formation rests unconformably upon crystalline or metamorphic Paleozoic rocks. Exposures appear only in the narrow valleys of a few streams that cross its outcrop from the east, or from the northeast, as on the branches of Chico Creek, Butte Creek, Dry Creek (Pentz), and on the south branch of the latter. No exposures are known on the east border of the valley south of Oroville, although older beds of the Asuncion group are found farther north and farther south.

The complete thickness of the Chico is probably not exposed on any of these streams, since its upper beds are overlain by the volcanic Tuscan formation. The greatest thickness of the Chico exposed in this area is on Big Chico Creek, for which Taff, Hanna and Cross (1940) gave an estimate of about 2000 feet. The section here begins with a basal conglomerate 50 feet thick resting directly upon metamorphic slates and limestones. Overlying these basal beds the formation consists almost wholly of bedded sandstones, having a dip of about 10° or less to the southwest.

At some levels, the beds are very fossiliferous but well cemented, though in a large part they are relatively soft and easily eroded. The best exposures are in the stream channel, where fossil collecting can be done only at low water stages of the stream, and often with much difficulty. On Butte Creek, a few miles southeast, the same thickness and lithological conditions exist, but the exposures are less accessible, and fossils are less numerous, though good collections have been made and include some species not yet found on Chico Creek.

The most important feature of the Chico in its type area, Chico and Butte creeks, is the unique character of its cephalopod fauna, unlike that of any other formation in the Upper Cretaceous on the West Coast. Large collections of fossils from Chico Creek have been made by Taff, Hanna, and Cross (1940), and are deposited in the California Academy of Sciences. The most nearly representative fauna of the formation is the collection made from locality 27838 (C. A. S.) near the middle of the exposed section, 1225 feet above its base, and which includes the following species:

Mortoniceras randalli n. sp.
Mortoniceras buttense (Anderson)
Mortoniceras chicoense (Trask)
Mortoniceras (Submortoniceras) gabbi
    (Anderson)
Mortoniceras (Submortoniceras) pentzanum
    n. sp.
Hauericeras mickeyi n. sp.
Butticeras studleyi n. sp.
Oxybeloceras taffi n. sp.
Parapachydiscus bidwelli n. sp.
Canadoceras fraternum (Gabb)
Baculites chicoensis Trask

Baculites buttensis n. sp.
Anchura falciformis (Gabb)
Volutoderma californica Dall
Volutoderma averillii (Gabb)
Perissitys brevirostris (Gabb)
Oligoptycha obliqua (Gabb)
Trigonocallista bowersiana (Cooper)
Cucullaea aff. *C. youngi* Waring
Tenea inflata (Gabb)
Inoceramus chicoensis n. sp.
Inoceramus sp. indet.
Trigonia hemphilli n. sp.
Acila (Truncacila) demessa Finlay

At locality 28171 (C. A. S.) near the top of the exposed section on Chico Creek, the following species were collected by Taff, Hanna and Cross:

Canadoceras fraternum (Gabb)　　　　　　Perissitys brevirostris (Gabb)
Inoceramus aff. I. vancouverensis Shumard　　Anchura falciformis (Gabb)
Inoceramus turgidus n. sp.

Three of these species occur in the preceding list, and show a measure of unity in the sequence of beds exposed here.

On Butte Creek, 4 miles southeast of Chico Creek, the sequence of beds and their lithologic character are essentially the same although the exposed section is not so thick.

From outcrops between Helltown and the junction of the stream branches below Diamondville, the following species have been collected, partly by Popenoe and Sharf and partly by Bennison and the writer:

Mortoniceras (Submortoniceras) gabbi　　　Trigonia aff. T. evansana Meek
　(Anderson)　　　　　　　　　　　　　Oligoptycha obliqua (Gabb)
Butticeras sp.　　　　　　　　　　　　　Perissitys brevirostris (Gabb)
Butticeras studleyi n. sp.　　　　　　　　Cymbophora gabbiana (Anderson)
Trigonia leana Gabb　　　　　　　　　　Trigonocallista nitida (Gabb)

All strata exposed on Butte Creek are also exposed on Chico Creek, though the faunas found in both are probably not completely known. Most of the species in the above list probably occur also on Chico Creek, though not yet found.

Near Pentz ("Pence's ranch"), 12 miles north of Oroville, Butte County, the Chico formation has a thickness of only a few hundred feet, and is not regarded as representing the span exposed on Chico Creek. From locality 1125 (C. A. S.) 1.5 miles west of Pentz P.O., the following species have been listed by Gabb, or later collected by Hanna, Bennison and the writer, or others:

Mortoniceras (Submortoniceras) pentzanum　"Astarte" tuscana (Gabb)
　n. sp.　　　　　　　　　　　　　　　Glycymeris veatchii (Gabb)
Canadoceras fraternum (Gabb)　　　　　　Acila (Truncacila) demessa Finlay
Bostrychoceras brewerii (Gabb)　　　　　Oligoptycha obliqua (Gabb)
Bostrychoceras decliva (Gabb)　　　　　　Anchura falciformis (Gabb)
Baculites chicoensis Trask　　　　　　　Volutoderma californica Dall
Trigonia aff. T. evansana Meek　　　　　Scaphander (Microscapha) costatus (Gabb)

Although the strata along Dry Creek and near Pentz are only a few hundred feet thick and rest directly upon basement rocks (slates and limestone), they contain a fauna not essentially different, except in number of species, from the upper beds exposed on Chico Creek or on Butte Creek. Insofar as the fauna differs, it may be regarded as being supplementary to that of locality 27838 (C. A. S.) near the middle of the Chico Creek section.

The fauna of the more representative part of the Chico formation is well characterized by cephalopods of the genera Mortoniceras, Butticeras, Canadoceras, and specific types of Trigonia, Inoceramus, and other forms not known in earlier West Coast formations. These cephalopods contrast strongly with those known at present in the Coniacian, as do the Inocerami and some other mollusks. However, many gastropod and pelecypod genera seem to have continued from late Coniacian into the Santonian. The nearest analogues of the mortoniceratids here listed or described from the Santonian are geographically far removed from West

Coast or from Indo-Pacific influences, and pertain to an Atlantic or a Mediterranean province, or to such as are known on both borders of the Atlantic, New Jersey and western Europe. It seems that some unusual event had taken place following the close of Coniacian time, that had permitted migrations of invertebrates from Atlantic to Pacific waters and into the Great Valley trough, where they are now found.

The age and chronological span of the Chico formation are indicated by its stratigraphic position and its paleontologic relations to the upper Coniacian, and by its position between the latter and the highest beds of the Lower Asuncion group, which terminate with Senonian time. As in the Joaquin embayment where the record is most complete, its position indicates that it can hardly be younger than Middle Campanian time.

It may be assumed that the mortoniceratids were contemporary with their nearest analogues on the American East Coast, and in Europe. In Europe the species most nearly allied to *Mortoniceras randalli* n. sp. is *M. campaniense* Grossouvre, and on the American East Coast, it is *M. delawarense* (Morton). Both these species are assigned by Spath (1921, T. opp. p. 50) to an upper Senonian (Campanian) age, and other writers have agreed.

The presence of various species of *Canadoceras* in the Chico and its correlatives in the San Joaquin Valley indicates that a major portion of the sequence was deposited during Santonian time.

Strata probably correlative to the Chico formation are recognizable or indicated stratigraphically or faunally on the west border of the San Joaquin Valley, where they are exposed on various streams that cross the outcrop south of Puerto Creek. On Puerto Creek itself no direct evidence of beds of this age has been found, although they should be found between strata that are recognizable faunally below and above its position. At base its outcrop should begin with the conglomerate beds that diagonally cross sec. 35, T. 5 S., R. 6 E., immediately overlying the Coniacian deposits, and extending eastward to the west border of the Moreno formation. Farther south on Crow Creek, at locality 27855 (C. A. S.), on the E ½ of sec. 5, T. 7 S., R. 7 E., the upper beds of the Santonian are indicated by the following species collected by Taff, Hanna and Cross:

Canadoceras aff. *C. subtilobatum* Jimbo	*Inoceramus* cf. *I angulatus* Jimbo
Baculites aff. *B. chicoensis* Trask	*Baculites* sp.

The stratigraphic and topographic relations of the belt containing these species conforms to those of the Santonian farther south. In the Pacheco Pass Quadrangle, deposits of this age have been more definitely proved. Bennison discovered on Garzas Creek, on the SE ¼ of sec. 23, T. 8 S., R. 7 E., in a bed of sandy shale, a number of diagnostic species, including the following:

Submortoniceras sp. (a fragment)	*Inoceramus chicoensis* n. sp.
Oxybeloceras taffi n. sp. (a fragment)	

Insofar as these species are known, all are found in the Chico formation in its typical localities in Butte County and near Altamont, Alameda County.

On the east flank of the Panoche Hills, north of Big Panoche Valley, Santonian deposits are well developed, about 4500 feet thick, consisting of clay shales alternating with beds of sandy shale containing calcareous concretions, some fossiliferous. The higher beds of the sequence are more or less sandy, are readily eroded and deeply trenched. This unit is traceable by its lithologic and topographic features, and where it crosses Moreno Gulch the beds are deeply cut by ravines which run almost parallel to the strike. In the south branch of Moreno Gulch, at locality 28542 (C. A. S.), near the center of sec. 15, T. 14 S., R. 11 E., Donald Birch and associates collected the following species:

Phylloceras gargantuum n. sp.	*Baculites* sp. (very large)
Parapachydiscus panochensis n. sp.	*Inoceramus* sp. (a fragment)

At locality 28339 (C. A. S.) on the NW ¼ sec. 14, of the same township, Taff and Cross discovered a large fragment of *Canadoceras* n. sp., in sandy beds above the top of this unit. The species here listed probably represent a horizon near the top of the Santonian.

Northwest of Coalinga, Fresno County, the Santonian and Campanian constitute the highest exposed portion of the Asuncion group. The basal conglomerates outcrop in many places, resting unconformably upon the Pacheco group, the Shasta series, or the Franciscan rocks in different areas on the Valley borders for a distance of 50 miles. The Coniacian, which in the Pacheco Pass Quadrangle attains a thickness of 2500 feet, is overlapped in the Coalinga region by the Santonian between Big Panoche Valley at the north, and the north border of McLure Valley on the south. In a brief note the writer (1905, p. 161) first called attention to the "Upper Chico" deposits (Maestrichtian) outcropping north of Los Gatos Creek, with a mention of their character and structural attitude. A brief list of invertebrate fossils from the lower part of the sequence indicated that the strata were high in the Upper Cretaceous succession, as then understood. Later Arnold and R. Anderson extended field work in this area west to White Creek, and their account (1910, p. 54–59) contains more complete data, with a suggestion as to the grouping of the strata. They also collected additional fossils, which they listed (p. 60). Following this work R. Anderson and R. W. Pack (1915, p. 40–42) recognized their divisions, describing them in somewhat different terms, giving their thickness as respectively 4400 and 4000 feet. The fossils in the upper half of the "Lowest member" of Anderson and Pack, or more definitely from the lowest member of the Lower Asuncion group of the present terminology in this area, include the following emended list:

Parapachydiscus (?)	*Glycymeris veatchii* (Gabb)
Baculites chicoensis Trask	*Legumen oöides* (Gabb)
Cymbophora ashburnerii Gabb	*Nucula* sp. indet.
"*Aphrodina*" *varians* (Gabb)	*Perissitys brevirostris* (Gabb)
Anomia lineata Gabb	*Volutoderma gabbi* (White)
Parallelodon vancouverensis (Meek)	*Oligoptycha obliqua* (Gabb)
Inoceramus chicoensis n. sp.	

At least 11 of these 12 are characteristic and plentiful in the Chico formation in its type area in Butte County, and are representative of this formation wherever they are found. The deposit from which these fossils were obtained consists mainly of black shales dipping steeply southward. In this direction, in the Waltham Creek district, the same member, as described by Arnold and Anderson (1910, p. 54) :

"Comprises a thick series of alternating thin beds of dark shale and sandstone with the . . . heavy conglomerate at the base, and with characteristic massive concretionary sandstone beds that form the upper division, overlying. Its thickness, including the conglomerate zone, measures at least 4,500 feet in the Alcalde Canyon section. . . ."

According to these writers the basal conglomerate, 200 to 300 feet in thickness ". . . represents throughout the district . . . an important stratigraphic horizon, characterized by a coarsening of the sediment. . . ." This conglomerate is essentially that described by Pack and English (1914, p. 128, 129) as traversing Juniper Ridge, with an overlying succession of shales. The thickness of the formation, including its basal conglomerate, is given by Pack and English as 4800 feet. At the top of the section west of Coalinga *Baculites chicoensis* Trask and other characteristic fossils of the Chico formation occur. The basal conglomerate traversing Juniper Ridge was traced at intervals (Arnold and Anderson, 1910, p. 35) southeast to the border of McLure Valley, and north to the head of White Creek, a distance of about 40 miles. In these areas this horizon is less fossiliferous than in Butte County, or at Altamont, although enough fossils have been collected to prove its identity, and to aid in its correlation.

According to Arnold and Anderson (1910, p. 54) : "Near the head of Big Tar Canyon, at the west edge of the mapped area, a thickness of 1200 feet or more of coarse, hard conglomerate occurs within the Cretaceous shale" probably at the same horizon as that at Juniper Ridge.

At locality 31313 (C. A. S.) on sec. 20, T. 25 S., R. 17 E., Hanna collected, from boulders from this conglomerate, many invertebrate species characteristic of upper Coniacian beds outcropping at Tuscan Springs, Tehama County. The lower beds of the Coniacian outcropping on Avenal Creek have already been mentioned. Certain beds in Big Tar Canyon can readily be shown to be faunally correlative with beds in Chico Creek.

The conglomerate marks in both areas the basal beds of the Santonian, and an important diastrophic event, followed by subsidence and a wide-spread overlap of the same upon older terrains, here as in Butte County, at Brushy Peak, and on Garzas Creek. It is evident that, at the close of Coniacian time, earth movements had taken place that later were followed by wide-spread subsidence, a wide expansion of marine seaways, and the deposition of the Santonian sediments upon older terrains in both embayments of the Great Valley. The coast-wise extent of these events and movements are not yet known; species of *Mortoniceras,* so prominent in the Chico formation in its type areas, occur also in the Joaquin embayment, near Altamont, and southward to Garzas Creek. Many other species characteristic of the Chico formation have been listed or mentioned by Popenoe as occurring in the Santiago district in Orange County, and in the Santa Monica Mountains, Los Angeles County.

In the Altamont district, Alameda County, the *Mortoniceras* horizon begins about 3500 feet above the base of the Santonian deposits; that is, a little below the middle of the Campanian stage. In the more complete sections of the formation from which the fossils have been collected, they have come almost wholly from its upper portion. It appears that the *Mortoniceras* horizons in the Great Valley should be assigned to a position in early-middle Campanian time. The extensive overlaps and unconformities of these deposits upon older terrains on the borders of the trough indicate source areas primarily toward the south, with a progressive spread northward. No trace of it has been found farther north than Red Bluff in the Great Valley, although equivalents have been recognized much farther north outside of California.

Vancouver Island, etc.—In the published accounts of the Upper Cretaceous deposits on Vancouver Island, the stratigraphic sequence of its faunas are not always clear, though many remarkable species from it have been described and well illustrated by Shumard (1858), Meek (1876), Whiteaves (1879–1903) and others. It appears that no faunal assemblage described from it is referable to any part of the Pacheco as found in California or Oregon. Some equivalents of the Chico formation are recognizable faunally although both older and younger Senonian formations are found there. Among the most representative species recorded from the Nanaimo series on the Island are the following:

Phylloceras ramosum Meek
Lytoceras (Gaudryceras) denmanense Whiteaves
Placenticeras vancouverense Meek
?*Eupachydiscus suciensis* (Meek)
Desmophyllites selwynianus (Whiteaves),
Canadoceras newberryanum (Meek)
Hauericeras gardeni Bailey
Diplomoceras ("Hamites") obstrictus Jimbo

Cymatoceras campbelli (Meek)
Baculites inornatus Meek
Tessarolax distorta Gabb
Hindsia nodulosa Whiteaves
Inoceramus subundatus Meek
Inoceramus vancouverensis Shumard
Inoceramus undulatoplicatus Roemer
Thyasira cretacea Whiteaves

This fauna seems to represent the Campanian. No occurrence of the genus *Metaplacenticeras* (Spath) has been recorded. Near analogues of many of the above species are found in the Forbes shale in its type area, and this fact should be a major factor in attempting a correlation between the fossil-bearing beds on Vancouver Island and the Lower Asuncion group in the Great Valley of California.

The exposures of Upper Cretaceous strata on Sucia Island are limited, but they seem to represent some part of the Nanaimo series on Vancouver Island. The species listed from this island by Whiteaves, or those collected there by Bruce Martin (1913) for the California Academy of Sciences, include six contained in the above list. No example of *Metaplacenticeras* (Spath) has been reported from Sucia Island, although its horizon might be regarded as represented by *Placenticeras vancouverense* Meek.

The thickness of the Nanaimo series, as given by Clapp (1911) is 6785 feet, or somewhat greater than that of the correlative deposits in the Rumsey Hills in California.

There is little evidence of equivalents of the Chico formation on or near the Queen Charlotte Island group, though older Upper Cretaceous strata have already been noted by the writer (1938).

On the Alaskan peninsula and in the Matanuska and Chitina valleys, Chico-like deposits have been described. As reviewed by Martin (1926, p. 470–475), they undoubtedly include strata correlating with the Chico formation.

CLOSE OF LOWER ASUNCION TIME: During Lower Asuncion time, the sea made its greatest advance into the Great Valley of California and other Pacific Coast areas. Within the Great Valley, it extended north to the latitude of Red Bluff, and south to Kern County. Outside the Great Valley, it extended much farther north and south, to southern Oregon and on the Klamath River, and at the south in Orange County (Packard, 1916a; 1921; Popenoe, 1937; 1941; 1942). Near the close of the Lower Asuncion epoch, a wide-spread uplift of the continental border led to a retreat of the sea. During the Santonian, the sea had reached a great areal expansion within the Great Valley; it withdrew during Campanian time to its minimum extent near the close of Lower Asuncion time.

These physiographic changes in West Coast areas during Lower Asuncion time and subsequent to it cannot be measured at present, but they can be partly known from the resulting biological changes. The latest faunal elements of importance before the close of Lower Asuncion time included mortoniceratids and associated types: *Canadoceras, Butticeras, Hauericeras, Muniericeras,* and others. These types disappeared by the close of the Lower Asuncion time. The biological changes can be best illustrated by contrasts, but until the succeeding forms are known, this cannot be done directly. They are, however, comparable to those between middle Campanian and Maestrichtian in other parts of the world.

UPPER ASUNCION GROUP

The Upper Asuncion group is represented by deposits of Maestrichtian and possible Danian age that are fairly widely distributed on the West Coast. As early as 1883, deposits of this age were described by White from Lower California and the Northern Coast Ranges.

The Upper Asuncion group forms a distinct belt along the east slope of the Diablo Range north from a point near Coalinga to Carquinez Strait with almost unbroken continuity and is also present in the Sacramento Valley, as at Marysville Buttes.

The group varies greatly in thickness, owing partly to its unconformable relation to the underlying terrains and partly to overlap by the Paleocene. In the San Joaquin Valley, its outcrop is 1 to 3 miles wide, and varys in thickness from a few hundred feet to much greater, for the most part in excess of 5000 feet, though often approaching 7000 feet, as estimated by Taff (1934, p. 1088).

The group is composed largely of moderately coarse sandstone beds and silty shales, but at base it often has a moderately thick conglomerate, rarely exceeding 125 feet, including some pebbly sandstones.

As traced along the east flank of the Diablo Range, the lithology and thickness of Upper Asuncion group vary in accord with background conditions, the drainage areas of its streams, the source rocks of its sediments, and also as affected by overlapping Tertiary deposits. On Los Gatos Creek and northward for some miles, the upper members of the group are overlapped by marine Paleocene beds. The exposed thickness of the group in this area has been estimated at near 2000 feet. Farther north on Joaquin Ridge, its thickness is estimated at 3800 feet.

Between the Big Panoche Valley and Puerto Creek, the thickness of the group varies greatly from that farther south, although in general the succession of its members remains the same, with the more sandy strata in ith lower portion; thick beds of shale in its middle part; a thick, persistent sandy member, usually fossil-bearing, above; and a more or less organic shale member near the top.

In the northern area near Puerto Creek, the upper member is overlapped by Tertiary beds. In other areas near the discharge points of large streams, as in the Pacheco Pass Quadrangle and northwest of Mount Diablo, delta-like deposits have been developed, in which the width of outcrop and thickness are greatly increased. In such areas, or at some levels in the group, are found facies where cephalopods are rare and other classes of Mollusca more tolerant of brackish water are more plentiful.

Estimates of thickness (in feet) in a number of sections on the west border of the Valley are as follows:

Los Gatos Creek	2000	Puerto Creek	2500
Joaquin Ridge	3800	Hospital Creek	3600
Panoche Hills	2300	Hetch Hetchy Tunnel	4000
Pacheco Pass Quad.	6900	Mt. Diablo Quad.	5800
Orestimba Creek	5000	Berkeley Hills	3500

Divisions of the Upper Asuncion group.—The Upper Asuncion group is the product of sedimentation during a long epoch of subsidence that led the sea into many coastal areas following an interval of moderate elevation and relative quiet. The group is well developed in the trough of the Great Valley, in which it is most complete in its southern embayment. Outside this area in California, it occurs to the north in central Mendocino County or farther and southward in the coastal areas of southern California (Los Angeles and Orange counties) and on the peninsula of Lower California. The rate of this subsidence and its net results were differential. In certain areas in the Great Valley, there are evidences of minor and repeated impulses of uplift or subsidence during sedimentation. The lithological changes in the upper Asuncion group in the Great Valley trough may be due to these facts. A sequence of faunal changes is readily seen in the column between its lowest member and the top. The faunal succession appears to be associated with lithological changes, though the relationships are not clear. They furnish some criteria for a subdivision of the group into a number of units, not all of them of equal magnitude or importance.

MAESTRICHTIAN AND DANIAN? DEPOSITS: Anderson and Pack (1915) described the Moreno formation which they regarded as the highest Upper Cretaceous on the West Coast. Since then further work on the Moreno formation has resulted in the recognition of two distinct sequences.

South of Los Banos Creek, the formation consists largely of shale with minor but persistent sand lenses. Payne (1941) described the subdivisions in this southern area. North of Los Banos Creek, the Moreno becomes more sandy (Bennison, 1940).

Anderson and Pack (1915, p. 46) state that:

"The name Moreno is applied to the formation from Moreno Gulch on the east flank of the Panoche Hills where it is typically exposed. Here the formation has a thickness of 1700 to 2000 feet and is composed predominantly of thin-bedded, rather brittle brownish and lav- ender-colored shales, that weather into small bits and flakes. In the lower part of the forma- tion there are numerous beds of sandstone. . . ."

Because of its stratigraphic position at the top of the Cretaceous in California and probably on the West Coast, the Moreno claims unusual interest as repre- senting the closing stage of the Cretaceous period, as well as of Mesozoic time.

In its lithologic and organic character, with few molluscan types but an abundant micro-organic content, the Moreno is not unlike certain correlative for- mations in western Europe, India, and other regions of the world. Throughout the extent of its outcrops, it can be separated from older strata both lithologically and biologically.

The fauna and flora of the Moreno contrast strongly with that of the Panoche formation with its abundant molluscan types, pelecypods, gastropods and am- monites. The disappearance of these and their replacement in the Moreno forma- tion by a rich and varied fauna and flora of micro-organisms, appears to mark an event of exceptional import. Concerning the Moreno formation, Anderson and Pack state (1915, p. 47–48) that:

"They are separated as a distinct formation because they constitute an individual and per- sistent lithologic division, unique among the Cretaceous beds in that they are composed largely of the remains of organisms such as diatoms and foraminifers, and they were evidently formed during an epoch when the physical conditions were different from those prevailing during the rest of Creataceous time. If they do not represent an entirely separate epoch of deposition, as it is possible that they may, they at least afford a record of marked and pro- longed change of conditions."

This aspect of the formation will be recalled when considering its possible disconformity upon the Panoche formation. Possibly for the above reasons, as well as the prospective economic importance, its type area has been re-examined in much detail by representatives of petroleum companies. Its upper shales con- tain a large flora of diatoms, and a rich fauna of foraminifera, radiolarians, and other micro-organisms. From a body of white shale 200 feet thick near its top, Hanna was able to isolate as many as 36 species of diatoms, and many others were indicated by fragmentary remains. The lower part of the sequence was closely searched, and it was stated that "Besides foraminifers, fossil mollusks occur sparingly, among them being *Hamites* or *Anisoceras,* characteristic Cretaceous fossils. . . ."

Payne (1941, p. 1953) restricted the Moreno formation to its original defi- nition and scope, based upon its type area, and separated the strata into four lithologic members, aggregating 2745 feet thick, which he traced northward to near Ortigalita Creek. Payne's divisions were based upon a section about 6 miles south of Moreno Gulch on the east flank of the Panoche Hills in Escarpado Canyon. Its several members were described as follows:

(1) Dos Palos shale, 1045 feet thick, composed primarily of brown shale, including a local 60-foot bed, the "Cima sandstone" lens, 185 feet below the top.

(2) The Marca shale, chiefly organic shale, with abundant *Siphogenerinoides*.

(3) Tierra Loma shale, consisting principally of brown shale, including the "Mercy sandstone" lens 190 feet thick, 70 feet below its top.

(4) Dosados sand and shale, 200 feet thick, "lying conformably above the Panoche formation" (Anderson and Pack), consisting partly of concretionary sandstone.

It is doubtful whether these members are traceable throughout the areas of the exposed Moreno formation. Schenck (1943) gave more precise data pertaining to the limits of the Moreno formation in the district immediately north of Laguna Seca Creek, about 14 miles north of Moreno Gulch. His views provide added information about the fauna. The Tierra Loma member is immediately overlain by Paleocene strata, thus giving evidence of a greater overlap of the Paleocene, as compared to that to the south. Schenck also described a new species of mollusk, *Acila princeps*, from a sand lentil near the top of the Tierra Loma member, and gave some data concerning the subjacent Panoche formation. The base of the Moreno, as determined by Payne (1941) and confirmed by Schenck, if extended northward shows its probable relation to the area on Ortigalita Creek mentioned by Payne (p. 1954), as being "some 1800 feet stratigraphically lower than their (Anderson and Pack's) type Moreno in Moreno Gulch."

The lowest member on Los Gatos Creek, northwest of Coalinga, is composed of bedded sandstones and sandy shale, with a fossiferous interval less than 600 feet thick characterized by cephalopods such as *Baculites, Nautilus,* large *Parapachydiscus,* and various nostocerids as well as *Inoceramus* and other pelecypods. This member has a thickness on Los Gatos Creek of at least 2000 feet and is overlain and partly concealed by Tertiary beds. Farther north it becomes thicker. The following species have been collected by C. C. Church, Hanna, or the writer:

Nautilus (two indet. species)
Lytoceras (Gaudryceras) coalingense n. sp.
Lytoceras (Gaudryceras) birkhauseri n. sp.
Lytoceras (Tetragonites) epigonum Kossmat
Neokotoceras fresnoense n. sp.
Hauericeras aff. *H. gardeni* Bailey
Nostoceras sp.
Parapachydiscus catarinae Anderson and Hanna
Parapachydiscus coalingensis n. sp.
Parapachydiscus aff. *P. peninsularis* Anderson and Hanna

Baculites occidentalis Meek
Baculites lomaensis n. sp.
Baculites aff. *B. anceps* Lamarck
Exiteloceras aff. *E. vancouverense* (Gabb)
Cophocara stantoni Stewart
Turritella aff. *T. peninsularis* Anderson and Hanna
Tessarolax aff. *T. distorta* Gabb
Dentalium (Entalis) whiteavesi Anderson and Hanna
Inoceramus sp.
Parallelodon sp.

Here the lowest fossil-bearing zone is underlain by carbonaceous shales, with a thickness of 200 feet or more. About 10 miles north of the above locality on Joaquin Ridge, at locality 2361 (C. A. S.), on the SE 1/4 of sec. 7, T. 19 S., R. 15 E., Church, Hanna and Huett collected from the above horizon the following additional species:

Nautilus *(Cymatoceras) hermosus* n. sp.
Parapachydiscus catarinae Anderson
  and Hanna
Joaquinites fascicostatus n. sp.
Nostoceras sp.

Exiteloceras vancouverense (Gabb)
Exiteloceras desertense n. sp.
Bostrychoceras sp.
Inoceramus sp.

Immediately north of the Panoche Hills, at locality 28306 (C. A. S.), Taff, Hanna, and Cross collected a small but diagnostic fauna near the center of the N ½ of sec. 24, T. 12 S., R. 10 E., containing the following species:

Lytoceras (Gaudryceras) coalingense n. sp.
Exiteloceras vancouverense (Gabb)

Anchura sp.
Macrocallista aff. *M. cordata* Waring

This faunule represents the lower part of the Moreno formation as found farther north on Salt Creek, where Bennison discovered the holotype of *Lytoceras (Gaudryceras) aurem* n. sp.

Near Ortigalita Creek, in a sandy belt mapped as Moreno at Locality 29656 (C. A. S.), Bennison, and later J. Bryan and others collected the following invertebrate species:

Phylloceras pachecoense n. sp.
Phylloceras sp.
Pachecocrinus joaquinensis n. sp.

Exiteloceras ortigalitoense n. sp.
Diplomoceras jimboi n. sp.

From data given by the collectors, these fossils were found on the E ½ of sec. 33, T. 11 S., R. 10 E., in part near the center of the east line of the section, in an area mapped as Moreno. These species indicate that the strata are referable to the Upper Asuncion group. Species of *Diplomoceras* range almost throughout the Upper Asuncion group, but rarely occur in older beds.

Schenck (after Payne, 1941) has supplied more precise data concerning the lower boundary of the Moreno formation as found on Laguna Seca Creek, 12 miles north of its type locality. Fossil localities are also noted, including locality 2383 (Leland Stanford, Jr. University), near the center of sec. 11, T. 12 S., R. 10 E., from which Schenck (p. 62) lists:

Diplomoceras ("Hamites") ellipticum
  Anderson
Cophocara sp.
Tenea inflata (Gabb)

Acila (Truncacila) sp.
Parallelodon sp.
Glycymeris veatchii (Gabb)

From the data given in Payne's sketch map (Schenck, 1943, p. 61), the local thickness of the Moreno formation may be reckoned as 2098 feet, somewhat less than at its type locality, which may be a result of an overlap by Tertiary deposits.

Southward from its type area, the Moreno formation has been identified in a narrow belt between Cantua Creek and "Oil City," and at intervals in outcrop, or in deep wells, as far south as the north border of Kern County, where for the most part it is covered by later deposits. The Moreno has been reported in wells drilled on the valley borders as far north as Tracy, Alameda County, and in wells on the border of the Sacramento Valley. It is not definitely known in any areas outside the Great Valley of California.

In the type area of the Moreno some uncertain ammonoids (*"Hamites"* or *Anisoceras*) and *Baculites* have been recognized, as well as foraminifera such as *Siphogenerinoides whitei* Church, *Bulimina prolixa* and *Gaudryina filiformis*

Cushman, *Valvulinaria* sp., *Dentalina* sp., *Robulina* sp., *Textularia, Nodosaria,* and *Eponides,* most of which occur in the lower part of the formation.

In the Pacheco Pass quadrangle and areas farther north, the Moreno formation is represented by at least four stratigraphic members (Bennison, 1940), differing much in lithological character and in faunal contents from those described by Payne (1941). In stratigraphic order these members from the top down are:

(1) Volta Sand—consisting of about 300 feet of gray, calcareous sand grading upward into a yellow biotitic sand, with local thin pebble beds in the base. The fauna consists mainly of small gastropods and pelecypods.

(2) Garzas Sand—mainly buff to grey, well-bedded sands, with minor white sands with intercalated light brown, calcareous sandstone. To the south this member tends to become silty. The fauna of the Garzas is characteristic and abundant.

(3) Quinto Silt—1500 to nearly 3000 feet of silty shale and clay shale. To the south of the Pacheco Pass road, three divisions can be recognized on the basis of local unconformities with the development of thin, pebble conglomerates. The shales become organic in various localities, with numerous foraminifera and other micro-organisms, and with small molluscan types, including aberrant cephalopods.

(4) Mustang Shale—consists of 1400 to 1800 feet of silty shale with local limestone concretions and basal conglomerate. The fauna of this member is less plentiful but contains numerous micro-organisms and a few aberrant cephalopods.

From Pacheco Pass quadrangle north to Hospital Creek and Corral Hollow the Mustang shales directly overly the Panoche formation. These shales weather easily and form prominent strike valleys between the more resistant sandstones of the Panoche and the basal sandy beds of the Quinto silts.

From the "Lower Shale" of Anderson and Pack (1915), Bennison collected at locality 29123 (C. A. S.), on the SE ¼ sec. 19, T. 8 S., R. 8 E., the following species, representing a single horizon in the Mustang shale member:

Turrilites excelsus n. sp.	*Inoceramus (Endocostea) stanislausensis*
Solenoceras sp. indet.	n. sp.
Diplomoceras sp. indet.	*Inoceramus* (large species)
Inoceramus aff. *I. regularis* d'Orbigny	*Acila (Truncacila)* aff. *A. demessa* Finlay

As indicated by the above list of species, the age of this locality is not younger than Maestrichtian. On Little Salado Creek, similar shales overlying the Panoche outcrop on the west borders of secs. 15 and 22, T. 6 S., R. 7 E. On the W ½ of the SW ¼ sec. 15, Bennison and Williams discovered in an irregular concretion in these shales "numerous ammonites and fossil wood," not otherwise reported.

On Puerto Creek a similar belt of clay shale is well exposed, crossing the stream on the north border of the NW ¼ of sec. 29, T. 5 S., R. 7 E. On the south side of the creek Bennison found the holotypes of *Bostrychoceras californicum* n. sp., and of *Exiteloceras bennisoni* n. sp.; neither can be assigned to a horizon older than lower Maestrichtian. A similar body of shales, with a smaller percentage of clay and mapped as Moreno, is exposed at the mouth of Hospital Creek, with a thickness of 1950 feet.

In their upper portion these shales consist of thin-bedded, siliceous strata; their lower part is somewhat calcareous, with abundant foraminifera. From the lower 600 feet the following invertebrate species of diminutive size were collected by H. E. Vokes, the writer, and students of B. L. Clark:

Lytoceras (Gaudryceras) sp.	*Inoceramus* (fragments)
Axonoceras sp.	*Parallelodon* (small species)
Solenoceras (2 species)	numerous foraminifera
Baculites aff. *B. anceps* Lamarck	

This body of shale, dipping 30° NE., is overlain by late Tertiary deposits which may conceal later members of the Cretaceous as in southern Merced County. At locality 28399 (C. A. S.), sec. 15, T. 2 S., R. 5 E., north of Tracy, a deep well penetrated the lower part of these shales, and from a depth of 3400 feet, the following molluscan species were obtained:

Lytoceras (Gaudryceras) sp.	*Solenoceras* sp. indet.
Axonoceras sp. indet.	*Baculites* aff. *B. anceps* Lamarck

as well as numerous species of foraminifera.

Farther west on the south border of Corral Hollow, similar shales outcrop in a narrow belt extending east to west. No molluscan fossils have been reported from the shales of this locality, although Anderson and Pack (1915) state indirectly that they are largely of organic nature, and have referred them to the "Lower shale" (p. 56).

Campbell and Clark, who have studied these organic shales, have described a radiolarian fauna (approximately 100 species) obtained from about 1 cubic inch of limestone. The fauna included 9 families and 25 genera. This limestone was part of the matrix surrounding a specimen of *Lytoceras (Tegragonites)* aff. *epigonum* Kossmat (Campbell and Clark, 1944, p. 1).

In the Pacheco Pass quadrangle, on Quinto Creek and about the Howard ranch house, a broad belt of claylike, partly organic shales called the Quinto silt by Bennison is well exposed north and south of the creek. This belt is traceable south to Los Banos Creek, and north to Garzas Creek, Salado Creek, and Puerto Creek. In some places as near as the Pacheco Pass highway this belt is covered by valley alluvium. Otherwise, the outcrop of these shades and the overlying sandstones is well exposed, and were included by Anderson and Pack (1915) in the Moreno formation.

Anderson and Pack described these shales as follows:

"Lithologically the shale north of Pacheco Pass differs somewhat from the typical shale of the Moreno farther south. . . . Through the northern part of the district the shale is sandy toward the base, showing a perfect gradation into the Panoche formation, from typical clay shale, sandy shale, and finally to concretionary sandstone. Although in several places the shale appears to be largely of organic origin, this member north of Pacheco Pass is predominantly a carbonaceous clay shale, as distinguished from the typical shale of the Moreno in the southern part of the region, ..."

In the Pacheco Pass quadrangle, these shales vary in thickness from about

1400 feet near Puerto Creek to 1600 feet on Quinto Creek, and an apparently similar thickness on Los Banos Creek. South of Los Banos Creek, they are less readily traceable, being overlapped by Tertiary deposits, or alluvium. However, on Los Banos Creek, a thick body of shales is exposed overlying the Los Gatos sandstone, as at locality 28118 (C. A. S.). Few fossils have been collected from these shales, although J. Bryan discovered in them the holotype of *Neocyrtochilus bryani* n. sp., and a single example, the holotype of *Nonacteonina stephensoni* n. sp., and another gastropod resembling *Cophocara* sp., at locality 30563 (C. A. S.), near the center of the NW ¼ sec. 7, T. 11 S., R. 10 E. The Quinto shales of this area have been but little searched for fossils, but would probably richly reward such work.

In the same stratigraphic interval on N ½ sec. 2, T. 11 S., R. 9 E., Bennison found an example of *Parapachydiscus coalingensis* n. sp., in the lower part of the Upper Asuncion group.

The base of the Quinto Silt on the north bank of Los Banos Creek, at locality 28118 (C. A. S.), on the NE ¼ sec. 12, T. 11 S., R. 9 E., is a belt of hard pebbly sandstone 125 feet thick, which appears to be a part of a much thicker body, including a conglomerate bed outcropping a little north of the creek. From the sandstones outcropping on the north bank of the creek, Taff, Hanna, and Cross, and later Bennison, McCoy, and the writer, collected the following invertebrate species :

Polinices mercedensis n. sp.	*Opisoma pacifica* n. sp.
Phasianella garzana n. sp.	*Crassatellites triangulatus* Waring
Pseudogaleodea sp.	*Glycymeris banosensis* n. sp.
Cymbophora ashburnerii Gabb	*Trigonocallista nitida* (Gabb)
Corbis aff. *C. peninsularis* Anderson	*Exogyra* sp.,
and Hanna	*Ostrea* sp.

Overlying this sandstone is a thick body of clay shales outcropping on the north bank of the creek, having an estimated thickness of about 3300 feet. The upper limit of these shales appears to be exposed on the east border of the SE ¼ sec. 26, T. 10 S., R. 9 E.

On Mustang gulch, at locality 28312 (C. A. S.), in Pacheco Pass quadrangle, Bennison collected from a similar belt of sandstone the following species:

Rhynchonella sp.	*Opisoma pacifica* n. sp.
Baculites aff. *B. occidentalis* Meek	*Trigonocallista nitida* (Gabb)
Baculites aff. *B. lomaensis* n. sp.	*Pugnellus* aff. *P. hamulus* Gabb
Diplomoceras mustangense n. sp.	*Phasianella garzana* n. sp.

The holotype of *Cerithium mustangense* n. sp. was probably found in this belt of the Upper Asuncion group.

Other areas of the same horizon show the continuity of its outcrop toward the north in the Pacheco Pass quadrangle. Incidentally, various molluscan species in this horizon have been found also in synchronous and equivalent beds in the coastal areas of California, as well as the peninsula of Lower California.

Near Quinto Creek, at the west line of the NW ¼ sec. 15, near the Howard ranch house, fragments of *Parapachydiscus* sp., *Bostrychoceras* sp., and *Oxybeloceras* sp. were found.

Near the center of the S ½ sec. 16, T. 6 S., R. 7 E., near Little Salado Creek, Bennison and Williams found *Parapachydiscus* sp., which, with supporting evidence in the strata below and above, may show the existence here of the Quinto silt. This member has been traced north to Puerto Creek, where it is overlain on the east by higher beds of the group. From the lower beds of the Quinto silt, Jack Frame, of Patterson, obtained the holotype of *Bostrychoceras puertoense* n. sp., and from the dark shales above in the same section, Bennison collected on the south side of Puerto Creek, the following diagnostic species:

Parapachydiscus coalingensis n. sp.
Didymoceras californicum n. sp.
Exiteloceras bennisoni n. sp.

Oxybeloceras sp. indet.
Inoceramus (Endocostea) stanislausensis n. sp.

On the NW ¼ sec. 29, T. 8 S., R. 8 E., Bennison collected *Baculites* sp., and *Tessarolax* sp., and from the NE ¼ sec. 30, adjoining, he obtained the holotype of *Parapachydiscus stanislausensis* n. sp., from the lower beds of the Quinto silt.

On the north and east sides of Mt. Diablo, a shale, similar to that exposed in Hospital Creek, overlies the Los Gatos member of the Upper Asuncion group on the north border of Briones Valley, and extends west into Long Valley. At the mouth of Briones Creek, near the old John Marsh home, these shales have an estimated thickness of 1200 feet, though their highest beds may be overlapped and concealed by Tertiary.

The exposed part of these shales consists of thin-bedded organic shale, in which a few molluscan species were collected by Taff, Church, Cross, and the writer, in part associated with many types of foraminifera and other microorganisms. The Mollusca included:

Lytoceras (Gaudryceras) sp.
Exicrioceras aff. *E. diabloense* n. sp.
Baculites subcircularis n. sp.
Baculites aff. *B. teres* Forbes
Lucina sp.

Acila sp.
Bulla sp.
Pecten (Propeapecten) sp. indet.
Parallelodon sp.,
Cycad (fragmentary)

On the north border of Briones Valley, on the SE ¼ sec. 29, T. 1 N., R. 2 E., the writer collected fragments of a large *Inoceramus*, and fragmentary fronds of cycads. The above fossils probably represent an upper portion of the Quinto shale member of the Moreno formation, here overlain by the Garzas member.

Reference has been made to the "Upper concretionary member" described by Anderson and Pack (1915, p. 41, 42, 56). This sandstone body was thought by the authors to form the upper part of the Moreno formation, but in other areas was regarded as a part of the Panoche formation. On the geologic map of Bull. 603 a dotted line traverses the belt mapped as Moreno extending from Quinto Creek north to Puerto Creek. As explained in the legend this line marks "the base of the upper sandstone member of the Moreno formation (north of Pacheco Pass)." This same member has been called the Garzas sandstone by Bennison (1940).

Between Quinto Creek and the north border of the quadrangle, numerous fossil Mollusca have been collected at 12 localities, from strata indicated as the "upper sandstone of the Moreno formation."

This "Upper sandstone" is described by Anderson and Pack (p. 56) in part as follows:

"Between Quinto and Garzas Creeks occurs a gray sandstone with numerous layers of conglomerate, in which most of the pebbles are small but which contain a few rounded fragments 7 to 10 inches in diameter. Fossil mollusks are present through almost the entire zone and in places are so plentiful that the rock is virtually an impure limestone. Concretionary sandstone is almost if not entirely lacking.

"North of Garzas Creek the sandstone is less conglomeratic and large brownish sandstone concretions are prominent in the lower part. On Orestimba Creek the sandstone is about 1,150 feet, and near Salado Creek almost 1,450 feet thick."

In its stratigraphic position and lithologic character, it seems to constitute a thick sandy member of the Upper Asuncion group. This sandy, pebbly, and fossiliferous member extends entirely across the Panoche Pass quadrangle. Between Los Banos Creek and the Pacheco Pass highway, it occupies the eastern part of the low hills belt and attains a thickness of about 1500 feet.

In the Volta quadrangle the upper beds of the Garzas member of the Moreno formation are partly exposed on the east border of sec. 26, T. 10 S., R. 9 E., where Bennison collected the following molluscan species:

Lytoceras (*Tetragonites*) aff. *L. epigonum* Kossmat	*Trigonia* sp.
Pugnellus hamulus Gabb	*Exogyra* sp.
Tessarolax sp. indet.	*Ostrea* sp. indet.

North of Los Banos Creek, the Garzas member is traceable by its position, lithology, and fauna to Orestimba Creek, Salado Creek, and farther, maintaining the same relation to the fossiliferous Quinto silt beneath. North of Orestimba Creek, the Garzas member is progressively overlapped on the east by marine Paleocene. Near Little Salado Creek the Garzas is fossil-bearing. On Puerto Creek its outcrop is much reduced in breadth by the Paleocene overlap, so that only about 1000 feet are exposed, without known fossils. On Hospital Creek, the Garzas member is concealed by Tertiary beds, so that the Quinto shales constitute the highest exposure of the Moreno formation. In the Mount Diablo quadrangle, the Garzas member is again exposed, and is recognizable by its field position, lithologic character, and faunal contents. North of lower Marsh Creek, the Garzas member occupies the ridge between the Briones and Deer valleys. Northeast of Clayton it is again overlapped by Paleocene deposits in the Nortonville district.

In a section across the outcrop of the Upper Asuncion near the west border of sec. 29, T. 1 N., R. 2 E., the Garzas member has an estimated thickness of 1690 feet, and is fossil-bearing at bottom and at top. Its lower sandy beds overlying the Quinto shales are concretionary, as exposed on the NW. ¼ of Section 29. Church, Cross and the writer collected from the concretions a number of undescribed ammonoids, including *Diplomoceras* aff. *D. recticostatum* (Seunes), *Diplomoceras* sp. indet., and *Axonoceras* sp.

Above this concretionary sandstone are other sandstones about 1000 feet thick. At the top, on the south side of Deer Valley, at locality 2359 (C. A. S.) the writer collected on the NE ¼ sec. 24, T. 1 N., R. 1 E., the following species:

Gyrodes expansus Gabb
Gyrodes californicus Packard
Oligoptycha obliqua (Gabb)
Dentalium (Entalis) whiteavesi Anderson
  and Hanna

Corbis peninsularis Anderson and Hanna
Meekia sella Gabb
Mytilus aff. *M. quadratus* Gabb
Trigonocallista nitida (Gabb)

Two miles farther east, in the same zone, SW ¼ sec. 20, T. 1 N., R. 2 E., Taff and Cross collected a small fauna including most of the species in the above list. Still farther east, at locality 25707 (C. A. S.) on the SW ¼ sec. 27, T. 1 N., R. 2 E., B. L. Clark and the writer collected from a similar sandstone in the same zone the following species:

Baculites sp. indet.
Pugnellus hamulus Gabb
Ampullina oviformis (Gabb)
Oligoptycha obliqua (Gabb)
Pharella alta Gabb
Cophocara stantoni Stewart

Corbis peninsularis Anderson and Hanna
Meekia sella Gabb
Tellina paralis Gabb
Tellina oöides Gabb
Cymbophora ashburnerii Gabb
Trigonocallista nitida (Gabb)

A probably correlative horizon occurs in the vicinity of Arroyo del Hambre. At this locality Merriam obtained the fossils listed below. This list was included by Lawson (1914, p. 8) as representing an Upper Chico horizon in the Concord quadrangle. This appears to be the locality from which Gabb obtained the holotypes of many species described by him (1864) and reported as found "south of Martinez." For the completion of the record in this area a list of species from this locality, as emended, is here included:

Bostrychoceras vermiculare (Gabb)
Oligoptycha obliqua (Gabb)
Gyrodes expansa Gabb
Meekia sella Gabb
Meekia navis Gabb
Mytilus quadratus Gabb
Perissitys aff. *P. brevirostris* (Gabb)
Pugnellus hamulus Gabb
Margarites inornatus (Gabb)

Dentalium cf. *D. whiteavesi* Anderson and
  Hanna
"Aphrodina" varians (Gabb)
Acila demessa Finlay
Glycymeris aff. *G. banosensis* n. sp.
Tellina hoffmannii Gabb
Teleost fish scales
Shark teeth

In the Berkeley Hills, probably only the upper portion of the Upper Asuncion group is at present recognizable, although older beds may be found. The relationship of the beds occurring here to those found in the Mount Diablo and the northern part of the Concord quadrangles is suggested by Lawson (1914, p. 8) as follows:

"The outcrop of Cretaceous rocks along the Berkeley Hills is thus the southwest limb of a great synclinorium, the northeast limb of which appears in the northern part of Concord quadrangle, south of the town of Martinez, and also more extensively in the Mount Diablo quadrangle, which adjoins the Concord quadrangle on the east. . . . In the Berkeley Hills the principal part of the Chico formation . . . comprizes a thick accumulation of sandstone and shales, the sandstones predominating. . . . The outcrop of the sandstones and shales occupies a broad belt along the summit of the Berkeley Hills parallel to the belts occupied by the Knoxville formation and the Oakland conglomerate. . . ."

The strata in this area are described as dipping to the northeast at angles ranging from 30 to 80 degrees. The thickness of the sequence is not definitely known, although in some representative sections of the group it is hardly less than 3500 feet. It consists chiefly of sandstone, but also includes some light-colored, partly organic shale, the latter nearly 1000 feet thick, overlain by beds of sandstone. The sequence in this area suggests a marginal part of the basin embracing the synclinorium described by Lawson (1914). Few molluscan fossils have been found here, although fragmentary tests of echinoids and broken shells of *Inoceramus* sp. have been reported. On the west slope of the hills, somewhat below the middle of the sandstones, on the SW ¼ sec. 7, T. 1 S., R. 3 W., B. L. Clark obtained, and sent to the Academy of Sciences some incomplete specimens of *Turrilites* aff. *T. splendidus* Shumard and *Desmoceras* sp.

A species of *Desmoceras* apparently identical with the latter has been described from the upper part of the Garzas in the Volta quadrangle, Merced County. The former was described by Shumard, and later was found in the Nacatoch sand, of the Navarro group in east-central Texas. As these fossils are significant in determining the age of the sandstones outcropping in the Berkeley Hills, they may be regarded as supplementary to the above list from the west border of Arroyo del Hambre, or they may be somewhat higher, but at all events the beds are high in the Upper Asuncion group.

Ten miles south of Tracy, Alameda County, the Hetch Hetchy aqueduct tunnel penetrates the Upper Ascuncion group. From the map and profile of the bore, these beds here underlie the S ½ sec. 32, T. 3 S., R. 5 E. The beds consist of alternating sandstones and hard shale, standing at angles of 30–45 degrees, dipping to the southwest. The lowest beds are fossil-bearing, and at top the group is overlain by marine Tertiary strata. The total thickness of the Upper Asuncion beds cut by the aqueduct tunnel is more than 4000 feet. From the fossil-bearing beds, F. A. Menkin, of the Associated Oil Company, and others, collected the following species:

Lytoceras (Gaudryceras) sp. indet.
Parapachydiscus aff. *P. catarinae* Anderson
   and Hanna
Parapachydiscus ootacodensis (Stoliczka)?
Nostoceras sp.
Exiteloceras vancouverense (Gabb)

Baculites sp. indet.
Baculites occidentalis Meek
Gyrodes californica Packard
Parallelodon brewerianus (Gabb)
"*Nucula*" aff. *N. solitaria* Gabb

To the above list should be added *Diplomoceras o'shaughnessyi* n. sp., donated to the Academy of Sciences by the Chief Engineer in charge of the tunnel construction work.

The thickness of the strata is not the full measure of the Upper Asuncion group in this area, although it is greater than in other sections farther south, and not so thick as in sections in the Mount Diablo quadrangle.

No older Cretaceous beds are known in the vicinity of the east portal to the tunnel where it appears that the Upper Asuncion deposits, as in the Mount Diablo area, were laid down in an open seaway that had extended to the northwest, and had reached the sea in this direction, whereas toward the southeast it had less clearly connected with the San Joaquin embayment. The Upper Asuncion group is well exposed between the center of Section 31, and a point near the SW corner of sec. 20, T. 1 N., R. 2 E., where it is overlain by Paleocene beds. Taff (1935) gave a small scale map of the area, and a profile section in which the Upper Asuncion group (Moreno formation) was given an estimated thickness of 7000 feet. A more conservative estimate of the thickness, free from duplication, would be 5800 feet. The lower part of the group is sparingly fossil-bearing, with cephalopods and other molluscs.

At locality 2256 (C. A. S.) on the north ½ sec. 32, T. 1 N., R. 2 E., the following invertebrate species were collected:

Parapachydiscus aff. *P. catarinae* Anderson and Hanna
Baculites occidentalis Meek
Baculites aff. *B. vagina* Forbes
Diplomoceras aff. *D. notabile* Whiteaves
Thyasira cretacea Whiteaves
?*Periploma quadrata* (Gabb)
Inoceramus sp. indet.

The foregoing list may represent the Garzas members of the Moreno formation. A similar horizon outcrops near Kellogg Creek, on the SW ¼ sec. 13, T. 1 S., R. 2 E., where B. L. Clark and his students have collected a small fauna now in the collections of the California Academy of Sciences, including the following species:

Phylloceras sp. indet.
Lytoceras (Gaudryceras) sp. indet.
Lytoceras (Tetragonites) epigonum Kossmat
Parapachydiscus sp. indet.
Baculites occidentalis Meek
Parallelodon aff. *P. brewerianus* (Gabb)

In all the foregoing (and following) lists, the presence of *Parapachydiscus* sp. may be regarded as nearly conclusive evidence of a Maestrichtian age for these deposits, correlative with those at Los Gatos Creek near Coalinga, and on the peninsula of Lower California, Point Loma, and La Jolla, San Diego County.

In the several localities in the Mount Diablo area where the foregoing species have been found, the beds in which they occur rests directly upon sandstone or sandy shale, and they are overlain by organic shales, not unlike those earlier referred to the Quinto farther south.

The several members of the group recognized in the Mount Diablo and Concord quadrangles follow the stratigraphic order, are commensurate with and lithologically similar to those in the Pacheco Pass quadrangle. Faunally they are correlative with them, as seen in the lists of species. In both regions, the Garzas includes thick belts of sandstone in the upper part of the Upper Asuncion, resting directly upon a thick body of shales referable to the Quinto member, as in the Pacheco Pass quadrangle. In both regions the uppermost beds are overlapped in part by marine Paleocene deposits, as if these widely separated areas had been synchronously disturbed by the same earth movements.

The proximity of the Berkeley Hills and neighboring areas of the Upper Asuncion group to the present coast line suggests an outlet to the sea during later Cretaceous time, but positive evidence is not yet known. Strata of the late Upper Cretaceous time are known in many parts of the California Coast, but no direct correlation of these deposits with those in the Great Valley has yet been made. It is possible, however, that outlets to the sea can be shown in other localities farther north or farther south.

Sacramento Valley.—Few exposures of strata referable to the Upper Asuncion group are recognizable north of Carquinez Strait, although Gabb (1864, p. 220–236) included in his synopsis, and in other lists, the names of various species described by himself that occur in this group though not confined to it. However, the following notes bearing upon species representing the Upper Asuncion group obtained from the Sacramento Valley may be given.

At Marysville Buttes, northwest of Marysville, Upper Cretaceous beds have been partly described by later writers. Watts (1894, p. 10) gave a list of invertebrate species obtained from this area, as identified by Cooper, a small number of which are of later Cretaceous age. Williams (1929) gave a brief account and sketch map of the district, with a note on the later Cretaceous strata outcropping in it, with lists of species that had been collected from them. Bennison and others have since collected additional Upper Cretaceous fossils from the area. From an inspection of the fossils that have been collected here, the following list is believed to fairly represent the Cretaceous fauna occurring in the Marysville Buttes area:

Parapachydiscus aff. *P. catarinae* Anderson
  and Hanna
Parapachydiscus aff. *P. ganesa* Stoliczka
Parapachydiscus sp. indet.
Gyrodes expansa Gabb
Acila (Truncacila) demessa Finlay

Inoceramus sp. indet.
"*Aphrodina*" *varians* (Gabb)
Cymbophora ashburnerii Gabb
"*Nucula*" *solitaria* Gabb
Modiolus aff. *M. cylindricus* Gabb

Most of the species have been collected from the Upper Asuncion group in other areas in the Great Valley, or from the coastal areas in California and on the peninsula of Lower California. None of them are characteristic of older beds.

According to Williams the Upper Cretaceous outcropping on the west border of the Marysville Buttes area is as much as 1500 feet thick. The lower part appears to be somewhat sandy, and the upper part more shaly (Williams, 1929, Fig. 4, p. 116). Since in other areas of the Upper Asuncion group its lowest beds rest discordantly upon older terrains, the same condition probably exists here also. The species of *Parapachydiscus* may be taken as evidence of the Maestrichtian age of these beds.

No surface outcrops have yet been described from the west side of the Sacramento Valley, although William Kennett recently obtained a single example of *Diplomoceras* aff. *D. notabile* Whiteaves from a point 1 mile north of the Red Bluff-Beegum road, on the west side of the Sacramento Valley, which possibly indicates the occurrence of the group in this area.

Lower California.—A cursory account of the later Cretaceous geology of Lower California south of Todos Santos Bay, based chiefly upon the work of earlier writers, and upon fossil collections made by Fairbanks, Sternberg, Santillan and Barrera, and by Hertlein and Jordan, was given by Anderson and Hanna (1935). Many fossil lists and collections were studied in the light of past and current literature, and of faunas assembled from various localities on the Peninsula. A correlation was attempted based generally upon the views then current. A few localities were prominent in this treatment, one on the south shore of Todos Santos Bay, the type locality of most of the species named by White (1885), and one near the mouth of Arroyo Santa Catarina, thought to be somewhat higher in the column, since none of the species mentioned by White had been found in it. Many fossils have been collected from the south shore of

Todos Santos Bay, and therefore from the chief area included by White in his Gualala group.

The age assignment of this group as given by White was based primarily upon the supposed resemblance of the limited fauna known to him to that of the Gosau formation in Europe. This assignment was accepted by Böse and Wittich (1913), Burckhardt (1930), and later writers.

Subsequent study of the faunas listed and those of other late Cretaceous beds in the coastal areas of California and in the Great Valley, as compared to those of western Europe, India, and Madagascar (Collignon, 1938), has thrown unexpected light upon the faunal aspect of the Gualala group of White, and its stratigraphic position. Clearly, there are faunal relationships with the strata outcropping in the coastal areas of California and those in the Great Valley.

The following list of species from locality 1431 (C. A. S.) near the mouth of Arroyo Santa Catarina is taken from Anderson and Hanna (1935) :

Parapachydiscus catarinae Anderson and Hanna
Parapachydiscus peninsularis Anderson and Hanna
Parapachydiscus ootacodensis (Stoliczka*)*
Exiteloceras vancouverense (Gabb)
Nostoceras sternbergi Anderson and Hanna
Baculites occidentalis Meek
Baculites vagina Forbes
Cymatoceras? campbelli (Meek)

"Nucula" solitaria Gabb
Oligoptycha obliqua (Gabb)
Gyrodes conradiana Gabb
Turritella peninsularis Anderson and Hanna
Nerinea parallela (Anderson and Hanna)
Volutoderma cf. *V. magna* Packard
Clisocolus cordatus Whiteaves
Glycymeris veatchii (Gabb)
Trigonocallista major (Packard)
Acila (Truncacila) demessa Finlay

From a second locality a little farther north on the Arroyo Santa Catarina others were collected later by Arthur Bridge, including *Parapachydiscus princeps* n. sp., and *Nostoceras mexicanum* n. sp.

From San Antonio del Mar, Sternberg collected the following invertebrate species :

Gyrodes conradiana Gabb
Tessarolax incrustata Anderson and Hanna
Turritella peninsularis Anderson and Hanna
Dentalium (Entalis) whiteavesi Anderson and Hanna
Spondylus cf. *S. rugosus* Packard
Gryphaea sp.

Ostrea sp.
Parallelodon aff. *P. brewerianus* (Gabb)
Parallelodon vancouverensis (Meek)
Crassatella aff. *C. tuscana* (Gabb)
Inoceramus sp.
Inoceramus pacificus Anderson and Hanna

At locality 948 (C. A. S.), about 6 miles north of San Antonio del Mar, Hertlein and Jordan collected, from sandstone outcropping in the sea cliffs, *Parapachydiscus* sp. indet., *Paleoechinoneus hannai* Grant and Hertlein, *Spondylus* sp. indet.

A large number of species have been collected from the south shore of Todos Santos Bay. Only a partial list is given here, taken partly from the account of Fairbanks (1893c), as emended, in part from White (1885b), as emended by Anderson and Hanna, and in part collected by Sternberg, and by others :

Baculites aff. *B. chicoensis* Trask
Baculites occidentalis Meek
Baculites aff. *B. fairbanksi* Anderson
Oxybeloceras lineatum (Gabb)
Acteon inornatus White

Lysis (Stomatia) intermedia (Cooper)
Cerithium pillingi White
Cerithium totium-sanctorum White
Trochus euryostomus White
Volutoderma gabbi (White)

Trigonocallista major (Packard)
Glycymeris veatchii (Gabb)
Tellina monilifera Gabb
Meekia navis Gabb

Coralliochama orcutti White
Crassatellites aff. *C. tuscana* (Gabb)
Acila (Truncacila) demessa Finlay
Gyrodes californica Packard

From locality 963 (C. A. S.), 9 miles northwest from Todos Santos Bay, Hertlein and Jordan collected from an exposure of about 600 feet of sandy shale, having a strike nearly parallel with that of the preceding beds on the south shore of the Bay, and a dip of 11°–14° SW., the following species:

Parapachydiscus sp. indet.
Baculites lomaensis n. sp.
Baculites aff. *B. vagina* Forbes
Bostrychoceras sp. indet.
Tessarolax sp. indet.
Oligoptycha aff. *O. obliqua* (Gabb)

Perissitys sp. indet.
Spondylus sp. indet.
Diplomoceras o'shaughnessyi n. sp.
Solenoceras mexicanum n. sp.
Lima sp. indet.
Parallelodon aff. *P. brewerianus* (Gabb)

The precise stratigraphic relation of the beds at this locality to those on the south shore of Todos Santos Bay is not known, although they appear to be slightly higher in the section, and represent a deeper water facies. All the preceding localities and faunas, undoubtedly belong in the Gualala group of C. A. White. The same group has been traced northward by Fairbanks and others.

On the east side of Point Loma, near San Diego, from a thin section of Upper Cretaceous beds exposed partly below high tide, Fairbanks (1893c, p. 476) collected a considerable invertebrate fauna, said to have been determined by J. G. Cooper. Some of the species in his list are undoubtedly Eocene, perhaps coming from overlying strata, and a few are doubtfully determined. Cooper later (1894) described other Cretaceous species from this locality, and more recently others have been obtained from the same place by C. G. Abbott, for the Natural History Museum, San Diego.

From these several collections an emended and enlarged list of species from this locality has been compiled, including the following:

Parapachydiscus abbottii n. sp.
Parapachydiscus sp. indet.
Baculites lomaensis n. sp.
Baculites sp. indet.
Pholadomya diegoensis n. sp.
Crassatella lomana Cooper
Parallelodon vancouverensis (Meek)
Inoceramus sp.
Haliotis lomana Anderson
Cerithium pillingi White

Cerithium fairbanksi Cooper
Cophocara stantoni Stewart
Calliostoma kempiana Cooper
Tornatella normalis Cooper
Coralliochama orcutti White
Opis triangulata (Cooper)
Avicula pellucida Gabb
Crenella santana Cooper
Corbis peninsularis Anderson and Hanna
Glycymeris veatchii (Gabb)

From La Jolla, about 12 miles north of Point Loma, San Diego County, Fairbanks (1893c, p. 477) gave a short list of species, which, as here emended, includes the following invertebrates:

Baculites lomaensis n. sp.
Exiteloceras vancouverense (Gabb)
Helcion dichotoma Cooper
Mergerlia dubitanda Cooper

Coralliochama orcutti White
Inoceramus sp.
Glycymeris veatchii (Gabb)
"Aphrodina" sp. indet.
Oligoptycha obliqua (Gabb)

The stratigraphic position of the beds exposed at La Jolla is that of those exposed at Point Loma, as stated by Fairbanks (1893c), and, as shown by the above fauna, is assignable to the *Parapachydiscus* horizon of the Gualala group of C. A. White. Fairbanks, who had studied the stratigraphic relations of the beds exposed at Todos Santos Bay and northward, reports (p. 477):

"The conclusion to be drawn from these facts warrants the assumption that the *Coralliochama* is a distinctly Chico fossil in the three known localities on the southern coast, namely, Todos Santos Bay, Point Loma and La Jolla, and though there are no stratigraphic relations shown near Wallala (Gualala), yet the general character of the beds and the resemblance of the fauna to that of the localities here described, lead me to the belief that they are all approximately synchronous."

North of La Jolla, few exposures of Upper Cretaceous deposits are known south of the Santa Ynez Range, Santa Barbara County. On Jalama Creek, a little north of Point Concepcion, at locality 1788 (C. A. S.), Hanna, Church and Gilbert collected a small fauna of invertebrate fossils from a tawny brown sandstone, including:

Gyrodes conradiana Gabb
Volutoderma magna Packard
Oligoptycha obliqua (Gabb)
Cerithium pillingi White
Cerithium totium-sanctorum White
Cerithium sp. indet.

Coralliochama orcutti White
Trigonocallista major (Packard)
Trigonia churchi n. sp.
Tellina oöides Gabb
Parallelodon aff. *P. brewerianus* (Gabb)
Solen sp. indet.

Twelve miles northwest from this locality, on the south flank of the Santa Ynez Range, at locality 1658 (C. A. S.), Kew and Bremner collected from a similar sandstone the following invertebrate species:

Echinoid (? *Salenia* Gray) sp.
Nostoceras aff. *N. elongata* Whiteaves
Polinices sp. indet.
Oligoptycha obliqua (Gabb)
Paladmete aff. *P. corbuliformis* Stephenson
Acteon sp. indet.
Lysis californiensis Packard
Dentalium (Entalis) whiteavesi Anderson and Hanna

Crassatella lomana Cooper
Crassatellites conradiana (Gabb)
Anatina sp. indet.
Glycymeris veatchii (Gabb)
Tellina oöides Gabb
Mytilus pauperculus Gabb
Lima appressa Gabb
Clisocolus dubius Gabb

The above localities are apparently correlative with the deposits at Todos Santos Bay. Their stratigraphic relations at the base are not known, although no older Upper Cretaceous beds are known or reported in this area. Both Shasta and Franciscan beds outcrop in the general region, but are not known here.

North of the Santa Ynez Range, no outcrop of the Upper Asuncion or of other Upper Cretaceous strata is known for a distance of more than 50 miles.

Fairbanks (1896) described thick beds of sandstone outcropping on the northeast flank of the Santa Lucia Range west of Santa Margarita on and near the Eagle Ranch. From these beds Fairbanks and the writer collected the following species, among others:

"Pentacrinus" fairbanksi n. sp.
Baculites aff. *B. chicoensis* Trask
Cucullaea sp. indet.

Trigonia aff. *T. evansana* Meek
Glycymeris aff. *G. banosensis* n. sp.
Scales of teleost fishes.

Later (1904) Fairbanks included this area in the Atascadero formation on the map of the San Luis quadrangle, with a width of outcrop of 1 to 2 miles and a longitudinal extent of 20 miles or more; but as traced by him and the writer it extended along the west border of the Salinas Valley and on the flanks of the

Santa Lucia Range for a much greater distance. In the columnar section of the Atascadero formation given by Fairbanks (1904), the formation attains a thickness of 3000 to 4000 feet, consisting of thick and thin-bedded sandstones, which terminate below in a conglomerate, resting unconformably upon the Toro formation (Lower Cretaceous).

As elsewhere shown under the genus *Pentacrinus,* the beds here referred to should be regarded as correlative of the Gualala group of White. Farther northwest, on the west border of the Salinas Valley, in the Adelaida and Bryson quadrangles, Upper Cretaceous deposits embraced in the same group have been included by Taliaferro (1944) in the Asuncion group. He gives these beds a thickness of 6000 feet. Taliaferro's description of these beds on the west side of the valley is somewhat more complete than that by Fairbanks. These beds appear to be continuations of the Atascadero formation.

The invertebrate fauna compiled from these beds as determined by B. L. Clark, Schenck and others is of much interest, showing a total of 14 definitely determined species (Taliaferro, 1944 p. 502) in the following slightly emended list:

Acila (Truncacila) demessa Finlay	*Opis triangulata* Cooper
"Aphrodina" nitida (Gabb)	*Parapachydiscus* sp.
Astarte cf. *A. lapidis* Packard	*Pugnellus (Conchothyra) hamulus* (Gabb)
Clisocolus dubius Gabb	*Tessarolax distorta* Gabb
Coralliochama orcutti White	*Trigonocallista varians* (Gabb)
Glycymeris veatchii (Gabb)	*Turritella chaneyi* Merriam
Inoceramus cf. *I. whitneyi* Gabb	*Volutoderma averillii* (Gabb)

Toward the northwest, in Section 23, T. 22 S., R. 5 E., Taliaferro, Clark, and Schenck collected from a gravelly conglomerate other species, including *Coralliochama orcutti* White and *Opis (Opisoma) vancouverensis* Whiteaves. Farther to the northwest these beds rise to an elevation of 4800 feet in the Lucia quadrangle, T. 21 S., R. 4 E., showing a more or less continuous outcrop of the formation across the axis of the Santa Lucia Range.

On the east side of the Salinas Valley, fossils found in the vicinity of Lonoak, appear referable to the same horizon. No Upper Cretaceous beds older than the Upper Asuncion group have yet been reported within the Salinas Valley, although older Cretaceous beds occur on the axis of the range west of Santa Margarita.

C. A. White (1885a, p. 27) published a brief note concerning Upper Cretaceous strata and invertebrate fossils found by G. F. Becker near the village of Gualala, Mendocino County, mentioning among them the following genera, without descriptions: *Spherulites* ?, *Ostrea, Inoceramus, Pecten, Turritella,* and *Solarium.* He considered similar fossils collected at Todos Santos Bay, near San Diego, by C. R. Orcutt, and sent by him to the National Museum, as the same species.

After further study, White (1885b) gave a more extended account, describing one of them *(Solarium wallalaense* n. sp.) and including the following species from Todos Santos Bay: *Coralliochama orcutti* White, *Cerithium pillingi* White, *Trochus euryostomus* White, and *Cerithium totium-sanctorum* White.

White (1891, p. 192) named the strata exposed at both localities "Wallala Group" in the belief that they represent a distinct group in the California Upper

Cretaceous column; he stated that, according to Becker, the strata near Gualala were "some thousands of feet in thickness." White supposed them to lie beneath the so-called "Chico-Tejon series" described by himself and Becker (1885).

White had supposed his Gualala group to be correlative with the "Gosau Beds" of the northeast Alps, and placed it below the top of the Upper Cretaceous; later writers have accepted this view without question. Franz Kossmat of Vienna, who had given aid and advice to Whiteaves concerning certain forms of *Parapachydiscus* and *Diplomoceras,* compared them with Indian species only, without indicating their chronological age. In his brief synopsis of the Upper Cretaceous of Pondicherri and Trichinopoly districts, Kossmat (1897) referred their highest beds to late Campanian-Maestrichtian and Danian stages. Many cephalopods and other mollusca included in his "Mucronatenkreide" (Maestrichtian) have close allies or synchronous forms on the West Coast, in California and in western Canada. Some of these forms were described by Gabb, Meek, Whiteaves, or others. Various other closely analogous or identical species have since been discovered; some are described in the present work. However, in view of the great variety of biotic and ecological conditions, with opportunity for the development of related types at all stages in contemporary deposits on the borders of the Pacific basin, it seems pointless to insist upon detailed identity in form, size, and other features in order to arrive at sound scientific conclusions as to the essential synchronism of stratigraphic groups on opposite sides of the Pacific basin. More reliance should be placed upon the evidence of large groups of related types as guides for correlation. Many species in the Gualala group on the West Coast have been held by excellent authority to be identical with species listed by Kossmat from the late Cretaceous deposits in southern India.

Weaver (1944) has briefly reviewed the work of the earlier writers on the areas near Gualala, has added much stratigraphic and structural detail about the district between Fort Ross and Gualala, and farther north, and has further discussed the faunal relations of the strata at Gualala and Todos Santos Bay, first noted by White and confirmed by Fairbanks.

The Upper Cretaceous invertebrates recorded from the Gualala district by Weaver (1944) include:

Inoceramus pacificus Anderson and Hanna
Pecten sp. indet.
Ostrea sp. indet.
Opis triangulata (Cooper)
Coralliochama orcutti White
Cylichna sp. indet.

Neverita sp. indet.
Cerithium totium-sanctorium White
Trochus euryostomus White
Turritella peninsularis Anderson and Hanna
Solarium wallalaense White

The following were collected by S. G. Clark, and determined by the writer:

Inoceramus aff. *I. lucianus* Davis
Inoceramus sp.
Glycymeris veatchii Gabb
Opis (Opisoma) aff. *O. vancouverensis* Whiteaves
Coralliochama orcutti White

Cymbophora sp. indet.
Cerithium mustangense n. sp.
Cerithium aff. *C. detectum* Stoliczka
Cypraea sp.
Cypraea sp. indet.
Turritella sp. indet.

These lists include 15 determined species, and 6 mollusks determined only generically. Four of these species have been found also in the Upper Asuncion group in the Great Valley, in a different habitat, though all appear to be of the same geologic age. Some of the species have been found in correlative beds on Vancouver Island, but a greater number occur in similar beds on the peninsula of Lower California.

In the Museum of Paleontology, University of California, there is a large, but not complete example of *Inoceramus,* slightly distorted, that appears to belong in the group of large *Inoceramus* found at Point Loma; it bears the label "near Gualala." With it is a smaller specimen resembling *Inoceramus lucianus* Davis from the Lucia quadrangle. *Cerithium mustangense* n. sp. has been found near the base of the Upper Asuncion group, north of the Panoche Hills, near Garzas Creek, on the west border of the San Joaquin Valley.

Many large areas of sandstone and shales in the Coast Ranges north of San Francisco Bay, lithologically similar to those in the Diablo and Concord quadrangles, are here assigned to the Upper Asuncion group, although in most of them fossils are lacking.

In the Russian River Valley and in the valley of Clear Lake, similar deposits are known. No late Cretaceous fossils have been reported from them, but their positions, lithology, and structures resemble those in the southern Coast Range areas in which fossils of the Upper Asuncion group are abundant, such as the Salinas Valley, the Concord and Diablo quadrangles, and farther south.

In the western part of Round Valley, Mendocino County, sandstones and shales of the same character have long been known, and fossils have been collected from them, but without full consideration of their significance. Clark (1940) has described some of these deposits in an area nearly 2 miles wide and 6 miles or more long, crossing the middle fork of Eel River southwest of Covelo. The beds consist of shales, tawny sandstones, and pebbly conglomerates, standing at a high angle, with an easterly dip, and with a thickness of about 4000 feet. From these rocks Clark has collected many fossils at various localities many of them new, but clearly indicating the character and age of the deposits. At localities 46, 49, and 85, he obtained the following molluscan species (Clark collection) :

Parapachydiscus sp. indet.	*Scaphander* sp. indet.
Exiteloceras aff. *E. bennisoni* n. sp.	*Inoceramus mendocinoensis* n. sp.
Nostoceras (?*Didymoceras*) sp. indet.	*Inoceramus* sp.
Baculites occidentalis Meek	*Meekia sella* Gabb

At locality 64, on Henley Creek, on the NW ¼ sec. 26, T. 22 N., R. 13 W., Clark collected from a tawny sandstone the following species:

Baculites occidentalis Meek	*Inoceramus mendocinoensis* n. sp.
Baculites lomaensis n. sp.	*Inoceramus* sp.
Parapachydiscus aff. *P. coalingensis* n. sp.	*Pholadmya* aff. *P. diegoensis* n. sp.

Most of these species are found in the lower part of the Upper Asuncion group on the west border of the San Joaquin Valley and some of them in the coastal areas in southern California, though a few are new. The assemblage can hardly, be regarded as correlative of any other than the lower part of the Upper Asuncion group.

MAESTRICHTIAN AND DANIAN? VERTEBRATE REMAINS: In the years 1937–1942, a number of more or less complete skeletons of saurians have been discovered in Upper Asuncion strata on the west border of the San Joaquin Valley. Most of them have been described by C. L. Camp (1942), with notes bearing upon their stratigraphic position.

All the species and many of the genera are new. They include mosasaurs, tylosaurs, and hadrosaurs, with two new genera of the mosasaurs, and perhaps new genera of the others, but the relationships are not clear.

Fragmentary remains of other types have been found, including an unidentified tooth Camp (1942, p. 11). Only a summary of the forms thus far recovered, with notes as to their stratigraphic position, can be presented here. They include:

MOSASAURINAE

Kolposaurus bennisoni CAMP, n. gen., n. sp., Mem. Univ. Calif., vol. 13, no. 1, 1942, p. 2, pl. 1; figs. 1, 2, 3; loc. V 3718 (Univ. Calif. Mus. Pal.), found on the SW ¼ sec. 20, T. 8 S., R. 8 E., Mt. D. B. and M., Stanislaus County, in the upper part of the Garzas sandtone of the Moreno formation. Maestrichtian or (?) Danian.

Kolposaurus tuckeri CAMP, n. sp., Mem. Univ. Calif., vol. 13, no. 1, 1942, p. 8, pl. 3; figs. 4, 5, 6, 7, 8, 9, 10; loc. V 3736 (Univ. Calif. Mus. Pal.), found 900 feet E., 1,050 feet S. of the NW cor. of sec. 13, T. 14 S., R. 11 E., Mt. D. B. and M., Fresno County, in the type area of the Moreno formation. Maestrichtian or (?) Danian.

TYLOSAURINAE

Plesiotylosaurus crassidens CAMP, n. gen., n. sp., Mem. Univ. Calif., vol. 13, no. 1, 1942, p. 18, pl. 4; figs 11, 12, 13; loc. 328 (C. I. T.); found 800 feet S., 300 feet W. of the SE cor. sec. 36, T. 14 S., R. 11 E., Mt. D. B. and M., Fresno County in the lower part of the Moreno formation. Maestrichtian or (?) Danian.

HADROSAURINAE

Duckbill dinosaur (? *Trachodon*) HESSE AND WELLES, 1936, discussed also by CAMP; Mem. Univ. Calif., vol. 13, no. 1, 1942, p. 10 (not figured). Loc. V 3622 (Univ. Calif. Mus. Pal.); found on the SW ¼ of the SW ¼ sec. 20, T. 5 S., R. 7 E., Mt. D. B. and M., on Puerto Creek, Stanislaus County, 600 feet N., 800 feet E., of the SE cor. sec. 10, township as given above. It occurs in the lower part of the Quinto member of the Moreno formation. Maestrichtian.

Duckbill dinosaur (rel. to *Hadrosaurus*) STOCK, Bull. Geol. Soc. Am., vol. 52, no. 12, 1941, p. 1950 (abstract); (C. I. T.), definite locality not given, *fide* Payne, 150 feet beneath the zone of *Siphogenerinoides*, in the Tumey Hills, western Fresno County. Maestrichtian.

CORRELATION OF THE PACIFIC COAST
UPPER CRETACEOUS

The lowest known fossil-bearing beds of the Upper Asuncion group, the *Parapachydiscus* horizon, is more than 1200 feet above its base in some areas, as on Joaquin Ridge and in the Mount Diablo quadrangle. The upper limit of the group is at the top of the Moreno formation, of possible Danian age.

In the monumental work of Stephenson (1941), much needed information has been assembled concerning equivalents of the Navarro group, within and outside the United States. In his notes devoted to other areas (p. 34-46), all valid correlations made with Navarro group apply equally well to the Upper Asuncion group of California and the West Coast. Among the indices of the Maestrichtian stage in the south of France, Seunes (1890) has included: *Pachydiscus jacquoti* Seunes, *Pachydiscus fresvillensis* Seunes, *Diplomoceras recticostatum* (Seunes), *Baculites anceps* Lamarck, *Bostrychoceras polyplocum* (d'Orbigny), and other types, to which Kossmat (1897) added many others, including: *Parapachydiscus ootacodensis* (Stoliczka), *Lytoceras (Pseudophyllites) indra* (Forbes), *Baculites vagina* Forbes, and others. Many of these species have identical or closely allied forms in the uppermost Cretaceous in western Canada, as shown by Whiteaves (1903). According to Grossouvre (1893), *Pachydiscus fresvillensis* Seunes is identical with *Pachydiscus colligatus* (Binckhorst), and should indicate the same age. To these may be added *Parapachydiscus peninsularis* Anderson and Hanna, and *Parapachydiscus coalingensis* n. sp., both closely akin to *P. colligatus* (Binckhorst). Associated with these are various types of *Nostoceras* described from California, from Baja California (Anderson and Hanna, 1935), and from Hornby Island (Whiteaves, 1903).

The *Parapachydiscus* horizon of the Upper Asuncion group may be directly correlated with the Maestrichtian of southern France (Seunes, 1890; Grossouvre, 1894; and others). According to Seunes, in the south of France, at the base of the Pyrenees, the highest part of the Cretaceous embraces two distinctly different groups of beds. The lower (Maestrichtian) is characterized by types of *Parapachydiscus, Inoceramus* aff. *I. impressus* d'Orbigny *Inoceramus* aff. *I. regularis* d'Orbigny, *Ostrea* aff. *O. vesicularis* Lamarck, and other molluscan types that occur in the *Parapachydiscus* horizon within or outside the Great Valley trough. The higher members correspond in both fauna and stratigraphy to the upper Maestrichtian and Danian stages of southern France.

The Moreno has stratigraphic and some lithologic resemblances to the Danian of southern Europe. The lower Danian consists chiefly of limestones and marls, with remains of echinoids and *Nautilus danicus* Schlotheim. In the upper Garumnian, Seunes mentions bryozoans, *Orbitoides,* Miliolids, *Dentalina, Baculina, Textularia, Lithothamnium,* and other forms. In the Pondicherri and Trichinopoly districts of southern India, according to Kossmat (1897), the strata at the top resemble the Moreno formation in its type area.

The faunas of the Atlantic coastal region contain more European and Mediterranean elements, while those of the West Coast are largely Indo-Pacific types. The faunal assemblages of the Western Interior and of the West Coast contain elements of boreal aspect, with few echinoids or rudistids, but a commingling of elements from the north, the east, and the west, with few from tropical or southern sources. The faunal contributions from the Indo-Pacific basin to the Western Interior and to the Gulf and central Texas regions have been but little known.

The deposits of the Western Interior cover a great region that includes parts of the Rocky Mountains and the Great Plains between northeast British Columbia and the Rio Grande. The exposed correlative deposits of central Texas and the Gulf extend across Texas in a relatively narrow belt from northeast to southwest; the two contrasted regions are separated by a belt of Paleozoic rocks, 400–500 miles broad, reaching from the Great Lakes southwest to central New Mexico. The nearest approach of the Western Interior deposits to the Pacific is near the Canadian border, or southwest of New Mexico, across the Cordilleran axis. Although Stephenson and Reeside (1938) have shown that the deposits in the Western Interior and the Gulf and central Texas regions are in part correlative, it is not obvious that their diastrophic or faunal records are parallel. They are dissimilar in stratigraphic character and thickness. Their lithologic contrasts have long been known. One is detrital; the other partly of organic origin, has marls and calcareous deposits, rarely with terriginous detritus.

The deposits of the Western Interior resemble those of the West Coast, in British Columbia, Oregon, and California, in their detrital character, which contrasts with the chalks, marls and other calcareous deposits in the Gulf region (Texas and east Mexico), as described by Stephenson (1941, p. 9).

A chronological correlation of the Upper Cretaceous of the Western Interior and on the West Coast seems entirely possible, although the diastrophic record and the faunal changes of the former have not been studied in detail. The faunas of the Western Interior are thought to be in part of boreal origin, as are those of the Pacific border regions—more boreal toward the north and more subtropical toward the south. The faunas of both the Western Interior and the Gulf region contain many elements that pertain to Indo-Pacific assemblages, sufficient to indicate that marine connections may have existed by way of Pacific shores.

There are group resemblances, many cases of close specific relationship, and some of apparent specific identity found at correlative levels in the Western Interior and the Pacific border. These parallels increase in frequency and in effect reaching a maximum in Maestrichtian time. These parallels appear in many invertebrate families, as in the Ostreidae, among Inocerami, and other pelecypod races, among gastropods (Naticidae, Turritellidae, Strombidae, Volutidae), and in cephalopod stocks (prionotropids, mortoniceratids, scaphitids, baculitids, turrilitids, nostoceratids and others).

From stratigraphic and faunal correlations in the Upper Cretaceous of the West Coast and of the Western Interior during successive stages (Cenomanian to Maestrichtian), partial lists in Table 3 illustrate the faunal relations between them.

TABLE 3.—*Closely related or identical invertebrate species in the Upper Cretaceous deposits on the West Coast and in the Western Interior region*

West Coast	Western Interior
Maestrichtian	
Inoceramus (Endocostea) stanislausensis n. sp.	*Inoceramus (Endocostea) typica* Whitfield
Inoceramus aff. *I. simpsoni* Meek	*Inoceramus simpsoni* Meek
Pholadomya diegoensis n. sp.	*Pholadomya coloradoensis* Stanton
Solenoceras sp. indet.	*Solenoceras crassum* (Whitfield)
Lower Senonian	
Peroniceras aff. *P. leei* Reeside	*Peroniceras leei* Reeside
Scaphites hippocrepis DeKay	*Scaphites hippocrepis* Dekay
Scaphites gillisi Anderson	*Scaphites warreni* Meek and Hayden
Scaphites klamathensis Anderson	*Scaphites larvaeformis* Meek
Turonian	
Acteon politus Gabb	*Actaeon propingus* Stanton
Prionotropis bakeri Anderson	*Prionotropis woolgari* Meek (not Mantell)
Prionotropis casperi n. sp.	*Prionotropis hyatti* Stanton
Inoceramus aff. *I. labiatus* Schlotheim	*Inoceramus labiatus* Schlotheim
Cenomanian	
Cyrtochilus stylus n. sp.	*Cyrtochilus gracilus* Shumard
Diplomoceras phoenixense (Anderson)	*"Helicoceras" pariense* White
Acanthoceras newboldi Kossmat	*Acanthoceras kanabense* Stanton

Closely related or identical invertebrate species from the Upper Asuncion group on the West Coast and the Navarro group of the Gulf Coast and the central Texas regions are shown in Table 4.

TABLE 4.—*Closely related or identical invertebrate species from the Upper Asuncion group on the West Coast and the Navarro group of the Gulf Coast and the central Texas region*

West Coast	Gulf Coast and Central Texas
Coralliochama orcutti White	*Coralliochama sp.* (east Mexico)
Exogyra sp.	*Exogyra costata* Say
Tellina mathewsonii Gabb	*Tellina munda* Stephenson
Tenea inflata (Gabb)	*Tenea parilis* Conrad
Astarte sulcata Packard	*Astarte culebrensis* Stephenson
Nonacteonina stephensoni n. sp.	*Nonacteonina graphoides* Stephenson
Turritella chicoensis (part ?) Popenoe (not Gabb)	*Turritella vertebroides* Shumard
Parapachydiscus quiriquinae (Philippi)	*Parapachydiscus arkansanus* Stephenson
Parapachydiscus ootacodensis (Stoliczka)	*Parapachydiscus scotti* Stephenson
Baculites lomaensis n. sp.	*Baculites* sp. Stephenson
Bostrychoceras puertoense n. sp.	*Bostrychoceras colubriforme* (Stephenson)
Turrilites aff. *T. splendidus* (Shumard)	*Turrilites splendidus* Shumard
Solenoceras sp.	*Solenoceras multicostatum* Stephenson
Exicrioceras diabloense n. sp.	*Axonoceras compressum* Stephenson

Table 4 could probably be greatly extended by a careful search leading back to early Senonian, or to Turonian times, or farther, as is indicated by early Cenomanian species of *Cyrtochilus, Lyelliceras,* and certain acanthoceratids. Table 5 lists characteristic species of the Upper Cretaceous in the Sacramento and San Joaquin Valleys.

TABLE 5.—*Representative zones and faunal lists from the Upper Cretaceous Series in the Great Valley of California*

		Sacramento Valley	San Joaquin Valley
Upper Asuncion Group	Maestrichtian–Danian	*Solarium inornatum* Gabb *Bostrychoceras vermiculare* Gabb *Solenoceras* sp. *Exicrioceras diabloense* n. sp. *Diplomoceras* aff. *D. notabile* Whiteaves *Lytoceras* (*Gaudryceras*) sp. *Parapachydiscus* sp. indet. *Parapachydiscus* aff. *P. ganesa* Forbes *Parapachydiscus* aff. *P. catarinae* Anderson and Hanna *Baculites* aff. *B. vagina* Forbes *Baculites occidentalis* Meek	*Acila* (*Truncacila princeps* Schenck *Glycymeris veatchii* (Gabb) *Tenea inflata* (Gabb) Saurian remains *Exicrioceras diabloense* n. sp. *Lytoceras* (*Gaudryceras*) sp. *Lytoceras* (*Gaudryceras*) *aureum* n. sp. *Parapachydiscus coalingensis* n. sp. *Parapachydiscus* aff. *P. peninsularis* Anderson and Hanna *Parapachydiscus catarinae* Anderson and Hanna *Nostoceras fresnoense* n. sp.
Lower Asuncion Group	Santonian-Campanian	*Inoceramus turgidus* n. sp. *Butticeras studleyi* n. sp. *Mortoniceras randalli* n. sp. *Mortoniceras buttense* n. sp. *Mortoniceras gabbi* Anderson *Oxybeloceras taffi* n. sp. *Hauericeras mickeyi* n. sp.	*Baculites chicoensis* Trask *Inoceramus chicoensis* n. sp. *Phylloceras gargantuum* n. sp. *Mortoniceras randalli* n. sp. *Mortoniceras templetoni* Hall and Ambrose *Oxybeloceras taffi* n. sp. *Perissitys brevirostris* (Gabb) *Hauericeras* aff. *H. gardeni* Bailey
	Coniacian	*Phylloceras ramosum* Meek *Metaplacenticeras pacificum* Smith *Metaplacenticeras californicum* Anderson *Lytoceras* (*Gaudryceras*) *alamedense* (Smith) *Prionocycloceras crenulatum* (Anderson) *Prionocyclus californicus* n. sp. *Peroniceras tehamaense* (Gabb)	*Metaplacenticeras pacificum* Smith *Metaplacenticeras californicum* Anderson *Phylloceras alamedense* Smith *Phylloceras ramosum* Meek *Desmoceras selwynianum* Whiteaves *Peroniceras quintoense* n. sp.
Pacheco Group	Turonian	*Prionotropis bakeri* Anderson *Gaudryceras tenuiliratum* Yabe *Oregoniceras oregonense* (Anderson) *Scaphites condoni* Anderson *Scaphites pittensis* n. sp. *Fagesia californica* Anderson *Inoceramus* aff. *I. labiatus* Schlotheim *Mammites rancheria* n. sp.	*Prionotropis bakeri* Anderson *Oregoniceras oregonense* (Anderson) *Oregoniceras knighteni* (Anderson) *Scaphites condoni* Anderson
	Cenomanian	*Phylloceras velledae* Michelin *Forbesiceras* sp. *Puzosia* aff. *P. planulatum* var. *Turrilites petersoni* n. sp. "*Acanthoceras*" *turneri* White *Puzosia* sp.	*Turrilites* aff. *T. oregonensis* Gabb *Acanthoceras* cf. *A. cunningtoni* Sharpe *Puzosia* sp.
	Albian	*Beudanticeras haydenii* (Gabb) *Beudanticeras alamoense* n. sp. *Stoliczkaia clavigera* var. *Pervinquieria inflata* var. *Beudanticeras brewerii* (Gabb)	*Pervinquieria* sp. *Sonneratia stantoni* Anderson

PALEOGEOGRAPHY
GREAT VALLEY TROUGH

The Great Valley and its subdivisions were briefly described by the author in relation to the Shasta series (1938b). The thickness and other characteristics of the Upper Cretaceous deposits within the trough, nearly 400 miles in extent, show that events and their results in the different parts of the embayment did not run parallel throughout the period. The maximum thickness of the Upper Cretaceous sediments in the northern embayment is hardly more than half that in the southern embayment. More surprising are the contrasts on opposite sides of the trough in the two embayments, though less than 50 miles in breadth. At no place on the east side of the Great Valley do these sediments aggregate a tenth of the thickness exposed on its western side. Clearly, the trough lay between nearly parallel shores; that on the eastern side was nearly straight along margin, whereas, that on the western side was more sinuous, following the contours of mountainous terrains that constituted the forelands of the time. From these and other equally important aspects, it may be inferred that the Upper Cretaceous sediments throughout the trough came largely from western sources, as did the sediments of the Shasta series. The broader continental areas lay toward the east, but their drainage toward the Great Valley was almost negligible as contrasted with that from the western mountains.

These facts indicate that the regional extent and altitude during Shasta time continue with only moderate changes throughout Upper Cretaceous. The Upper Cretaceous deposits of the Great Valley were best developed and best preserved in its southern embayment. This reflects the areal extension and the altitude of the forelands that constituted the source areas of the sediments, the climate and the volumes and gradients of the streams that entered from the west.

There is evidence here that, during Upper Cretaceous times, the foreland areas of the continental border were very great, with corresponding elevations, heavy precipitation and erosion that built up thick deposits of sediments within the trough on its western border.

BORDERLANDS

The forelands of the Far West during later Mesozoic times were partly described by the writer (1938b). The sea and land relationships described by Schuchert (1935, p. 118) during late Cretaceous times, evidently extended from Mexico northward to southern Alaska, and west of the "Pacific geosyncline" there existed a broad, mountainous chain of islands that included Sonoria (Schuchert), Salinia (Reed) and Klamathonia (Anderson). Others probably existed farther to the north. Klamathonia is now most completely preserved. Only remnants of Sonoria still exist in the mountains of western Mexico, and in its off-shore islands, on some of which continental rocks are reported. Similar but larger areas of Klamathonia are recognizable in the coastal areas of northwest

California and southwest Oregon. Farther north in the Olympic mountains, on Vancouver Island, and in the Queen Charlotte Islands, other large remnants of forelands are recognizable.

Klamathonia.—The late Mesozoic foreland that occupied much of northwest California and southwest Oregon, and probably a marginal part of the sea during Knoxville and Shasta times, may have continued with little change through the Upper Cretaceous. It had suffered from denudation and tectonic disturbances prior to, during, and after the Shasta period.

The physical features of Klamathonia during the Upper Cretaceous may be partly inferred from those described for the preceding Shasta time (Anderson, 1938), and partly from the great masses of Upper Cretaceous sediments on the west borders of the Sacramento Valley between Redding at the north and Fairfield at the south. It appears that the river systems of the Knoxville and Shasta periods still continue to carry the drainage and its detritus from the hinterland, although the strandlines of Upper Cretaceous time lay farther toward the east.

Many streams carried and discharged their detritus into the Great Valley embayments of the Upper Cretaceous epoch, from the same regional background across intervening belts of Knoxville and Shasta deposits. They built up this latest series of sediments within the Great Valley trough. The stream channels of Upper Cretaceous time were no doubt largely inherited from earlier epochs, though diastrophic episodes, thrusts, displacements and other changes had occurred.

Salinia.—R. D. Reed (1933) described an ancient land area lying west of the Joaquin embayment of the Great Valley trough and proposed the name Salinia for it. Reed described the area as having contained pre-Mesozoic rock systems, including granites, schists, quartzites, crystalline limestones and other types, and as structurally resembling Mohavia in being divisible into variously constituted areas. It may be understood that Salinia included all the pre-Cretaceous terrains now known in the Coast Ranges between the latitude of Mount Hamilton on the north and the Santa Ynez Range on the south, and extensive western land areas now submerged beneath the sea.

The tectonic history of Salinia cannot now be traced in detail. Its areas have been eroded, particularly in its western half, far in excess of other areas on the California coast north of Point Concepcion. It appears probable that the San Andreas rift had its inception prior to Upper Cretaceous time, with an uplift of areas to the west since no early Upper Cretaceous deposits are west of it.

The Upper Cretaceous Series on the flanks of Salinia exhibits its greatest thickness, and yet contains evidence of a near maximum of diastrophic results from thrusting normal to the continental border. These conditions may also reflect the fact that Salinia occupies a position intermediate between Klamathonia at the north and Sonoria at the south. Sonoria has suffered even greater losses from erosion, faulting, and submergence than any of the known forelands of the continental border.

Mohavia.—There can be no doubt that, on the continental side of the Great Valley trough in all its latitudes, broad land areas existed throughout Upper Cretaceous times, although its coast line and other features are generally obscure.

At the south were the land areas which Reed (1933) named Mohavia, and which Hulin (1935) described as extending toward the north. The boundaries of Mohavia, its altitude, drainage direction, climatic features, and geologic history have not yet been determined. It lay upon the eastern border of the "Pacific Geosyncline" of Schuchert (1935) and may be regarded as having been co-extensive with it, although at the north much evidence is hidden beneath volcanic ejecta. There is little evidence that the eastern border land contributed important volumes of sediment to the trough during Upper Cretaceous times. During Tertiary times, it did so in certain areas. Only in the northern part of the Great Valley (Cow Creek district) are found evidences of lower Upper Cretaceous (Turonian) strand lines. Farther south, the strand lines lay farther east along the Mohavian coast. The coastal borders are now hidden in many places beneath later volcanics.

The invertebrate faunas on the east border of the trough are almost wholly marine and little affected by fresh or brackish water at any place.

The thickness of the Upper Cretaceous deposits on the east border of the trough nowhere exceeds 2500 feet, and for the most part is less than 1500 feet, the maximum being at the north end of the Great Valley. The thickness of sediment on the east side of the Valley is only a tenth that on the west which ranges from 4000–15,000 feet.

This difference probably results from altitude differences in the background on opposite sides of the trough, or climatic differences (rainfall) on the west. Climatic differences on the west and on the Mohavian border of the trough in these latitudes might be attributable to differences in altitude only—Mohavia possibly was a low-lying, semi-desert plain, from which only small streams entered the trough except at the north. The strictly marine faunas, ranging from Turonian to middle or upper Campanian in age, support this view of the eastern strand line.

VOLUME OF SEDIMENT

Adequate source areas have been described for the Upper Cretaceous deposits on the west side of the Sacramento Valley, (Anderson, 1938) in the mountains of Klamathonia toward the west and north. Similar source areas for the greater volumes of sediment on the west border of the Joaquin embayment are found in the broader areas of Salinia as they existed in Late Cretaceous time. From this viewpoint, these deposits may be subjected to comparative computations in the manner employed for the Shasta series on the flanks of Klamathonia (Anderson, 1938).

In the exposures within the latitude of Mount Hamilton on the north and Castle Mountain below Coalinga on the south, the present volume of Upper Cretaceous sediments may be estimated as more than 4500 cubic miles. Assuming an average of 1 vertical mile of denudation in the source areas, it would require 4500 square miles of surface to supply it. If the volume of sediment was greater, or if the vertical denudation was less, the areas of origin should be computed as greater.

The high angle of inclination in the Upper Cretaceous strata (50°–80°), and that of the Tertiary beds on the flanks of the Diablo and Santa Lucia Ranges, may be taken as evidence of large-scale post-Upper Cretaceous thrusting from the southwest to the northeast. The resulting compression, folding, and faulting in the source areas of the Upper Cretaceous sediments, and in contiguous belts, would have greatly reduced the breadth of all areas of Salinia. It could thus be shown that the present topographic and geologic maps of these regions do not correctly represent the areas of denudation that existed on Salinia during Late Cretaceous time, but that these areas occupied twice the areas shown on the present maps. Large parts of the source areas may have lain beyond the locus of the present coast line and are now submerged.

Almost all the Upper Cretaceous sediments consist of sandstones, shales, and conglomerates, though not in any significant order. Sandstones predominate in most sections, emphasizing the detrital character of the Great Valley trough, and are repeated at intervals in the column.

The writer believes that most of the conglomerates indicate diastrophic incidents such as have marked the record of the Upper Cretaceous in other parts of the West Coast. Shales are more frequent in the upper-middle part of the general section, and indicate intervals of relative stability. Few occurrences of limestone are known, and none of notable thickness or extent in any part of the section.

The thickness of the series and of its components differ greatly in the northern and southern embayments. The thickest and best preserved Upper Cretaceous deposits occur at the south, on the flanks of Salinia. As the source of the sediments upon its flanks, its areas were in some measure proportional to those of Klamathonia, which has remained more nearly intact, without great loss to its general area. In contrast, Salinia has suffered enormous losses by compressive thrusting, faulting and submergence, as its deposits and structures show at present.

Salinia is very similar to the region in southern Argentina described by Burckhardt (1900) as containing "Traces of an ancient continent," although not on the same great scale. Thick aggregates of boulder conglomerates on the flanks of Salinia, in the lower and middle portions of the series give material evidence of the entrance into the trough of one or more large rivers, near to and south of the present positions of Quinto and Los Banos creeks. These boulder conglomerates and their aggregates of mixed rock types show unmistakably a great variety of terrains in the region from which they came, and from which they have been carried by streams of considerable volumes and steep gradients. Their roundness indicates long distances of travel. The earlier parts of the Upper Cretaceous series yields important data indicating that the source areas, of at least a large proportion of their materials, were not close at hand, that they lay toward the west in large tracts, probably now partly submerged by the sea. From these boulder conglomerates, aggregating some 2000 to 3000 feet, some estimate could be made of the altitude of the source areas, the stream volumes and their gradients, and of the time required for their accumulation.

For the somewhat thicker but similar Shasta series, of the Sacremento embayment the source areas were reckoned (Anderson, 1938) at about 65,000 square miles; a commensurate area should be held as the source of the Upper Cretaceous sediment on the west border of that valley.

GEOLOGIC HISTORY

The complete Upper Cretaceous section shows evidence of diastrophic events, such as were described for the Shasta series (Anderson, 1938). For the Upper Cretaceous Series, the evidence is more extensive and more impressive when traced throughout the Great Valley toward the west.

The first of these events was described by Haug (1900) under the title, "The Cenomanian Transgression." It here began in latest Albian time, with strata containing species of *Pervinquieria,* rather than later, as Haug believed, probably upon evidence taken from other regions. The Cenomanian transgression was followed by a prolonged subsidence which led to a rapid spread of marine sedimentation upon land areas in later Turonian time, ending at the opening of Senonian time. This sequence of events corresponds to the Pacheco group on the Pacific coast. The closing Turonian interval was characterized in California by the presence of *Fagesia, Scaphites, Hyphantoceras* and prionotropid ammonites.

An uplift on the borders of the trough, of short duration, was terminated by widespread subsidence at the beginning of Senonian time. This event initiated another long cycle of sedimentation, with distinct marine faunas—species of *Peroniceras, Prionocyclus, Prionocycloceras,* and later, species of *Metaplacenticeras* in both embayments of the trough and in areas to the north and to the south. The ammonites indicate that this sequence is to be correlated with the Coniacian. The sedimentary deposits of this interval reach their greatest development in Yolo County, but extend to many areas on the West Coast.

An upward movement led to retraction of shore lines in both embayments, with the introduction of new faunal elements, *Inoceramus undulatoplicatus* (Roemer), *Parapuzosia* sp., *Eupachydiscus* sp., and *Canadoceras.* This reduction of seaways in the trough led to erosion on its borders, which continued for a short time only. This event was followed by rapid subsidence, and by a wide lateral expansion of marine areas in both embayments, marked by such species of *Mortoniceras* as *M. randalli* n. sp., *M. chicoense* (Trask), and *M. (Submortoniceras) pentzanum* n. sp., and by *Inoceramus chicoensis* n. sp., *Butticeras studleyi* n. sp., and numerous gastropods and pelecypods new to the trough.

The species of *Mortoniceras* are thought to indicate a lower-middle Campanian age, correlating with the stage of *Mortoniceras delawarense* (Morton), and *M. campaniense* Grossouvre. Members of this group occur in both embayments of the trough, but are more numerous at the north.

This interval was closed in later Campanian time by another retraction of the seas in the trough, erosion on its borders, and the removal of large volumes of sediment from extra-strandline exposures. The end of Campanian time brought a return of subsidence and of marine expansion within and outside the trough, with the deposition of the Gualala group on the coastal border and of the Lower Asuncion group within the Great Valley. This subsidence was felt in many latitudes on the West Coast and over wide areas of the continent, and probably extended to South America, Africa, and Europe, India, and other parts of the world. It was characterized by the development of many large and often eccentric types of cephalopods in protected areas, of the genera *Parapachydiscus, Nostoceras, Baculites, Axonoceras;* gastropods of the genera *Cerithium, Solarium,* and *Trochus;* and pelecypods *(Coralliochama, Inoceramus, Opisoma),* most of which are new.

Among the notable cephalopods in protected areas of the coastal border were parapachydiscids, some of large size *(Parapachydiscus catarinae* Anderson and Hanna, *P. princeps* n. sp. and *P. coalingensis* n. sp.).

The Upper Asuncion group is traceable from Lower California northward along the coastal border, into the Great Valley trough as far north as Marysville Buttes, and in the Coast Ranges of Mendocino County. With similar stratigraphic relations, its correlatives occur on Vancouver Island and in other areas farther north and west.

A distinct phase of Cretaceous sedimentation, generally known as the Moreno formation, marked the close of Asuncion time. This formation is not now known to be unconformable upon the preceding strata. In part, it is characterized by numerous microorganisms, foraminifera, radiolaria, diatoms, and a considerable number of mollusca. Probably the most important discovery from a purely biological viewpoint are the remains of vertebrates in the Moreno formation. These include various types of marine or shore-inhabiting saurians. The Moreno has not been recognized outside the Great Valley of California.

SYSTEMATIC PALEONTOLOGY

Phylum COELENTERATA
Genus **Favites** Link
Favites gabbi n. sp.
(Plate 71, figures 2, 2a, 3, 3a)

Corallum small, cerioid, massive; corallites irregularly polygonal; walls septothecal, thin; calices moderately deep; septa in 3 cycles, those of first 2 reaching moderately developed parietal columella; septa just slightly exsert, not continuous from one calyx to another; details of upper ends of septa poorly preserved, but slight indications of paliform lobes on first and second cycles; third cycle septa extending in about two-thirds distance to columella; septal interspaces 3 to 4 times as wide as septa; lateral faces of septa only moderately granulated.

Corallites 5 to 8 mm in diameter; height of corallum about 27 mm; major diameter of corallum 47.5 mm; the calices appear to have been about 2 mm or more deep.

This is the earliest recorded species of this genus. There are no other known species from the later strata of the Pacific Coast region with which to compare it. *Astrocoenia irregularis* Whiteaves from the Cretaceous of Maude Island is the only other described Pacific Coast Cretaceous coral with which it might be confused; but the corallites of that species are only 4 to 5 mm in diameter, the calices are shallow, and it has a prominent styliform columella. *Favites mexicana* Vaughan from the Oligocene San Rafael formation, in the State of Tamaulipas, Mexico, has corallites of slightly greater diameter and about twice as many septa, with tertiaries fusing to the secondaries.

This species is from locality 29121 (C. A. S.), NE ¼ of SW. ¼ sec. 28, T. 11 S., R. 10 E., Mt. Diablo base, from a fossiliferous conglomerate bed on Ortigalita Creek, probably near the base of the Quinto. Holotype (C. A. S. Type Coll.).

Phylum ECHINODERMATA
Class CRINOIDEA Miller
Family PENTACRINIDAE Gray
Genus **Pachecocrinus** Anderson n. gen.

This genus is proposed for a number of crinoid remains found in the upper part of the Asuncion group in the Great Valley of California.

The taxonomic position of the genus may be indicated by the accompanying figures and notes based upon the incomplete remains now at hand. It seems improbable that the genus could belong to the subtribe of *Uintacrinus* Zittel, since it differs greatly from the known remains of the latter. Furthermore, sections of crinoid stems found associated with the heads indicate its probable relationship to *Pentacrinus* and to related types. The two crinoid heads thus far found have had small and poorly defined bases that seem to have been connected with stems. The arms, of which 17 may be counted on the holotype, are for the most part in trios, although one of the arms may have been lost or suppressed to a mere rudimentary arm. Viewed from a basal position, the arms appear to be set in six groups; one group has only two instead of three arms that diverge from a central axis. The precise relation of these groups to the divisions of a pentagonal stem must await further evidence. The generic features of the group, insofar as they can be given at present, are seen in the brachial attachments of the two individual heads found in the same stratigraphic zone, although at different localities. Though not attached to the stem of the organism, the joints and joint faces of stems were found associated with the head itself. If only stem sections had been found, they might have led to placing it in the genus *Isocrinus* von Meyer.

Pachecocrinus joaquinensis Anderson n. sp.
(Plate 6, figures 3a, 3b)

The holotype was found at Loc. 29650 (C. A. S.) in the NE ¼ of the SE ¼ sec. 4, T. 9

S. R. 8 E., M. D. B. and M., by Allan Bennison; the paratype was found by Bennison on Salt Creek at location 29121 (C. A. S.), about 800 feet N., and 2400 feet W., of the SE corner of sec. 18, T. 11 S., R. 10 E., in a stratigraphic position nearly identical with that of the holotype. With the holotype were found various portions of a stem, and other fragmentary remains, some of which expose the joint face, and the internal figure characteristic of the same. Presumably these fragments represent the stem belonging to the head itself, or to another individual. The holotype (C. A. S.), Type Coll.) has the following dimensions: length, 30 mm; width, 19 mm; maximum transverse measure (thickness), 12 mm; thickness of single arm, 2 mm.

The zone in which these examples were found is in the lower part of the Upper Asuncion group, mapped on the geologic sheet of Bull. 603 (U. S. Geol. Survey) as the Moreno formation. The chronological position of the species, as determined from the stratigraphic sequence underlying it, and as determined by the faunas of the underlying and overlying beds, is that of the middle or lower part of the Maestrichtian stage.

Genus Pentacrinus Blumenbach
"Pentacrinus" fairbanksi Anderson n. sp.
(Plate 6, figure 4)

This genus was included by H. W. Fairbanks (1895, p. 427) in a list of Upper Cretaceous invertebrate fossils found on Eagle Ranch in northern San Luis Obispo County, without any further data. The genus is not abundant in the Upper Cretaceous on the West Coast. The present writer accompanied Fairbanks in this reconnaissance work and aided in the collection and identification of these fossils; he may therefore be permitted to add at this time some further data taken from his personal notes concerning this species. Fragments of the stems of crinoids were found somewhat plentifully in the sandstones. The collections included two or three well preserved sections, showing joint faces and the interior aspect of the stems, in which the pentagonal petaloid divisions were clearly exposed. The petaloid figures seen in these joint faces of the stem, however, are narrower than those of *Pentacrinus bryani* Gabb, from the Upper Cretaceous of New Jersey, but more nearly resemble those from the Upper Triassic, namely, *Pentacrinus asteriscus* Meek and Hayden. It is possible that the species belongs to the subgenus *Isocrinus* Phillips.

As shown by the associated molluscan species, which included *Baculites* aff. *B. vagina* Forbes, and *Glycymeras* aff. *G. banosensis* n. sp., the species should be regarded as belonging in the lower part of the Upper Asuncion.

Class ECHINOIDEA

Few species of echinoids have been found in the Upper Cretaceous series of the West Coast, and most have been described or reviewed by Kew (1920) who says (p. 29):

"The Cretaceous forms are mainly of the cassidulid and spatangid types. *Hemiaster* seems to be the most characteristic form, no species of this genus being reported from any later age. One species, *Catopygus* (?) is present in the Upper Cretaceous, but the genus is not confined to this horizon."

The following genera and species are here summarized from Kew's treatment:

Genus Epiaster d'Orbigny
Epiaster depressus Kew

Epiaster depressus Kew, Univ. Calif. Pub. Bull. Dept. Geol., vol. 12, no. 2, 1920, p. 143, Pl. 40, figs. 3a, 3b, 3c, 3d; Chico Series, northern California. Probably of lower Senonian age.

Hemiaster Desor
Hemiaster alamedensis Kew

Hemiaster alamedensis Kew, Univ. Calif. Pub. Bull. Dept. Geol., vol. 12, no. 2, 1920, p. 144, Pl. 40, figs. 5a, 5b, 5c, 5d; Shepherd Canyon, San Leandro Hills, Alameda County, Upper Cretaceous. Probably from the Upper Asuncion group.

Hemiaster californicus W. B. Clark

Hemiaster californicus W. B. CLARK, John Hopkins University, Circ. vol. 10, no. 87, 1891, p. 77 . . . CLARK AND TWITCHELL, U. S. Geol. Survey, Mon. vol. 54, 1915, p. 96, Pl. 50, figs. 1a, 1b, 1c, 1d; . . . KEW, Univ. Calif. Pub. Bull. Dept. Geol., vol. 12, no. 2, 1920, p. 145, Pl. 40, figs. 4a, 4b, 4c; near Redding, Shasta County, and reported from the Santa Ana Mountains, Orange County. Probably of Turonian age.

Hemiaster cholamensis Kew

Hemiaster cholamensis KEW, Univ. Calif. Pub. Bull. Dept. Geol., vol. 12, no. 2, 1920, p. 146, Pl. 41, figs. 1a, 1b, 1c, 1d; center sec. 5, T. 24 S., R. 16 E.; in southeast corner of Monterey County. Probably from the Upper Asuncion group.

Hemiaster oregonensis Kew

Hemiaster oregonensis KEW, Univ. Calif. Pub. Bull. Dept. Geol., vol. 12, no. 2, 1920, p. 147, Pl. 41, figs. 2a, 2b, 2c, 2d; found on the old Dollarhide ranch, north slope of Siskiyou Mountains, Pacific Highway, Jackson County. Probably of lower Senonian age.

Family ANANCHYTIDAE Desor
Genus **Echinocorys** Breynius
Echinocorys yoloensis Anderson n. sp.
(Plate 6, figures 1a, 1b, 1c, 1d)

This genus has not before been recorded from the Cretaceous of the West Coast, although it has been found in the Arrialoor group in southern India, and a somewhat similar form has been described by Cragin from Medina County, Texas, under the name *Ananchites texana*.

Two examples of the species were found, the holotype and another, both in a poor state of preservation, in western Yolo County. The holotype is a much weathered and somewhat distorted example, especially as to the base, and its essential features are not completely preserved. Only enough of the test remains for a tentative generic determination, but as it is the only example of the genus, and as its stratigraphic position is correctly known it may be given a name and preliminary description. The holotype (C. A. S., Type Coll.) here sketched has the following dimensions: length, 64 mm; breadth, about 54 mm; height, 50 mm.

The test is broadly ovate in plan, broader in its posterior portion, narrowing slightly toward the front; base moderately convex; peristome rather small, transverse, but poorly defined; the periproct apparently subterminal, since it is not elsewhere shown; the apical system not well exposed, but its position, and some of its features are indicated. The test is apetalous; the ambulacra, diverge from the apex, which is situated 4 or 5 mm in advance of the center of the test; the frontal pair of ambulacra diverging at an angle of about 75 degrees.

The species appears to be related to *Ananchites texana* Cragin, although it is not so large, and differs in many details, and perhaps in its horizon. The holotype and its companion fragment were found by the writer at location 1343 (C. A. S.) at the north end of Pleasant Valley, Yolo County. It is early Senonian, as determined by associated cephalopod species, and by stratigraphic data.

Family CASSIDULIDAE Agassiz
Genus **Cassidulus** Lamarck
Cassidulus mercedensis Anderson n. sp.
(Plate 6, figures 2a, 2b)

This genus was not previously reported from the Upper Cretaceous of the West Coast; its earliest appearance has been in the upper Eocene of the Great Valley, although it is not unknown elsewhere in the later Cretaceous.

Small, slightly depressed, oval in outline, a little longer than broad, slightly broader behind middle of test; upper surface convex, lower surface concave; apical system subcentral, but not wholly distinct, a little in advance of the center; floscelle fairly well exposed, petals open; mouth subcentral, slightly in advance of center; periproct nearly terminal. Petals of bivium narrow, spreading at an angle of about 30 degrees. The species has much resemblance to *Cassidulus lapis-cancri* Lamarck, though it is probably more closely related to *Cassidulus umbonatus* Woods from South Africa. Dimensions are as follows: length, 18 mm; greatest breadth, posterior to mouth, 16 mm; height, about 8 mm. The holotype (C. A. S., Type Coll.) and another example were found by Allan Bennison, at Loc. 29106 (C. A. S.), about 2000 feet south of the NW corner sec. 20, T. 8 S., R. 8 E., and about 200 feet beneath the white sand, thought to be Eocene. The stratigraphic position is very near the Upper limit of the Asuncion group, and is probably referable to the Garzas member of the Moreno. The species described by Desor is said to be from the upper Danian beds of France; that described by Woods is from beds near the coast of Pondoland, and regarded as Senonian. A number of clublike echinoid spines, resembling spines of *Cidaris*, have been found in nearly the same horizon in the Garzas in the Pacheco Pass quadrangle.

Phylum BRACHIOPODA Dumeril

Not many genera and species of brachiopods have been described from the Upper Cretaceous of the West Coast. None appear to have descended from stocks known in the older Cretaceous (Shasta Series), in which few forms are known.

Two species earlier described, but referred to upper beds of the Horsetown group, are here reconsidered upon stratigraphic grounds and regarded as properly belonging in the lowest beds of the Upper Cretaceous, which accords with the views of Stanton (in Merriam, 1901, p. 284). These species of the genus *Rhynchonella* occur at the site of old Horsetown, in the upper beds of this locality, and at Texas Springs, 3 miles to the east, at both points in strata that can readily be shown to be referable to the Upper Cretaceous Series, though regarded as older in the early literature. These species, with a large molluscan fauna, first appeared in deposits laid down during the early Upper Cretaceous transgression, upon both older Cretaceous beds, and upon the basement terrains in the areas here described. They belong to late-Albian or to early-Cenomanian time.

Later stages of diastrophism in early Senonian time, in California, Oregon, and in British Columbia, brought other brachiopod species into the Lower Asuncion group, and its equivalents, including two or more genera (*Rhynchonella, Terebratella*, and probably *Kingena*), although the precise horizon of each is not clear.

Following the diastrophism (and subsidence) that introduced the Upper Asuncion group, other genera and species of brachiopods were brought into the later part of the Upper Cretaceous column on the West Coast, constituting on the whole 5 genera and 7 species known at present.

Family RHYNCHONELLIDAE Fischer
Genus **Rhynchonella** Fisher
Rhynchonella densleonis Anderson
(Plate 1, figures 3, 4)

Rhynchonella densleonis ANDERSON, Proc. Calif. Acad. Sci., 3d ser., vol. 2, 1902, p. 72, Pl. 7, figs. 157, 158; Horsetown, Shasta County, California.

The following description of this species is taken directly from the original account (1902, p. 72):

"Shell of medium size, attaining a diameter of 11 to 12 mm; trigonal; gibbous; when full grown, the greatest convexity being near the middle; posterior lateral margin straight, sloping from the beak at an angle of about 90 degrees; anterior margin somewhat broadly rounded; dorsal valve more convex than the ventral, nearly globose; ventral valve flattened, though bearing a deep sinus; anterior half of each valve bearing strong, rounded or angular plications which disappear on the posterior portion of the shell; surface of both valves bearing fine striations most plainly seen on the posterior half of the shell. The sinus of the ventral valve bears three or four plications, while the corresponding prominence on the dorsal valve bears four or more; beak not very prominent and only slightly curved; deltidium small; width of shell greater than length."

This species is very closely related to *Rhynchonella gnathophora* Meek, from the Jurassic of California.

This species is not uncommon at the site of old Horsetown, and Texas Springs, Shasta County, in the lowest beds of the Upper Cretaceous series, which were formerly thought to belong in the upper part of the Horsetown group, of the Shasto series.

Rhynchonella whiteana Anderson

Rhynchonella whiteana ANDERSON, Proc. Calif. Acad. Sci., 3d ser., vol. 2, 1902, p. 72, Pl. 7, figs. 160, 161; Horsetown, Shasta County, California.

In the original account of this species it was stated that:

"Associated with the (preceding) species is another somewhat related form, with a finer and more subdued sculpture. The ventral sinus bears about nine or ten plications of uniform size, and none of the strong folds of the other. The shell is rather circular in outline. The dorsal valve is crossed by two diverging ridges meeting on the anterior margin the borders of the ventral sinus." Locality, Horsetown and Texas Springs.

Rhynchonella suciensis Whiteaves

Rhynchonella sp. indet., WHITEAVES, Mes. Foss., vol. 1, pt. 2, 1879, p. 177 (not figured); Sucia Islands, western Washington.
Rhynchonella suciensis WHITEAVES, Royal Soc. Canada, Trans., 1875, 2d ser., vol. 1, p. 119, Pl. 3, fig. 1; ... Whiteaves, Mes. Foss., vol. 1, pt. 5, 1903, p. 402, Pl. 51, figs. 3, 3a, and 4; Sucia Islands; lower Senonian; correlative with the Lower Asuncion group.

Genus Terebratella d'Orbigny
Terebratella harveyi Whiteaves

Terebratella harveyi WHITEAVES, Mes. Foss., vol. 1, pt. 5, 1903, p. 403, Pl. 51, figs. 5, 6; Extension mine, Nanaimo district, and Texada Island; Mr. Harvey, Coll.; lower Senonian, lower Asuncion group.

Genus Kingena Davidson (Kingia Schloenbach)
Kingena occidentalis Whiteaves

Terebratula wacoensis WHITEAVES, Mes. Foss., vol. 1, pt. 2, 1877 (? not *Terebratula wacoensis* Roemer, 1852).
Kingena occidentalis WHITEAVES, Mes. Foss., vol. 1, pt. 5, 1903, p. 404, Pl. 51, figs. 7, 7a; Trent River, Vancouver Island, British Columbia; probably from Lower Asuncion group, Lower Senonian.

Subfamily DALLININAE Beecher
Genus Megerlia King
Megerlia dubitanda Cooper

Megerlia dubitanda COOPER, Calif. State Min. Bur., Bull. No. 4, 1894, p. 50, Pl. 3, figs. 48, 49; Point Loma, San Diego County.

Subfamily MAGELLANIINAE Beecher
Genus Waldheimia King
Waldheimia imbricata Cooper

Waldheimia imbricata COOPER, Calif. State Min. Bur., Bull. No. 4, 1894, p. 51, Pl. 3, figs. 50, 51; La Jolla, San Diego County, California; H. W. Fairbanks Coll.; Maestrichtian.

Phylum MOLLUSCA
Class PELECYPODA
Family CUCULLAEIDAE
Genus Cucullaea Lamarck
Subgenus Idonearca Conrad[3]

In neither California nor Oregon has the genus *Cucullaea* been recorded from any strata

[3] Stephenson (1941, p. 89–90) has reviewed the subgenus *Idonearca* Conrad, and *Cyphoxis* Rafinesque, and concludes as follows: "On the basis of reasonable doubt as to the source and true nature of the material on which *Cyphoxis* was based, I prefer to continue the use of *Idonearca* Conrad." Accordingly Conrad's name is adopted in the present work.

older than the lowest beds of the Upper Cretaceous Series. It enters the stratigraphic record in the lowest beds of the Pacheco group, as it apparently does in western Canada (Queen Charlotte series). It appears first in the early part of this group, in which it plays an important role, ranging upward to its top, and continuing with various specific changes into the upper horizons of the Upper Asuncion group. This genus, like the rudistids, and various ammonites *(Parapuzosia, Calycoceras, Pervinquieria)* serves to illustrate the great faunistic (and probably physical) changes that took place on the West Coast about the close of Albian time. In the record of this genus during Upper Cretaceous times three or more diverse types of the genus appear at successive intervals, corresponding to the diastrophic record, and the stratigraphic changes that have taken place.

In the following pages these several types, as far as they are known, are taken up in the order of their stratigraphic occurrence.

Cucullaea (Idonearca) grossaforma Hertlein

Cucullaea (?) sp. indet., WHITEAVES, Meso. Foss., vol. 1, pt. 1, 1876, p. 73; locality indefinite.
Cucullaea (Idonearca) sp. indet., WHITEAVES, Meso. Foss., vol. 1, pt. 3, 1884, p. 235; east end of Maud Island (Queen Charlotte Island group).
Cucullaea ponderosa WHITEAVES (not Hutton, 1873), Meso. Foss., vol. 1, pt. 4, 1900, p. 294; Skidegate Channel, west of Alliford Bay, and probably Maud Island.
Cucullaea grossaforma HERTLEIN, Journ. Paleont., vol. 3, 1929, p. 296; loc. as above.

Whiteaves states (1900, p. 294) concerning this species:

"Shell large, ventricose, subtrapezoidal, and very inequilateral; valves so strongly convex in the umbonal region that their maximum breadth or thickness when closed exceeds their greatest height, inclusive of the beaks; test thick" . . . etc.

According to MacKenzie (1916), the stratigraphic position of the area, as shown on the map, is that of the "Haida formation," which with its fauna containing *Desmoceras (Puzosia) planulatum* Sowerby ?, *Desmoceras (Puzosia) perezianum* Whiteaves, and *Lytoceras (Tetragonites) timotheanum* (Mayor), etc., should be assigned to a lower Cenomanian, or older horizon, corresponds to the lower part of the Upper Cretaceous in California. The holotype of *Cucullaea "ponderosa"* Whiteaves, has the following dimensions: length, 117 mm; height, 86 mm; greatest breadth or thickness, 100 mm. The precise equivalent of this species has perhaps not been recorded from California or Oregon, although a closely related form occurs on the North fork of Cottonwood Creek, in Shasta County.

Cucullaea (Idonearca) aff. C. (I.) grossaforma Hertlein

This species is closely related to the preceding, although smaller, the corresponding dimensions being about 63 per cent of those given by Whiteaves for the type from Maude Island (Pl. 38), and perhaps occurs somewhat higher in the Pacheco group. No specimen satisfactory for illustration has been obtained, although the following measurements have been taken from a representative example: length (incomplete), 75 mm (est. 78 mm); height, 60 mm; width of cast, 60 mm (original shell, est. 65 mm).

In section, the form is broadly cordate; surface is marked by rough concentric lines; beaks distant, ligamental area gaping, showing 10 or more spreading chevronlike grooves above hinge line; hinge long, nearly straight, with 8–10 short, vertical teeth in its central part, and 2 or 3 laterals at each end of hinge. This species was found on the North fork of Cottonwood Creek, at location 1346C (C. A. S.), in a coarse sandy conglomerate, associated with other species of the genus, and with *Trigonia* sp.

Cucullaea (Idonearca) alamoensis Anderson n. sp.
(Plate 49, figure 5)

The shell is of medium size, subtriangular in outline, elongated, length exceeding height, moderately inflated; umbones tumid, with strongly angulated umbonal ridges sloping to the rear; shell somewhat squarely truncated in front, bearing brief winglike expansions before and behind; base broadly rounded; hinge long, set with about 8 short, nearly vertical teeth, and 3 strong lateral teeth before, and apparently the same number behind; ligamental area of moderate height, showing 6 or 7 chevronlike grooves beneath beak; beaks small, prominent, incurved, but not closely approximate; test thick, surface smooth, though marked by numerous growth lines, and also by radial lines below beak, most clearly seen on median layers of shell, especially on anterior half.

This species is related to *Cucullaea truncata* Gabb, and may have a similar stratigraphic significance, but hardly the same stratigraphic range, as far as known.

The holotype (C. A. S. Type Coll.) has the following dimensions: length, 55 mm; height, 46.3 mm. Found by the writer at location 1346 (C. A. S.), in the third conglomerate above the base of the upper Cretaceous series, on the north fork of Cottonwood Creek, below the mouth of Hulen Creek. This bed is regarded as in the upper part of the Cenomanian. It was associated with the preceding species, *Trigonia* sp., and *Trigonocallista* sp.

The same, or a closely allied species was found by R. M. Kleinpell and E. Wayne Galliher on Graham Island, at location 77, Richfield Oil Company, associated with *Lytoceras (Tetragonites) timotheanum* (Mayor), a well-known Cenomanian ammonite.

Cucullaea (Idonearca) gravida (Gabb)
(Plate 26, figures 1, 2, 3)

Arca gravida GABB, Paleont. Calif. vol. 1, 1864, p. 194, Pl. 30, fig. 264; Wragg ("Rag") Canyon, eastern Napa County. . . . vol. 2, 1869, p. 248.
Arca decurtata GABB, Paleont. Calif., vol. 1, 1864, p. 195, Pl. 31, figs. 265, 265a; Wragg ("Rag") Canyon, eastern Napa County. . . . vol. 2, 1869, p. 248; locality as given above. ANDERSON, Proc. Calif. Acad. Sci. 3rd ser., vol. 2, 1902, p. 30, included "*Cucullaea decurta*" Gabb in a list of "Lower Chico" fossils from Henley, and from Silverado Canyon, the latter collected by H. W. Fairbanks. STEWART, Acad. Nat. Sci. Phila., Special Pub., No. 3, 1930, p. 77.

Concerning "*Arca decurtata*" Gabb, Stewart remarks (1930, p. 77): "It may be a large specimen of *Cucullaea gravida,* and the name therefore is a synonym of that name."

Both types were obtained by Gabb from the belt crossed by Wragg Canyon, on the west slope of Vaca Mountain. On the basis of a comparative study and geographic and stratigraphic evidence, the present writer agrees with Stewart as to the identity of the above types, both collected from the same zone in the Turonian on the west slope of Vaca Mountain.

Cucullaea (Idonearca) gravida (Gabb) is abundant about Frazier Corners, Shasta County, where numerous examples have been collected by John Melhase, by B. L. Cunningham, the writer, and Taff, Hanna, and Cross. All are now in the collections of the California Academy of Sciences. These include specimens of all stages of growth. It is readily seen that examples representing its younger stages are relatively thinner and flatter than those of mature and older stages.

Dimensions of the three hypotypes figured: (1) Exterior of right valve. Length, 36.5 mm; height, 28.5 mm; (2) Fragment of left valve, showing dentition. Length, 22.4 mm; height (incomplete), 19.6 mm; (3) Immature example, showing dentition. Length, 33 mm; height, 26.9 mm. Locality 1293C (C. A. S.), Bella Vista District, Shasta County.

Cucullaea (Idonearca) truncata (Gabb)

Cucullaea truncata GABB, Paleont. Calif., vol. 1, 1864, p. 196, Pl. 25, fig. 182; Curry Canyon, south of Mount Diablo.
Cucullaea (Idonearca) truncata (GABB), WHITEAVES (in part), Meso. Foss., vol. 1, pt. 2, 1879, p. 165–167, (? not Pl. 19, figs. 2, 2a; Middle shale, division D; Hornby Island, Straits of Georgia).
Cucullaea (Cyphoxis) truncata (Gabb), STEWART, Acad. Nat. Sci. Phila., Special Publ., No. 3, 1930, p. 75–76; Pl. 2, fig. 7.

The first locality mentioned by Gabb in his description should be the type locality, and correctly represent the horizon of the species. This is Curry's, southeast of Mount Diablo, Contra Costa County. This locality has been repeatedly searched by the writer, and by others. The age of these beds has been clearly indicated by "*Ammonites*" *turneri* White, and a closely related form, namely, *Calycoceras (Eucalycoceras) diabloense* n. sp. The lowest beds are of Cenomanian age; above the Turonian is also exposed. Correlative beds are found on the North fork of Cottonwood Creek, Shasta County, and are characterized by a similar fauna.

Gabb also cited the species from 2 miles north of Benicia, a locality where other Turonian fossils have been collected. According to Gabb's figure and account of *Cucullaea truncata,* the species is characterized by a narrow umbonal area, and by narrow beaks, strongly incurved but not closely approximate; of which he says:

"hinge robust, broad at the ends and narrow in the middle; composed of three or four long angular teeth at each end, and a few small, variable, transverse ones in the center. Internal plate robust, but not very elevated."

The beaks are nearly central, very prominent, but distant, and inclined slightly forward. Emphasis is here placed upon the character of the hinge plate and the teeth.

The writer records (1902a, p. 76) finding this species on the north slope of the Siskiyou Mountains, (south of Ashland), associated with *"Desmoceras" ashlandicus* Anderson (= *Pachydiscus ashlandicus*), and other diagnostic Turonian species.

Cucullaea (Idonearca) melhaseana Anderson n. sp.
(Plate 75, figures 1, 1a)

Test thick, outline of valves subtrigonal, umbones rounded, low, extended posteriorly, with short winglike extensions before and behind, as seen from the side; beaks a little in advance of central, incurved above the ligamental area, not closely approximate; shell slightly flattened on the sides; basal margin broadly rounded or nearly straight; surface of shell almost smooth, marked by concentric lines of growth and by faint radial lines on anterior part of shell. Hinge line long, with numerous short vertical teeth in central third of hinge, and long lateral teeth, 2 or more at each end; ligamental area marked by 6–8 chevronlike grooves, sloping outwardly to hinge line. This species in some respects resembles *Cucullaea truncata* Gabb, and appears to belong in its group, but it has broader and more rounded umbones, a longer hinge line, more numerous central, vertical teeth, and less conspicuous radial lines, which are confined to the anterior part of the shell.

Three valves of this species were collected by Taff, Hanna and Cross, at locality 27833 (C. A. S.) from east bank of Dry Creek near center of NE ¼ sec. 7, T. 32 N. R. 3 W., M. D. M., 0.8 of a mile north of Frazier Corners, Shasta County, northwest of Little Cow Creek, in the upper part of the Turonian, about 600 feet beneath the highest fossil-bearing zone marked by species of *Oregoniceras.*

Holotype (C. A. S. Type Coll.) has the following dimensions: length, 63 mm; height, 50 mm; and paratype (C. A. S. Type Coll.) has the following dimensions: length (incomplete), 55 mm; height, 50 mm.

This species is named in remembrance of John Melhase, well-known geologist and Mining Engineer of California. He had collected many of the invertebrate species from the Upper Cretaceous of this area.

Cucullaea (Idonearca) youngi Waring
(Plate 61, figure 4)

Cucullaea youngi WARING, Proc. Calif. Acad. Sci., 4th ser., vol. 7, 1917, p. 59, Pl. 8, fig. 12; Loc. 2 (L. S. J. U.), Bell Canyon, Camulos quadrangle, Los Angeles County.

The description of the species given by Waring reads in (part) as follows:

"Shell large, thick, ventricose; strongly convex, so that the maximum umbonal breadth across both valves about equals the height, older individuals of the species tending to have the height considerably greater than the length. . . . Umbones broad, curved slightly anteriorly, and deeply excavated both anteriorly and posteriorly; anterior margin broadly rounded, basal margin nearly straight, posterior truncated; posterior umbonal angle sharp; anterior umbonal angle broadly rounded; hinge area broad and long, extending about two-thirds length of the shell;"

In the collection of the California Academy of Sciences are two examples of this species from Waldron Island, collected by Bruce Martin, one of which (hypotype, C. A. S. Type Coll.) is here figured. Its dimensions are as follows: length, 43.8 mm; height, 41 mm; thickness of right valve, 22 mm; length of hinge, 32 mm; dimensions of the large example: 61.5 mm in height; 66 mm in length (incomplete); thickness of left valve, 32 mm. Fragmentary examples of the same species from Sucia Island, collected by Martin, show a length of 85 mm, a height of 76 mm; and a thickness of 40 mm.

Cucullaea (Idonearca) calabaza Anderson, n. sp.
(Plate 70, figures 1, 1a)

This species is probably one of the largest yet recorded from the Upper Cretaceous on the West Coast. It appears to belong to the group represented by *Cucullaea (Idonearca) youngi* Waring, although it differs from the latter in many important features.

Shell is large, massive, somewhat trapezoidal in outline, as viewed from the side, though from the front or rear its inflated sides give it a rotund, almost spherical appearance. Umbones are broad and rounded, though truncated behind; apex of beak being nearly central, though relatively low, beak depressed above the ligamental area; base of valves broadly rounded curving rapidly upward at anterior end, but meeting its border at nearly right angles; surface of shell generally smooth, showing only fine concentric lines of growth; at nearly uniform intervals interspersed with coarser threads or grooves, producing a wave-like surface unlike that of any other known species. Hinge is long and straight at top, but broadly arched beneath, set with normal cucullaeaid teeth, consisting of a short interval of vertical denticles near the middle, 8–10 in number, and long laterals at the ends, 3 or 4 in number, nearly parallel with hinge margin, or slightly inclined to front or rear. Holotype (C. A. S. Type Coll.) has the following dimensions: length, 102 mm; height, 90 mm; thickness of each valve, 48 mm; giving the umbonal diameter of the shell a measure greater than its height.

The holotype was found by C. E. Leach, at locality 30536 (C. A. S.) in the Santa Monica Mountains, southwest of Chatsworth, on sec. 28, T. 2 N., R. 17 W., S. B. M. Los Angeles County, California. Its stratigraphic position is considerably above that of the Pleasants member, characterized by *Metaplacenticeras pacificum* (Smith) found in this area by Popenoe. Numerous examples of the species are in the Academy of Sciences from the same area, collected by Stephen Bowers, associated with *Metaplacenticeras bowersi* n. sp.

Cucullaea (Idonearca) cordiformis Packard

Cucullaea (?) cordiformis PACKARD, Univ. Calif. Pub., Geol., Bull. vol. 13, 1922, p. 417, Pl. 24, fig. 1; zone of *Turritella pescaderoensis*, Loc. 2158 (Univ Calif. Coll.), 600 feet east of the Pleasant's home, Santiago district, Orange County.

According to Packard's description, the shell of this species is—

"large, trigonal in outline, height greater than length; umbones widely separated, with narrow, acute, incurving beaks. Hinge line relatively short. Length 64 mm; height 75 mm; diameter 70 mm."

The horizon of this species is probably within the Lower Asuncion group, and may be Santonian.

Cucullaea (Idonearca) lirata Packard

Cucullaea lirata PACKARD, Univ. Calif. Pub., Geol., Bull., vol. 13, 1922, p. 417, Pl. 24, fig. 2; Pl. 25, fig. 3; the holotype found at Loc. 2149 (Univ. Calif., Coll.), at 1100 feet elevation.

Packard states:

"Several specimens of this species have been found at three collecting localities." Its horizon is said to be in the zones of *Acteonella oviformis,* and *Turritella pescaderoensis,* which do not appear to be the same. The species may be regarded as having a considerable range in the Lower Asuncion group.

Cucullaea (Idonearca) sp. undet.

Whiteaves (1879 p. 165, Pl. 19, figs. 2, 2a) figures and discusses two types of *Cucullaea* under the heading *C. (Idonearca) truncata* Gabb, but neither of these have been specifically described, and it appears to the present writer that it can be conclusively shown that neither of them conform to Gabb's species, and neither can be shown to be referable to a Turonian horizon, whereas, each is referable to a much later position in the stratigraphic column, and are perhaps distinct species.

The present note is entered here only to clear the record of these interesting types, which require appropriate names, and a determination of the true position.

Cucullaea (Idonearca) buttensis Anderson, n. sp.
(Plate 61, figures 5, 5a, 5b)

Cucullaea truncata Gabb, TAFF, HANNA, AND CROSS, Geol. Soc. Am., Bull. vol. 51, 1940, p. 1321, Pl. 1, figs. 5, 6; locality 28172 (C. A. S.) near top of Chico Creek section, Butte County, California.

Test thick, shell triangular in outline, as seen from the side; umbones high, broad, rounded, inflated; beaks central, or a little in advance of center, incurved, approximate, nearly touching, or less than 8 mm apart; posterior umbonal ridge somewhat angulate, with an abrupt posterior slope, more rounded in front; sides of valves slightly flattened; base of shell broadly rounded. Surface of shell smooth, though marked by numerous concentric lines of growth and by radial lines, the latter most clearly seen on the posterior part of the shell; base broadly rounded.

The holotype (C. A. S. Type Coll.) has the following dimensions: length, 72 mm; height, 64 mm; convexity of single valve, 31 mm. The holotype was found by Taff, Hanna, and Cross at locality 28172 (C. A. S.), near the top of the Chico Creek section of the type Chico formation, where it was associated with other species, including *Inoceramus turgidus* n. sp. and *Canadoceras* sp. aff. *C. fraternus* Gabb.

This species differs considerably from *Cucullaea (Idonearca) truncata* (Gabb) in the breadth and inflation of its umbonal region, in the inward curvature of the beaks, and in the proximity of the opposite beaks, which in *Cucullaea truncata* Gabb are distant and inclined slightly forward. In the present species, the curvature is in the opposite direction. The hinge also differs from that of Gabb's species in being longer, with 10 to 12 small, central, vertical teeth between the horizontal laterals.

The two species also differ widely in their positions in the stratigraphic column. *C. (Idonearca) truncata* occurs in the Turonian, and this species occupies a position in the upper part of the Chico formation, near the middle of the Campanian stage. The holotype is one of two examples collected by Taff, Hanna, and Cross. The other example was the basis of their description and figure.

Family PARALLELODONTIDAE Dall

This family is well represented and varied in the Upper Cretaceous of the West Coast; one or more species occur in each of the major groups. Most of the species are of moderate or small size; only one is more than 2 inches long.

These forms serve well as index fossils, although as a family they have a long time range. Most of them occupied a restricted habitus, living in neritic, though moderate depths of water below the littoral, and for this reason may have been more susceptible to changes in depths which would not seriously disturb other Mollusca.

Genus Parallelodon Meek
Subgenus Nanonavis Stewart
Parallelodon (Nanonavis) brewerianus (Gabb)

Arca Breweriana GABB, Paleont. Calif., vol. 1, 1864, p. 193, Pl. 25, fig. 181, Cottonwood Creek, Shasta County . . . vol. 2, 1869, p. 248; (probably near mouth of Hulen Creek). *Nemodon (Arca) breweriana* WARING, Proc. Calif. Acad. Sci., 4th ser., vol. 7, 1917, p. 57, Pl. 7, (? figs. 5 and 6; locality 2, L. S. J. U.), Calabasas quadrangle, California. . . . NELSON, Univ. Calif. Publ., Geol. Sci. Dept. Bull., vol. 5, 1925, p. 406 (?). . . . ANDERSON, Geol. Soc. Am., Special Papers, No. 16, 1938, p. 96, Pl. 2, figs. 3, 4; Loc. 1346,

(C. A. S.) ; North fork of Cottonwood Creek, half a mile above the mouth of Hulen Creek.

Parallelodon (Nanonavis) brewerianus (GABB), STEWART, Acad. Nat. Sci. Phila., Special Publ., No. 3, 1930, p. 69, Pl. 3, fig. 1; probably Cottonwood Creek, Shasta County. . . . POPENOE, Am. Ass. Petr. Geol., Bull., vol. 26, 1942, fig. 4 (?); Holz Shale, Santiago Dist., Orange County.

Gabb's description of this species reads, in part, as follows:

"Shell small, longer than wide; beaks prominent, incurved, approximate, and inclined forward, placed in advance of the middle; umbones broad; anterior end rounded, and sloping inward; posterior end obliquely truncated and uniting with the base by an abrupt angle; basal margin slightly rounded in front, straight behind, and parallel with the hinge, or sloping upward; umbonal angle sharp, with the surface in front of it very convex, behind it somewhat excavated; area narrow, almost as long as the shell; marked by a few small, closely placed angular lines. . . . Hinge slender; teeth below beaks, to the number of two or three only, are transverse; those adjoining are oblique, the angle rapidly growing wider, and those at the extremities are all horizontal; this is most strongly marked posteriorly, the *upper* tooth on that side extending for nearly half the length of the hinge."

Gabb's description of this species, like that of its occurrence, is difficult to interpret, and for either specific diagnosis or for stratigraphic use is valueless. The North fork of Cottonwood Creek below Ono, crosses as much as 7000 feet of Cretaceous strata, of which 6000 feet are assignable to the Horsetown group, and the remainder is referable to the Pacheco group of the Upper Cretaceous series. Two forms of *Parallelodon* have been found, one near Ono, at the base of the Horsetown group, and the other at the base of the Upper Cretaceous series, near Hulen Creek. The specimen figured by the writer (1938b, Pl. 2), was from Loc. 1346 (C. A. S.) on the North fork, half a mile above Hulen Creek, from which point most of Gabb's material was taken, including the example figured by Stewart (Pl. 3, fig. 1). A distinct form of the genus has been found at Ono, and from it certain surface features found in Gabb's description may have been obtained. At all events, neither Stewart's figure nor that of the writer exhibits the sculpture described in the later part of Gabb's account, whereas samples found at Ono show them perfectly.

Parallelodon (Nanonavis) vancouverensis (Meek)

Arca vancouverensis MEEK, Trans. Albany Inst., vol. 4, 1867, p. 40; The type is said to have been obtained at Nanaimo, Vancouver Island, 1856.

Grammatodon (?) *vancouverensis* MEEK, Bull. Geol. and Geogr. Survey Terr., vol. 2, No. 4, 1876, p. 256, Pl. 3, figs. 5, 5a; Komoox, Vancouver Island.

Grammatodon vancouverensis WHITE, U. S. Geol. Survey, Bull. 51, 1889, p. 39; Sucia Island, Strait of Georgia.

Arca vancouverensis Meek, WHITEAVES, Meso. Foss., vol. 1, pt. 5, 1903, p. 392; localities as given above (not p. 163, Pl. 19, figs. 1, 1a).

(? not) *Nemodon vancouverensis* (Meek), PACKARD, Univ. Calif. Pub. Geol., Bull., vol. 9, 1916, p. 147; *Turritella pescaderoensis* zone, Santiago district, Orange County.

(?) *Parallelodon (Nanonavis) vancouverensis* (Meek), REINHART, Geol. Soc. Am., Special Paper, No. 47, 1943, p. 85.

As stated by Meek (1876) "the type of *Arca vancouverensis* Meek was collected at Nanaimo, V. I." Its dimensions are: length, 0.74 inch; height, 0.44 inch; breadth, 0.40 inch.

According to Whiteaves: "This species" Meek says "will be readily distinguished by its vertically truncated posterior extremity, and the distantly separated radiating costae, with smaller ones between, on the anterior end."

Concerning this species Whiteaves continues:

"The specimens upon which the description of *Grammatodon* ? *vancouverensis* was based, are said to be from Comox . . . the dimensions of the specimen figured are given as: length, 0.75 inch; height, 0.47 inch; breadth, or convexity, 0.40 inch."

In both accounts the types are small, not exceeding 19 mm, and the description given by Meek does not warrant any other interpretation. Other specimens of a small "*Arca*" in this area are mentioned by Whiteaves; he is uncertain as to their specific relation to others of a larger size, of which he states (p. 393):

"But it is still uncertain whether the two large single valves from Blunden Point, V. I., that are figured on Plate 19 (figs. 1, 1a), of the second part of this volume, and the two casts of the interior of large single valves collected on Sable River, V. I., . . . should be regarded as adult specimens of *Arca vancouverensis,* or a distinct species."

In the light of material obtained from the Gualala group in California, and on the Peninsula of Lower California (San Antonio del Mar), it appears certain that the examples figured by Whiteaves (Pl. 19) represent a distinct species, not closely related to *"Arca" vancouverensis* Meek, having a length of only 19 mm. or less.

The figures, description, and dimensions given by Meek for the examples of the present species do not constitute a basis for including the larger forms described and figured by Whiteaves, nor do the stratigraphic horizons of the latter support such deductions.

Parallelodon (Nanonavis) nanainoenis Anderson, n. sp.

Nemodon vancouverensis WHITEAVES, Meso. Foss., vol. 1, pt. 2, 1879, p. 163, Pl. 19, figs. 1, 1a; near Blunden Point, Nanaimo River, Vancouver Island (not *Arca vancouverensis* Meek; not *Grammatodon ? vancouverensis* Meek, 1876, p. 356, Pl. 3, figs. 5, 5a).
Parallelodon (Nanonavis) brewerianus (Gabb), STEWART, (in part), Acad. Nat. Sci. Phila., Special Pub., No. 3, 1930, p. 69.
Nemodon vancouverensis (Meek), ANDERSON AND HANNA, Proc. Calif. Acad. Sci., 4th ser., vol. 23, 1935, p. 28; Coalinga, California, and San Antonio del Mar (= Johnson's ranch, Lower California.
Parallelodon (Nanonavis) vancouverensis REINHART, Geol. Soc. Am., Special Paper, No. 47, 1943, p. 85.

This species, not before distinguished from certain of its congeners, is said by Whiteaves (1879, p. 163), to "Attain to a length of upwards of three inches, and a height of about twenty-two lines" (= 1.83 inches).

In California and on the Peninsula of Lower California, and perhaps in many other areas of the Maestrichtian extending along the West Coast, this species will probably be found associated with its characteristic faunal types, parapachydiscids, *Coralliochama,* and nostoceratids, as at Santa Catarina, Point Loma, and in the Great Valley of California. An example of the species found by Sternberg, at San Antonio del Mar, and now at the California Academy of Sciences, has a length of 110 mm; a height of 53 mm; and a breadth of 58 mm; with ribs averaging about 10 to an inch between its extremities.

The shell is brittle, breaks readily, and as a result disintegrates rapidly, and perhaps for this reason has not often been recovered.

Parallelodon (Nanonavis) cumshewensis (Whiteaves)

Grammatodon inornatus WHITEAVES, Meso. Foss., vol. 1, pt. 3, 1884, p. 235, Pl. 31, figs. 8, 8a and 8b; north shore of Cumshewa Inlet, and the south side of Alliford Bay, etc.
Arca (Nemodon) cumshewensis WHITEAVES, Meso. Foss., vol. 1, pt. 4, 1900, p. 294; locality as given above.
Parallelodon (Nanonavis) cumshewensis (Whiteaves), REINHART, Geol. Soc. Am., Special Paper, No. 47, 1943, p. 85; locality as given above.

Neither the stratigraphic position, nor age of this species has been directly stated by Whiteaves, though it may be inferred from related data that it is not younger than Cenomanian, and that it may be Albian.

The coal-bearing strata of Cumshewa and Skidegate inlets have been shown by Whiteaves, and by McKenzie (1916, p. 54–66), on the authority of Stanton to fall within the limits of the Queen Charlotte series, and to be referable to the Haida formation, not older than late Albian, but possibly of Cenomanian age, although the species is not mentioned in the lists of better known species supplied by Stanton.

Parallelodon (Nanonavis) simillima Whiteaves

Nemodon Fisheri d'Orbigny, WHITEAVES, Meso. Foss., vol. 1, pt. 3, 1884, p. 234; east end of Maud Island. . . . south side of Maud Island; a cast of a left valve. Species figured on

Arca (Nemodon) simillima WHITEAVES, Meso. Foss., vol. 1, pt. 4, 1900, p. 393, (not *Arca Fisheri* d'Orbigny, a Russian Jurassic species).
Parallelodon (Nanonavis) simillima (Whiteaves), REINHART, Geol. Soc. Am., Special Paper, No. 47, 1943, p. 85.

Whiteaves states (1900, p. 293) that:
"Several well-preserved, and nearly perfect specimens" had been collected at the east end of Maud Island. The surface is said to be:

"marked by very numerous, small radiating ribs, and by concentric striae and lines of growth. . . . Hinge dentition apparently as in *Nemodon* (Conrad) and consisting of three short, longitudinal, anterior teeth, parallel to the cardinal border, with some granulous teeth opposite the beaks, and of two very long, laminar posterior teeth, which are also parallel to the cardinal border."

MacKenzie (1916) makes no mention of this species, but shows the east end of Maud Island to be occupied by the Haida formation, and therefore referable to the lower part of the Queen Charlotte series, probably not older than upper Albian.

Parallelodon (Nanonavis) bremneri Anderson n. sp.
(Plate 61, figure 6)

Shell small, ovate in outline, or somewhat pear-shaped; umbonal area rounded, a little inflated; base nearly straight, curving roundly upward at anterior end, more rapidly at posterior terminus; umbonal ridge sloping uniformly downward to the rear; posterior slope long, descending obliquely behind; beaks situated about 15 mm from anterior end of shell, or about a third of its length; anterior slope rapid, excavated beneath beaks; dorsal border ridgelike; hinge marked by long parallel teeth, 3 or more in number on posterior end of shell; fewer in front.

The species is a thin-shelled form, represented by 6 entire individuals, and about 20 single halves, all casts from which the shell matter has been removed, but yet retaining the outward sculpture. The figure has been made from the holotype. The surface, chiefly without shell, preserves the form, the number and character of the radial ribs, escutcheon, and other details quite distinctly; surface of cast well marked by numerous ribs (12 per 1 cm), of which as many as 52 may be seen with a lens, radiating uniformly from the beaks, which are low and incurved. The holotype (C. A. S. Type Coll.) has the following dimensions: length, 34 mm; height, 18 mm; breadth across both valves, about 12 mm. loc. 1658 (C. A. S.).

The species was found associated with the following:

Nostoceratid, large form with coarse oblique ribs
Lysis californiensis Packard
Acteon sp. indet.
Dentalium (Entalis) whiteavesi Anderson and Hanna

Lima cf. *L. appressa* Gabb
Ostrea sp.
Glycymeris cf. *G. veatchii* (Gabb)
Crassatella lomana Cooper
Mytilus sp. indet.

This fauna is Maestrichtian. It was collected by Kew and Bremner; the species is named for the latter.

Genus Trigonarca Conrad
Trigonarca excavata Packard

Trigonarca excavata PACKARD, Univ. Calif. Pub. Bull. Dept. Geol. Sci., vol. 13, 1922, p. 418, Pl. 25, figs. 1, 1a; Santa Ana Mountains, Orange County.

This species, as described by Packard, is characterized by a medium size, triangular outline, a nearly straight umbonal ridge and a relatively straight basal border; it is found in the "zone" of *Acteonella oviformis* Gabb (Turonian) and possibly somewhat earlier beds.

The species is also abundant on the west border of the Sacramento Valley, in Yolo and Glenn counties, and at nearly the same horizon in the Pioneer district, north of the Pioneer road, 2.5 miles southwest of Phoenix, Oregon, where it is associated with *Gryphaea, Trigonia, Cucullaea,* and other mollusca.

Trigonarca californica Packard

Trigonarca californica PACKARD, Univ. Calif. Pub. Bull. Dept. Geol. Sci., vol. 13, 1922, p. 418, Pl. 25, figs. 2b, 2c; Santa Ana Mountains, Orange County.

This species differs from the preceding in being shorter, less angular, with the anterior end and base line more rounded, and with a hinge plate more rounded, and a broader dorsal area. Surface of shell marked by irregular lines of growth. Dentition, as described by Packard, consisting of "ten short, straight, posterior teeth, placed obliquely upon the hinge plate, and a less number of short, heavy, anterior teeth."

Like the preceding species, this form occurs in the *Acteonella oviformis* "zone," though apparently not found associated with it.

A similar species found by Wm. E. Kennett, southwest of Willows, near Logan Creek, Glenn County, and at locality 31918 (C. A. S.), on Thompson Creek, western Yolo County, was associated with the preceding species, and with *Acteonina californica* and *Trigonocallista nitida* (Gabb), in the lowest beds of the Turonian.

Trigonarca sectilis Packard

Trigonarca sectilis PACKARD, Univ. Calif. Pub. Bull. Dept. Geol. Sci., vol. 13, 1922, p. 419, Pl. 26, figs. 1a, b, c; Santa Ana Mountains, Orange County.

According to Packard, this species is characterized by a somewhat distinctive form, of which he states:

"Shell small, trigonal, inequilateral, ventricose, the diameter being nearly equal to length. Anterior extremity short, evenly rounded. Posterior dorsal side of the shell conspicuously flattened; basal margin nearly straight. Beaks small, widely separated." This species was also found in the *Acteonella oviformis* "zone" in Orange County. It has not yet been recognized in the Great Valley, or farther north in California or Oregon.

Trigonarca jacksonensis Anderson n. sp.
(Plate 2, figures 6, 6a, 6b)

The shell of this species is larger than any yet seen in California in the Upper Cretaceous, and differs in both exterior and internal features. It is subtriangular in outline, umbonal ridge oblique, forming angles with hinge line and basal border of about 40 and 50 degrees respectively; surface nearly smooth, showing only lines of growth and faint or nearly obsolete radial sculpture; anterior end abruptly rounded; posterior end more prolonged, margins forming an angle of about 47 degrees. Ratio of length to height varies somewhat, so that the angle varies accordingly. The ligamental area is triangular, with about 7 diverging folds; the outer, heavier teeth not plainly seen in the rear, but on the anterior part of the hinge plate they diverge outwardly; the hinge plate resembles that of *Trigonarca gamana* (Forbes) from the Ootatoor group, to which it may be related.

The holotype (C. A. S. Type Coll.) has the following dimensions: maximum length, 75 mm; height, 45 mm; thickness of right valve, 25 mm.

This example was found on the former Sheble ranch, 2.5 miles southwest of Phoenix, Oregon, where it was associated with *Exogyra, Trigonia,* etc.

The nearest California ally of the species may be *Trigonarca excavata* Packard, from which it differs in size, outline, and form of the hinge plate.

The same or a related species has been collected from a lower zone on the Schutte ranch near the base of the upper Cretaceous, where it is associated with rudistids.

Family GLYCYMERIDAE
Genus Glycymeris da Costa
Glycymeris veatchii (Gabb)

Axinea veatchii GABB, Paleont. Calif., vol. 1, 1864, p. 187, Pl. 25, figs. 183, 183a; Tuscan Springs, Tehama County. . . . vol. 2, 1869, p. 249 (in part).

Pectunculus veatchii STANTON, U. S. Geol. Survey, Ann. Rept., pt. 1, p. 1039, Pl. 54, fig. 1, (not figs. 2, 3).
Glycymeris veatchii (Gabb), STEWART (in part), Acad. Nat. Sci. Phila., Special Pub., No. 3, 1930, p. 71, text-figure 1; Tuscan Springs, Tehama County; (not Pl. 1, fig. 7).

Gabb's records of this species are not entirely clear, and probably include more than a single species, and his figure seems to have been incorrect in the number of ribs, and in other details. In typical examples of the species from its type locality, only 26 to 30 ribs can be counted on each valve, as shown in Stewart's figure of the lectotype. Two distinct species occur at Tuscan Springs, namely, *Glycymeris veatchii* (Gabb), and *Glycymeris shastensis* n. sp., the latter seems to have been also figured by Stewart (Pl. 1, fig. 7), as "*Glycymeris veatchii* Gabb," although it differs greatly from the lectotype figured by himself (p. 71, text-figure 1).

Only a few examples of *Glycymeris veatchii* (Gabb) have been found on the west side of the Sacramento Valley, though it is abundant on the west side of the San Joaquin Valley in many parts of the Panoche formation. It is found on the west side of the Sacramento Valley, on the east slope of the Rumsey Hills, on Buckeye Creek, in the upper part of the Coniacian, but it is not abundant. The exact stratigraphical span of its occurrence is not yet definitely known, although it appears to be confined to the Panoche group (Senonian stage). Normal examples from Tuscan Springs contain as many as 16 cardinal teeth on the interior of the shell, including about six small central, partly vertical teeth, beneath the beak, and five larger, oblique teeth on either side; on the interior of the basal margin, and rising on the sides, are about 28 strong crenulations. It was believed by Gabb, and by some later writers that this species occurred also in lower Eocene strata in California, but this view appears to have been abandoned.

Glycymeris pacificus (Anderson)
(Plate 18, figure 7)

Pectunculus pacificus ANDERSON, Proc. Calif. Acad. Sci., 3d ser., vol. 2, 1902, p. 74, Pl. 7, fig. 159; Santiago Creek, Orange County.

This species was first described as follows:

"Shell subcircular, compressed; beaks central, low, sometimes a little prominent; surface mostly smooth, yet marked with fine radiating striae and a few faint lines of growth; thickness of shell two-thirds the vertical diameter; hinge margin angularly truncated in some specimens, both anteriorly and posteriorly; diameter generally 1.5 to 3 cm."

The holotype was found at Santiago Creek, Orange County, associated with *Baculites fairbanksi* Anderson. It has also been found at the old "Forty-nine" mine in southern Oregon, and more recently at locality 1293A (C. A. S.) in the Turonian 1 mile north of Frazier Corners, Shasta County. It is not abundant at any place. Its stratigraphic position is in upper, or upper-middle Turonian strata. A reproduction of the original figure of this species is on Plate 18, figure 7. Holotype was originally in the collection of Dr. H. N. Fairbanks. Approximately nautral size.

Glycymeris shastensis Anderson n. sp.
(Plate 18, figures 8, 9, 10)

Glycymeris veatchii (Gabb), STEWART, Acad. Nat. Sci. Phila., Special Pub., No. 3, p. 1030, Pl. 1, fig. 7; (not p. 71, text fig. 1).

The shell is of moderate size, subcircular in outline or often subquadrate; shell inflated, surface marked by fine radial riblets near the beak, becoming coarser with growth; beaks central, the sides forming an angle of about 125 degrees; hinge plate as shown (Fig. 10), having about 8 or 10 nearly vertical teeth near the center, and about 6 heavier and more oblique teeth; interior margin in more mature examples set with about 36 denticles.

This species is found abundantly in the Turonian along the highway north of Redding, Shasta County, and in the same stratigraphic position 4 miles east of Millville, near the

Herford ranch. It differs from *Glycymeris pacificus* Anderson in having a somewhat more inflated shell, and fewer but coarser radial ribs. The holotype and a paratype were found at locality 27830 (C. A. S.) by Taff, Hanna, and Cross, 4 miles or more east of Millville, Shasta County, in the upper part of the Frazier formation. The species has since been found at Tuscan Springs, Tehama County, at a higher horizon. Holotype length, 29.5 mm; height, 28.5 mm; convexity (1 valve), 13 mm; Paratype length, 20.2 mm; height, 20.4 mm; convexity (1 valve), 7.7 mm. Normal horizon, Turonian.

Glycymeris pentzana Anderson n. sp.
(Plate 74, figures 2, 2a)

Shell of medium size, a little inflated, subcircular in outline, nearly equilateral, with low beaks, scarcely rising above margin of valves; shell of moderate thickness; surface marked by concentric growth lines and by slight undulations, crossed by numerous (30-35) rather fine radial ribs extending from beak to basal margin of shell; hinge plate of holotype only partly exposed, but set with radially arranged cardinal teeth, 10 or more on either side of the median line, curving outward and downward at ends of hinge plate; inner margin of the shell smooth at the front and rear, denticulate only at the base of the shell opposite the beak, for about 10 mm. The holotype (C. A. S. Type Coll.) was found by Bennison and the writer at locality 1125 (C.A.S.), about 1 mile west of Pentz, Butte County, in sandy strata dipping southward. The dimensions of the holotype are as follows: length, 28 mm; height, 28 mm; thickness of each valve about 8 mm. About six good examples of the species have been obtained here, and a single example was found by Hanna and the writer at Tuscan Springs. Two examples of the species were also found by Hanna and Hertlein at a near-by locality about three-fourths of a mile northwest of locality 1125 (C.A.S.), and north of the road running west from Pentz.

The species has some resemblance to *G. veatchii* (Gabb), but it is more compressed, the two valves together not exceeding 18 mm. in thickness, in a shell having a diameter of 30 mm.

At its type locality, the species was found associated with *Canadoceras* sp., *Mortoniceras gabbi* Anderson, *Bostrychoceras brewerii* (Gabb), *Bostrychoceras declive* (Gabb), and *Baculites chicoensis* Trask.

Glycymeris banosensis Anderson n. sp.
(Plate 73, figures 1, 2, 3)

The shell of this species differs much from those of all the preceding West Coast forms in the Upper Cretaceous, in size, form, and details of ornamentation. Outwardly, it resembles *Glycymeris veatchii* (Gabb), though its beak is less prominent and its radiating ribs are heavier. Also, in older stages of growth, the anterior and posterior margins of the shell, in the line of the hinge, become winglike and are oblique to the line of the hinge, recalling certain Tertiary and living Arcidae.

Internally, the roundly arched base of the hinge plate, the crenulated border, and the dentition show departures from the same features in all preceding species. The hinge plate is relatively more massive, its base more roundly curved, the small vertical teeth near the center of the hinge are more numerous (8 to 10) and are bordered at each end of the plate by 4 or 5 larger, oblique teeth that curve outward with progressive divergence until they become nearly horizontal, or even slope downward. The marginal crenulations are strongest at the base of the shell and weaken progressively outward and upward, and a little below the hinge plate become reduced in strength or obsolete. The development of internal flangelike shelves beneath the posterior muscle scars in the left, and probably also in the right valve, is a common feature, though possibly not occurring in all examples.

The species occurs plentifully in the Quinto member of the Moreno formation in the Pacheco Pass quadrangle, Lower California, at Gualala on the Mendocino Coast, and in the Salinas Valley.

The holotype and numerous other examples were collected by Taff, Hanna, and Cross on Los Banos Creek in pebbly sandstone on the north bank in the NE ¼ sec. 12, T. 11 S., R. 9 E. This locality is regarded as lower Maestrichtian.

Dimensions of holotype and two paratypes (C. A. S. Type Coll.) : Paratype (Pl. 73, fig. 1). Length, 52 mm; height, 56.4 mm; convexity (1 valve), 23.8 mm; locality 29117 (C. A. S.). Holotype (fig. 2). Length, 59.4 mm; height, 59.8 mm; convexity (1 valve) approximately 26.6 mm; locality 28310 (C. A. S.). Paratype (fig. 3). Length, 47 mm; height, 48.5 mm; convexity (1 valve), 20.8 mm. locality 29116 (C. A. S.). All on Los Banos Creek, Merced County.

Family PERNIDAE Fittel
Genus Inoceramus Sowerby

The genus *Inoceramus* attains a great development in the Upper Cretaceous, occurring in notable variety and often in great numbers. The genus is found in the Great Valley in much earlier strata (Knoxville and Shasta series), but distinctive types, mostly small or medium in size, are introduced into the lower beds of the Pacheco group.

In the Turonian, its species are not large, and are grouped about *Inoceramus labiatus* (*Auct.*), although this species itself is rare or not found at all; its place is apparently taken by forms related to *Inoceramus glennensis* n. sp.

The following synopsis of the genus, taken largely from the Great Valley, indicates its development in the Pacific Coast Upper Cretaceous.

Maestrichtian
Inoceramus (*Endocostea*) *stanislausensis* n. sp.
Inoceramus pacificus Anderson and Hanna
Inoceramus mendocinoensis n. sp.
Inoceramus aff. *I. simpsoni* Meek

Campanian

Inoceramus contracostae n. sp.
Inoceramus chicoensis n. sp., large form
Inoceramus aff *I. chicoensis* n. sp., very large form, elongated
Inoceramus turgidus n. sp., very thick form

Santonian-Coniacian

Inoceramus aff. *I. schmidti* (Michael) Sokolow

Inoceramus vancouverensis Shumard
Inoceramus aff *I. digitatus* Sowerby
Inoceramus subundatus Meek
Inoceramus meekianus n. sp.
Inoceramus undulatoplicatus Roemer
Inoceramus aff. *I. whitneyi* Gabb

Turonian

Inoceramus aduncus Anderson
Inoceramus glennensis n. sp.
Inoceramus duplicostatus n. sp.
Inoceramus jacksonensis n. sp.

Cenomanian

Inoceramus eolobatus n. sp.

Inoceramus eolobatus Anderson n. sp.
(Plate 18, figure 13)

The shell is of moderate size, oval in outline, beaks terminal, surface traversed by rather broad undulations, concentric and symmetrically placed about the unbonal ridge, not unlike those of *Inoceramus labiatus* Schlotheim, although the shell is considerably broader relative to its length, and occurs at a lower horizon.

The holotype (C. A. S. Type Coll.) has the following dimensions: length (incomplete), 78 mm; width (incomplete), 45 mm; thickness of one valve, 12 mm.

This example was found on the Peterson ranch, 4 miles north of Sites, western Colusa County, where it was associated with *Parapuzosia colusaensis* (Anderson), *Beudanticeras alamoense* n. sp., and fragments of *Durania*(?) *californica* n. sp. The species is regarded as early Cenomanian.

Inoceramus glennensis Anderson n. sp.
(Plate 17, figures 1, 2)

Shell is of medium size, inequivalve, inequilateral, elongate ovate in outline, beaks terminal, borders regularly curved; hinge line short, oblique; left valve thicker and more highly arched than right; umbonal ridges curving upward toward anterior end of shell; surface marked by low concentric undulations, but otherwise almost smooth; concentric folds showing a tendency to occur in pairs near anterior end of umbonal ridge.

The holotype (C. A. S. Type Coll.) is an incomplete right valve, having the following dimensions: length (incomplete), 67 mm; width (incomplete), approximately 33 mm; thickness, approximately 10 mm. The paratype (C. A. S. Type Coll.) is an incomplete left valve of another individual, length (incomplete), 66.8 mm; width, 31.5 mm; thickness, 10 mm; found at the same locality. The locality is 3 miles south of Fruto, Glenn County, about 800 feet above the zone of *Acanthoceras shastense* Reagan. It should represent a horizon not higher than lower Turonian, or possibly upper Cenomanian.

In some respects the shell resembles that of *Inoceramus duplicostatus* n. sp., to which it may be related, although the shell is more oblique, more strongly curved, and more inequivalve, the left valve being more highly arched than the right. A right valve in the collections of Stanford University, was found by J. M. Kirby on the south border of Capay Valley (SW ¼ sec. 24, T. 10 N., R. 3 W., M. D. M.), in beds that are possibly correlative.

Inoceramus duplicostatus Anderson n. sp.
(Plate 17, figures 3, 4)

Shell is small or of medium size, narrowly ovate in outline, inequilateral, and slightly curved, umbonal ridge curving gently upward toward anterior end. Beaks terminal, narrowly acuminate; surface characteristically marked by narrow, concentric folds (undulations) that show a decided disposition to duplication, appearing as doubles or triplets. The species resembles *Inoceramus glennensis,* to which it is probably related, although, as far as known, it belongs to a somewhat higher stratigraphic level.

The figured examples (Holotype mould and plaster cast (C. A. S. Type Coll.) have the following dimensions: length, 41.4 mm; maximum width, 20.2 mm. Found at locality 444A (C. A. S.), on the north border of "Rocky Gulch," 1.5 miles southwest of Henley, Siskiyou County, California. It is associated with *Oregoniceras jillsoni* n. sp. and *O. siskiyouense* Anderson, and many pelecypods. Its horizon is probably lower or middle Turonian.

Earlier reference to *Inoceramus labiatus* in the Upper Cretaceous of California and Oregon may have been based upon an incorrect identification of this species, although materials are not now at hand for comparison, since many were lost in the San Francisco fire.

Inoceramus aduncus Anderson
(Plate 18, figures 11, 12)

Inoceramus adunca ANDERSON, Proc. Calif. Acad. Sci., 3d ser., vol. 2, 1902, p. 73, Pl. 9, figs. 288, 289; "Forty-nine" mine, south of Phoenix, Oregon.

The original description of this species reads as follows:

"Shell equivalve, or nearly so, narrowly oval; margin elliptical; anterior side short, rounded, sloping rapidly from the beaks; base forming a broad curve; posterior side longer than high, meeting the basal margin in a rounded point; beaks high, very prominent and full, forming a strongly curved beak; surface having moderately strong concentric ridges, not regularly disposed."

A single example of this shell (Holotype No. 43, C. A. S. Type Coll.) was found at the "Forty-nine" mine, 2 miles south of Phoenix, Oregon, associated with *Oregoniceras, Scaphites, Pachydiscus,* and *Lytoceras* in beds regarded as Turonian. Dimension of Holotype No. 43 (C. A. S. Type Coll.): length (incomplete), 58 mm; height, 31.5 mm; thickness of valves, 22.5 mm.

Inoceramus jacksonensis Anderson n. sp.
(Plate 43, figures 1, 2)

This species resembles *Inoceramus meekianus* n. sp., but belongs to an older horizon and differs in form and sculptural details. The hinge line is longer and better developed, and differs slightly in the obliquity of its umbonal ridge to the line of the hinge. This feature is better seen in the average of several examples than in the holotypes of the two species. The holotype of the present species (Univ. Calif. Coll.) has the following dimensions: height, 45.5 mm; length, 41 mm; convexity, 10 mm. The figured examples were found by the writer at the Fitch ranch, 3 miles west of Phoenix, Jackson County, Oregon, associated with *Prionotropis fitchi* n. sp., *Oregoniceras knighteni* (Anderson), *Pachydiscus ashlandicus* Anderson, and *Fagesia californica* Anderson, and therefore in the upper part of the Turonian, whereas the holotype of *Inoceramus meekianus* n. sp. was obtained from the lower Senonian beds on Sucia Island.

In the present species the hinge is elevated, forming the top of a flangelike ridge, rising above the body of the shell, and the beaks are subterminal, not at the apex of the umbonal ridge, as in *Inoceramus meekianus* n. sp.

Inoceramus meekianus Anderson n. sp.

(Plate 22, figures 5, 6)

This species greatly resembles Meek's representation of *Inoceramus barabini* (Morton), drawn from the type specimen of the same (1876, p. 358). It was this species, perhaps, that caused Meek to alter his first determination of *Inoceramus subundatus* and to include it as a variety of *Inoceramus cripsii* Morton, which it probably is not.

In form and outline the present species resembles *Inoceramus subundatus* Meek, but it lacks the prominent and slightly elevated beak shown in Meek's figures of the adult shell. The beak of *Inoceramus meekianus* n. sp. is terminal, is usually depressed a little below the level of the dorsal margin (hinge line). In the holotype, from Sucia Island (C. A. S. Type Coll.), the outline is subquadrate or ovate, narrowing in front, much expanded toward the rear; surface marked by concentric undulations, which become progressively broader toward the rear. The holotype, which is a left valve, has the following dimensions: length (incomplete), 56 mm; height, 55 mm; thickness of one valve, approximately 8.5 mm. It was found by Bruce Martin at locality 228 (C. A. S.) on the south side of Sucia Island; the other figured example (Paratype, C. A. S. Type Coll.) is from locality 444A (C. A. S.) and shows the same outline and surface features, but is a little larger and more robust, having a length of 66 mm; height 55 mm; thickness of both valves, 27 mm. Larger examples have been found, but they are not well preserved.

Inoceramus subundatus Meek

(Plate 22, figures 1, 2, 3; Plate 26, figure 4)

Inoceramus subundatus Meek, Acad. Nat. Sci. Phila., Proc., vol. 13, 1861, p. 315; Komoox, Vancouver Island, B. C.

Inoceramus cripsii var. *subundatus* Meek, Geol. and George. Survey Terr., vol. 2, No. 4, 1876, p. 358, Pl. 1, fig. 6; Pl. 3, figs. 1, 1a; 3, 3a; Sucia Island, western Washington.

Inoceramus subundatus (Meek), Whiteaves, Trans. Royal Soc., Canada, vol. 1, 1895, p. 112; Comox and Sucia Island, Strait of Georgia.

Good examples of this species are in the collection of the California Academy of Sciences from Sucia Island. The same species is abundant in northern California, Siskiyou County, at locality 444 (C. A. S.) and at neighboring localities near Henley, and in the same zone south of the Klamath River, associated with *Metaplacenticeras pacificum* Smith, and other species of *Inoceramus*.

In California the examples are a little more robust than those from Vancouver and Sucia Islands, and there are other minor differences. Many of the casts of this species are deeply pitted, as if from pearls developed under the shells during the life of the animal. The species was found also on the South fork of Cow Creek, not far above the Waggoner home, eastern Shasta County, and by Dana Russell (1929, p. 416) in the same belt, near Oak Run, who has described and figured fossil pearls that he had collected with specimens of this species. In all cases for which definite information has been obtained it is found only in the lower beds of the Coniacian. The species is allied to *Inoceramus pembertoni* Waring, which also occurs in the same zone at other places in the lower part of the Senonian in California.

Inoceramus whitneyi Gabb

Inoceramus Whitneyi GABB, Paleont. Calif., vol. 2, 1869, p. 193, Pl. 32, fig. 91; Folsom, California; . . . STEWART, Acad. Nat. Sci., Phila., Special Pub., No. 3, 1930, p. 105, Pl. 2, fig. 1; near Folsom, California.

Stewart has included in his account of this species numerous references to the literature in which the name occurs. For the correct determination of this species, its point of discovery and its horizon should be kept in view. Gabb's figure and description are excellent, and hardly need repeating. Its precise horizon was not indicated by Gabb, although he reported an ammonite species as having been found at the same place, namely, *Ammonites suciaensis* (Meek), described from Sucia Island, and reported also from Comox, Vancouver Island, by Whiteaves (1903, p. 344). More recently, H. O. Jenkins showed the writer an excellent specimen of *Nautilus campbelli* Meek, found at the type locality. Thus far only the two cephalopod species and a small *Parallelodon* constitute the known associates. None are wholly conclusive as to age.

The horizon of the exposures at Folsom should be near that of Texas Flat (? Rock Creek), about 4 miles to the northwest, which has supplied a larger fauna, though none of these species have been reported from this place. Both of the cephalopods, namely, *Parapachydiscus suciensis* and *Nautilus campbelli* Meek occur at Sucia Island, and the present species, *Inoceramus whitneyi,* or a very similar species occurs at Enos canyon, on the opposite side of the Sacramento Valley.

Inoceramus undulatoplicatus Roemer
(Plate 22, figure 4; Plate 43, figures 3, 4, 5)

Inoceramus undulato-plicatus ROEMER, Die Kriedebild. von Texas . . . , p. 59, Pl. 7, fig. 1, 1852.

This species belongs to the group represented by *Inoceramus digitatus* Sowerby and *Inoceramus diversus* Stoliczka. As indicated by the name the species is noted for its variability in size, form, and ornamentation. Schmidt (1873) has illustrated the variability of the species (or group) in a 30-foot bed of calcareous marl in Russian Sakhalin, that has attracted much interest among paleontologists.

For the Pacific basin, and particularly for the West Coast, it seems better to adopt the name used by Roemer and more recent geologists in Texas, and on the American West Coast.

The characteristics of this group, its divergent ribs and concentric undulations, resulting in its bizarre ornamentation, makes its description almost unnecessary. The figured example (Pl. 43, fig. 3) is a plaster cast made from a rock mold of a large fragment, exposing only the interior portion of a right valve, still retaining much of its original shell.

A large fragment of the shell found at the same locality (locality 25730, C. A. S.), shows more correctly its external ornamentation, ribs and interspaces. The species attained a very large size in its more mature stages.

The cast of the Stanford example (Pl. 43, fig. 3), hypotype, a right valve, has the following dimensions: height (incomplete), 165 mm; greatest width (incomplete), 105 mm; thickness of valve, 25 mm. One fragment of the shell indicated a height of 12 inches (304 mm).

The species (or group) has been found in Texas, and recognized in California only in the lower Senonian horizons (Austin Chalk in Texas). Farther north it has been recognized by Whiteaves (1879; 1903) in the "Productive Coal Measures" on Vancouver Island, and it is now known in the Upper Cretaceous beds on Sucia Island.

Its chronological position on the West Coast is indicated by characteristic cephalopod faunas, which include *Nowakites dobbinsi* n. sp., *Canadoceras newberryanum* (Meek), *Metaplacenticeras pacificum* (Smith), and by its stratigraphical position immediately following the latest beds of Turonian age, with species of *Prionotropis, Oregoniceras,* and *Fagesia.* In the Rumsey Hills district, western Colusa and Yolo counties, the species characterizes the Forbes shale.

Inoceramus aff. I. schmidti (Michael), Sokolow
(Plate 74, figure 1)

Inoceramus schmidti (Michael), SOKOLOW, Mem. Comm. Geol. n. ser., 1914, p. 67, Pls. 1, 2, 3, figs. 1, 2; Northern Sachalin Island.

The incomplete specimen here figured is either identical with, or closely related to the form illustrated by Sokolow from Russian Sakhalin, as representing *Inoceramus schmidti* Michael. Only the lower portion of the valve has been obtained, the beak and adjacent parts of the valve are missing. The peculiar form and ornamentation of the lower part of the valves and the stratigraphic position of the specimen supports its identification with the Sakhalin species. According to Yabe and Shimizu (1923), the latter is from the lower part of Urakawa series (lower Senonian), and the example here figured is from the same stage, or possibly a little higher in the Senonian. It was found by Allan Bennison on Garzas Creek on the east border of sec. 23, T. 8 S., R. 7 E., M. D. M. He also found an incomplete specimen of enormous size, having concentric undulations and radial markings that recall the note by Sokolow that an example seen by him was 1.5 feet high. The diverging, noded, radial ribs of the early-mature shell form one of its striking features, not found in any other known species. The fragmentary examples thus far found hardly permit a more definite identification.

Dimensions of hypotype (Pl. 74, fig. 1) (C. A. S. Type Coll.) : length (incomplete), 160 mm; height (incomplete), 138 mm.

Inoceramus chicoensis Anderson, n. sp.
(Plate 55, figures 1, 2)

Shell large at maturity, subcircular in outline, equivalve, somewhat lenticular in form; hinge line straight, beaks subterminal, small, forming the apex of an angle of about 95° or more between the hinge line and the anterior margin of the shell; surface marked by concentric ridges, or undulations; the spaces between the ridges widening rapidly with growth; surface otherwise smooth.

The holotype (C. A. S. Type Coll.) measures: length (incomplete), 71.5 mm; height, 95 mm; convexity (both valves together), 34 mm. This example and other specimens were found at locality 27838 (C. A. S.) in the Chico formation of Chico Creek, Butte County, by Taff, Hanna, and Cross.

In the holotype the inner layers of the shell show faint radial lines extending from the beak to the basal border of the shell. The species greatly resembles "the flat variety" of *Inoceramus 'cripsianus'* Stoliczka from the Arrialoor group of southern India. A larger example of the species, 12 or more inches (305 mm) in diameter, was found by O. L. Campbell of Chico, near its type locality. An example of *Inoceramus* resembling that here described has been found in southern Oregon, near Ashland, by W. W. Wells of the Ashland schools. It measures 18 inches in diameter.

A similar species, *Inoceramus* aff. *I. chicoensis,* n. sp., is known in the Panoche formation in the Great Valley, examples have been reported by Taff, Hanna, and Cross. Some of these specimens, always too badly broken to collect, measured 18 inches in length.

Inoceramus contracostae Anderson n. sp.
(Plate 18, figures 3, 4; Plate 55, figure 3)

The shell is small, thin, subovate in outline; beaks terminal, hinge line short; posterior border nearly straight, base broadly rounded; surface marked by fine, sharp concentric ridges separated by broader interspaces; valves little inflated, compressed; in young stages of growth the beak is narrow and high; in older stages the shell becomes elongated and more narrowly ovate.

The holotype (C. A. S. Type Coll.) has the following dimensions: length (incomplete), 55 mm; width (incomplete), 25 mm; convexity (1 valve), approximately 5.8 mm. Found at locality 29084 (C. A. S.) in Round Valley, east of Mount Diablo, with *Baculites* aff.

B. teres Forbes, and fragmentary specimens of *Parapachydiscus* sp., resembling *Parapachydiscus diabloensis* n. name.

The species is related to *Inoceramus klamathensis* Anderson, from a similar horizon on Willow Creek, Siskiyou County, north of Montague.

Inoceramus klamathensis Anderson
(Plate 18, figures 1, 2)

Inoceramus klamathensis ANDERSON, Proc. Calif. Acad. Sci., 3d ser., vol. 2, No. 1, 1902, p. 73, Pl. 9, figs. 185, 186; Willow Creek, Siskiyou County, California.

The original description is as follows:

"Shell small, not attaining a size much above that shown in the figure, inequivalve, the left valve being much more strongly arched, the right being somewhat flattened, or compressed; left valve showing tendency to form an umbonal angle and depression at mature age; hinge line short, and forming an angle of 60 degrees with the anterior margin." Lower Senonian, probably representing the Chico formation. Syntypes nos. 45, 46 (C. A. S. Type Coll.)

Inoceramus turgidus Anderson n. sp.
(Plate 61, figures 1, 2)

Shell large and unusually thick, roundly robust; beaks elevated above hinge line, tumid, approximate; hinge line straight; surface marked by heavy concentric ridges, showing a tendency to form beadlike nodes on the concentric ridges. The external measurements of the holotype are as follows: length, 100 mm; height, 90 mm; breadth of both valves, 80 mm; number of concentric undulations, 10 or more. The form is unique among Inocerami of the West Coast.

The holotype (C. A. S. Type Coll.) was found by Taff, Hanna, and Cross, at locality 28171 (C. A. S.) on Chico Creek, near the top of the Chico formation. The chronological position of this species is probably in the lower Campanian, but above that of *Mortoniceras randalli* n. sp., and *Inoceramus chicoensis* n. sp.

Inoceramus aff. I. simpsoni Meek

Inoceramus Simpsoni MEEK, Acad. Nat. Sci., Phila., Proc., vol. 12, 1860. p. 312. . . . Report of Exploration across the Great Basin of Utah, p. 360, Pl. 4, fig. 4.

The California species to which the above name is here attached is in the Collection of the University of California and is labelled "Gualala," Mendocino County, California.

The specimen is incomplete and is the cast of a right valve of a large *Inoceramus,* having the following dimensions: length, 223 mm; maximum height, 140 mm; thickness of valve, 33 mm. The original length of the valve was not less than 260 mm Meek gave no figure of the species, but as described and illustrated by R. P. Whitfield (1880, p. 395, Pl. 8), the species has quite definite and characteristic size, form, and surface markings, which are not imitated in any other species. The species occurs in the Fort Pierre group ("group 4") described by Whitfield. The California example from Gualala is somewhat larger, roughly pear-shaped by its posterior expansion and narrow anterior, and relatively thin, not gibbous.

Whitfield describes the characteristic markings on the cast as "oblique curving lines, or lines of pustules, which incline slightly forward as they approach the basal margin."

These lines appear distinctly on the California form. Its resemblance to that figured by Whitfield is so close that if it is not identical with that from "Old Woman Fork," it is a very closely allied form or an analogue of it.

Inoceramus pacificus Anderson and Hanna

Inoceramus pacificus ANDERSON AND HANNA, Proc. Calif. Acad. Sci., 4th ser., vol. 23, 1935, p. 29, Pl. 10, fig. 4.

Shell large, subquadrate, elongate, beaks almost terminal, strongly incurved; hinge margin extended, straight, elevated behind; anterior ends abruptly truncated, rounded below; basal margin broadly curved in outline; surface marked by strong concentric undulations on the upper half of shell, becoming obsolete below. The holotype No. 4266 (C. A. S. Type Coll.) has the following dimensions: length, 142 mm; height, 88 mm; thickness (est.), 70 mm. The holotype was found at locality 1430 (C. A. S.) on the Johnson ranch (San Antonio del Mar), Lower California. The species belongs to the group of *Inoceramus cripsianus* (Mantell) as determined by Stoliczka, although differing from it in some features. Its chronological position is probably early Maestrichtian.

Inoceramus mendocinoensis Anderson n. sp.
(Plate 73, figure 4)

Large, ovate in outline, moderately inflated; beaks small, terminal, acute, rising but little above hinge line; hinge relatively short, straight, rounding to posterior margin; surface smooth, or marked only by concentric undulations, best shown in young stages of growth (near the beak), becoming obsolete with age and larger growth. The holotype was found by Jerold Henney, on the Covelo-Dos Rios highway, southwest of Kelly Creek, at a horizon correlative with the Moreno formation in the Great Valley. The holotype (C. A. S. Type Coll.) measures as follows: height, 234 mm; maximum length (est.), 170 mm; length of hinge (incomplete), 95 mm; maximum thickness (both valves), 67 mm. This species belongs in the group of *Inoceramus lucianus* Davis, found near Slate's Springs, on the coast of Monterey County, although it differs from the latter in having a smaller and more pointed beak, and a more rounded outline. It appears to be a contemporary of the latter species, and represents the same transgressive overlap of the late Upper Cretaceous seas upon pre-Chico terrains in the inter-Coast Range valleys of California.

Subgenus Endocostea Whitfield

D'Orbigny (1843–1847, p. 515 [1845]) described a species of Senonian *Inoceramus* under the name *Inoceramus impressus,* stating that "At the middle of each side is seen a large depression," extending from behind the beak obliquely downward to its posterior margin.

Without referring to this species, or to d'Orbigny's account, Whitfield (1880, p. 402) described and figured a closely related species under the generic name *Endocostea,* of which the type is given as *Endocostea typica* Whitfield, perhaps intending the name to cover a subgenus of *Inoceramus* Sowerby. His brief diagnosis of the genus follows:

"Shell resembling *Inoceramus,* being bivalve, with both sides convex, but more or less unequal, and composed of two layers, an outer vertically fibrous coating, and an inner nacreous, or pearly lining; hinge line straight, edentulous, with a narrow linear external cartilage area on each valve.

"Valves provided with an oblique internal rib passing from behind the beaks, along the postero-cardinal slope, toward the postero-basal margin, marking the position of the posterior muscular imprint; other muscular markings unknown. Type, *E. typica* Whitfield."

Clearly the generic name connotes the internal rib of the shell thus described, and presumably included the species described by d'Orbigny.

One or more species of the subgenus has been found in the upper part of the Panoche formation (upper Campanian), in the Garzas Creek district (NW ¼ sec. 19, T. 8 S., R. 8 E., M. D. B. and M.).

Inoceramus (Endocostea) stanislausensis Anderson n. sp.
(Plate 74, figures 3, 4, 5, 6)

Shell of medium size, subovate as viewed laterally, slightly compressed behind, somewhat inflated before, especially in umbonal region; concentrically costate, ribs narrow and ridgelike, separated by rather broad concentric interspaces which become broader with growth of shell, especially near its basal border.

The holotype of the present species (C. A. S. Type Coll.) is the larger and more mature of the two examples figured, but it does not show the thickness and prominent ribbing in the younger stages of growth seen in the smaller example, which may be regarded as a paratype (C. A. S. Type Coll.). Dimensions of holotype (right valve, incomplete) length, 87.5

mm; height, 52 mm; dimensions of paratype (right valve, incomplete) length 58 mm; height, 36.4 mm; convexity (one valve) 20 mm. These examples were found by Bennison in the upper part of the Moreno formation, at locality 29123 (C. A. S.) a mile or more south of Garzas Creek, near the south border of Stanislaus County, or more precisely, on the NW ¼ of the SE ¼ sec. 19, T. 8 S., R. 8 E., M. D. B. and M.

This species closely resembles *Inoceramus impressus* d'Orbigny, to which is apparently analogous in stratigraphic position. As shown by Seunes (1890, p. 186) the European species is associated with *Inoceramus regularis* d'Orbigny, and *Diplomoceras recticostatus* Seunes, in the "Lower Danian" beds of southern France, with which the upper part of the Moreno formation may be correlated.

Family PTERIIDAE Meek

Genus **Avicula** Bruguiere

Avicula gainsana Anderson n. sp.

(Plate 1, figure 7)

Shell of moderate size, obliquely elongated, compressed, smooth, slightly inequivalve; lower margin ventricose, dorsal margin nearly straight; ears rather small, anterior ear minute, posterior ear more expanded; surface marked only by concentric lines of growth, and faint undulations; shell thin and somewhat nacreous. The holotype (C. A. S. Type Coll.) has the following dimensions: length, 57 mm; maximum width, 26 mm; thickness, 8.6 mm; angle of hinge-line with major axis, acute, about 40 degrees. Five well-preserved examples were found in a single concretion in the second conglomerate of the Upper Cretaceous series on the North fork of Cottonwood Creek, 0.6 miles above the mouth of Hulen Creek, where they were associated with *Beudanticeras haydeni* (Gabb), *Pervinquieria tehamaensis* (Reagan), *Durania* (?) *californica,* and various other species of upper Albian age. The species resembles figures of *Avicula subplicatus* d'Orbigny, from the lower Turonian of France, although it is larger.

Avicula roguensis Anderson n. sp.

(Plate 38, figure 7)

Shell small, narrowly ovate in outline, with short, oblique hinge line, and an acuminate terminal beak. The holotype (C. A. S. Type Coll.) has the following dimensions: length, 15 mm; greater width, 10.3 mm; little inflated, about 2.5 mm. The surface is smooth. The holotype was found at the old "Forty-nine mine" south of Phoenix, Oregon, associated with species of *Oregoniceras, Scaphites condoni* Anderson, and with *Pachydiscus oregonensis* n. sp., in the upper part of the Turonian. This species has not been reported from any other locality or horizon as far as known.

Family OSTREIDAE Lamarck

Members of this family are not abundant in the Upper Cretaceous of the West Coast in any latitude. Two species of *Ostrea* were described by Gabb (1864, p. 204) from the Chico series of California, and others are now known.

Other genera of the family are likewise little known in the Upper Cretaceous. Gabb (1869), Meek (1876), and Whiteaves (1903) mention or list *Gryphaea vesicularis* Lamarck in the "Chico" of California, or of British Columbia, and *Exogyra parasitica* Gabb has been recognized by Whiteaves in western Canada.

Packard (1922) adds two species each of *Ostrea* and *Exogyra,* which were not abundant. A few others may now be added to the species already known in California, but none are plentiful. No members of the family flourished at any epoch of the Upper Cretaceous, as compared with comtemporary beds in the American Interior (Texas and Mexico), where many types occur in great numbers. The known representatives of the family are generically and numerically few.

Ostrea brewerii Gabb

Ostrea Brewerii GABB, Paleont. Calif., vol. 1, 1864, p. 204, Pl. 26, fig. 191; Cow Creek, Shasta County.

This species is common on the Little Cow Creek, 1 to 2 miles east of Frazier Corners, 10 miles east of Redding. It occurs near the basal beds of the Upper Cretaceous, in the horizon of *Phylloceras vaculae* n. sp., and *Kotôceras frazierense* n. sp. The species is large, with a squamose surface, and is sometimes found massed in small numbers, but it forms no important shell beds.

Ostrea malleiformis Gabb

Ostrea malleiformis GABB, Paleont. Calif., vol. 1, 1864, p. 204, Pl. 31, fig. 272; Siskiyou Mountains, California, and in southern Oregon.

This species is common near Frazier Corners, east of Redding, and is found on both sides of the Siskiyou mountains near the present Oregon—California highway, in beds that are regarded as upper Turonian in the horizon of *Prionotropis hiltensis* n. sp., and in overlying beds.

Genus **Gryphaea** Lamarck
Gryphaea distorta Anderson n. sp.
(Plate 2, figures 3, 3a, 4, 4a)

Shell small, or of moderate size, subtriangular in outline, otherwise somewhat irregular in shape, umbones a little bent; anterior and posterior borders of the shell expanded; beak nearly terminal, and spiral, small; lower valve deep and rather broad, central depression extending from beak to basal border of the valve, which is marked by a slight sinus; upper part of umbone narrow but rounded; shell not squamose, smooth and nacreous, ornamented with concentric lines of growth.

The holotype and paratype (C. A. S. Type Coll.) was donated to the Academy of Sciences by the California State Mining Bureau, and was said to have been found on the Petersen Ranch, 4 miles north of Sites, Colusa County. In general form, the species is similar to *"Exogyra" suborbiculata* Lamarck, as illustrated by Stoliczka (1871, p. 462, Pl. 38, figs. 1–4). The species belongs to the group of *Gryphaea corrugata* Say, coming within its range of variation. The holotype (Pl. 2, figs. 3, 3a) has the following dimensions: height (incomplete), 30 mm; length (incomplete), 35 mm; depth of lower valve, 13 mm; restored height, 35 mm; paratype (Pl. 2, figs. 4, 4a): height (incomplete), 21 mm.

The exact stratigraphic level to which the species belongs is not definite; the lowest beds of the Upper Cretaceous series exposed where the holotype was found are not younger than early Cenomanian, and contain *Beudanticeras alamoense* n. sp., *Parapuzosia colusaensis* (Anderson), and fragments of a rudistid-like shell, seemingly referable to *Durania? californica* n. sp.

Gryphaea accipiter Anderson n. sp.
(Plate 2, figures 5, 5a, 5b)

Shell small, inequivalve, lower valve deep, narrow, and beaklike; upper valve smaller and less strongly arched, beak elevated, narrow, spirally coiled; valve triangular in outline, expanded behind; surface smooth, or polished, marked only by concentric growth lines; upper valve smaller, shallow, beak coiling oppositely.

This species resembles Morton's original type of *Gryphaea pitcheri* as figured by Hill and Vaughan (1898, Pl. 6, figs. 5–7), although it is higher relative to its width, with high, narrow umbones and incurved beak and expanded borders. The holotype (C. A. S. Type Coll.) was donated to the Academy of Sciences by the California State Mining Bureau, and was said to have been found on the Peterson Ranch, Colusa County at locality 12779 (Calif. State Mining Bur.), with the preceding.

The holotype, lower valve, has the following dimensions: height (incomplete), 28 mm; length, 21 mm; thickness 18 mm. Its age is the same as that of the preceding (early Cenomanian).

Genus **Exogyra** Say

Few species of *Exogyra* have been noted in the Cretaceous deposits of California or Oregon. The genus did not flourish in any part of the Cretaceous on the West Coast, as compared to its abundance in contemporary deposits in the American Interior (Texas and Mexico), where the family is represented by many species in great numbers. At present at least six species of *Exogyra* have been recognized in the lower part of the Upper Cretaceous, and there are others in its upper beds. Packard (1922, p. 420, 421) has described and illustrated two species from the lower beds (lower Turonian) exposed on the west flank of the Santa Ana Mountains, Orange County, and others have been described from contemporary or from later beds.

Exogyra parasitica Gabb

Exogyra parasitica GABB, Paleont. Calif., vol. 1, 1864, p. 205, Pl. 26, figs. 192a, b; Pl. 31, figs. 273, 273a; Texas Flat, Placer County. . . . vol. 2, 1869, p. 253; locality as above.

Probably more than one species has been included under this name in the literature of the Chico series. Gabb mentioned Texas Flat, northwest of Folsom, as the type locality of the species, and the species has been found in the vicinity near Rock Creek, and a similar but undescribed form near Folsom, by Eldridge Drew.

Gabb noted the species also on the Cottonwood Creek, Shasta County, and other writers believed that it occurred below the 2500 foot conglomerate of the Upper Cretaceous on Elder Creek, Tehama County, and at Texas Springs, Shasta County. It has been listed at the "Forty-nine" mine, in southern Oregon.

Whiteaves (1903, p. 401) states that a single valve obtained at Departure Bay, Vancouver Island, and two specimens with both valves, now in the collections of the California Academy of Sciences from Sucia Island, are probably referable to *Exogyra parasitica* Gabb. Similar forms have been collected by the writer at Enos Canyon, Yolo County, where they are associated with *Metaplacenticeras pacificum* Smith, and other species characteristic of the lower Coniacian.

Exogyra californica Packard

Exogyra californica PACKARD, Univ. Calif. Pub., Bull. Dept. Geol. Sci., vol. 13, 1922, p. 421, Pl. 27, fig. 5; type specimen No. 12320 (Univ. Calif. Type Coll.).

Packard's description reads, in part:

"Shell small, much higher than long, irregular in outline. Umbones prominent, with an umbonal ridge extending to the base. Surface marked by crude radiating ribs." *Acteonella oviformis* zone, Santa Ana Mountains, California. This zone is characteristic of the lower Turonian.

Exogyra inornata Packard

Exogyra inornata PACKARD, Univ. Calif. Pub. Bull. Dept. Geol. Sci., vol. 13, 1922, p. 420, Pl. 27, fig. 1; *Acteonella oviformis* zone, Silverado Canyon, Orange County, California.

Packard's description reads, in part, as follows:

"Shell small, rather thin, smooth, very tumid, somewhat elliptical in outline; beaks large, conspicuously twisted; lower valve of the cotype (not figured) is circular, irregular, margins smooth. The upper valve of the cotype is similar to that of the type. Height of the type about 35 mm; length, about 25 mm."

Family TRIGONIIDAE Lamarck
Genus **Trigonia** Bruguiere

The genus *Trigonia* is well known on the West Coast, especially in California and Oregon, from the Valanginian to the later Senonian stages. It has not yet been reported from the Knoxville (Upper Jurassic), although known in Jurassic deposits in other parts of the world. It is not well known in the highest Cretaceous of the West Coast, although it occurs there sparingly. The earliest appearance of the genus on the coast is in the Paskenta group (*Trigonia kayana* Anderson) of early Cretaceous time.

The genus attained its greatest development on the West Coast in middle Upper Cretaceous times, though it appeared in important numbers in almost the earliest Upper Cretaceous. As many as five species appeared in quick succession, following the widespread subsidence and overlap of late Albian and Cenomanian times, though only fragmentary remains of one or two of them are known.

In Turonian and early Senonian times, the number and variety became greatly increased, but in later stages they declined. Few of the species known in early Upper Cretaceous times survived the diastrophism that initiated Senonian deposition on the West Coast.

Packard (1921) enumerates about 18 Upper Cretaceous species of *Trigonia,* some were described as varieties. Additional forms are now known, either as described species or as fragmentary and undescribed forms, and though the number has been enlarged, it is not yet complete, and the possible varieties are numerous. Of all the species known in early and middle Upper Cretaceous times, not more than three or four can be counted in the Maestrichtian.

TABLE 6.—*Stratigraphic distribution of the Trigoniidae
in the West Coast Upper Cretaceous*

MAESTRICHTIAN

Trigonia sp.   several undescribed forms

SENONIAN

Trigonia tryoniana Gabb	*Trigonia inezana* Packard
Trigonia hemphilli n.sp.	*Trigonia oregona* (Packard)
Trigonia evansana Meek	*Trigonia wheelerensis* n. sp.

TURONIAN

Trigonia branneri n. sp.	*Trigonia fitchi* Packard
Trigonia jacksonensis Packard	*Trigonia condoni* Packard
Trigonia deschutesensis Packard	*Trigonia californiana* Packard
Trigonia klamathonia n.sp.	*Trigonia leana* Gabb.

CENOMANIAN

Trigonia colusaensis n.sp.	*Trigonia aequicostata* Gabb.
Trigonia perrinsmithi n.sp.	*Trigonia packardi* n.sp.

None of the species can be shown to be descended from types known in earlier Mesozoic deposits on the West Coast. They appear to have reached these areas by migrations, following epochs of diastrophism, such as in late-Albian time, preceding the beginning of Senonian time, and later, preceding Maestrichtian time.

In the Queen Charlotte Series, other species are known, although their vertical distribution has not yet been determined. The list of these are probably not yet complete, although Packard (1921) noted the following species. These forms include the following:

Trigonia flexicosta Burwash	*Trigonia maudensis* Whiteaves
Trigonia newcombi Packard	*Trigonia charlottensis* Packard
Trigonia dawsoni Whiteaves	*Trigonia diversicostata* Whiteaves
Trigonia whiteavesi (Packard)	*Trigonia columbiana* Packard

Some of these species have been reported as occurring in the Haida formation, which may be correlated with some part of the Cenomanian and Turonian in Oregon and California, whereas the Honna and Skidegate formations, as shown by MacKenzie (1916) are not older than Turonian.

Trigonia packardi Anderson n. sp.
(Plate 1, figure 5)

The shell is of medium size, trigonal, or pear-shaped in general outline, broadly rounded in front and in its anterior basal part; beaks high, approximate, not terminal; surface costate, bearing about 16 prominent ribs that appear to have been regularly beaded; ribs on anterior third of shell radiating from the beak, those on the posterior portion nearly vertical; corselet ovate, elevated, and ridge-like in its median area with outward sloping sides. Size, form and ornamentation resembling those of *Trigonia condoni* Packard, but lacking the anterior tubercules. In other details of ornamentation there are considerable differences. The dimensions of the holotype (C. A. S. Type Coll.) are as follows: length, 55.6 mm, height, 40 mm; convexity (both valves together) 26 mm; sides tapering to a narrow posterior terminus.

The species recalls the group represented by *Trigonia mooreana* Gabb, and *Trigonia emoryi* Conrad, or at any rate approaches it in time and in form, though its weathered condition hardly permits a detailed comparison.

The species was found by the writer in the basal beds at locality 1345 (C. A. S.), at Texas Springs, 2 miles east of old Horsetown, Shasta County, where it was associated with other species of *Trigonia,* in the horizon of *Trigonia perrinsmithi* n. sp., *Sonnerata stantoni,* and *Neohibolites fontinalis* Anderson, and fragments of rudistids.

Trigonia mooreana Gabb

Trigonia mooreana GABB, Synop. Cret. Moll., Acad. Nat. Sci. Phila., Proc., 1861, p. 176. . . . GABB, Paleont. Calif., vol. 2, 1869, p. 269; Arivechi, Sonora, Mexico. . . . Böse, Bol. Inst. Geol., de Mexico, No. 25, 1910, p. 124, Pl. 25, figs. 2, 9; Pl. 26, fig. 2; Vraconian, Sonora, Mexico.

Böse describes the differences between this form and *Trigonia emoryi* Conrad, as being very small and suggests that they may be synonomous, although in Colombian examples the differences may be greater. Two fairly well-preserved examples of Gabb's species were found by the writer near locality 759 (C. A. S.), near Barichara, Colombia, and a well-preserved example was also obtained from the district of Leiva, Colombia.

To this group could be added various others, probably including *Trigonia packardi* n. sp., and perhaps *Trigonia kayana* Anderson, from the Paskenta group, near Riddle, Oregon, first figured by Diller and Kay (1924).

Trigonia perrinsmithi Anderson n. sp.
(Plate 2, figure 7)

This species belongs to the group of *Trigonia leana* Gabb, and is large, with thick shell, with ovate outline, broader in front and narrowing toward rear; beaks subterminal, slightly raised, but not high; hinge line nearly straight for two-thirds the length of shell, posterior margin curving downward from hinge line to posterior angle; anterior border at first descending nearly vertical, rounded below to the more broadly rounded base; umbonal ridge little prominent, descending at an angle of about 17 degrees from the line of the hinge to the posterior angle; shell nearly smooth above, but showing two shallow depressions sloping back from beak; sides costate below, with about 10 coarse tuberculate ribs, curving slightly forward near the base; tubercules low, scattered and little developed. The holotype, No. 2691 (Stanford Univ. Coll.), has the following dimensions: length, 126 mm; height, 80 mm; thickness of left valve, 25 mm.

This example was found by Jas. Perrin Smith about a mile east of the site of old Horsetown, Shasta County, in the basal beds of the Upper Cretaceous.

It somewhat resembles *Trigonia hemphilli* n. sp., found near Pescadero, San Mateo County, which represents a higher horizon. The stratigraphic position of the present species is regarded as lower Cenomanian; its nearest allied species, are, in the order of their occurrence, *Trigonia colusaensis* n.sp., *T. branneri* n.sp., and *T. leana* Gabb.

Trigonia colusaensis Anderson n. sp.
(Plate 1, figure 6)

Shell large, thick, subtrigonal in outline, anterior part ventricose; posterior half produced and almost smooth, showing only lines of growth; anterior lower third of shell strongly tuberculate, giving to the ribs in this area, six or more in number, a noded appearance; beaks anterior, slightly elevated but not prominent. The species may belong to the group of *Trigonia californiana* Packard, although it is older and possesses a pronounced umbonal ridge extending from the beak backward and downward to basal posterior end, in a manner not seen in any other West Coast species thus far described. The beaks are near terminal, and strongly incurved, almost approximate. In these respects the shell differs from *Trigonia californiana*. The holotype (C. A. S. Type Coll.) is the specimen referred to by Packard (1921, p. 15) as having been found near Sites, Colusa County. A critical comparison of this example with others found in the Cenomanian, and with a plaster cast of *Trigonia california,* supplied by Dr. Packard, discloses the fact that they are distinct in form and in ornamentation, as well as in their stratigraphic levels.

Trigonia colusaensis n. sp. has been found at three widely separated localities in the Cenomanian, namely, at its type locality 1291 (C. A. S.), near Sites, Colusa County; at Hulen Creek, Shasta County and at Curry Creek, southeast of Mount Diablo. The holotype has the following dimensions: maximum length, 102 mm; height, 71 mm; greatest breadth, 48 mm. It was found associated with *Parapuzosia colusaensis* (Anderson), *Trigonia aequicostata* Gabb, and fragments of *Durania ? californica* n. sp.

Trigonia aequicostata Gabb

Trigonia sp. indet., GABB, Paleont. Calif., vol. 1, 1864, p. 209, Pl. 26, fig. 198; Orestimba Canyon, Stanislaus County.
Trigonia aequicostata GABB, Paleont. Calif., vol. 2, 1869, p. 196; locality as above. . . . PACKARD, Univ. Oregon Pub., vol. 1, No. 9, 1921, p. 27, Pl. 9, fig. 3; reproduction of Gabb's figure. . . . STEWART, Acad. Nat. Sci. Phila., Special Paper, No. 3, 1930, p. 90, Pl. 5, fig. 7, 8.

This species was poorly figured and described by Gabb, and the holotype, if any existed, has been lost. As a result the species has not been clearly understood by subsequent writers. Since it is desirable to indicate a satisfactory lectotype, Stewart proposed the type of his figure 8, as seeming "the less unsatisfactory" etc. He says, however (p. 91) :

"The only unquestionable specimen (in Mus. Comp. Zool.?) which shows the external surface is here figured (Pl. 5, fig. 7)," which was labelled as coming from "Orestimba." As this was the first locality mentioned by Gabb in his descriptions, it is not unlikely that this example was the basis of his description and drawing, in part, at least. Although no complete example of the species has since been illustrated, it has been found at various localities by the writer and by others, but always in the lower beds of the Cenomanian. It has been found on Hulen Creek, Shasta County; at Petersen's ranch, north of Sites, Colusa County; at the lowest horizon of the Upper Cretaceous in Curry Canyon, Contra Costa County; and at its type locality on Orestimba Creek, Stanislaus County. The reported occurrence of the species in the Horsetown "group," is subject to some doubt.

Trigonia whiteavesi (Packard)

Trigonia sp. indet. WHITEAVES, Mes. Foss., vol. 1, pt. 1, 1876, p. 70; pt. 3, 1884, Pl. 10, figs. 2, 2a; Upper Cretaceous, Skidegate Inlet, Queen Charlotte Islands.
Trigonia leana, var. *whiteavesi* PACKARD, Univ. Oregon Pub., vol. 1, 1921, p. 21, Pl. 6, fig. 2, only, copy of Whiteaves' figure; Haida formation, locality as given above.

A careful reading of Whiteaves' description of this species (p. 70), readily shows that the original example from which figure 2, Plate 10 was drawn should be regarded as the holotype of this species, and that the status of figure 2a, can hardly rank as such, and appears to be a partial restoration (possibly a composite reconstruction) of the species found on Skidegate Channel.

Packard believed that this form represented only a variety of *Trigonia leana* Gabb, but the form figured by Whiteaves exhibits various features that seem irreconcilable with Gabb's figure and description of his holotype.

In both figures of the Skidegate species given by Whiteaves (Pl. 10), the tubercules are coarse and beadlike, and are said to constitute "thirteen or fourteen obliquely transverse, concavely, curved rows of separate raised tubercules."

In Gabb's figure of *Trigonia leana,* only nine rows, or ribs, are shown, although it is stated in his text that there are "about thirteen nodose ribs." Gabb's description of *T. leana* cannot be accepted in detail, since it is based upon two quite dissimilar species that are not stratigraphically contemporary.

Trigonia branneri Anderson n. sp.
(Plate 17, figure 5)

This species is probably most closely related to *Trigonia whiteavesi* (Packard) from the Haida formation of Queen Charlotte Islands, and may be contemporary with it.

The shell is rather large, subquadrate in outline, moderately inflated, numerously costate and tuberculate; beaks nearly terminal, not elevated, hinge line nearly straight; anterior border descending from the beaks at an angle of little more than 90 degrees from hinge line, rounded below to meet the more broadly rounded base; posterior end somewhat narrowed and obliquely truncated; umbonal ridge not prominent, descending obliquely at an angle of about 20 degrees from hingle line, rounded below to meet posterior basal angle; upper part of posterior surface nearly smooth, showing only concentric growth lines; lower two-thirds of shell costate; ribs about 16 in number, descending somewhat vertically above, but irregularly below and turning sharply forward near base. Ribs are tuberculate, with rounded, beadlike tubercules; ribs shorter behind than in front.

The holotype, No. 2786 (Stanford Univ. Coll.) has the following dimensions: length, 86 mm; height, 60 mm; thickness of left valve, 17 mm. The holotype was found at "Rocky Gulch," 2.5 miles southwest of Hornbrook, Siskiyou County, by R. A. Diggles. Its stratigraphic position is in the lower beds of the Turonian. It has not yet been recognized at any other horizon in California or Oregon.

Trigonia klamathonia Anderson n. sp.
(Plate 30, figure 4)

Trigonia evansana Auct., (in part) of the California Upper Cretaceous. *Non* Meek, 1861.

This species is a close relative of *Trigonia scabra* Lamarck. The shell is of medium size, subtrigonal in outline, gibbous in the anterior-ventral area, where it is deeply rounded; beaks near terminal; anterior border short, rounded upward to nearly vertical near beaks; posterior border sloping upward from base to terminal end, nearly straight; dorsal margin concave in outline, concavity being about 5 mm near its middle; dorsal border between the side and the escutcheon rounded, doubled by a longitudinal groove; escutcheon narrowly ovate, or lanceolate, divided on its median line by an elevated ridge, narrowing at the rear, and terminating in an acute angle of closure; each half of the escutcheon slightly concave above, and crossed transversely by about ten horizontal, or slightly curved ridges; outer surface of the valves bearing about 14 curved and beaded riblets; between which are transverse hollows.

The holotype (C. A. S. Type Coll.) is an almost complete mold of a single valve, from which a plaster cast was obtained, showing clearly the outer aspect of the shell and nearly half the corselet in detail; this valve has the following dimensions: length, (partly estimated), 45 mm; maximum height, 27 mm; convexity of valve, 12 mm. The mold was found about 4 miles south of Hilt, on the west border of the small Cottonwood Valley, above Hornbrook, Siskiyou County where it was associated with *Prionotropis hiltensis* n. sp., about 100 feet above the zone of *Oregoniceras,* and a few hundred feet beneath the local overlap by the basal beds of the Coniacian. Its chronological position is accordingly in upper Turonian strata.

A somewhat similar, but a more slender and graceful species has been collected in the lowest beds of the Cenomanian in the Cottonwood district, Shasta County, and on Griffin Creek, west of Medford, Oregon.

Trigonia californiana Packard

Trigonia californiana PACKARD, Univ. Oregon Pub., vol. 1, 1921, p. 17, Pl. 2, fig. 2; near Ager, Siskiyou County, California.

This species has been well described and figured by Packard from the holotype in the Condon collection at the University of Oregon. The horizon of the holotype is now known to be upper Senonian. It has not been recorded from any lower beds in California or Oregon. Packard's description reads in part as follows:

"Shell large, elongate, subquadrate; compressed posteriorly; anterior dorsal margin short, curving regularly to meet the broad curve of the anterior end, base only slightly curved; posterior end irregularly rounded; . . . Umbones inconspicuous, beaks small, nearly adjacent. Surface of shell ornamented by a very few irregular low elevations and by concentric lines of growth. Length of type, 111 mm; height, 80 mm; diameter 35 mm.

The text of this description conforms to the figure given by Packard, and to the cast of the holotype itself. Shell is thick and heavy, with a broad open escutcheon extending half the length of shell. Beaks are low, scarcely rising above dorsal line, and in this respect differs much from the holotype of *Trigonia colusaensis* n. sp.

A large, but incomplete example of a related species was found by Taff, Hanna and Cross at locality 27 830 (C. A. S.) 4.9 miles east of Millville, Shasta County, associated with other lower Senonian pelecypods and gastropods.

Trigonia leana Gabb

Trigonia gibboniana GABB, Paleont. Calif., vol. 1, 1864, p. 190 (in part), Pl. 31, fig. 262; ? Jacksonville, Oregon . . . vol. 2, 1869, p. 248 (in part).
Trigonia leana GABB, Acad. Nat. Sci. Phila., Proc., 1876, p. 312. . . . PACKARD, Univ. Oregon Pub., vol. 1, No. 9, 1921, p. 20, Pl. 5, figs. 1, 6 (not fig. 3, Martinez; not fig. 4, Pescadero, San Mateo County) . . . STEWART, Acad. Nat. Sci. Phila., Special Pub., No. 3, 1930, p. 92.

In Gabb's original description and in his figures illustrating this form, two distinct species were confused, one from beds outcropping near Martinez, and probably of late Cretaceous age, and the other from older strata exposed near Jacksonville, Oregon. The specimen illustrated by Gabb (1864, Pl. 25, fig. 178) was from near Martinez, and it is in the Museum of Paleontology, University of California, lectotype No. 12131. The other, and larger, form was from Oregon. Gabb's description of the species was based upon the latter, but he adds: "on the specimen from Martinez is a single row of small isolated tubercules, placed between the two rows of ribs." This latter feature is not again mentioned by Gabb, or by any later writer who has attempted to interpret his description. The example, described in his text (p. 190) was later (1876) given the name *Trigonia leana* Gabb, and needs no further comment.

Gabb's smaller form (Pl. 25, fig. 178) can hardly be regarded as the same species, but it was included by Merriam (1895) under this name in his check list of type species at the University of California.

Packard stated (p. 21) that *Trigonia leana* is abundant in the Chico Cretaceous of the Bear Creek Valley area of Oregon. Since Jacksonville is in this area, there is little doubt that the species is Turonian.

Trigonia melhasei Anderson n. sp.
(Plate 26, figures 7, 7a)

This species is related to the preceding and accordingly belongs in the group of *Trigonia scabra* Lamarck, but differs from it slightly in size and form, and in its surface ornamentation. It is somewhat longer than *Trigonia klamathonia* n. sp., more graceful in outline and form, though rougher in its external sculpture, and has about 17 ribs on each valve, similarly spaced to those of the preceding form. The escutcheon is longer and narrower and is crossed by about 16 transverse riblets that slope slightly backward toward the median ridge, or axis; The surface ornamentation of the valves consists of rows of numerous scale-like tubercules arising on the ribs, and connected with those on the neighboring ribs by slightly obscure lines of growth, that give the tubercules a curved alignment on the sides of the valves; four examples of the species were found by John Melhase, about a mile east of Frazier Corners, Shasta County, in the upper part of the Turonian. The holotype (C. A. S. Type Coll.) has the following dimensions: length, 54 mm; height of valve between the base and its upper border, 29 mm; thickness (convexity) of valve, about 13 mm. The stratigraphic position of the species is near the top of the Turonian, a little above the zone of *Oregoniceras oregonense* (Anderson), and beneath the base of the overlying Coniacian with *Phylloceras ramosum* Meek. The species is named in remembrance of the late John Melhase, a long-time geologist of the Southern Pacific Company in California.

Trigonia tryoniana Gabb

Trigonia tryoniana GABB, Paleont. Calif., vol. 1, 1864, p. 188, Pl. 25, fig. 176; Tuscan Springs, Tehama County. . . . PACKARD, Univ. Oregon Pub., vol. 1, no. 9, 1921, p. 19, Pl. 4; a reproduction of Gabb's holotype. . . . STEWART, Acad. Nat. Sci. Phila., Special Paper No. 3, 1930, p. 93–95; locality as given above.

As the stratigraphical (and chronological) station of each species of *Trigonia* constitutes a most important consideration, the following notes are offered.

The holotype (No. 11955) is in the collections of the Museum of Paleontology, University of California. Packard (1916, p. 147) reported the species as occurring in the *"Turritella* zone" of the strata exposed on the west flank of the Santa Ana Mountains, Orange County.

The holotype was found at Tuscan Springs, Tehama County, where it was associated with numerous pelecypods and gastropods characteristic of this limited horizon.

Of the 38 species appearing in Gabb's list (1864, p. 220-236) from Tuscan Springs some are Coniacian in age; many, including the less diagnostic species, also occur in the later (Campanian) beds of the Chico formation exposed on Chico Creek.

The precise age of the species, as determined by its associates cannot be younger than Santonian; its horizon lacks the Campanian cephalopods of the Chico formation (*Mortoniceras randalli* n. sp., of the group of *M. delawarense* Morton, and *M. campaniense* Grossouvre, *Hauericeras* sp., and the nostoceratids). It also is without any species of *Submortoniceras,* of the group of *S. woodsi* Spath, well represented in the Chico formation of Butte and Chico Creeks, and of Pentz, all referable to an early Campanian horizon.

Trigonia evansana Meek

Trigonia Evansana MEEK, Albany Inst., Trans., vol. 4, 1861, p. 42 (type not figured); Nanaimo, Vancouver Island.
Trigonia evansii (Meek), GABB (in part), Paleont. Calif., vol. 1, 1864, p. 189, (not Pl. 25, fig. 177); "Tuscan Springs," Tehama County. . . . (Not *Trigonia evansana* Meek, Gabb, Paleont. Calif., vol. 2, 1869, p. 247) . . . MEEK, U .S. Geol. and Geogr. Surv. Terr., Bull. vol. 2, No. 4, 1876, p. 369, Pl. 2, fig. 7 only, (not figs. 7a, 7b).
Trigonia evansana MEEK, PACKARD (in part), Univ. Oregon Pub., vol. 1, No. 9, 1921, p. 25, Pl. 9, fig. 6 only (not fig. 5, nor fig. 7), probably from Crooked River, Oregon. . . . ; STEWART, Acad. Nat. Sci. Phila., Special Pub., No. 3, 1930, p. 93; the holotype said to be represented by Meek's figure (1876, Pl. 2, fig. 7 only; not figs. 7a, 7b; probably from Crooked River, Oregon).

Various species of *Trigonia* have been figured and described under this name, resulting in much confusion, apparently beginning with Meek himself. Yet, as described, and especially as figured by Meek (1876, Pl. 2, fig. 7) his species is clearly recognizable. The dimensions are given as follows:

Length, 67.3 mm; height, about 47.2 mm; convexity, 38.2 mm; and bearing about 18 curving, and more or less distinctly beaded ribs.

The "corselet" (escutcheon) is comparatively narrow, tapering gradually to a narrow accuminate point at the posterior extremity; escutcheon bordered by a narrow, rounded longitudinal rib, rendered double by an impressed groove, and crossed obliquely by numerous slightly impressed lines; escutcheon traversed by a central ridge, along which the valves divide, each being ornamented, or bearing numerous transverse riblets; these are more or less oblique to the axis of division.

The holotype was found at Nanaimo, seemingly associated with *Canadoceras newberryanum* Meek, in beds that are referable to the lower part of the section, correlative with the lower part of the Coniacian in the Great Valley of California.

A closely related if not identical species occurs on Sucia Island; it is somewhat larger, more than 80 mm long; and corresponding other dimensions. Similar forms found in California are referable to the same species.

Trigonia inezana Packard

Trigonia inezana PACKARD, Univ. Oregon Pub., vol. 1, No. 9, 1921, p. 27, Pl. 8, figs. 1a, 1b; Pl. 9, fig. 1; Santa Ynez Mountains (not Pl. 10, fig. 1; Chico Creek, Butte County, California).

Trigonia inezana Packard, is clearly akin to *Trigonia evansana* Meek, but differs from it specifically in its critical measurements and their proportions, although apparently found in nearly correlative strata. The holotype of *T. inezana* Packard is in the Museum of Paleontology, University of California. Packard's excellent description and figures of the latter renders its comparison with Meek's species relatively simple, although neither writer directly stated the position of his species in the West Coast Upper Cretaceous. Stewart (1930, p. 94) has questioned the basis of the separation of *Trigonia inezana* Packard from *Trigonia evansana* Meek. These forms do not occur together, and critical measurements of the two do not support Stewart's suggestion as to their identity. It seems probable, however, that *T. inezana* Packard was mistaken by Gabb in many of his references to *T. evansana* Meek (= *T. evansi* Meek). In this view of the matter it may be recalled that both Gabb and Packard record the occurrence in the Chico formation of Chico Creek, of a *Trigonia* species, the former referring it to *T. evansana*, Meek, and the latter to *T. inezana* Packard. The form figured by Packard (1921, Pl. 10, fig. 1) as *Trigonia inezana*, cannot be shown by critical measurements to belong to either species, but more probably represents a distinct species, relatively shorter and broader than either. Specimens found by the writer on Chico Creek, a few hundred feet above the basement rocks, seem to confirm this view.

Trigonia hemphilli Anderson n. sp.
(Plate 52, figures 9, 9a, 9b)

Trigonia leana Gabb, var. *"whiteavesi"* PACKARD, Univ. Oregon Pub., vol. 1, no. 9, 1921, Pl. 5, fig. 4 only; Pescadero, San Mateo County, California (Not Pl. 6, fig. 2.)

The holotype of this species (no. 994, C. A. S. Type Coll.) is from the Hemphill Collection, now in the California Academy of Sciences. It is said to have been obtained from the Upper Cretaceous beds near Pescadero, California, at locality 12123 (C. A. S.). This example was figured by Packard (1921, Pl. 5, fig. 4) in the belief that it represented an undetermined species figured by Whiteaves (1884, Pl. 10, figs. 2, 2a) from Queen Charlotte Islands. A comparison of the holotype with the figure given by Whiteaves, shows many specific characters not possessed by *T. leana*, or by any other West Coast species previously described. Its resemblance to *T. leana* Gabb is chiefly in its general outline, not in its ornamentation.

The shell is large, robust, thick, and heavily costate in its forward portion, ribs tending to become shortened, and the tubercules to be reduced in number or to disappear entirely toward the rear; posterior part smooth, or showing only concentric lines of growth; beaks terminal, little elevated; ribs 10–12 in number, elevated, heavily beaded; escutcheon rather broad, also costate and beaded; ribs standing at right angles to dorsal border; hinge line straight, but curving downward at rear; umbonal ridge obscure, showing two hardly visible grooves, extending backward from beak; ligament prominent and thickened; forward end of shell rounded, broadly rounded base.

The species has been found at localities 27834 and 28175 (C. A. S.) in the Chico formation on Chico Creek, associated with many other species characteristic of this horizon, and also at Jalama Creek, Santa Barbara County, probably in beds of the same horizon.

The holotype 994 (C. A. S. Type Coll.) has the following dimensions: length (incomplete), 67 mm; height, 69 mm; total length of shell (estimated), 105 mm; convexity (both valves together), 48.5 mm. In all cases in which satisfactory information is at hand, its horizon is lower Campanian.

Trigonia churchi Anderson n. sp.
(Plate 17, figures 6, 7)

Shell large, moderately thick, subquadrate in outline, strongly ribbed, with 10–13 nearly straight, smooth, elevated ribs crossing the sides from the border of the escutcheon at an angle of about 80 degrees, becoming more elevated and curving forward near base of shell; escutcheon area deep, concave, ovate, broader in front, narrowing behind, upper surface crossed by 12–15 transverse, elevated ridges at nearly right angles to hinge line; beaks elevated, incurved, crossed by a few ribs descending obliquely to anterior margin of valve; posterior end broadly rounded, crossed by about 4 straight, elevated, smooth ribs which meet border at nearly right angles.

The holotype (C. A. S. Type Coll.), consists of a single right valve, of which the dimensions follow: length, about 80 mm; height from base to upper margin, 58 mm; apparent width of escutcheon, 38 mm; thickness of entire shell (est.), 54 mm. The holotype was found by C. C. Church and G. D. Hanna at locality 1788 (C. A. S.) in the Jalama Creek area, Santa Barbara County, a mile east of the mouth of Arroyo Escondido. Another example was found by J. C. May on the NW ¼ sec. 5, T. 5 N., R. 33 W., S.B.M. The holotype was found associated with *Trigonia hemphilli* n. sp., *Macrocallista cordata* Waring, *"Meretrix" major* (Packard), *Volutoderma magna* Packard, and other species. As all these species occur in the West Coast Campanian, we may assume that the present species represents the same horizon. The same, or a similar species was found at locality 28173 (C. A. S.) in the lower third of the strata exposed on Chico Creek, Butte County.

Trigonia oregona (Packard)

Trigonia evansana var. *oregona* PACKARD, Univ. Oregon Pub., vol. 1, No. 9, 1921, p. 26 Pl. 9, fig. 7; Crooked River, Wheeler County Oregon . . . STEWART, Acad. Nat. Sci. Phila., Special Pub., No. 3, 1930, p. 93.

In Packard's figure of *"Trigonia evansana* var. *oregona,"* both Packard and Stewart seem not to have compared it with Meek's figure, reproduced by the former on the same plate (Pl. 9, fig. 6); *Trigonia oregona* (Packard) has not the form of *T. evansana* Meek, as seen in its posterior portion. Concerning the former Packard gives the following account:

"Shell crescentic, elongate; anterior dorsal margin converging regularly to meet the even curve of the base; posterior dorsal margin concave, meeting the truncated attenuated posterior end; posterior area strongly differentiated from the median area of the shell by an ornamental dorsal area which is more conspicuous near the posterior end."

This description is sufficient to show that the present species cannot properly be referred to *T. evansana* Meek, as figured on the same plate; the two types show more contrast than resemblance, and should not be confused.

Trigonia bowersiana Anderson n. sp.
(Plate 26, figure 8)

This species may be related to *Trigonia evansana* Meek, which it resembles in size and form, though possessing features that distinguish it from all other Upper Cretaceous forms. The holotype is broader relative to its length, the concave curvature of its upper borders is deeper, the umbonal width of the shell is greater, and the external ornamentation of the shell differs much in showing traces of stronger vertical ribs on the anterior part of the valves and also traces of horizontal concentric ribs on the central posterior lower quarter of the shell. The escutcheon is not well exposed. The beaks are not terminal and are high, strongly incurved, and approximate. The holotype (C. A. S. Type Coll.) has the following dimensions: total length, 60 mm; maximum height, 50 mm; thickness of the valve, 35 mm. The holotype consists of a single valve, found by Stephen Bowers at locality 252 (C. A. S.), in the Santiago district, Orange County, on the south border of Silverado Canyon, where it was associated with other species of *Trigonia, Acteonella oviformis* var. *major,* and *Cucullaea (Idonearca) youngi* Waring and other types of Mollusca, commonly found in the lower portion of the Coniacian in the southern part of the state.

Trigonia wheelerensis Anderson n. sp.

Trigonia leana Gabb, PACKARD, Univ. Oregon Pub., vol. 1, No. 9, 1921 (in part), p. 20, Pl. 7, fig. 1; locality 92 (Univ. Oregon Coll.), Wheeler County, Oregon. (Not *Trigonia leana* Gabb).

The shell is large, and as shown in the figure and in the text given by Packard, it has some resemblance to *Trigonia leana* Gabb (1864), but differs from it in form and in outline, has not the same number of ribs, and these are differently placed and more heavily noded, with nodes more irregularly disposed on the sides of the shell, giving it a rougher appearance than that of *Trigonia leana* Gabb. Stewart (1930, p. 93) has regarded this species as related to *T. leana* Gabb.

Family PECTINIDAE Lamarck

Genus **Syncyclonema** Meek

Syncyclonema latum Anderson n. sp.

(Plate 2, figures 1, 2)

Shell compressed, thin and flat, nearly circular in outline, with a narrow, angular beak, the borders of the umbone meeting in an angle of about 70°; hinge line is short, straight, nearly at right angles to axis of umbone, ears a little unequal, anterior ear larger than the other, showing only a faint sinus, if any; surface marked chiefly by concentric growth lines, with only a faint radial sculpture near axis, seen more clearly in reflected light. The holotype (C. A. S. Type Coll.) has the following dimensions: height (incomplete), 45 mm; transverse diameter, 45 mm; thickness of both valves hardly exceeding 5 mm. Both the holotype and the paratype were found in the lower beds of the Upper Cretaceous, on the old Pioneer road, about 4 miles southwest of Phoenix, Oregon, where it was associated with *Beudanticeras alamoensis* n. sp., *Dipoloceras sp., Mantelliceras oregonense* n. sp., and many other species. The biological relations of the species to *Syncyclonema operculiformis* (Gabb) is not definitely known, although the latter is thought to have a stratigraphic range throughout the Horsetown "group" in the Shasta series, and to also occur in the lower beds of the upper Cretaceous. In size and form the two are quite unlike, the present species being larger, and probably confined to the lower part of the upper Cretaceous.

Syncyclonema operculiformis (Gabb)

Pecten operculiformis GABB, Paleont. Calif., vol. 1, 1864, p. 201, Pl. 26, fig. 188; Cottonwood and Hulen Creeks, and Curry Canyon. . . . vol. 2, 1869, p. 200, 251; locality as above. . . . STANTON, U. S. Geol. Survey, Bull. 133, 1895, p. 10, 18, 22, and 37; North fork of Cottonwood Creek, lower Horsetown group.
Syncyclonema operculiformis (Gabb), STEWART, Acad. Nat. Sci. Phila. Special Pub. No. 3, 1930, p. 120; locality not given. . . . ANDERSON, Geol. Soc. Am., Special Paper, No. 16, 1938, p. 109; Shasta, and lower "Chico Series."

Shell flatly lenticular, subcircular in outline below the auricles; interior of shell silky in texture, outwardly smooth or polished, but showing fine concentric growth lines; left valve with nearly equal auricles, right valve less well known. The "lectotype," as named by Stewart (1930), is in the Museum of Paleontology, University of California. It has the following dimensions: length, 22 mm; height, 26.5 mm; thickness, about 3 mm. According to Stewart, the umbonal angle of the holotype is 100°; if this angle is correctly regarded as a diagnostic feature of the species, there may be various species capable of recognition in the Shasta series, and in the basal beds of the Upper Cretaceous.

Genus **Pecten** Müller

Pecten traskii Gabb

Pecten Traskii GABB, Paleont. Calif., vol. 1, 1864, p. 200, Pl. 26, fig. 187, 187a; Texas Flat, Placer County.

According to Gabb, the shell is "compressed, elongate, outline of the lower half forming two-thirds of a circle; margins of the body, above the curve, rapidly converging and straight. Right valve, anterior auricle long, truncated at the end, deeply excavated below; posterior auricle broad and obliquely truncated. Surface marked by numerous, radiating, squamose ribs, with sometimes smaller intermediate ones; the interspaces are marked by oblique lines, producing, under a glass, a woven appearance."

Gabb remarks: "The species seems to be rare, as there are remains of but two valves in the collection."

The holotype of this species was probably lost in the San Francisco fire

Pecten (Propeamusium) cowperi Waring

Pecten (Propeamusium) cowperi WARING, Proc. Calif. Acad. Sci., 4th ser., vol. 7, 1917, p. 63, Pl. 7, figs. 1, 2; locality 2, (L. S. J. U.) near Santa Monica, California.

Waring gives a detailed description of this species, which reads in part as follows:

"The shell is small, subcircular, equivalve, equilateral, compressed, thin; upper valve, ears equal, moderately large; lower (right) valve, right ear long, deeply and narrowly emarginate; right valve with about nine large internal ribs, equally spaced, which are rounded and extend from the umbone nearly to the margin where they are abruptly truncated; external surface ornamented with many fine equally spaced concentric lines; upper valve with four to eight rather large rounded internal riblets which extend from the umbone nearly to the margins."

In addition to the concentric lines, the external surface is marked by many fine radial ribs, nearly obsolete near the anterior and posterior borders of the shell. Waring adds: "This species has also been found by the writer in the Chico shales of the Tesla sheet." This appears to be the Quinto shales, of the Moreno formation which are middle Maestrichtian.

The writer has collected the species also from the North fork of Cottonwood Creek, 1½ miles above Gas Point, Shasta County, from beds of the upper Turonian, where it is associated with *Prionotropis bakeri* Anderson, *Gaudryceras tenuiliratum* Yabe, and other diagnostic types of cephalopods, and species of corals, characteristic of the horizon.

The holotype from near Santa Monica, occurs there with species of *Metaplacenticeras* Spath, and *Hauericeras,* characteristic of the lower Senonian. It appears that this species ranges from upper Turonian strata to middle Maestrichtian.

Family ANATINIDAE Dall
Genus **Anatina** Lamarck
Anatina tryoniana Gabb

Anatina Tryoniana GABB, Paleont. Calif., vol. 1, 1864, p. 150, Pl. 29, fig. 240; Martinez, Contra Costa County, California. . . . vol. 2, 1869, p. 234; Martinez, as above. . . . WHITE-AVES, Meso. Foss., vol. 1, pt. 2, 1879, p. 140; Gabriola Island, near Vancouver Island, B. C., . . . ARNOLD, U. S. Nat. Museum, Proc., vol. 34, 1908, p. 374; Santa Cruz quadrangle, California. . . . ARNOLD, Santa Cruz Folio, No. 163, 1909, p. 3.
"Periplomya" tryoniana (Gabb), STEWART, Acad. Nat. Sci. Phila., Special Pub., No. 3, 1930, p. 298, Pl. 3, fig. 13; specimen figured as the lectotype cannot be considered authentic.

Unfortunately the figure given by Stewart for *"Periplomya" tryoniana* (Gabb) cannot be proved to be Gabb's holotype of *Anatina tryoniana,* since it has neither the outline, the form, nor the dimensions and proportions belonging to it; it is higher in relation to its length; its roundly inflated umbonal area, and its broad extremities exclude it from a claim to be the holotype. It may prove to be a *Periplomya,* as Stewart claims.

Anatina sulcatina (?) Shumard

Anatina sulcatina Shumard WHITEAVES, Meso. Foss., vol. 1, pt. 2, 1879, p. 139, Pl. 17, figs 5, 5a; Sucia Island; western Washington.
Anatina sulcatina Shumard ? WHITE, U. S. Geol. Survey, Bull. 51, 1889, p. 43, Pl. 6, fig. 1; Sucia Island.

White expressed doubt as to the propriety of referring this form to Schumard's species, which he states was never figured. Whiteaves (1879) admits defects in the record of the species. For these defects the species is not here regarded as wholly removed from doubt, though it may later be proved to occur on the West Coast.

Genus **Periplomya** Conrad
"**Periplomya**" whitneyi (Gabb)

Tellina (?*Sanguilolaria*) *Whitneyi* GABB, Paleont. Calif., vol. 1, 1864, p. 160, Pl. 30, fig.
    242; Jacksonville, Oregon. . . . vol. 2, 1869, p. 238; locality as above.
Periplomya ? *whitneyi* (Gabb), STEWART, Acad. Nat. Sci. Phila., Special Pub., No. 3, 1930,
    p. 299, Pl. 3, fig. 12; holotype figured, which for the most part is an internal cast of a right
    valve, with a rather prominent umbo.

There is little to add regarding the taxonomic position of this species. Its stratigraphic
place is indicated by its associated species to be within the Turonian. According to Stewart
the holotype has the following dimensions: length, 52 mm; height, 35 mm; thickness, about
4 mm.

"**Periplomya**" oregonensis (Gabb)

Siliqua oregonensis GABB, Paleont. Calif., vol. 1, 1864, p. 147, Pl. 29, fig. 237; near Toll
    House on the north side of the Siskiyou Mountains in southern Oregon. . . . vol. 2, 1869,
    p. 233; locality as above.
Periplomya ? *oregonensis* (GABB) STEWART, Acad. Nat. Sci. Phila., Special Pub., No. 3,
    1930, p. 300, Pl. 5, fig. 3 (the example figured by Stewart seems to be the holotype of the
    species, although his figure differs slightly from that of Gabb).

The locality of the holotype is well known to the writer, and forms a part of the belt
which skirts the Bear Creek Valley between the Siskiyou highway and Jacksonville. Numerous molluscan species have been collected here, including *Parapachydiscus ashlandicus* (Anderson), *Pugnellus manubriatus* Gabb, and various types of pelecypods characteristic of the
Turonian.

Family POROMYACIDAE Dall
Genus **Liopistha** Meek
Liopistha (s. s.) anaana (Anderson)
(Plate 15, figure 3)

Pholadomya anaana ANDERSON, Proc. Calif. Acad. Sci., 3rd ser., vol. 2, 1902, p. 72, Pl. 7,
    fig. 151; Santiago district, Orange County, (Coll. by H. W. Fairbanks).
Liopistha anaana, PACKARD, Univ. Calif. Pub. Bull. Dept. Geol., vol. 9, No. 12, 1916, p. 146;
    "*Actaeonina oviformis* zone," Santiago district, Orange County. . . . POPENOE, Jour.
    Paleont., vol. 11, 1937, p. 384, Pl. 46, figs. 1, 3; Baker member of the Ladd formation;
    abundant and characteristic. . . . POPENOE, Am. Ass. of Petrol. Geol., Bull., vol. 26, 1942,
    fig. 4; Baker Canyon; horizon as above; in sandstone.

As shown by Popenoe, this species is associated with *Trigonarca californica* Packard,
Syncyclonema operculiformis (Gabb), and other molluscan forms characteristic of the Turonian in northern California, and as found by the present writer, it occurs above the zone of
Oregoniceras knighteni (Anderson) and *O. siskiyouense* (Anderson) and of other prionotropids. The fauna occurring in the lower beds in the Santiago district, including the Baker
sandstone, should be regarded as middle Turonian in age, though some of the forms are
found at higher stages in northern California.

Subgenus **Psilomya** Meek
Liopistha (Psilomya) hardingensis (Packard)

Homomya hardingensis PACKARD, Univ. Calif. Pub., Bull. Dept. Geol. Sci., Vol. 13, No. 10,
    1922, p. 425, Pl. 32, figs. 1a, 1b; "Chico group," "*Actaeonella oviformis* zone," Santiago
    district, Orange County. Dimensions of the type: length, 100 mm; height, *ca.* 75 mm;
    breadth, 70 mm.
Liopistha (Psilomya) hardingensis (Packard), POPENOE, Jour. Paleont., vol. 11, No. 5,
    1937, p. 383, Pl. 45, fig. 8; Pl. 46, fig. 16; Baker member of the Ladd formation; Santiago
    district, Orange County. Turonian, rare.

This large species belongs to the group of *Liopistha superba* Stoliczka, from the Trichinopoly group of southern India, and of the Blackmore beds in the Upper Cretaceous in
England, but it differs from both. The hinge structure is not yet well known.

Family PLEUROPHORIDAE Dall (CYPRINIDAE Authors)
Genus **Trapezium** Megerle
Subgenus **Schedotrapezium** Stewart
Trapezium (Schedotrapezium) carinatum (Gabb)

Trapezium carinatum GABB, Paleont. Calif., vol. 1, 1864, p. 170, Pl. 23, fig. 150; Texas Flat, Placer County. . . . vol. 2, 1869, p. 241; Chico group, Texas Flat, etc.
Trapezium (Schedotrapezium) carinatum (Gabb), STEWART, Acad. Nat. Sci., Phila., Special Pub., No. 3, 1930, p. 174; locality as above.

Stewart appears to have re-discovered Gabb's holotype of this species at the Museum of Comparative Zoology, and it may perhaps be a part of the original collection made by Trask from this locality. According to Stewart (p. 175) it has the following dimensions: "length, 9.1 mm; height, 5.7 mm; breadth of right valve, 2 mm; no. 15030.

The external surface is not well preserved, though it still retains some of the more important features that permit its recognition. The chief part of the collection made by Trask at this locality was destroyed in the San Francisco fire, 1906, and the exact locality itself is no longer known. The locality and its fauna are best known from the records left by Whitney (1865, p. 202, 203), and by Gabb, in his accounts of the several species.

Genus **Veniella** Stoliczka
Veniella crassa Whiteaves

Veniella crassa WHITEAVES, Meso. Foss., vol. 1, pt. 2, 1879, p. 153, Pl. 18, fig. 1; Sucia Island (not frequent).

Neither this species, nor its genus, has yet been recognized in California. Its resemblance to certain forms of *"Crassatellites"* warrants the record here made of its occurrence in western Washington.

Genus **Cyprina** Lamarck (**Arctica** Schumacher)
"Cyprina" denmanensis Whiteaves
(Plate 47, figure 3)

Cyprina denmanensis WHITEAVES, Meso. Foss., vol. 1, pt. 5, 1903, p. 380; text-figure 25; west side of Denman Island, British Columbia.

Whiteaves has figured and described under the above name a single, imperfect right valve of a large pelecypod shell found on Denman Island, without giving further data. Its exact horizon is not known, nor has the author named any of its associates, if such are known, and only from its geographic position may one infer a lower Senonian horizon for it.

In the lower Senonian, on the west border of the Great Valley, a similar species has been found at two distinct localities at the same stratigraphic level.

At locality 1345 (C. A. S.), about 4 miles southwest of Winters, at the north end of Pleasants Valley, two large but imperfect examples of a pelecypod shell that appears to be referable to *"Cyprina"* denmanensis Whiteaves have been collected, associated with *Phylloceras ramosum* Meek, *Gaudryceras alamedense* (Smith), *Desmoceras selwynianum* (Whiteaves) and *Thyasira cretacea* Whiteaves.

Also at locality 1467 (C. A. S.) in the same zone, 7 miles northwest of Winters, Yolo County, similar pelecypod shells collected by McCoy and the writer are referable to *"Cyprina"* denmanensis Whiteaves. A little lower stratigraphically than the *"Cyprina,"* were collected *Phylloceras ramosum* Meek, *Desmoceras* sp., *Gaudryceras* sp., *Metaplacenticeras californicum* (Anderson), and *M. pacificum* (Smith).

In the examples of *"Cyprina"* denmanensis from locality 1345 (C. A. S.), the hinge is partly exposed, with the muscle scars and other features that seem to conform to those of the genus *Cyprina* Lamarck.

Specimen figured is imperfect, with the following dimensions: length, 97.8 mm; height (incomplete), 80.5 mm; convexity, both valves together, approximately 36.5 mm.

Genus Etea Conrad
Etea angulata (Packard)

Meretrix angulata PACKARD, Univ. Calif. Pub., Bull. Dept. Geol. Sci., vol. 13, no. 10, 1922, p. 425, Pl. 33, fig. 5.
Etea angulata (Packard), POPENOE, Jour. Paleont., vol. 11, no. 5, 1937, p. 385, Pl. 46, fig. 4.

Packard's original description reads, in part, as follows:

"Shell medium sized; inequilateral; posterior dorsal slope nearly straight; anterior end evenly rounded; posterior extremity truncated; base broadly rounded. Umbones tumid, with blunt beaks. Anterior dorsal margin slightly excavated underneath the beak; lunule ill-defined; a prominent ridge extends from the beak to the posterior ventral margin; inner margin smooth, hinge showing, imperfectly, three cardinals and two laterals. Length of type, 59 mm; height, about 45 mm; convexity, 15 mm."

HORIZON: *Turritella pescaderoensis* zone, Santiago district, Orange County.

It is not readily seen how the figure given by Popenoe of the hinge features of the species harmonize with the statement by Packard (p. 425) of the hinge "showing three cardinals and two laterals," though probably this is explainable.

The horizon of the species, as shown by Popenoe (1942, fig. 4), is largely confined to the lower part of the Holz shale, (*"Turritella chicoensis* Division").

Family ASTARTIDAE d'Orbigny (emend. Dall)

According to Dall (*in* Zittel, 1913), few representatives of this family are found in the West Coast Upper Cretaceous. Most of the species formerly assigned to the genus *Astarte* have been otherwise placed, chiefly in Crassatellidae, leaving but few types under Astartidae, including *Astarte* Sowerby, *Opis* Defrance, *Opisoma* Stoliczka, and *Eriphyla* Gabb. Stewart (1930), in reviewing Gabb's California types, found no species assignable to *Astarte* itself, and placed the two species so named by Gabb in the genus *Crassatella*. However, other species have since been described and assigned to *Astarte*.

Packard (1922) described three forms placed by him under *Astarte,* two of which have been regarded by Popenoe (1937) as being better assigned to *Eriphyla* Gabb. The following two species accordingly have been here placed in the genus *Astarte,* since both seem to have the essential features of this genus and have not been questioned.

Genus Astarte Sowerby
Astarte carlottensis Whiteaves

Astarte packardi WHITE, U. S. Geol. Survey, Contrib. Paleont., Nos. 2–3, 1860, p. 149, Pl. 37, figs. 6a, 6b; . . . WHITEAVES, Meso. Foss., vol. 1, pt. 3, 1880, p. 229, Pl. 30, figs. 6, 6a, 6b; East side of Alliford Bay. Upper Cretaceous.
Astarte carlottensis WHITEAVES, Meso. Foss., vol. 1, pt. 4, 1900, p. 292, Pl. 30, figs. 6, 6a, 6b.

Locality as given above.

From the figures and the description of this species, its outward form, ornamentation, and hinge elements, conform to the requirements of this genus, and no basis for questioning its assignment is apparent.

Astarte (?) earllergyi Anderson, n. name

Astarte sulcatus PACKARD (Not of FLEMING, 1826, nor of ROEMER, 1836), Univ. Calif. Pub. Bull. Dept. Geol. Sci., vol. 13, 1922, p. 424, Pl. 33, fig. 6; *Acteonella oviformis* zone, Santiago district, Orange County. . . . POPENOE, Jour. Paleont., vol. 11, 1937, p. 386, Pl. 46, figs. 5–8; Baker member of the Ladd formation; . . . Am. Ass. Petrol. Geol., Bull., vol. 26, 1942, fig. 4; listed as occurring in the *Trigonarca californica* zone, Santiago district, Orange County. Turonian.

Popenoe states (1937, p. 386) that:

"The genus *Astarte* (s. l.) has been divided into many sections and subgenera, of which distinctions are both confused and confusing. The subdivision of the genus to which *Astarte sulcatus* is to be referred is yet uncertain."

It is certain, however, that it belongs in that portion of the Santiago sequence that may properly be referred to the middle Turonian, as found in the northern part of the Great Valley and farther north in Oregon.

Genus **Opis** Defrance
Opis triangulata (Cooper)

Corbula triangulata COOPER, Calif. State Min. Bur., Bull. No. 4, 1894, p. 49, Pl. 4, fig. 42; Upper Cretaceous, Point Loma, California.
Opis triangulata (Cooper), STANTON, U. S. Geol. Survey, Bull. 133, 1895, p. 59; Point Loma, near San Diego, California.

Cooper's description of this species reads, in part, as follows:

"Shell doubly trigonal, higher than long, with four nearly equal triangular surfaces, valves equal, the disks being nearly right angled triangles, higher than wide; the beaks prominent, acute; anterior margin slightly incurved; posterior straight, more acutely ridged laterally; surface crossed by about thirty undulations parallel to lines of growth.—Anterior face of shell triangular-cordate, slightly concave."

Length of base, 0.30 inch (= 7.6 mm); anterior height, 0.30 inch (= 7.6 mm); posterior, 0.40 inch (= 10.16 mm).

Stanton, who later examined the holotype states that:

"Under the name *Corbula triangulata* Cooper has recently described an *Opis* from the Chico beds on Point Loma, near San Diego, California."

The holotype No. 624 (C. A. S. Type Coll.) agrees with Cooper's description, and with Stanton's determination. Its horizon is the lower part of the Gualala group of White, and is correctly assignable to the Maestrichtian.

Opis rosarioensis Anderson and Hanna

Opis rosarioensis ANDERSON AND HANNA, Proc. Calif. Acad. Sci., 4th ser., vol. 23, 1935, p. 31; Pl. 10, figs. 2, 3; collected by Barrera and Santillan, near Rosario Landing, Lower California.

The description given by its authors reads, in part, as follows:
"Shell subtriangular, broadly rounded at the base, straight on the anterior border, rounded behind; umbones strongly incurved; lunule deep, ovate in outline, bordered within by an impressed marginal groove, bordered without by a slightly broader, almost smooth area surrounded by a thin raised lamella; holotype (broken on lower margin) measuring 58 mm in length; 66 mm in height; depth of single valve, 25.4 mm; lunule 23 mm in height; . . . dentition not shown."

The holotype (Univ. Calif. Coll.) is from locality A-426, near Rosario. Its horizon is apparently Maestrichtian, as indicated by the occurrence of *Parapachydiscus* sp. in the same beds a few miles farther north, near San Antonio del Mar.

Genus **Opisoma** Stoliczka
Opisoma pacifica Anderson n. sp.
(Plate 26, figures 5, 6)

In size, thickness of test, form and outline, and in other external features, this species greatly resembles and appears to be closely related to *Opisoma geinitziana*, figured and described by Stoliczka (1871), from the Ootatoor group of southern India (p. 288, Pl. 10, figs. 11, 11a, 11b). Stoliczka illustrated only a right valve, probably a mature example, showing its side, front and interior details, but not those of the left valve. The present species is a much later form from the Maestrichtian in the Great Valley, thus far found only in the Pacheco Pass quadrangle. It is represented by no less than six right, and nine left valves, some of which are larger than the figured type. In outward aspects the species varies considerably in size, surface markings, and the ratio of length to height.

In the interior features of the shell, the species departs farther from the Indian type, having in part more prominent but shorter teeth, of very unequal size and length; in the right valve, the anterior tooth is shorter and much more prominent than in the Indian type, and more prominent and longer than the posterior in the same valve, the latter being only one-third the length of the former, and it rises to only half the height of the anterior tooth. In the left valve the teeth are also of unequal size, though their respective length and prominence are reversed; the posterior tooth greatly exceeds the anterior in length and prominence.

The holotype (C. A. S. Type Coll.), a left valve, has the following dimensions: maximum length, 48 mm; height, 66 mm; thickness (convexity) of valve, 28 mm; other examples vary greatly from these measures, due to age and other circumstances.

The stratigraphic position of the several examples is essentially the same, all occurring in the lower beds of the Moreno formation, which in neighboring areas is characterized by species of *Parapachydiscus* and *Nostoceras,* and by numerous gastropods and pelecypods. The holotype and most of the other examples were found by Bennison, half a mile south of Mustang Creek, at locality 29118 (C. A. S.), on the S½ sec. 33, T. 8 S., R. 8 E., M. D. M. Other examples were found in the same zone south of Garzas Creek, associated with *Glycymeris banosensis* n. sp., in the zone of *Parapachydiscus coalingensis* n. sp.

Opisoma vancouverensis (Whiteaves)

Opis vancouverensis WHITEAVES, Meso. Foss., vol. 1, pt. 2, 1879, p. 158, Pl. 18, figs. 4, 4a; southwest side of Denman Island; Division B. . . . vol. 1, pt. 5, p. 385; reports the imperfect condition of the material known concerning the species.

Whiteaves originally described a right valve, which in size, general form, ornamentation, and all external features seemed to conform to the genus *Opisoma* Stoliczka, rather than to *Opis* Defrance, although the hinge features as illustrated by him vary somewhat from those of the genotype, *Opisoma geinitziana,* as illustrated by Stoliczka, and from those of the form described from Los Banos Creek. However, in form, size, and outward aspects, his figure (Pl. 18) resembles *Opisoma geinitziana* described by Stoliczka from southern India.

The locality is on the southwest side of Denman Island, which contained "*Cyprina*" *denmanensis* Whiteaves and a few other forms. The evidence as to its precise horizon is not yet clear, although it has been assigned to Division B, of the Nanaimo section, which may be tentatively correlated with the lower part of the Senonian in California.

Genus **Eriphyla** Gabb

Gabb (1864, p. 180) characterized this genus as follows:

"Shell subtrigonal, surface of valves concentrically ribbed or striated. Hinge composed of two primary teeth in the right valve, and one in the left, and an anterior and posterior lateral tooth in each valve. Ligament external; lunule deep. . . . This shell is closely allied to *Astarte* and *Gouldia,* but differs from both in the presence of a well-marked posterior tooth in each valve. On the left valve there is a rudiment of a second cardinal tooth, which enters a depression in the opposite side, behind the large, posterior, cardinal tooth of that valve."

Genotype, **Eriphyla umbonata** Gabb

Eriphyla umbonata GABB, Paleont. Calif., vol. 1, 1864, p. 180, Pl. 24, figs. 62, 62a; Cow Creek, Shasta County, and Curry's, south side of Mount Diablo. . . . vol. 2, 1869, p. 244; locality as above.

This species is the only member of the genus described by Gabb, and its characterization is essentially that given above, to which Gabb adds the following:

"Lunule profound, subcordate. Internal margin with a minute rim or thickening running parallel with the edge. Surface ornamented with numerous regular, concentric ribs, which in some specimens become obsolete on the middle of the shell."

This species is common in the Turonian of northern California, whence came the type of the species. Popenoe (1937, p. 387) reports the species, with some doubt, as occurring on Clover Creek.

Whiteaves (1879, p. 151) reported the occurrence of this species on the Nanaimo River and at Sucia Island, in "Division A," which by their faunas, containing *Canadoceras newberryanum* (Meek), *"Hamites" obstrictum* Jimbo, *"Desmoceras" selwynianum* Whiteaves, and *Inoceramus* aff. *I. undulato-plicatus* Roemer, can hardly be older than lower Senonian.

Eriphyla ovoides (Packard)

Astarte ovoides PACKARD, Univ. Calif. Publ. Bull. Dept. Geol. Sci., vol. 13, 1922, p. 424, Pl. 30, fig. 1; locality 2157 (Univ. Calif.); Santiago Canyon, Corona Sheet "stream bed just above Williams Canyon."
Eriphyla ovoides (Packard), POPENOE, Jour. Paleont., vol. 11, 1937, p. 386, Pl. 46, figs. 9, 10; definition extended.

The description of the species given by Packard reads (in part) as follows:

"Shell nearly circular in outline, slightly inequilateral; quite tumid at a point about one-third the distance from the beak to the ventral margin; anterior dorsal slope slightly concave, but rapidly becoming convex and changing into an evenly rounded anterior extremity; base regularly rounded, forming with the anterior end an arc of a circle whose diameter is but slightly greater than the height of the shell; . . . Umbones very prominent; beaks sharply pointed, situated anteriorly. Lunule present, but imperfectly preserved," etc.

Popenoe adds the following to the original description:

"Dentition consists of two cardinal teeth in each valve, and of a posterior lateral tooth in the right valve and a corresponding posterior lateral socket in the left valve; right posterior cardinal heavy, oblique, trigonal." etc. "Distribution: Ladd formation, Baker member *rare,* Holz shale member, *rare."*

This position in the sequence in the Santiago district is shown by Popenoe in his later work (1942, Fig. 4), wherein it appears that the stratigraphic position of the species is referable to the Turonian.

Eriphyla lapidis (Packard)

Astarte lapidis PACKARD, Univ. Calif. Publ. Bull. Dept. Geol. Sci., vol. 13, 1922, p. 423, Pl. 30, figs. 4a, 4b; locality 2135 (Univ. Calif. Coll.), Santiago district, a quarter mile N., 15° E. of B. M. 1271, Corona Sheet, Santiago Canyon.
Eriphyla lapidis (Packard), POPENOE, Jour. Paleont., vol. 11, 1937, p. 387, Pl. 46, figs. 11, 12; description extended, and distribution discussed, with its relation to other species of the genus.

The description of the species given by Packard (in part) follows:

"Shell small, nearly circular in outline, slightly inequilateral; rather tumid. Anterior dorsal margin concave, set off by an ill-defined lunule; anterior end and base rounded, forming nearly a segment of a circle; posterior dorsal margin convex, meeting the even curve of the base and the posterior end at a point about halfway to the ventral margin." etc.

Popenoe adds the following:

"Distribution: Ladd formation, Holz shale member, *common."*
"Hinges of both valves of the species have been revealed and agree fully with Gabb's diagnosis of *Eriphyla."*

The position of the species in the stratigraphic column of the Santiago district is shown by Popenoe (1942, Fig. 4), in which it appears in the lower part of the Holz shale, referable to the lower Senonian.

Family CAPRINIDAE d'Orbigny
Genus **Lithocalamus** Lupher and Packard

Lithocalamus colonicus LUPHER AND PACKARD, Univ. Oregon Publ. Geol., vol. 1, 1930, p. 206, Pl. 4, figs. 2, 3; Pl. 5, fig. 6; textfigure, p. 210; "Forty-nine" mine, near Phoenix, Oregon.

Lower (attached) valve elongated, tapering at about 12.5 per cent per unit of length in upper portion, and at 30 per cent in lower; the lower valves of many individuals grow together and partially coalesce throughout their lengths; in cross-section the individual valves are variable, piriform, ovate, or sub-elliptical; inner cavity more regular. Shell thick at ends of ellipse, but thinner on the sides. Walls of "body cavity" bear fine striations as well as heavier longitudinal riblets.

According to the authors of the genus and species:

"A microscopic study of the polished sections of the lower valve shows the shell substance to be composed of a mass of thin-walled, parallel canals extending from the apex to the lip" . . . "These canals are quite variable in size, shape, and arrangement. In some areas they are of a uniform size, while in others small canals fill in the interspaces between the larger ones. The predominating shapes are pentagonal, hexagonal, or circular, but they may be occasionally quadrilateral or even trigonal," etc.

The genus is placed in Caprinidae because of its dentition and shell structure, and because it is apparently related to *Coralliochama* White. It is stated that:

"*Lithocalamus* differs from *Coralliochama* in several important respects; it has no ligamental grooves, nor porcelaneous inner layer, and the hinge bears in the upper valve two large closely set teeth and a smaller one in the lower valve."

LOCALITY: . . . Univ. Oregon locality 67, . . . the "Forty-nine" mine, near Phoenix, Oregon. Little more is known at present regarding the exact chronological position of the species, although it occurs within the lower part of the upper Cretaceous series. The species appears to have been a near-beach dweller, since at all points where it has been found it is associated with partially rounded and fragmentary beach shells of various types and with rolled pebbles. The shell itself readily breaks up by beach action, forming prismatic fragments, or even single small prisms, which are easily recognized as such. Larger and smaller fragments of shells resembling those of the lower valve have been found at many points in the lowest beds of the upper Cretaceous, as at the Shutte ranch, at the head of an east branch of Coleman Creek, southwest of Phoenix, Oregon.

Genus Coralliochama White
Coralliochama orcutti White

Coralliochama Orcutti WHITE, U. S. Geol. Survey, Bull. 22, 1885, p. 10–12; Todos Santos Bay, Lower California.

This species has been sufficiently described and illustrated by White, and needs no further characterization, although its geographical occurrence and stratigraphical position in the upper Cretaceous have now become better known than when it was first described. It had been reported as occurring in the lower beds of the upper Cretaceous in Shasta County, on the west side of the Sacramento Valley, and in other places on its northern border, but later investigations have proved this to be in error. In all cases in which adequate material from these areas has been obtained for determination, it has proved to be remains of rudistids other than *Coralliochama*.

On the peninsula of Lower California, *Coralliochama* has been found as far south as San Antonia del Mar (Johnson's ranch) and at many places farther north. Darton (1921) has reported it at Arroyo Hondo, 15 miles north of Rosario, and its type locality is on the south shore of Todos Santos Bay, where White obtained his original material. It has been collected at Point Loma near San Diego and at La Jolla by Fairbanks, and farther north. It was later found by Hanna, Church, and Gilbert, on Jalama Creek, on the south flank of the Santa Ynez Range, not far east of Point Concepcion, and more recently by Taliaferro, B. L. Clark and Schenck, at locality A-3435 (Univ. Calif.), near the north border of the San Martin quadrangle, associated with *Opis vancouverensis* Whiteaves.

White (1885b) reported the occurrence of the species near Gualala, and the writer has since found it there associated with species of *Inoceramus* and various gastropods. It has been found farther north by other collectors.

The chronological position of this species should be regarded as Maestrichtian, rather than earlier; there is abundant proof of this at and near its type locality. The species has not yet been recorded from the Great Valley trough, although many of its associated species in its coastal areas have been found in strata of the same age on the west border of the trough in the Moreno formation. More particularly, as may be seen in its character and proved habitats, the species lived in rough water in the littoral areas of the sea, rather than in enclosed basins.

Family RADIOLITIDAE Gray (emend.)

Many fragmentary remains of rudistids resembling radiolitids occur in the Cottonwood district of western Shasta County and farther south on the west border of the Sacramento Valley. Near the mouth of Hulen Creek they have been found in the lowest beds of the Upper Cretaceous series, namely, in the first and second conglomerates, as well as farther south in Tehama, Glenn, Colusa, and Yolo counties, and farther north in southern Oregon. They have their beginning in the lowest beds of the Cenomanian formation. None have yet been recorded from the underlying beds of the Shasta series in any part of the West Coast, but they appear to have entered the Great Valley trough, as did other genera, with the submergence that followed the interval of uplift closing the Horsetown epoch. These rudistid remains illustrate the faunal changes that took place in the Cretaceous history of the West Coast.

These fragments vary greatly in size, from roughly conical pieces of fist size to small bits, or elongated prisms 1 mm. in diameter. In form and structure of shell, and in their associates, these fragments are so characteristic that they indicate the lower beds of the series where other types of invertebrates are lacking.

Numerous types of rudistids are known in the Upper Cretaceous of north Andean countries, as shown by Gerth (1928) and by other writers, and in southern Mexico, as described by Palmer (1928). Palmer has described and illustrated forms of *Radiolites* (p. 74–84), but they do not possess the characters apparent in the fragmentary remains in the deposits of California and Oregon. Without claiming special knowledge of this interesting group of invertebrates, it appears to the writer that none of the genera described and illustrated from the northern California area conform to the types of rudistids found abundantly in southern Mexico, as described by Palmer.

The California types, resemble the genus *Durania,* or possibly *Sauvegesia,* described by Pervinquiere (1912), probably the former. Various types of rudistids have been described or are known from southern Oregon, but it is by no means certain that they represent only a single genus, either in Oregon or California. In the examples found in California, the internal cavities, the structure of the shell, and the fluted form of the exterior resemble those of *Durania,* as illustrated by Toucas and by Pervinquiere.

Genus **Durania** H. Douville
Durania ? californica Anderson n. sp.
(Plate 1, figures 1, 2)

A complete characterization of this species cannot be given for lack of sufficiently well preserved specimens. The lower valve, which was evidently attached, was erect, conical in form, expanding rapidly with growth; section subcircular, walls thick, composed of irregular hexagonal prisms or prismatic columns, surrounded by membranous sheaths; outer side of walls apparently ribbed, similar to *Radiolites;* ribs narrow, separated by narrower impressed grooves, forming a fluted exterior surface on the lower valve. Only fragmentary examples have been found of the opercular valve; these are relatively small and show only faintly the ribbing seen on the lower valve; the surface of the ribs are striated; valve composed of crowded prismatic columns, covering toward the narrow base of the valve. The species appears to be related to *Durania pervinquieri* Toucas, from the lower Cenomanian beds of Mrhila, North Africa.

The holotype (C. A. S. Type Coll.) [Pl. 1, fig. 1] has the following dimensions: length (incomplete), 110 mm; breadth at top, 75 mm; from locality 1346 (C. A. S.), mouth of Hulen Creek, Shasta County. The interior of the lower valve is usually narrow and tubelike, rarely more than a fourth the diameter of the valve itself, and is filled with sediment. The species has been found in the basal bed of the upper Cretaceous, and in the second conglomerate bed 450 feet above the base, on the North fork of Cottonwood Creek, associated with *Pervinquieria gainsana* n. sp., *Beudanticeras alamoense* n. sp., and (?) *Turrilites* sp. and other types of mollusks indicative of Albian strata.

Similar rudistid fragments, some of them egg-sized or larger, have been found in the lowest beds of the upper Cretaceous in the Coleman Creek district, on the south border of the Bear Creek Valley in southern Oregon, south of Medford, in beds that contain *Beudanticeras* and *Diplomoceras,* and at other places, a species of *Brancoceras.*

Family CRASSATELLIDAE

Stewart (1930, p. 134–140) has reviewed with much care and insight the several members of this family known in California. Few of these are found in the Upper Cretaceous.

Genus Crassatella Lamarck
Crassatella conradiana (Gabb)

Astarte conradiana GABB, Paleont. Calif., vol. 1, 1864, p. 178, Pl. 24, fig. 161; Texas Flat,
   Placer County, northwest of Folsom. . . . vol. 2, 1869, p. 244; locality as given above. . . .
   not WHITEAVES, Meso. Foss., vol. 1, pt. 2, 1879, p. 160, Pl. 18, figs. 5, 5a; Sucia Islands;
   . . . not *Crassatella conradiana* (Gabb) WHITEAVES, Meso. Foss., vol. 1, pt. 5, 1903, p. 384;
   Sucia Islands. Not *Crassatellites conradianus* (Gabb), WARING, Proc. Calif. Acad. Sci.,
   4th ser., vol. 7, 1917, p. 56, Pl. 7, figs. 3, 4; near Santa Monica.
Crassatella conradiana (Gabb) STEWART, Acad. Nat. Sci. Phila., Special Pub., No. 3, 1930,
   p. 145, Pl. 5, fig. 4; provisionally designated as the neotype; Texas Flat, Placer County.

The material upon which the original figure and description were based was taken from a shaft, at a depth of 40 feet (Whitney, 1865, p. 202, 203). This material was deposited in the California Academy of Sciences, where it remained until 1906, when it was destroyed in the San Francisco fire.

The site of the old shaft has become lost, and although there are certain accessible outcrops in the district, it is unlikely that a search would supply a specimen any more satisfactory than that figured by Stewart (Pl. 5, fig. 4).

This figure is of a right valve, and presumably from it Stewart obtained the hinge character shown by him (Pl. 17, fig. 2). Gabb's figure (1864, Pl. 24, fig. 161) is natural size, and measures: length, 27 mm; maximum height, 19 mm; and is said to be 'compressed.' Stewart's "Neotype" has a length (almost complete) of 15.5 mm; a height of 11.4 mm; and a thickness (of right valve) of 3 mm. The dimensional proportions are, therefore, nearly those of Gabb's type, and accordingly may be accepted, as proposed by Stewart, as a neotype of the species.

Crassatella tuscana (Gabb)

Astarte tuscana GABB, Paleont. Calif., vol. 1, 1864, p. 179, Pl. 30, fig. 257; "Division A";
   Tuscan Springs, Tehama County. Not Pentz, Butte County. . . . vol. 2, 1869, p. 244;
   locality as above. Merriam, holotype recognized in the Museum of Paleontology, University of California, and included in a list of type specimens (1895).
Crassatella tuscana (Gabb), WHITE, U. S. Geol. Survey, Bull. No. 51, 1889, p. 39, not Pl. 6,
   figs. 2, 3, 4; Sucia and Waldron Islands, western Washington. The species is regarded as
   possibly synonomous with *Crassatella conradiana* (Gabb). . . . not *Astarte conradiana,* var.
   tuscana, WHITEAVES, Meso. Foss., vol. 1, pt. 2, 1879, p. 160, Pl. 18, fig. 6; Sucia Island
   and Vancouver Island, B. C. Not *Crassatella conradiana* var. *tuscana,* WHITEAVES, Meso.
   Foss., vol. 1, pt. 5, 1903, p. 384; Vancouver Island, etc. . . . Not *Crassatellites tuscana*
   (Gabb), WARING, Proc. Calif. Acad. Sci., 4th ser., vol. 7, 1917, p. 59, Pl. 8, fig. 4; locality
   2 (L. S. J. U.); Bell Canyon, Los Angeles County. . . .
"Astarte" tuscana Gabb, STEWART, Acad. Nat. Sci., Phila., Special Pub. No. 3, 1930, p. 145;
   states that "it is practically certain that the holotype of *Crassatella tuscana* is from Penz"
   (Pentz).

Gabb (1864, p. 179, 233, and 1869, p. 244), and Whitney (1865, p. 207) give its source as Tuscan Springs (Tehama County), and since these writers had the best opportunity to know the facts, their statement should be accepted as final.

The locality at Pentz, from which many molluscan species have been collected, and described, is undoubtedly equivalent to some part of the exposures on Chico Creek a few miles to the north. Its horizon is lower Campanian, and therefore much above that of Tuscan Springs, which is probably not higher than Santonian, though it could be lower. Gabb (1864, p. 179) states that:

"Two specimens in the collection of the Survey, from Chico Creek, resemble this species in most of the essential characters, except they are twice as large, are more robust, wider from beak to base, and slightly excavated on the anterior end, immediately under the beaks. They are also proportionally narrower posteriorly, than the present species, and may prove to be distinct; . . . ."

The localities at Pentz and on Chico Creek are included in the Chico formation, and as shown by their cephalopod faunas are distinct from that of Tuscan Springs.

Crassatella lomana Cooper (?)

Crassatella lomana COOPER, Calif. State Min. Bur., Bull. No. 4, 1894, p. 48, Pl. 3, fig. 47; Point Loma, "Division A." (Maestrichtian).
Crassatellites lomana (Cooper) PACKARD, Univ. Calif. Pub. Bull. Dept. Geol., vol. 9, 1916, p. 146; zone of *Turritella pescaderoensis,* Santiago district, Orange County.
Crassatella lomana Cooper, POPENOE, Jour. Paleont., vol. 11, 1937, p. 387; "Holz shale member of the Ladd formation"; Pl. 47, figs. 2, 3, showing hinge character of left and right valves. . . . POPENOE, Am. Assoc. Petrol. Geol., Bull. vol. 26, 1942, Fig. 4; locality as given above.

This species was collected by the writer at locality 252 (C. A. S.) on the south side of the valley of Silverado Creek, associated with *Turritella pescaderoensis* Arnold. *Crassatella lomana* Cooper, first found and described from Point Loma, and from the Gualala group of White, is above recorded from the Santiago district, Orange County.

If this species really had survived unchanged from early Senonian to Maestrichtian time, it would be one of the rare species to endure so long, but possibly it could do so in southern California. A comparison of specimens from Point Loma now in the Academy, with those from locality 252, Silverado Creek, noted above, show appreciable differences in form and ornamentation that could warrant divergent views as to their specific identity. The figures here given of a representative form from locality 252 (C. A. S.) may be compared with that given by Cooper (Pl. 3, fig. 47). The internal features of the type from Point Loma are still unknown.

Crassatella gamma Popenoe

Crassatella gamma POPENOE, Jour. Paleont., vol. 11, 1937, p. 288, Pl. 46, figs. 13-15; Pl. 47, fig. 1; Baker and Holz shale members of the Ladd formation; Santiago district, Orange County. . . . POPENOE, Am. Assoc. Petrol. Geol., Bull., vol. 26, 1942, Fig. 4; Turonian. (Holotype in the collection of Calif. Inst. Tech.)

This species closely resembles *Crassatella tuscana* (Gabb) in size, form, and ornamentation, showing only individual differences. The horizon differs, as given by the respective authors. Popenoe gives a detailed account, and an illustration of the hinge character of his paratype (Pl. 46, fig. 15), assigning the species to the Baker and Holz shale members, probably Turonian.

Crassatella tuscana (Gabb) is regarded as Santonian. From the viewpoint of stratigraphic and geologic history, it appears unlikely that the two types are closely related.

Crassatella? elongata Anderson n. sp.

Crassatellites tuscanus (Gabb), WARING, Proc. Calif. Acad. Sci., 4th ser., vol 7, 1917, p. 59, Pl. 8, fig. 4; not *Astarte tuscana* Gabb, Paleont. Calif. vol. 1, 1864, p. 179, Pl. 30, fig. 257. Not *Astarte conradiana* var. *tuscana* (Gabb), Whiteaves, Meso. Foss., vol. 1, pt. 2, 1879,

p. 160, Pl. 18, fig. 6; Northwest Bay, Vancouver Island. Not *Crassatella tuscana* (Gabb) Stewart, Acad. Nat. Sci. Phila., Special Pub., No. 3, 1930, p. 145 (an undescribed form).

The holotype of the present species was found by Waring at locality 2 (L. S. J. U.), in Bell Canyon, Los Angeles County, west of San Fernando Valley. The species was described by Waring as follows:

"Shell moderate in size, elongate; umbone inconspicuous and anterior; cardinal margin slightly convex and sloping gradually toward the posterior, which is broadly rounded; anterior margin truncated and rounded and basal margin broadly convex; surface ornamented by irregular fine to coarse lines of growth, and where worn, by fine radial lines; beaks excavated both posteriorly and anteriorly."

On page 108, opposite Plate 8, Waring gives dimensions of the holotype as follows: "Long. 43 mm; alt. 29 mm." By measurements the holotype has the height of about 22 mm; and a length of 42 mm, and accordingly has neither the form, dimensions nor proportions of *Crassatella tuscana* (Gabb), and is referable to a higher horizon, as shown by its associated species.

Crassatella triangulatus (Waring)

Crassatellites triangulatus WARING, Proc. Calif. Acad. Sci., 4th ser., vol. 7, 1917, p. 56, 59, Pl. 9, fig. 1; locality 3 (L. S. J. U.), near Santa Monica, Los Angeles County.

This species is included in a list of Upper Cretaceous fossils (p. 56, 57), and described by Waring (p. 59) from the area immediately north of Santa Monica, which according to the list, contains three species of *Metaplacenticeras* (Spath), which in other areas in California and Oregon characterizes the Coniacian. The species has not yet been found by other collectors, or if so, it has been unrecognized by them. Its hinge features have not been described.

Crassatella mercedensis Anderson n. sp.
(Plate 72, figure 9)

Shell large, thick and brittle, and usually firmly cemented in matrix; it is subtriangular in outline, having a nearly straight base, roundly upturned in front, but at the rear meeting the posterior dorsal slope at a subacute angle; surface marked by numerous concentric growth lines at slightly irregular intervals; beneath outer layer of shell appear radial lines, arising near beak and crossing sides; lunule small, pointed below, slightly rounded above; escutcheon long, and well defined; hinge plate heavy, right valve having a strong, rounded, or pear-shaped tooth, behind which is a triangular pit; anterior and posterior muscle scars, subcircular and impressed.

The holotype (C. A. S. Type Coll.) was collected by Taff, Hanna, and Cross at locality 29117 (C. A. S. = 28310) on the north bank of Los Banos Creek, on the NE ¼ of sec. 12, T. 11 S., R. 9 E., M. D. B., and M. It has the following dimensions: length, 80 mm; height, 60 mm; thickness of right valve, 16 mm. It was found associated with *Glycymeris banosensis* n. sp., and *Pseudogaleodea bennisoni*[4] n. sp., and other species The locality and its fauna were included in the belt mapped as Moreno on the geologic sheet of Bull. 603 (U. S. Geol. Survey). The chronological position is regarded as lower Maestrichtian.

Genus Anthonyia Gabb

Gabb only briefly characterized the genus, believing it to be allied to *Megalodon* Sowerby, and to *Opis* Defrance, and accordingly placed it in the family Crassatellidae. Stewart (1930, p. 147) referred it to the family Gouldiidae. The shell, as represented by its genotype, *Anthonyia cultriformis* Gabb, is very inequilateral, long and narrow, with beaks almost

---

[4] Shell large; sculptured with six rugose, slightly nodose, spiral ridges which are crossed by thickened axial lines of growth. Length (incomplete), 112.4 mm, maximum diameter, 68 mm, length of aperture, approximately 65.5 mm, height of spire, approximately 49 mm. Holotype (C. A. S. Type Coll.) from locality 28311 (C. A. S.), Los Banos Creek, 1½ miles West of B. M. 307, middle of SW ¼ of NE ¼ sec. 12, T. 11 S., R. 9 E., M.D. B. and M.

terminal at its anterior end. Insofar as known, the genus is represented on the West Coast only by its type species; the nearest ally of the genus being *Scambula* Conrad, occurring in contemporary deposits in central Texas, and in similar deposits farther east, in Tennessee and in New Jersey, etc. From a comparison of his types with those of *Scambula* Conrad, Gabb states (1876, p. 311): "it proves that they are generally identical, the hinges agreeing perfectly."

Although these types differ much in specific characters, it is not without a genetic significance, though one is found in California and the other in Texas, that they probably are contemporary, and are basically akin, as shown in their hinge structures.

Anthonyia cultriformis Gabb

Anthonya cultriformis Gabb, Paleont. Calif., vol. 1, 1864, p. 182, Pl. 30, figs. 236, 236a; near Martinez, Contra Costa County, California. . . . vol. 2, 1869, p. 248; . . . STEWART, Acad. Nat. Sci. Phila., Special Pub., No. 3, 1930, p. 147, 148, Pl. 4, fig. 5; a lecotype figured, apparently from the type locality near Martinez (? locality 1, Merriam, 1897).

The horizon of this locality, and of the species, from faunal and stratigraphic evidence, is in the upper part of the Upper Cretaceous, and is probably correlative with the Navarro group of Texas (Maestrichtian).

Genus Remondia Gabb
Genotype Remondia furcatus Gabb

This genus was proposed by Gabb for a new molluscan type occurring in a considerable faunal assemblage (24 species), brought by Agustus Rémond from the Sierra de las Conchas, near Arivechi, State of Sonora, Mexico, and given to the State Geological Survey. Gabb recognized the fauna as pertaining to the Cretaceous of Texas, and described it as such, although it was discovered in the western flank of the Sierra Madre, and, as he thought, within the domain of the Pacific Cretaceous faunas then known in California. Gabb's description of the genus was defective and in some respects misleading. It was later (1897) emended by Stanton, who also assigned *"Stearnsia" robbinsi* White, found in the Cretaceous of Texas to it. The brief review of the subject by Stanton and his illustration of the hinge structure are illuminating and important. He correctly placed the genus in the Crassatelludae, rather than in the Trigoniidae, as was done by Gabb. The fauna of which this genus forms a part was held by Roemer and by Gabb to belong to the horizon of the "Lower Chalk" (Cenomanian), which appears to be correct, though as here shown, it may bettter be assigned to a slightly lower (uppermost Albian) horizon.

A species of *Remondia* closely related to, or perhaps identical with the genotype, has been collected by the writer in southern Oregon, and a similar, but seemingly distinct species has been found in the same horizon, as judged from its associates, in the lowermost "Chico" beds in the Cottonwood district in Shasta County, California. The resemblance of these two species to each other, and to the genotype, though specifically distinct, is remarkable, but equally interesting is the associated fauna which determines the epoch of their occurrence. In both Oregon and California this epoch was the closing stage of Albian time, as is shown by the presence of *Pervinquieria, Beudanticeras,* and other upper Albian types (*Brancoceras, Dipoloceras,* etc.).

Remondia furcatus Gabb

Remondia furcatus GABB, Paleont. Calif., vol. 2, 1869, p. 270, Pl. 36, figs. 17, 17a; 4 miles east of Arivechi, Sonora, Mexico. . . . STANTON, U. S. Nat. Museum, Proc., vol. 19, 1897, p. 299–302, Pl. 26, figs. 1–5; locality as given by Gabb, in Cerro de las Conchas, near Arivechi, Sonora.

As described by later writers, the type locality of this species lies in the Valley of the Rio Sahuaripa, 4 miles east of Arivechi and almost directly east of Hermosillo, State of Sonora.

Stanton (1897, p. 299–301) has given a detailed account of the genotype of *Remondia,* with figures illustrating the essential features of the shell, its structure, its form and surface ornamentation. According to Stanton two species of *Remondia* are known in the Lower Cretaceous of Texas, namely, *Remondia furcatus* Gabb, and *Remondia robbinsi* (White), known only in Texas. Stanton gives the following description of the genus *Remondia,* based upon the genotype:

"Shell rather compressed, equivalve, or nearly so, elongate subquadrate to subtriangular in outline; lunule and escutcheon well marked and deeply excavated; ligament partly internal; hinge with three cardinal teeth, and an anterior lateral lamina in the right valve, and two cardinals with a posterior lateral lamina in the left; free margins smooth, or crenulate within; sculpture consisting of strong concentric ridges and furrows which may become obsolete in later stages of growth; posterior end usually (? always) emarginate."

Remondia oregonensis Anderson n. sp.
(Plate 1, figure 8)

Closely related to *Remondia furcatus* Gabb, and may be identical with it. The type is much larger, and perhaps more developed; it is without the open or divided posterior end sketched by Gabb; the basal border is nearly straight, rather than sinuous, although, as shown by Stanton (1897), Gabb's sketch of the posterior may have been erroneous.

Anterior end, near basal border, is partly eroded away, but as evidenced on the cast, it extended downward and forward, meeting the basal border at an angle of about 60 degrees, as is also indicated by the growth lines above the middle of the side; this angle well defined and gave outline of shell a trapezoidal form. Hinge line, long and almost straight, is seemingly channeled, showing the ligament to have been more or less internal. The cardinal teeth are partly exposed on right valve, and as far as can be seen, conform to the pattern illustrated by Stanton. Surface ornamentation is more clearly defined than shown by either Gabb or Stanton, and on its lower half consists of concentric undulations, or rounded ridges, separated by narrow grooves; the ridges are traversed by longitudinal threads, 3–5 on each ridge, all parallel with border of shell itself. One large example, the holotype (C. A. S. Type Coll.), and 4 or more smaller fragmentary specimens were collected, some showing the hinge structure, especially of the left valve, in which 3 cardinal teeth are exposed, with an elongated lateral. Posterior end of shell is entire, characterized by an extended angle, formed by the extended basal border, and a posterior slope beginning at the hinge line and meeting the upturned base line in a narrowly rounded curve. Basal anterior end of shell is similar to posterior, but less acute and more broadly rounded.

Dimensions of holotype, length about 80 mm, and height about 41 mm; the umbonal ridge is much more distinct on the type itself than is shown in the figure. From locality 445C (C. A. S.).

The horizon of this species, as shown by its associates, can hardly be higher than the uppermost beds of the Albian stage, as indicated by the following list of species associated with the holotype:

Pervinquieria sp. indet.
Beudanticeras haydenii (Gabb)
Beudanticeras alamoense n. sp.
Dipoloceras sp.
Mantelliceras conquistador n. sp.
Cucullaea (*Idonearca*) *alamoensis* n. sp.

Parallelodon (*Nanonavis*) *breweriana* (Gabb)
Syncyclonema latum n. sp.
Nautilus (*Cymatoceras*) *carlottensis* Whiteaves

From the same horizon not far to the east, came the holotype of *Brancoceras parvum* (Anderson), and many fragments of rudistids.

Remondia shastensis Anderson n. sp.
(Plate 64, figure 3)

Resembles *Remondia furcatus* Gabb in size, form, and general outline, as emended by Stanton (1897), although having a more regularly rounded basal border, more acute anterior and posterior angles, and a rougher and less readily traced surface ornamentation; its associated species are at least in part analogous to those of *Remondia oregonensis* n. sp., to which it is related. In outline, shell is trapezoidal, with an elongated, straight hinge line, nearly parallel to axis of shell, and a distinct umbonal ridge extending from beak diagonally downward to lower posterior angle, which is narrowly rounded; beak is small, low, and placed about a fourth the length of shell from its anterior end; basal border broadly and uniformly rounded, rather than straight, meeting anterior and posterior slopes at different acute angles; anterior slope of shell straight, or nearly so, to anterior angle; posterior slope less steeply inclined; surface of shell marked by numerous undulations concentric with basal border of shell, though slightly irregular in height normal to surface; growth lines and undulations curving gradually upward approaching the umbonal ridge, upon which they are bent sharply upward and forward to dorsal border of shell; upper surface above umbonal ridge, narrow as compared to abdominal area. The angles formed by anterior and posterior slopes with the axial line of the shell differ somewhat as follows: the anterior slope meeting the axial line at an angle of about 44 degrees; the posterior slope meeting this line at an angle of 36 degrees. Hinge features are not exposed. Dimensions of the holotype are: length, 62 mm; maximum height, 28 mm; thickness of valve, 6 mm; length of hinge line, 27 mm; the ratios are determinable from these figures.

The holotype (C. A. S. Type Coll.) was found by the writer at locality 1292 (C. A. S.), a mile northeast of the mouth of Hulen Creek, in the lowest beds of the Upper Cretaceous, where the sandy beds of this area overlie unconformably the shales of the later Horsetown group, with a distinct lithological and faunal change. The beds above the contact are sandy, with a succession of conglomerates, whereas the beds beneath are shales with occasional concretionary layers, many of them stocked with Albian types of Mollusca, as already shown (Anderson, 1938). The associated fauna found with the present species include the following:

rudistids, sp. indet.
"Lunatia" avellana Gabb
Dentalium stramineum Gabb
Cucullaea (Idonearca) sp.
Trigonia colusaensis n. sp.
Trigonia aff. *T. inezana* Packard

"Meretrix" arata Gabb
Parallelodon (Nanonavis) breweriana (Gabb)

and various other near-littoral species, the beds containing them being overlaid by sandy shales containing species of *Pervinquieria,* including *Pervinquieria inflata* (authors). Other uppermost Albian types, obtained in the strike of these beds within a distance of 1.5 miles southwest of the locality named above are:

Beudanticeras haydenii (Gabb)
Beudanticeras alamoense n. sp.

Parapuzosia colusaensis (Anderson)
Pervinquieria tehamaensis (Reagan)

Family PHOLADOMYACIDAE Gray
Genus **Pholadomya** Sowerby
Pholadomya diegoensis Anderson n. sp.
(Plate 69, figure 1)

In outline and general form, this species appears to be closely related to *Pholadomya breweri* Gabb, from the Upper Cretaceous (Chico formation), at Pentz, Butte County, which according to Gabb "approaches *P. subelongata* Meek from Vancouver Island," although it cannot be identified with either of these forms.

In the present species both anterior and posterior ends are rounded, cardinal margin behind beak is straight but rounded to posterior margin; beak anterior, but more prominent and more inflated than that of of *P. breweri,* and the radiating ribs are less numerous, and almost confined to the anterior end of shell. Only faint radial markings are seen on posterior half. The ribs on the anterior slope are not straight, as in Gabb's species, but are curved downward and backward; the posterior half of the shell is almost smooth.

The holotype (C. A. S. Type Coll.) has the following dimensions: length, 67 mm; height of beak above the base, 39 mm; breadth of shell, 20 mm, or more. This example was found on the south side of Point Loma, San Diego County, in the upper part of the Cretaceous

(Maestrichtian), associated with species of *Parapachydiscus, Didymoceras cooperi* Gabb, and *Baculites lomaensis* nov. in beds that are regarded as correlative with the Moreno formation in the Great Valley, and with the Catarina formation of Lower California.

Family THYASIRIDAE Dall
Genus **Thyasira** Leach
Thyasira cretacea Whiteaves
(Plate 15, figures 4, 5)

Conchocele cretacea WHITEAVES, Geol. Survey Canada, Rept. Prog., 1873–4, p. 266, Pl. of fossils, figs. 2, 2a ; below Dodd's Narrows, V. I.
Thyasira cretacea WHITEAVES, Meso. Foss., vol. 1, pt. 5, 1903, p. 383, locality as above.

Whiteaves original description of this species reads in part as follows :

"Shell eliptical, somewhat quadrangular, inflated, beaks terminal, anterior ; front end shallowly concave, making an acute angle with the ventral margin ; base broadly rounded ; posterior extremity slightly convex, forming an angle at its junction with the dorsal margin. Two keels extend on each valve from the beaks to the posterior end, each of which encloses an excavated space of which the interior is the smaller ; the outer area thus circumscribed is broadly lenticular, while the inner one is rather shorter and much narrower."

This species is readily identified from the figures and text and has been recognized at various places in the Great Valley of California. Dimensions of hypotypes (C. A. S. Type Coll.) (Pl. 15, fig. 4) Right valve (incomplete) : length, 32 mm (illustrated portion) ; (Pl. 15, fig. 5) left valve, view of top, showing ligamental area. Length, 37 mm ; thickness of valve, 10 mm. Found at locality 1467A (C. A. S.) in Enos Canyon, 7 miles northwest of Winters, Yolo County. Good examples have also been found at a higher horizon at locality 2212 (C. A. S.) north of Marsh Creek.

At Enos Canyon it was found associated with *Metaplacenticeras pacificum* Smith, and various other invertebrate species that fix its age as Coniacian.

Family CARDIIDAE Fisher
Genus **Cardium** Linné
Subgenus **Pachycardium** Conrad
Pachycardium ? remondianum Gabb

Cardium Remondianum GABB, Paleont. Calif., vol. 1, 1864, p. 172, Pl. 25, fig. 153 ; from near Benicia, California. . . . vol. 2, 1869, p. 242 ; locality as above. . . . ANDERSON, Proc. Calif. Acad. Sci., 3d ser., vol. 2, 1902, p. 30 ; "Forty-nine" mine, southern Oregon.
Pachycardium ? remondianum (Gabb), STEWART, Acad. Nat. Sci. Phila., Special Pub., No. 3, 1930, p. 270 ; locality as given by Gabb.

This species was not included by either Diller or Stanton (1893) in their lists of lower Chico fossils in California, although the writer has collected good specimens of it at various localities representing the lowest beds of the Upper Cretaceous in northern California, namely, at Texas Springs, the Middle fork of Cottonwood Creek, at Petersen's ranch, 4 miles north of Sites, and in the basal conglomerate of the Turonian, in Berryessa Canyon.

Family **Veneridae** Leach
Genus **Venus** Linné
"Venus" lenticularis Gabb

Venus lenticularis GABB, Paleont. Calif., vol. 1, 1864, p. 162, Pl. 30, fig. 246 ; Benicia, California . . . Vol. 2, 1869, p. 239 ; Chico Group, Benicia . . . STEWART, Acad. Nat. Sci. Phila., Special Pub., No. 3, 1930, p. 219, Pl. 1, fig. 12 ; Gabb's holotype figured ; length of valve, 28.4 mm ; height, 26.6 mm ; thickness of both valves, 18 mm.

According to Stewart, the lunule is deep and long, the escutcheon is not defined, the ligament is external, opisthodetic. Stewart further suggests that the holotype may be the adult of *"Venus" veatchii* Gabb.

"Venus" tetrahedra Gabb

Venus tetrahedra GABB, Paleont. Calif., vol. 1, 1864, p. 163, Pl. 30, fig. 247; near Martinez.
    Division A . . . vol. 2, 1869, p. 239; Chico group, Martinez . . . STEWART, Acad. Nat. Sci.
    Phila., Special Pub., No. 3, 1930, p. 219, Pl. 1, fig. 10.

Stewart figures a well-preserved right valve, which he proposes as the lectotype of the species. Length, 10.7 mm; height, 8.5 mm; thickness of right valve, 3.5 mm.

"Venus" veatchii Gabb

Venus veatchii GABB, Paleont. Calif., vol. 1, 1864, p. 162, Pl. 23, fig. 142; Tuscan Springs,
    Tehama County . . . Vol. 2, 1869, p. 238; locality as above . . . STEWART, Acad. Nat. Sci.
    Phila., Special Pub., no. 3, 1930, p. 219, Pl. 5, fig. 9.

By its position, this species should be regarded as Senonian rather than higher in the section, and for this reason can hardly be regarded as the adult form of *Venus lenticularis* Gabb. To support such view, both types should be shown to be referable to the same stratigraphic level, rather than to distinct groups of strata.

Genus **Flaventia** Jukes-Brown
Flaventia lens (Gabb)

Meretrix lens GABB, Paleont. Calif., vol. 1, 1864, p. 164, Pl. 23, fig. 143; Chico Creek, Butte
    County (not *'Cyprimeria lens'* Whiteaves).
Flaventia ? lens, STEWART, Acad. Nat. Sci. Phila., Special Pub., No. 3, 1930, p. 247, Pl. 4,
    fig. 6; Chico Creek, Butte County. . . . POPENOE, Jour. Paleont., vol. 11, 1937, p. 392, Pl.
    48, fig. 4; locality as above. . . . Am. Ass. Petrol. Geol., Bull. vol. 26, 1942, Fig. 4; occurs
    at various localities in the Santiago district, and in the Simi Hills, Los Angeles County,
    ranging throughout Senonian formations in these districts.

Popenoe (1937, p. 392) gives the hinge characters of the species, with an illustration of the same. For the Santiago district, he gives the following note:

"Distribution: Ladd formation. Holz member, *abundant;* Williams formation, *common."*

In his later contribution (Fig. 4) Popenoe shows the species to be limited to the Senonian portion of the Holz member. In its type area, Chico Creek, the species is limited to a lower-middle Campanian range, and this may be true in Orange County.

Flaventia hornbyensis Anderson, n. name

Cyprimeria lens WHITEAVES, Geol. Survey Canada, Meso. Foss., vol. 1, pt. 2, p. 152, Pl. 17,
    figs. 15, 15a; northwest side of Hornby Island. . . . Meso. Foss., vol. 1, pt. 5, 1903, p. 379;
    locality as above.
Cyprimeria lens (Gabb), WHITE, U. S. Geol. Survey, Bull. 51, 1889, p. 42; states that a
    single example of this form occurs in the collection from Waldron Island, (British Colum-
    bia). . . . WHITEAVES, Meso. Foss., vol. 1, pt. 5, 1903, p. 379; locality as above.
Flaventia ? lens (Whiteaves), STEWART, Acad. Nat. Sci. Phila., Special Pub. No. 3, 1930,
    p. 247, 248; suggests new name for Whiteaves' species. . . . POPENOE, Journ. Paleont., vol.
    11, 1937, p. 393; states that his study "verifies Stewart's determination of the generic
    position of *Flaventia lens* (Gabb)."

Much of the fauna described from northwest Hornby Island appears to be referable to an upper Senonian horizon, although the area also contains later Cretaceous deposits.

Flaventia zeta Popenoe

Flaventia zeta POPENOE, Jour. Paleont., vol. 11, 1937, p. 393, Pl. 48, figs. 9–11; "common
    in the Baker member and very rare in the lower part of the Holz shale," in the Santiago
    district, Orange County. . . . Am. Ass. Petrol. Geol., Bull., vol. 26, 1942, Fig. 4.

According to Popenoe (1937, p. 393) : *"Flaventia zeta* is to be distinguished from *F. lens* (Gabb) principally by its more elongate outline and by its higher beaks." As compared to Gabb's species he says:

"Stratigraphically, the two species are complementary. *F. zeta* being common in the Baker member, and very rare in the lower part of the Holz shale, whereas, *F. lens* (Gabb) is common in the upper part of the Holz shale, and rare in the Williams formation."

In his later contribution (1942, Fig. 4) the stratigraphic distribution of the two species is shown graphically. *Flaventia zeta* represents the basal Upper Cretaceous beds, as they occur at Henley, Siskiyou County.

Genus Dosinia Scopoli
Dosinia pertenuis Gabb

Dosinia pertenuis GABB, Paleont. Calif., vol. 1, 1864, p. 187, Pl. 30, fig. 253; north slope of the Siskiyou Mountains, (near old highway). . . . ANDERSON, Proc. Calif. Acad. Sci., 3d ser., vol. 2, 1902, p. 32; near Henley, Siskiyou County, California.
Venus pertenuis (Gabb), WARING, Proc. Calif. Acad. Sci., 4th ser., vol. 7, 1917, p. 57, 60; Calabasas quadrangle; locality 3 (L. S. J. U.), north of Santa Monica, Los Angeles County.
"Dosinia" pertenuis Gabb, STEWART, Acad. Nat. Sci. Phila., Special Pub., No. 3, 1930, p. 232, Pl. 6, fig. 7; locality as given by Gabb; the holotype figured. Length, 21.3 mm; height, 18.8 mm; thickness of left valve, *ca.* 4 mm; horizon, "Chico group."

The occurrence of this species on the north slope of the Siskiyou Mountains, near the railroad, may be taken as evidence of its upper Turonian age, since no strata of any other horizon is exposed in this area, although younger beds are found farther northwest, near Phoenix.

Dosinia milthoides Waring

Dosinia milthoides WARING, Proc. Calif. Acad. Sci., vol. 7, 1917, p. 60, Pl. 8, fig. 5; locality 2, (L. S. J. U.), Bell Canyon, Camulos quadrangle, Los Angeles County, California.

This species is described by Waring as follows:

"Shell of medium thickness, circular and inflated; beak small, excavated anteriorly; cardinal margin convex, sloping into the circular posterior margin; anterior and basal margins rounded; surface ornamented by fine concentric lines of growth, and three or four irregularly spaced major concentric lines."

Genus Tenea Conrad
Tenea inflata (Gabb)

Dosinia inflata GABB, Paleont. Calif. vol. 1, 1864, p. 168, Pl. 23, fig. 149; Chico Creek, Butte County. . . . STEWART, Acad. Nat. Sci. Phila., Special Pub., No. 3, 1930, p. 231; locality as above.
Tenea inflata (Gabb) POPENOE, Jour. Paleont., vol. 11, 1937, p. 391; locality as above. . . . TAFF, HANNA and CROSS, Geol. Soc. Am., Bull., vol. 51, 1940, p. 1322; locality as above. . . . POPENOE, Am. Ass. Petrol. Geol., Bull., vol. 26, Fig. 4; localities 982, 1173, 1160, 1158, etc. Santiago district, and Simi Hills; Holz shale member of Ladd formation. (upper Senonian).

In the Chico Creek area this species occurs in the Chico formation, having a considerable stratigraphic range both below and above the horizon of *Mortoniceras randalli* n. sp. and *M. chicoense* (Trask), assigned in this memoir to a lower-middle Campanian horizon. The stratigraphic range of the present species is somewhat greater, ranging from the Coniacian to the upper part of the Campanian.

According to Popenoe (1937, p. 392), a "dwarf variety" of the species occurs in the Baker member of the Ladd formation, and a "giant variety" is found in the Holz member of the same. The greatest abundance of the species in the Santiago area is in the Senonian part of the sequence. The Baker member in this area is certainly of Turonian age, as indicated by the presence in it of *Glycymeris pacificus, Cucullaea gravida,* and *Trigonarca californica,* besides the prionotropids included by Popenoe (1942, Fig. 4) in the lower part of his column.

It may be that one or both the "varieties" mentioned by him represent distinct, but closely allied species.

Genus **Chione** Megerle
? **Chione angulata** Gabb

? Chione angulata GABB, Paleont. Calif. vol. 1, 1864, p. 213, Pl. 32, fig. 231; west of Martinez. Division A. Cretaceous. . . . vol. 2, 1869, p. 239; Martinez group, near Martinez (Paleocene). . . . COOPER, Calif. State Min. Bur., Bull. No. 4, 1894, p. 60; referred to "Division B," near Kelley's. . . . STEWART, Acad. Nat. Sci. Phila., Special Pub., No. 3, 1930, p. 220, Pl. 1, fig. 6.

Stewart examined the holotype of this species (? Mus. Comp. Zool.), and upon such evidence as he could find, believed it to be Cretaceous. Concerning this form he states: "This is a fine species, and probably a new genus, but until its affinities have been recognized, or its hinge character discovered, it may be left where Gabb placed it."

Evidences as to the character, affinities, genus, and stratigraphic position of this species are still far from being satisfactory.

Genus **Cyprimeria** Conrad
Cyprimeria moorei Popenoe

Cyprimeria moorei POPENOE, Jour. Paleont., vol. 11, 1937, p. 391, Pl. 48, figs. 1, 2; Holz shale member of the Ladd formation; Santiago district, west flank of the Santa Ana Mountains, Orange County. . . . POPENOE, Amer. Ass. Petrol. Geol., Bull., vol. 26, 1942, Fig. 4; localities 454, and 92; upper part of Holz shale member; Turonian.

According to Popenoe (1937, p. 391): *"Cyprimeria moorei* is probably the first *Cyprimeria* to be reported from the Pacific Coast Upper Cretaceous."

Whiteaves had reported the occurrence of *"Cyprimeria lens"* (Gabb), which later he referred to *Cyprimeria lens* Whiteaves, (not Gabb), Meso. Foss., vol. 1, pt. 5, p. 379, Pl. 17, figs. 15, 15a. This species was later shown by Stewart to be referable to the genus *Flaventia* Jukes-Brown, and so classed by himself, and this determination has been adopted by Popenoe (1937, p. 392; 1942, Fig. 4). By this interpretation few species of *Cyprimeria* have yet been found in the West Coast Upper Cretaceous, and none later than upper Turonian.

Genus **Meretrix** Lamarck
"Meretrix" coronada Anderson n. name

Meretrix (?) sp., PACKARD, Univ. Calif. Pub. Bull. Dept. Geol. Sci., vol. 13, 1922, p. 426, Pl. 33, fig. 2; *Turritella pescaderoensis* zone, locality 2167 (Univ. Calif.), 2 miles N. 10° W. of B. M. 1271, Corona sheet, half a mile below Mojeska Springs, in Williams Canyon, Orange County, California.

Packard's description of this species reads (in part) as follows:

"A large, elongate specimen, No. 12306, that is doubtfully referred to this genus was obtained at locality 2167. The specimen is devoid of shell except on the anterior end, which shows an ill-defined lunule, bounded by an impressed line. Irregular lines of growth are the only evidence of sculpture. The shell is elongate, very tumid, with prominent umbones but inconspicuous beaks. Length, 68 mm; height, 46 mm; diameter of cast, 35 mm."

Although it is unlikely that either this, or the following species is referable to the genus *Meretrix* Lamarck, they may be left under this name until some evidence has been obtained for a more satisfactory assignment. Meanwhile, their relationship will serve a useful stratigraphic purpose in fixing their position in the section.

"Meretrix" marshana Anderson n. sp.
(Plate 68, figure 3)

Shell of moderate size, elongate, subquadrate, rounded on anterior end; subtruncate behind; basal border broadly rounded, curvature merging gradually to that of either end; beaks depressed, subcentral, closely approximate; surface marked only by narrowly spaced, concentric growth lines; beaks without shell, and without a well defined lunule, if there is any.

Length (incomplete), 63 mm; height at beaks, 44 mm; approximate thickness, 35 mm; hinge structure not known.

This species is congeneric with, and similar to the preceding. It was found by the writer at locality 2356 (C. A. S.), on ridge between Marsh Creek and Briones Valley, 6 miles southwest of Brentwood, Contra Costa County, California, associated with *Parapachydiscus catarinae* Anderson and Hanna, *Baculites occidentalis* (Meek), *Diplomoceras notabile* Whiteaves, and other species. Although it cannot be shown that this species is identical with the foregoing, it is evident that their relationship is very close. The horizon of the present species is Maestrichtian.

Genus **Legumen** Conrad
"Legumen" ooides (Gabb)

Tellina ooides GABB, Paleont. Calif., vol. 1, 1864, p. 157, Pl. 22, figs. 135, 135a; west of
    Martinez (fig. 135); Pentz (fig. 135a). . . . vol. 2, 1869, p. 237; Chico group, Martinez,
    Pentz. . . . FAIRBANKS, Am. Journ. Sci., vol. 45, 1893, p. 474; gives a list of species con-
    taining *Tellina ooides,* (determined by Cooper). . . . COOPER, Calif. State Min. Bur., Bull.
    No. 4, 1894, p. 63; west base of Point Loma. . . . MERRIAM, name given in a list of "Type
    Specimens" at the University of California. . . . PACKARD, Univ. Calif. Pub. Dept. Geol.
    Sci. Bull., vol. 9, 1916, p. 147; Santiago district, Orange County; the species selected as
    the index fossil for the uppermost zone occurring in this area.
"Tellina" ooides Gabb, STEWART, Acad. Nat. Sci. Phila., Special Pub., No. 3, 1930, p. 202;
    Pl. 3, fig. 3; length, 61 mm; height, 45 mm; thickness of left valve *ca.* 6 mm.
Legumen ooides (Gabb), POPENOE, Jour. Paleont., vol. 11, 1937, p. 394, Pl. 48, figs. 8, 12;
    Pleasants member of Williams formation. . . . Am. Assn. Petrol. Geol., Bull. vol. 26,
    1942, Fig. 4; locality as given above.

The generic assignment of this species may still be questioned. It differs greatly in form at least, and seemingly in hinge characters, although not in stratigraphic horizon from the genotype of *Legumen* Conrad which has been studied and well illustrated by Stephenson (1941, p. 215, Pl. 42).

Packard (1916; 1922) selected *Tellina ooides* Gabb as an index fossil for a zone that he believed to be at the top of the section in the Santiago district. In 1922, Packard in reviewing the subject (p. 414), wrote:

"Three faunal zones were recognized within the Chico of this region, by the writer, and were named after distinctive fossils: The *Tellina ooides* zone, the uppermost horizon, etc. . . . ranging through the uppermost 300 feet."

Many species have been described by Packard, and by later writers, including *Trigonocallista major* (Packard), *Odostomia santana* Packard, *Parapachydiscus* sp., and others mentioned elsewhere in this volume.

Both of Gabb's examples are in the Museum of Paleontology, University of California, though neither show the hinge characters. Surficial differences in size, form and other features make their specific identity doubtful, but the Lectotype No. 12072 is the larger of the two, and its position appears to conform to that named by Packard, the *Tellina ooides* zone and the Pleasants member of the Williams formation.

Genus **Aphrodina** Conrad
"Aphrodina" arata (Gabb)

Meretrix arata GABB, Paleont. Calif., vol. 1, 1864, p. 166, 231, Pl. 30, fig. 250; Cottonwood
    Creek, Shasta County. . . . vol. 2, 1869, p. 246; locality as given above. . . . (? not Cooper),
    Calif. State Min. Bur., Bull. No. 4, 1894, p. 62; Cretaceous, Division A; west base of
    Point Loma, San Diego County. . . . STEWART, Acad. Nat. Sci. Phila., Special Pub., No.
    3, 1930, p. 247, Pl. 1, fig. 4; "Orestimba Canyon. Cal.," . . . .
Aphrodina ? *arata* (Gabb) POPENOE, Jour. Paleont., vol. 11, 1937, p. 397, Pl. 48, figs. 15, 16;
    Baker member of the Ladd formation; Santiago district, Orange County. . . . POPENOE,
    Am. Ass. Petrol. Geol., Bull. vol. 26, 1942, Fig. 4; locality as given above.

Concerning this species and its stratigraphic position, it may be said that no Cretaceous strata younger than the Turonian are known to outcrop on the Cottonwood Creek, Shasta

County, whence came the type material of Gabb. Most of the localities mentioned by Gabb appear to be referable to the Turonian, and the same is true of the Baker member of the Ladd formation of Orange County.

The species has been cited, however, as occurring in much later strata, Cooper (1894, p. 62) and Merriam (1897, p. 770) have believed that it had been found in higher parts of the column as well.

Genus **Trigonocallista** Rennie

W. P. Popenoe (1937, p. 394) proposed the name *Calva* to include a number of venerid types found abundantly in the Upper Cretaceous on the West Coast, especially in California and Oregon. Later (1940, p. 163) he concluded that the name was synonymous with the above genus of Rennie, and should be discontinued. Many of the West Coast types of the Veneridae in the Upper Cretaceous should be included in this genus, including species of *"Meretrix," "Chione," "Aphrodina,"* and the following.

Trigonocallista major (Packard)
(Plate 70, figures 2, 2a)

Meretrix nitida (Gabb) var. *major* PACKARD, Univ. Calif. Pub. Bull. Dept. Geol. Sci., vol. 13, 1922, p. 425, Pl. 31, fig. 2; locality 2169 (Univ. Calif.), Santa Ana Mountains.
Venus steinyi Hertlein, ANDERSON AND HANNA, Proc. Calif. Acad. Sci., vol. 23, 1935, p. 7 (not figured).

After a critical study of the materials now in the collections of the Academy of Sciences, the following supplementary notes can be added concerning the form named *Venus steinyi.*

The shell of the species is large, robust, rounded in outline, with prominent beaks overhanging the lunular area. In general contours, surface features, and hinge characters, the species greatly resembles the genotype named by Rennie *"Meretrix" umzambiensis* Woods, from the Upper Cretaceous of Pondoland, southeast Africa. In truth, the resemblance of the species to that of Woods (1906, p. 304, Pl. 36) is so close that identity might be claimed, although it cannot be proved.

The hinge plate is large, showing the normal venerid characters; the hinge teeth, 2 in number, are distinct, with a third, the anterior, connected with the anterior lateral, beneath the lunular area; lunule, relatively small and broad, is deeply impressed. The "holotype" of *"Venus steinyi"* was collected with other examples at locality 954 (C. A. S.), on the northeast side of Punta Banda (southwest border of Todos Santos Bay), Lower California, in the beach cliff, accessible at low tide, 3 miles from La Grulla gun club house, by E. K. Jordan and L. G. Hertlein.

The stratigraphic position as thus described is probably near the base of the exposed section, and, incidentally, at the base of the "Gualala group" described by White (1885b).

In view of the entire fauna collected from this section in the past, as reviewed by Anderson and Hanna (1935, p. 7), the horizon should be regarded as lower Maestrichtian, somewhat lower in the general section than that exposed at Point Loma and at Arroyo Santa Catarina, farther south on the peninsula.

The hypotype (C. A. S. Type Coll.) has the following dimensions: length, 88 mm; height (incomplete), 79.5 mm; convexity (1 valve), approximately 35 mm.

"Trigonocallista" varians (Gabb)

Venus (Mercenaria) varians GABB, Paleont. Calif., vol. 1, 1864, p. 161, Pl. 23, figs. 140, 140a; near Martinez, (? not Pentz, Butte County).
Chione varians GABB, Paleont. Calif., vol. 2, 1869, p. 239 (in part, ? not vol. 1, 1864, fig. 141, from Pentz).
Aphrodina varians (Gabb), STEWART, Acad. Nat. Sci. Phila., Special Pub., No. 3, 1930, p. 249, Pl. 6, fig. 6; believed to be the type figured by Gabb, vol. 1, Pl. 23, fig. 240a. Figured by Stewart, as lectotype.
Trigonocallista varians (Gabb), POPENOE, Jour. Paleont., vol. 14, 1940, p. 163; the name replacing '*Calva varians* (Gabb)', proposed earlier. . . . TAFF, HANNA, AND CROSS, Geol. Soc. Am., Bull., vol. 51, p. 1321, (? not Pl. 2, figs. 10, 11; Chico Creek).

This species was originally described and figured by Gabb from a locality near Martinez. Gabb supposed the same species to occur at Pentz, Butte County, and illustrated a specimen from that place (vol. 1, Pl. 23, fig. 141), although his figure is distinctly different from that of the lectotype illustrated by Stewart (Pl. 6, fig. 6; Martinez).

A specimen obained from Chico Creek, and thought to be referable to this species by Taff, Hanna, and Cross, was figured by them (1940, Pl. 2, figs. 10, 11), although a comparison of their figures with those of Gabb, and with that of the lectotype given by Sewart (Pl. 6, fig. 6), hardly supports this view. It appears to be more logical to regard the type from Chico Creek as being a distinct species.

"Trigonocallista" nitida (Gabb)

Meretrix nitida GABB, Paleont. Calif., vol. 1, 1864, p. 165, Pl. 23, figs. 145, 146; near Martinez "in loose blocks on the shores of the Straits of Carquinez."

Caryatis nitida GABB, Paleont. Calif., vol. 2, 1869, p. 186, Pl. 30, fig. 79; "a young shell from Martinez." Gabb stated that he had seen shells (of this species) "nearly two inches in length."

Aphrodina nitida (Gabb), STEWART, Acad. Nat. Sci. Phila., Special Pub. No. 3, 1930, p. 250, Pl. 5, fig. 10; Pl. 6, fig. 9; the type of Pl. 5, fig. 10 is provisionally designated as the lectotype, although that of Pl. 6, fig. 9 is said to be "a well-preserved right valve" of a larger shell of more maturity, for which the dimensions are stated by Stewart, and apparently could have served as a lectotype.

The complete record of this species as gathered from the literature leaves much to be desired, particularly as to an authentic representative, its correct name, and its position in the stratigraphic column.

Its record begins without a source for its material, and ends with only a provisional "lectotype," for which no hinge characters were given by either Gabb or Stewart, or by any subsequent writer. Popenoe (1937, p. 395) tentatively assigned *"Meretrix nitida* Gabb" to his genus *Calva,* which later (1940) he transferred to *Trigonocallista* (Rennie) although without any reference to its hinge characters.

Taff, Hanna, and Cross (1940, p. 1322) included under *Trigonocallista nitida* (Gabb) a specimen obtained from Chico Creek, which they illustrated (Pl. 2, figs. 3, 4), with notes pertaining to the same. The horizon of this species is, of course, within the Chico formation (lower Campanian). On a following page their specimen is named *"Trigonocallista" taffi,* n. sp.

"Trigonocallista" taffi Anderson n. sp.
(Plate 59, figures 2, 2a)

Trigonocallista nitida (Gabb), TAFF, HANNA, AND CROSS, Geol. Soc. Am., Bull., vol. 51, 1940, p. 1322, Pl. 2, figs. 3, 4; Chico Creek, Butte County. Not *Caryatis nitida* GABB, Paleont. Calif., vol. 2, 1869, p. 186, Pl. 30, fig. 79; near Martinez; not *Aphrodina nitida* (Gabb), STEWART, Acad. Nat. Sci. Phila., Special Pub. No. 3, 1930, p. 250, Pl. 5, fig. 10; Pl. 6, fig. 9; Carquinez Strait.

A specimen, hypotype No. 5789 (C. A. S. Type Coll.) referred to *Trigonocallista nitida* (Gabb) by Taff, Hanna, and Cross (1940, p. 1322), has the following dimensions: length, 27 mm; height, 25.8 mm; thickness (both valves), 17 mm. It was found by them at locality 27836 (C. A. S.), on Chico Creek, Butte County, 1.2 miles northeast of Frank Mickey ranch, which, as shown in their section (p. 1316), is near the base of the Chico formation. Their published note concerning this species reads (in part) as follows:

"The species is common in Chico Creek and seems to be constantly separable from *T. varians* (Gabb), by being shorter, higher, and more inflated. Both species are marked by prominent concentric grooves, widely spaced, representing rest periods in growth. Both species have been assigned to numerous genera."

The specimen illustrated by Taff, Hanna, and Cross represents a distinct species which can take the name *"Trigonocallista" taffi.*

"Trigonocallista" buttensis Anderson n. sp.
(Plate 59, figures 1, 1a)

Trigonocallista varians (Gabb), TAFF, HANNA, AND CROSS, Geol. Soc. Am. Bull., vol. 51, p. 1321, Pl. 2, figs. 10, 11; Chico Creek; (not *Venus varians* GABB, 1864, p. 161, Pl. 23, figs. 140, 140a, Martinez; not fig. 141, var. ? from Pentz, Butte County; not *Aphrodina varians* (Gabb), STEWART, Acad. Nat. Sci. Phila., Special Pub., No. 3, 1930, p. 249, Pl. 6, fig. 6; not *Chione varians* (Gabb) STANTON (in DILLER), 1893, p. 209, 210, Elder Creek, and other places.

Under the name of *Trigonocallista varians* (Gabb), Taff, Hanna, and Cross (1940, p. 1321) partly described and illustrated (Pl. 2, figs. 10, 11) a single pelecypod valve (hypotype 5788 C. A. S. Type Coll.) found on Chico Creek at locality 27838 (C. A. S.). Hypotype 5788 has the following dimensions: length, 48.2 mm; convexity (one valve), approximately 15.2 mm. If this, or any other specimen from Chico Creek could really be identified with either Gabb's holotype from near Martinez, or with Stewart's lectotype (Pl. 6, fig. 6), some progress might be made in showing the presence of equivalents of the Chico formation in the area about Martinez. The figure given by these writers for the Chico Creek specimen is at best not convincing, since it shows neither the form, the lunule, nor the hinge character attributed to Gabb's species.

A list of 20 molluscan species given by Merriam (1897, p. 770) contains *Venus varians* from locality 1, near Martinez, probably Gabb's type locality. The present species, illustrated by Taff, Hanna and Cross, appears to be referable to the genus, but not the species figured by Gabb, since it shows no lunule, and scarcely the anterior excavation illustrated by Gabb's figures (140, 140a).

Trigonocallista bowersiana (Cooper)

Cucullaea bowersiana COOPER, Calif. State Min. Bur., Bull. No. 4, 1894, p. 48, Pl. 5, figs. 61, 62; Santa Ana Mountains, Orange County.
Calva bowersiana (Cooper), POPENOE, Jour. Paleont., vol. 11, 1937, p. 396.
Trigonocallista bowersiana (Cooper), POPENOE, Am. Ass. Petrol. Geol., Bull. vol. 26, 1942, Fig. 4 [178], Pleasants member, and Holz shale.

Cooper's original description of this species reads:

"Shell large, thick, nearly equilateral; surface smooth, with coarse lines of growth; valves very convex, sub-truncate posteriorly, but with edges of valves prominent, rounded; umbonal ridge obtuse, nearly straight; beaks moderate, meeting in a medial line; anterior outline slightly incurved above, but rounded on lower half; base moderately curved, rounded posteriorly. Length of largest, 2.50 inches (63.5 mm); height, 2 (50.6) mm); diameter of shell, about 1.20 (30.5 mm)."
Locality, Santa Ana Mountains. (Stephen Bowers, coll.).

Trigonocallista regina Popenoe

Calva regina POPENOE, Jour. Paleont., vol. 11, 1937, p. 395, Pl. 48, figs. 6, 7, 13, 14; Baker member of Ladd formation. Santa Ana Mountains, Orange County.
Trigonocallista regina (Popenoe) POPENOE, Jour. Paleont., vol. 14, 1940, p. 163. . . . Am. Ass. Petrol. Geol., Bull. vol. 26, 1942, Fig. 4; locality as given above.

The description of the shell reads, in part, as follows:

"Shell of moderate size, nearly as high as long, inflated, rather thick; beaks prominent, rather high, placed anterior to the mid-length of the shell, prosogyrous; anterior dorsal border strongly concave; anterior end rather sharply rounded; ventral border broadly arched; posterior end bluntly truncate vertically; posterior dorsal border rather short, slightly arched;" . . . (Hinge elements described in detail, not quoted) . . . "Dimensions of syntypes: Right valve, height, 34.4 mm; length, 36.5 mm; thickness of one valve, approximately 8.5 mm; left valve, height, 33.2 mm; length, 37 mm; thickness of valve, approximately 10.8 mm." Baker member of Ladd formation (Turonian).

Family TELLINIDAE Deshayes
Genus **Tellina** Linnaeus
Tellina hoffmanniana Gabb

Tellina hoffmanniana GABB, Paleont. Calif., vol. 1, 1864, p. 156, Pl. 22, fig. 133; (? 133a); west of Martinez, (not Pentz, Butte County). . . . vol. 2, 1869, p. 237 (not p. 182; Martinez group, Martinez). . . . MERRIAM, Jour. Geol., vol. 5, No. 8, 1897, p. 770; locality No. 1, (Univ. Calif. Coll.). . . . PACKARD, Univ. Calif. Pub., Bull., Dept. Geol., vol. 9, No. 12, 1916, p. 147, 154 (?). (Santiago district, Orange County. Species in doubt). . . . STEWART, Acad. Nat. Sci. Phila., Special Pub., No. 3, 1930, p. 201, Pl. 6, fig. 12 (a topotype, possibly the holotype).

The example figured by Stewart (Pl. 6, fig. 12) was obtained from a well known locality (locality 1, of Merriam) a mile or more southwest of Martinez, referred to above, from which Gabb collected many type specimens described in Paleontology of California, vols. 1 and 2.

Tellina mathewsonii Gabb

Tellina mathewsonii GABB, Paleont. Calif., vol. 1, 1864, p. 158, Pl. 23, fig. 136; Division A, a mile north of Pacheco, Contra Costa County. . . . vol. 2, 1869, p. 237; Chico group, Martinez. . . . ANDERSON, Proc. Calif. Acad. Sci., 3d ser., vol. 2, 1902, p. 37, "Pacheco Pass," Contra Costa County. . . . STEWART, Acad. Nat. Sci. Phila., Special Pub., No. 3, 1930, p. 201, Pl. 3, fig. 2; locality, Martinez.

No later record of this species has been found for northern California, although its occurrence at Todos Santos Bay is mentioned by Anderson and Hanna (1935, p. 7), associated with *Coralliochama orcutti* White, and many other species characteristic of the Maestrichtian, thus supporting the view that locality 1 (Merriam), may also be the same age.

Tellina decurtata Gabb

Tellina decurtata GABB, Paleont. Calif., vol. 1, 1864, p. 158, Pl. 23, fig. 137; Pentz, 12 miles north of Oroville, Butte County. . . . vol. 2, 1869, p. 237, Chico group, Pentz (Pence's ranch), Butte County. . . . MERRIAM, *Tellina "decurta"* (Gabb), in published list of type specimens found at the Museum of Paleontology, 1895. . . . ANDERSON, Proc. Calif. Acad. Sci., 3d ser., vol. 2, 1902, p. 32, Pentz, Butte County. . . . STEWART, Acad. Nat. Sci. Phila., Special Pub., No. 3, 1930, p. 204; holotype found in the Museum of Paleontology, University of California.

This species is included in the list of molluscan species given by Gabb from Pentz, 1864, (p. 220–236), including the following:

Mortoniceras (Submortoniceras) chicoense (Trask)
"Ptychoceras (Hamites ?) quadratus Gabb
Baculites chicoensis Trask
Canadoceras aff. *C. newberryanum* Meek

"Helicoceras" brewerii Gabb
"Helicoceras" declive Gabb
Haydenia impressa Gabb
Volutoderma californica Dall

and many other species characteristic of the Chico formation, as found on Chico Creek. The horizon as indicated by its cephalopod fauna, is early, or early middle Campanian.

Tellina paralis Gabb

Tellina paralis GABB, Paleont. Calif., vol. 1, 1864, p. 160, Pl. 30, fig. 243; Martinez (Loc. 1, of Merriam), (1.5 miles southwest of the town of Martinez). . . . vol. 2, 1869, p. 238; Chico group, as shown above.
"Tellina" paralis Gabb, STEWART, Acad. Nat. Sci. Phila., Special Pub., No. 3, 1930, p. 203, Pl. 1, fig. 11; recognized as the holotype of the species. Concerning this specimen Stewart says:

"The specimen figured is the best of four specimens labelled 'types,' and is considered the holotype. It agrees very well with the size mark given for the original figure. The umbo is very small and, assuming the shell to be a left valve, just anterior to the middle. The posterior end is a little broader than the anterior end. The shell is highly polished and a trifle inflated. Length, 18.5 mm; height, 11.5 mm; thickness, *ca.* 3 mm." . . . "Two internal casts of this species from the same locality reveal anterior and posterior laminae distinct enough to be considered remote laterals. A suggestion of the pallial sinus may be present on the specimen."

This species, as does the general fauna from this locality given by Merriam, probably represents the Maestrichtian. This species was found by B. L. Clark and the writer at locality 25707 (C. A. S.).

Tellina aequalis Gabb

Tellina aequalis GABB, Paleont. Calif., vol. 2, 1869, p. 182, Pl. 29, fig. 73; "Martinez Group at Martinez" . . . FAIRBANKS, Am. Jour. Sci., vol. 45, 1893, p. 474, found at Todos Santos Bay, Lower California. . . . COOPER, Calif. State Min. Bur., Bull. No. 4, 1894, p. 63; west base of Point Loma, San Diego County. . . . MERRIAM, Jour. Geol., Nov.-Dec., 1897, p. 770; locality No. 1, near Martinez. . . . STEWART, Acad. Nat. Sci. Phila., Special Pub., No. 3, 1930, p. 203, Pl. 2, fig. 8; "presumably Gabb's 'type'" found at the Philadelphia Academy, and by Stewart is regarded as the holotype. "Horizon, Cretaceous: locality, Martinez."

Notwithstanding Gabb's statement that this species is referable to the "Martinez group, at Martinez," it becomes evident from the above record that it came from Locality 1, of Merriam, and represents the Maestrichtian, as at Todos Santos Bay, and at Point Loma, San Diego County. The example figured by Stewart, which has nearly the size of Gabb's figure, has the following dimensions:

Length (incomplete), 40 mm; height (practically complete), 28.2 mm; thickness, *ca.* 3.5 mm. According to Fairbanks (1893, p. 474-475), the species occurs at both Todos Santos Bay and near Point Loma, associated with *Coralliochama orcutti* White. It may accordingly be regarded as Maestrichtian in age.

"Tellina" alisoensis Packard

Tellina alisoensis PACKARD, Univ. Calif. Pub., Bull. Dept. Geol. Sci., vol. 13, No. 10, 1922, p. 426, Pl. 33, fig. 3; Horizon; Chico group, "*Tellina oöides* Zone," Santiago district, Orange County.

Packard gives the following description of the species:

"Shell small, elongated, inequilateral; dorsal margin slightly convex, approximately paralleling the nearly straight base line; posterior extremity bluntly pointed; anterior dorsal margin sloping abruptly to the slightly truncated extremity. Beaks inconspicuous, situated at about one-fourth the distance from the anterior to the posterior end; an indistinct ridge extends from the beak to the anterior end." . . . Length of type, 16.5 mm; height, 11 mm. "Horizon.—Chico group, *Tellina oöides* zone."

The horizon given by Packard is that of *Legumen ooides* (Gabb), which, as shown by Popenoe (1937, p. 394), is "rare in the Williams formation" in the Santiago district, Orange County. Its stratigraphic position in this area is shown by Popenoe (1942, Fig. 4), to be that of the Pleasants zone, characterized by *Metaplacenticeras pacificum* (Smith), and by its congener, *M. californicum* (Anderson), and is Coniacian in age.

Tellina (Arcopagia) tehama Anderson

Tellina (Arcopagia) tehama ANDERSON, Geol. Soc. Am., Special Paper, No. 16, 1938, p. 123, Pl. 7, figs. 3, 3a; Middle fork of Cottonwood Creek, and Dry Creek, Tehama County.

The shell resembles *Arcopagia circinalis* d'Orbigny, but it belongs to a lower stratigraphic horizon (lower Cenomanian or older). The author stated (1938, p. 123) that the species was found also in the uppermost beds of the Horsetown group, on Dry Creek, but later investigation has proved this statement to be in error. Its true position is in the basal beds of the Upper Cretaceous, which were not well exposed at the time of the earlier account. As now known, the species becomes a definite index fossil, though rare, of the lowest beds of the Upper Cretaceous series, occurring a little below the horizon of *Calycoceras newboldi* (Kossmat), found in the same zone in a neighboring section, that of the Middle fork, about 1000 feet above the basal bed of the series.

Tellina santana Packard

Tellina santana PACKARD, Univ. Calif. Publ., Bull. Dept. Geol. Sci., vol. 13, No. 10, 1922, p. 426, Pl. 33, fig. 4; "*Tellina oöides* zone" in the Santiago district, Orange County.

Packard's description of this species reads:

"Shell small, very thin, elongated, very nearly equilateral; posterior dorsal margin sloping with a straight line to the evenly rounded posterior end; anterior dorsal margin slightly concave near the beaks, then sloping in a broadly rounded curve, base arcuate. Beaks small; surface smooth, with indistinct, incremental lines of growth. Hinge unknown. Anterior adductor scar pear-shaped. Length of type, 35.5 mm; height, 18 mm; beak, 16 mm from the anterior extremity.

Horizon.—Chico group, *Tellina oöides* zone."

As shown for the preceding species, the horizon is that of the Pleasants zone in the Santiago district, and is characterized by *Metaplacenticeras pacificum* (Smith), and *M. californicum* (Anderson), Coniacian.

Genus **Agnomyax** Stewart
Agnomyax monilifera (Gabb)

Tellina monilifera GABB, Paleont. Calif., vol. 1, 1864, p. 157, Pl. 22, figs. 134, 134a; Texas Flat, Placer County. . . . Vol. 2, 1869, p. 257; Chico group, Texas Flat. . . . MERRIAM, doubtfully recognized in his list of type specimens in the Museum of Paleontology (1895).
Agnomyax monilifera (Gabb), STEWART, Acad. Nat. Sci. Phila., Special Pub., No. 3, 1930, p. 283, Pl. 17, fig. 9 (showing hinge characters).

On the basis of a fragment of a right valve, showing a small anterior cardinal (tooth), and a larger bifid cardinal, and other hinge parts, Stewart erected the genus *Agnomyax*.

The type was obtained at Texas Flat, Placer County. The fauna from this locality, as stated by Whitney (1865, p. 202–203), consists of a large number of Cretaceous fossils (30 species, as listed by Gabb), were collected by Trask from a shaft, 40 feet in depth. Eighteen of these species, including the present one, were peculiar to this locality. The collection was placed in the California Academy of Sciences, where it remained until 1906, when it was destroyed in the San Francisco fire.

Family MACTRIDAE Gray 1837
Genus **Cymbophora** Gabb
Cymbophora ashburnerii (Gabb)

Mactra ashburnerii GABB, Paleont. Calif., vol. 1, 1864, p. 153, Pl. 22, fig. 127; Pentz and Chico Creek, Butte County, California.
Cymbophora ashburnerii GABB, Paleont. Calif., vol. 2, 1869, p. 180, 181; Chico Creek, and Pentz, Butte County. (Senonian).
(?) Not *Mactra ashburneri* Gabb, WHITE, U. S. Geol. Survey, Bull. 51, 1889, p. 42, Vancouver and Sucia Islands, and at other places in British Columbia and in California. . . . ANDERSON, Proc. Calif. Acad. Sci., 3d ser., vol. 2, 1902, p. 31; Lower and Upper Chico beds.
Cymbophora ashburneri Gabb, WHITEAVES, Meso. Foss., vol. 1, pt. 2, 1879, p. 141; pt. 5, 1903, pp. 374, 408; Nanaimo group, Vancouver Island.
Spisula ashburnerii (Gabb), PACKARD, Univ. Calif., Pub. Bull. Dept. Geol., vol. 9, No. 12, 1916, p. 154; Chico Creek, Pentz and Santa Ana Mountains. . . . vol. 9, No. 15, 1916, p. 298, pl. 26, figs. 4, 5; pl. 27, fig. 1; locality not stated.
Cymbophora ashburnerii (Gabb), STEWART, Acad. Nat. Sci. Phila., Special Pub., No. 3, 1930, p. 212; (not Pl. 5, fig. 6; Texas Flat). Stewart gives a review of the record of this species on the West Coast.

The specimen figured by Stewart is from Texas Flat, Placer County. The horizon to which this locality is properly referable is not that of Pentz and Chico Creek, but older (? Santonian).

References have sometimes been made to the species in Horsetown strata of the Shasta series in California, but this appears to be an error.

After prolonged search in the field and in the literature pertaining to it, the writer is of the opinion that no authentic record exists of the occurrence of this species in strata older than the Turonian and it is doubtful whether it can be shown to occur below the horizon of the Chico formation.

Stanton (1894) makes no mention of this species in his account of the "Chico beds" on the North fork of the Cottonwood Creek, Shasta County, nor in the section of the same found on Elder Creek. Gabb's holotype was obtained at Pentz, and Ashburner found it on Chico Creek. Its horizon is normally that of the Chico formation (lower or middle Campanian), where it is associated with forms of *Mortoniceras,* of the group of M. *delewarense* (Morton), and with *Canadoceras* Spath.

Cymbophora gabbiana (Anderson)

Mactra gabbiana ANDERSON, Proc. Calif. Acad. Sci., 3d ser., vol. 2, 1902, p. 74, Pl. 7, fig. 156; lower Chico beds near Henley, and on Willow Creek, Siskiyou County, California.
Spisula gabbiana (Anderson), PACKARD, Univ. Calif. Pub. Bull. Dept. Geol., vol. 9, No. 12, 1916, p. 147; *Turritella pescaderoensis* zone, Santiago district, Orange County. . . . PACKARD, Univ. Calif. Pub. Bull. Dept. Geol., vol. 9, No. 15, p. 299, Pl. 27, fig. 2; Rancheria ("Henley") Creek, and Chico Creek, "and numerous other Chico localities of California."
Cymbophora gabbiana (Anderson), STEWART, Acad. Nat. Sci. Phila., Special Pub., No. 3, 1930, p. 211; referred to Upper Cretaceous, only. . . . POPENOE, Jour. Paleont., vol. 11, 1937, p. 398, Pl. 49, fig. 2; showing hinge features of the right valve; Holz member of Ladd formation, *rare;* Williams formation, very abundant. . . . POPENOE, Am. Ass. Petrol. Geol., Bull., vol. 26, 1942, Figure 4; showing the species to occur abundantly in, and above the Pleasants member of the Williams formation, and more rarely in the Schultz member of the same.

Packard (1916, p. 299), referring the species to *Spisula* (Gray), emended the original description, emphasizing the radial markings on the shell and in other respects contrasting it with *Cymbophora ashburneri* Gabb, which is related and in part contemporary. The species seems to have appeared during later Turonian time and therefore somewhat earlier than the preceding species, and to have run a parallel course, both terminating during the Senonian. There is little evidence that the species continued into the Maestrichtian, or later.

The holotype, as restored, had the following dimensions: length, 44 mm; height, 33 mm; apparent convexity of valve, 11 mm. It has been found at Pentz, and according to Popenoe, in the Santiago district, and most abundantly in the Pleasants zone of the Williams formation (lower Senonian), but continuing into the lower Campanian, although it has not yet been recorded from intervening stages.

(?) Cymbophora truncata Gabb

Lutraria truncata GABB, Paleont. Calif., vol. 1, 1864, p. 154, Pl. 22, fig. 128; Pentz (Pence's ranch), Butte County. . . . vol. 2, 1869, p. 236; Pentz and Chico Creek.
Spisula truncata (Gabb) DALL, Trans. Wagner Inst. Sci., vol. 3, pt. 4, 1898, p. 879; locality as given by Gabb.
Spisula chicoensis PACKARD, Univ. Calif. Pub., Bull. Dept. Geol., vol. 9, No. 15, 1916, p. 300, Pl. 27, figs. 6, 7; Pentz and Chico Creek, Butte County.
"Lutraria" truncata Gabb, STEWART, Acad. Nat. Sci. Phila., Special Pub., No. 3, 1930, p. 213, Pl. 4, fig. 10; "an incomplete internal cast" proposed as lectotype, with some reserve.

Stewart adheres to the name *"Lutraria" truncata* Gabb, to which attention had been called by Packard. This procedure seems hardly to be in the line of progress suggested by himself (1930, p. 211) of referring all Cretaceous Mactridae to the genus *Cymbophora* Gabb. However, this species was described by Gabb as follows:

"Shell thin, compressed, somewhat elongated, length compares with the breadth as about four to three; beaks nearly central, small, acute and slightly inclined forwards; anterior cardinal margin slightly sinuous, posterior convex, nearly straight; anterior end rounded; posterior obliquely truncated, gaping. Surface marked by faint irregular lines of growth."

Concerning the lunule, Stewart adds: "Though not defined, the lunule is large and slightly depressed, the anterior dorsal margin of the shell being sinuous." . . .

Packard's figure conforms very closely to that of Gabb, he gives the following dimensions: length, 50 mm; height, 35 mm; convexity, 8 mm. plus. As indicated by Gabb (1869, p. 236), the species occurs chiefly in the Chico formation, as at Pentz and Chico Creek, although it may later be found at the same horizon in other areas.

Cymbophora buttensis Anderson n. sp.
(Plate 61, figure 3)

Fully grown individuals are much larger than any previously described from the Upper Cretaceous on the West Coast. Larger forms are known in the Tertiary and in the living fauna, some resembling the form here figured, so that it is not striking except in the Upper Cretaceous. In size and form it may be compared with living stocks, such as the undescribed type, figured but not named by Packard (1916, Pl. 26, fig. 6).

The species is represented by the holotype and paratype (Calif. Acad. Sci. Type Coll.), the latter being much larger but less well preserved. The holotype is large, roundly triangular, and somewhat produced anteriorly; ratio of length to height about 5 to 4, and that of the paratype nearly the same. Both were found at Pentz, and show some individual differences. The lunular area, not visible from the side, is deep and slightly overhung by its borders; the surface, insofar as preserved, is smooth, or marked only by lines of growth.

The umbonal area is a little swollen, and the posterior border is roundly truncated, or more roundly curved than the anterior; the test is thick and brittle, and for this reason the larger part of the paratype has crumbled away, leaving an incomplete cast exposed.

The holotype and paratype were collected by Bennison and the writer at locality 1125 (C. A. S.), 1 mile west of Pentz, on the south side of the road, in the ravines leading to the southwest. The holotype has the following dimensions: length, 60 mm; height, 46 mm; thickness, a maximum width for a single valve, 12 mm.

The paratype has a length of 97 mm; a height of 77 mm; and an original thickness of 12 mm. Possibly the examples mentioned by Gabb (1864, p. 153) as being "a third larger" than the average size of *"Mactra" ashburneri,* belonged to this species.

Cymbophora stantoni (Arnold)

Mactra stantoni ARNOLD, U. S. Nat. Museum, Proc., vol. 34, 1908, p. 357, Pl. 31, fig. 3; locality 27, 1 mile north of Pigeon Point, Santa Cruz quadrangle. . . . Arnold, Santa Cruz Folio, No. 163, 1909, Explanations of Illustrations, Sheet 11, fig. 3 (reprint of above).
Mactra (?) stantoni ARNOLD, PACKARD, Univ. Calif. Pub. Bull. Dept. Geol., vol. 9, No. 15, p. 311; the author repeats description and dimensions given by Arnold; length of type, 50 mm; height, 34 mm; convexity (single valve), 12 mm. Umbonal angle, 120 degrees.

The definite horizon of this species is not yet known. From the two accounts given by Arnold, and from his lists of invertebrate species it appears certain that two distinct stratigraphic groups are present in the area shown on the map, the older of which represents some portion of the Campanian, and the other part of the Maestrichtian. From which of these units the holotype of the species was derived is not yet clear, though its resemblance to *Cymbophora ashburneri* Gabb, suggests the older. A similar form occurs also in the younger.

Family SAXICAVIDAE Gray
Genus Panope Menard
Panope concentrica (Gabb)

Panopaea concentrica GABB, Paleont. Calif., vol. 1, 1864, p. 148, Pl. 22, fig. 119; Cottonwood Creek, Shasta County (? not Martinez). . . .
Homomya (Panopaea) concentrica GABB, vol. 2, 1869, p. 179; Cottonwood Creek, etc. . . .
MERRIAM, 1895 (checklist of type specimens found in the Museum of Paleontology, University of California) . . . ANDERSON, Proc. Calif. Acad. Sci., 3d ser., vol. 2, 1902, p. 32, (gives a list of species compiled from existing literature).
Panopea ? concentrica Gabb, STEWART, Acad. Nat. Sci. Phila., Special Pub., No. 3, 1930, p. 249; Type specimen discussed; "Cottonwood."
Panope concentrica (Gabb), ANDERSON, Geol. Soc. Am., Special Papers, No. 16, 1938, p. 123; "Uppermost beds of Horsetown group; old Horsetown, Loc. 1344 (C. A. S.), Clear Creek, Shasta County, Calif.

The uppermost Cretaceous beds exposed at Horsetown, from which this species was obtained, should be regarded as properly belonging in the lowest part of the upper Cretaceous series. The hoiotype of the species was probably found on the Cottonwood Creek, but it occurs also at old Horsetown, and at Texas Springs, 3 miles to the east, in the basal beds of the series, where it overlaps upon the greenstones and metamorphic rocks of this area, associated with a considerable fauna regarded as early Cenomanian.

Class GASTROPODA
Genus Anisomyon Meek and Hayden
Anisomyon meekii Gabb

Anisomyon Meekii GABB, Paleont. Calif. vol. 1, 1864, p. 142; Pl. 21, fig. 105; North fork of Cottonwood Creek, Shasta County, California. . . . vol 2, 1869, p. 231; locality as above. . . . STEWART, Acad. Nat. Sci. Phila., Proc., vol. 78, 1926, p. 312; locality as above.

The exact locality of the holotype of this species is not known; the only indication given by Gabb was "Division A," North fork of the Cottonwood Creek. However, a good example of the species was found by the writer at locality 2233 (C. A. S.), about half a mile east of the mouth of Hulen Creek, in beds recognized as upper Cenomanian. This discovery confirms Gabb's record and fixes the stratigraphic position of the species. It was found here associated with *Phylloceras velledae* Forbes, *Puzosia* aff. *P. planulata,* and other invertebrate species usually regarded as Cenomanian. A second example was found near Jacksonville, Oregon, in strata of nearly the same horizon, which also contained *Turritlites oregonensis* Gabb.

The occurrence of this species in these localities indicates a near-shore position of these beds, and conforms to an early upper Cretaceous overlap upon older (basement) rocks in the near vicinity.

Genus Patella Linnaeus
Patella traskii Gabb

Patella Traskii GABB, Paleont. Calif., vol. 1, 1864, p. 140, Pl. 21, fig. 103; Texas Flat, Placer County, California. . . . vol. 2, 1869, p. 173, 230; Texas Flat, Placer County. . . . STEWART, Acad. Nat. Sci. Phila., Proc. vol. 78, 1926, p. 312; locality as above.

This small and rare species was found only at Texas Flat, where the holotype was obtained from a marine near-shore bed at the bottom of a deep shaft, now caved in.

Family HALIOTIDAE Fleming
Genus Haliotis Linnaeus
Haliotis lomaënsis Anderson
(Plate 21, figure 12)

Haliotis lomaënsis ANDERSON, Proc. Calif. Acad. Sci., 3d ser., vol. 2, 1902, p. 75, Pl. 9, fig. 183; Point Loma, near San Diego, California.

Shell is small, oval in outline, and depressed. Holotype No. 69 (C. A. S. Type Coll.) has the following dimensions: length, 13 mm; width, about 8.6 mm; thickness, little more than 3 mm; spire low and indistinct; margins of shell are equally curved; back is angled near the row of perforations, of which there are 4, equally spaced, and a slight marginal notch; surface of shell marked by concentric lines extending around body whorl near margin, and showing indistinct radial lines.

The species appears to belong to Tryon's group of *Haliotis iris.* The holotype, the only example known, is in the type collection of the Academy of Sciences, having been recovered from the ashes of the San Francisco fire of 1906. This example was discovered by H. W. Fairbanks at Point Loma and was given to the California State Mining Bureau, but at the time of the fire was at the Academy and was later given to this institution.

The species was supposed to represent an "upper Chico" horizon, and later investigation has proved that it occurs below the zone of *Coralliochama orcutti* White, and below that of *Parapachydiscus.* It is accordingly low in the Pacific Coast Maestrichtian and probably somewhat older than *Haliotis antiqua* Binkhorst.

Family TROCHIDAE Adams
Genus **Trochus** Linnaeus
Subgenus **Oxystele** Philippi
Trochus (Oxystele) euryostomus White

Trochus (Oxystele) euryostomus WHITE, U. S. Geol. Survey, Bull. 22, 1885, p. 12, Pl. 7, figs. 2, 10, 11; Todos Santos Bay, Lower California; Gualala group (Chico series).

The following description of the species was given by White:

"Shell small, depressed-subturbinate; volutions about four in number, rounded, and, at the distal border, more or less distinctly appressed against the preceding volution; aperture comparatively large, and in adult shells, the inner lip is appressed against the last volution as a callus covering of a portion of the base of the shell, but its margin being a little elevated, it forms, together with the thin outer lip, a continuous margin to the aperture. In immature shells the callus of the inner lip is not formed, and the margin of the aperture is therefore not then continuous. Surface marked by numerous sharply raised revolving, somewhat crumpled ridges, separated by grooves of similar width."

Height, 6mm; greatest diameter of the last volution, 8 mm.

Subgenus **Anadema** H. and A. Adams
Trochus (Anadema) gemiferus White

Trochus (Anadema) gemiferus WHITE, U. S. Geol. Survey, Bull 51, 1889, p. 17, Pl. 4, figs 8, 9; Chico group, near Pentz, Butte County.

For this species White gives the following description (in part):

"Shell small, depressed-conical, the height being somewhat less than the greatest diameter; aperture subcircular, oblique; umbilicus small and deep; inner lip with a callus at its upper portion, which borders a part of the umbilicus, slightly thickened below, where it bears just within its outer edge a small distinct tubercule-like tooth having somewhat the appearance of a small adherent pearl." Height 13 mm; greatest breadth, 16 mm; Position and locality, Chico formation, near Pentz, Butte County, California.

Genus **Calliostoma** Swainson
Calliostoma radiatum Gabb

Calliostoma radiatum GABB, Paleont. Calif., vol. 2, 1869, p. 170, Pl. 28, fig. 53; Texas Flat, Placer County, California.

Gabb's description reads (in part) as follows:

"Shell minute, broadly conical; whorls four (or more), sides flat, sloping; suture well marked. Surface ornamented by fourteen or fifteen large radiating ribs, which produce an undulation of the upper margin of the whorl, and abut against a strongly marked revolving rib bordering the lower angle; these are crossed by six or seven smaller revolving elevated lines; under surface marked by numerous minute, revolving striae. Aperture subquadrate; inner lip straight, slightly oblique and thickened."

Length, 4.06 mm; width, 4.57 mm; ? Santonian

Calliostoma constrictum Whiteaves

Calliostoma constrictum WHITEAVES, Meso. Foss., vol. 1, pt. 3, 1884, p. 217, Pl. 28, figs. 4, 4a; east end of Maud Island, Queen Charlotte Islands, B. C.

The description of this species reads (in part) as follows:

"Shell conical, trochiform, length and breadth about equal; whorls four or four and a half, those of the spire obliquely compressed; sutures distinct, flattened at nearly a right angle to the side of the whorls or somewhat excavated; last whorl about two-thirds of the entire length, (in a dosal view) concavely and shallowly constricted or grooved above the middle, most prominent a little below the center; axis imperforate."

Height, 17.5 mm; maximum breadth, 17 mm; height of body whorl, 11 mm.

According to MacKenzie's map, published by the Canadian Geologic Survey (1916) the horizon of its area is within the Haida formation, and should be considered to be not younger than Cenomanian.

Calliostoma kempiana Cooper

Calliostoma kempiana COOPER, Calif. State Min. Bur., Bull. No. 4, 1894, p. 46, Pl. 3, figs. 33, 34; West base of Point Loma, near San Diego, Calif.

The horizon of this species is near the base of the Maestrichtian in this area, occurring associated with *Coralliochama orcutti* White.

Genus Margarites, "Leach," Gray
Subgenus Atira Stewart
Margarites (Atira) ornatissima (Gabb)

Angaria ornatissima GABB, Paleont. Calif., vol. 1, 1864, p. 121, Pl. 20, fig. 78; Texas Flat, Placer County. . . . vol. 2, 1869, p. 229; locality as above.
Margarita ornatissima, WHITEAVES, Meso. Foss., vol. 1, pt. 2, 1879, p. 128; Hornby Island, near Vancouver Island. . . . Pt. 5, 1903, p. 368; Sucia Island, western Washington.
Margarites (Atira) ornatissima, STEWART, Acad. Nat. Sci. Phila., Proc., vol. 78, 1926, p. 316, Pl. 24, fig. 1; (enlarged, X 3).

The specimen figured by Stewart was proposed as the lectotype, of which he states:

"Beneath the thin, chalky, finely reticulate, ornamentation, the shell is nacreous. The umbilical angle is distinct but not ridged."

Height (of lectotype, the largest specimen), 9.9 mm; width, 10.1 mm.

The horizon from which Gabb obtained the holotype of this species is not certainly known, though it appears to be not younger than Santonian, as elsewhere shown, though it may be in the upper part of the Coniacian.

Margarites (Atira) inornata (Gabb)

Architectonica inornata GABB, Paleont. Calif., vol. 1, 1864, p. 118, Pl. 20, fig. 73; hills southwest of Martinez, Contra Costa County. . . . vol. 2, 1869, p. 224; locality as above. . . .
DALL, Trans. Wag. Inst., vol. 3, 1892, p. 330; referred to Trochidae. . . . ANDERSON, Proc. Calif. Acad. Sci., 3d ser., vol. 2, 1902, p. 29.
Solarium inornatum (Gabb), STANTON, U. S. Geol. Survey, Ann. Rept., vol. 17, pt. 1, p. 1023, etc. . . . MERRIAM, Jour. Geology, vol. 5, 1897, p. 770; listed from "locality 1," near Martinez (not Tuscan Springs).
Margarites(Atira) inornatus (Gabb), STEWART, Acad. Nat. Sci. Phila., Proc., vol. 78, 1926, p. 315, Pl. 24, fig. 2a (enlarged); height, 9.5 mm; width, 11.8 mm; near Martinez, as above.

As stated by Gabb, this species was first found near Martinez, and probably at the locality referred to by Merriam as "locality 1," a mile or more southwest of Martinez.

This locality was visited by the writer, with Merriam, in 1897, and was thought to be that often referred to by Gabb, from which many invertebrate fossils had been collected, and described by him.

Genus Margaritella Meek and Hayden
Margaritella globosa Gabb

Margaritella globosa GABB, Paleont. Calif., vol. 1, 1864, p. 119, Pl. 29, fig. 225; near Benicia, Solano County. . . . vol. 2, 1869, p. 228; locality as above. . . . ANDERSON, Proc. Calif. Acad. Sci., 3d ser., vol. 2, 1902, p. 29; "Forty-nine" mine, Jackson County, Oregon. . . .
"Margaritella" globosa Gabb, STEWART, Acad. Nat. Sci. Phila., Proc. vol. 78, 1926, p. 291. (type not found).

The type locality of this species is given as Benicia, California. Its horizon is not yet clear. Most of the Cretaceous invertebrates collected near the town in recent years represent the Senonian stage, rather than older beds, though older strata are indicated 2 miles north; to which horizon this species belongs has not been clearly determined. Cooper (in Fairbanks, 1893, p. 476) reports the species in a collection made at Point Loma, associated with *Coralliochama orcutti* White, from which the Maestrichtian might be inferred. Until more definite evidence has been found, little can be said as to the true horizon of the species.

Family NATICIDAE Forbes
Genus **Gyrodes** Conrad

According to Stephenson (1941, p. 279) the genotype of *Gyrodes* is *Natica (Gyrodes) crenata* Conrad, which he regards as synonymous with *Gyrodes supraplicatus* (Conrad) (Pl. 51, figs. 13–16).

Natica (Gyrodes) conradiana (Gabb)
(Plate 21, figures 2, 3)

?Lunatia (Gyrodes?) conradiana GABB, Paleont. Calif. vol. 1, 1864, p. 107, Pl. 29, fig. 219; San Luis Gonzaga Ranch, at east end of Pacheco Pass. . . . vol. 2, 1869, p. 222.
Gyrodes conradiana Gabb, STEWART, Acad. Nat. Sci. Phila., Proc., vol. 78, 1926, p. 329, (? pl. 22, fig. 2). Locality not stated.

Gabb's characterization is simple and sufficiently clear, although more emphasis should be given to the following statement:

"Umbilicus broadly open, perspective, forming about half the diameter of the lower aspect of the shell; margin subangular. Surface externally and in the umbilicus, marked by fine lines of growth."

These features are diagnostic of the species.

The holotype figured by Gabb was found at the "east end of The Pacheco Pass," where the lower beds of the Upper Cretaceous are well exposed. This species and others of Cenomanian age have been found by McCoy, Bennison and the writer, in this horizon farther north and farther south, near Los Banos Creek.

The 2 hypotypes (C. A. S. Type Coll.) here figured were collected by the writer on the North fork of Cottonwood Creek, Shasta County, at locality 1346A (C. A. S.) in the lower beds of the Upper Cretaceous series. They have the following dimensions: (Pl. 21, fig. 2) Height, incomplete, 31 mm; greatest width, 45 mm; greatest width of umbilicus, 18 mm; (Pl. 21, fig. 3) height, 23 mm; greatest width, 25 mm; greatest width of umbilicus, 10 mm. Smaller examples of the species were also collected at the same locality, all showing the sutural zones deeply excavated. This species greatly resembles the genotype of *Gyrodes*, as figured by Stephenson.

Gyrodes expansa Gabb

Gyrodes expansa GABB, Paleont, Calif. vol. 1, 1864, p. 108, Pl. 19, figs. 62, a, b, c; Hills southwest of Martinez, Contra Costa County. . . . vol. 2, 1869, p. 222; locality as above. . . . STEWART, Acad. Nat. Sci. Phila., Proc., vol. 78, 1926, p. 328, Pl. 22, figs. 1, 1a and 3; an example obtained by Gabb (no. 4245) chosen as the lectotype, with dimensions of the same given.

To ascertain the true stratigraphic habitus of this species, and others described by Gabb, it is assumed that the locality of the holotype is the first one mentioned in his statement as to its geographic distribution.

Gabb's characterization of the species appears to be sufficient, except as to the umbilical pit, which according to his statement is "patulous," meaning expanding, as is indicated by the name, but without a bordering angle, as in the preceding species.

Assuming that the zone of its occurrence is southwest and west of Martinez, where the higher beds of the Upper Cretaceous are exposed, the stratigraphic level of its occurrence would be equivalent to that of the Garzas formation near the top of the series. However, Gabb has named many localities at which he believed this species to occur. The species itself appears to have been strictly littoral in habitat, ranging from early Turonian to Maestrichtian time, and spanning various episodes of diastrophism.

Gyrodes dowelli White
(Plate 21, figures 8, 9)

Gyrodes dowelli WHITE, U. S. Geol. Survey, Bull. 51, 1889, p. 19, Pl. 3, figs. 8, 9; Chico group, near Jacksonville, Oregon.

White's description of the species reads in part as follows:

"Shell of medium size, depressed, oblique, spire slightly elevated; volutions, four or five in number, the last one much expanded, broadly rounded at the outer side and abruptly rounded and somewhat shouldered at the distal side; those of the spire convex; suture distinct, impressed; umbilicus somewhat narrow, deep; its border abruptly rounded and marked by numerous oblique crenulations. Somewhat similar flexuous crenulations mark the upper, or distal side of the volutions near the suture, with which exception the surface is plain; aperture obliquely suboval, outer lip, thin; inner lip bordering the umbilicus, thin and convex."

Hypotype (C. A. S. Type Coll.) has the following dimensions: height, 36 mm; width 32 mm; width umbilical pit, 12 mm. locality 1293-A (C. A. S.), 1 mile north of Frazier Corners, Shasta County.

Gyrodes siskiyouensis Anderson
(Plate 21, figures 6, 7)

Gyrodes siskiyouensis ANDERSON, Proc. Calif. Acad. Sci., 3d ser., vol. 2, 1902, p. 76, Pl. 8, figs. 167, 168; north slope of the Siskiyou Mountains, 4 miles southwest of Ashland, Jackson County, Oregon.

The account of this species given by the writer (1902, p. 76) reads in part:

"Shell moderate in size, subglobose, though a little compressed, spire low; upper surface a little flattened near the suture, forming a narrow ledge and angle; the whole surface plainly marked by revolving lines, most developed near the angle above; umbilicus open and slightly angled; no lines of growth visible, except on perfectly preserved shells."

The species is abundant on the north slope of the Siskiyou Mountains, as at an old quarry 4 miles southwest of Ashland, where it was found associated with *Pugnellus manubriatus* Gabb, and *Pachydiscus ashlandicus* (Anderson). The species is assigned to an upper Turonian age on the basis of its stratigraphic occurrence, and on that of its associates.

Holotype 41 (C. A. S. Type Coll.) has the following dimensions: height, 22 mm; width, 23 mm.

Genus Polinices Montfort
Polinices shumardiana (Gabb)

Lunatia Shumardiana GABB, Paleont. Calif., vol. 1, 1864, Pl. 19, fig. 61; Hills southwest of Martinez; . . . vol. 2, 1869, p. 222; locality as given above. . . .
Not *Polinices shumardianus* (Gabb), STEWART, Acad. Nat. Sci. Phila., Proc. vol. 78, 1926, p. 325; locality as given above.
Not *Euspira shumardiana* (Gabb) POPENOE, Jour. Paleont., vol. 11, 1937, p. 398, Pl. 49, fig. 3 (no. 3452); not *Gyrodes compressus* WARING, 1917, north slope of Santa Monica Mountains; not *Gyrodes californica* PACKARD, 1922, Pl. 35, figs. 2a, 2b; Chico group, Santa Ana Mountains.

Merriam did not include the name of Gabb's species in his list of Type Specimens found at the University of California in 1895, and its location is yet unknown.

Stewart remarks concerning the materials found at the University in 1926, that: "Of the numerous specimens so labelled, that figured here best agrees with the description and the figure (given by Gabb)."

His figured specimen is offered as the "lectotype" of the species. Gabb's figure of his type is said to be 'natural size,' and measurements taken from it show the following dimensions: height, 25 mm; width, 20 mm; the ratio of width to height is, therefore, 4 : 5. Stewart gives a ratio for his "lectotype" of 1 : 1. Although these two types are readily referable to the genus *Polinices* Montfort, the figure given by Stewart (Pl. 21, fig. 11) seems specifically distinct from that given by Gabb (1864, pl. 19, figure 61), as shown in the illustrations. The robust form figured by Stewart cannot be shown to conform to that figured by Gabb in any essential detail.

Popenoe seems to have accepted the example figured by Stewart (Pl. 21. fig. 11) as an authentic representation of *Polinices shumardiana* (Gabb), and has accordingly considered *Polinices compressus* (Waring) and *Polinices californica* (Packard), synonomous, although neither of them is equivalent to *Polinices shumardiana* (Gabb).

Polinices compressus (Waring)

Gyrodes compressus WARING, Proc. Calif. Acad. Sci., 4th ser., vol. 7, 1917, p. 67, Pl. 9, fig. 6; locality 1, (L. S. J. U. Pal. Coll.).
Gyrodes californica PACKARD, Univ. Calif. Pub. Bull. Dept. Geol. Sci., vol 13, 1922, p. 429, Pl. 35, figs. 2a, 2b; Santa Ana Mountains.
Euspira Shumardiana (Gabb), POPENOE, Jour. Paleont., vol. 11, 1937, p. 398, Pl. 49, fig. 3; Williams formation, Santa Ana Mountains, not *Polinices shumardiana* (Gabb).
Not *Polinices shumardianus* (Gabb), STEWART, as shown above.

A careful reading of the records of the above types will probably convince most students of the subject as to the essential correctness of the account here given. Not all of these types have been obtained from the same horizon.

Polinices gainesanus Anderson n. sp.
(Plate 30, figures 1, 1a)

This species is characterized by a thin shell, prominent spire, and a distinct, impressed suture, bordered by a narrow tabular zone at summit of whorl; base of whorls rounded; umbilicus open and deep; aperture broadly ovate, narrower in front than in its posterior half; surface marked only by distinct, oblique lines of growth. The holotype and an immature example were found at locality 1346A (C. A. S.), in the lower beds of the Cenomanian, on the North fork of Cottonwood Creek, beneath the second conglomerate, associated with *Parapuzosia colusaensis* Anderson, and *Desmoceras* aff. *D. barryae* n. sp. Holotype (C. A. S. Type Coll.) has the following dimensions: maximum height, 33 mm; maximum width of body-whorl, 34 mm; height of aperature, 24 mm. Lower Cenomanian.

Polinices mercedensis Anderson n. sp.
(Plate 70, figure 5)

Shell moderately large, globose, thick and smooth; spire consisting of three or four whorls, prominent; whorls marked by a slight depression below suture; surface smooth, or marked only by oblique lines of growth; aperture ovate, outer border circular; umbilicus small, forming a narrow but deep pit; outer lip thin, semicircular; inner lip smooth, bearing a narrow callus on its posterior half; surface marked by oblique lines of growth, curving backward from aperture. Holotype (C. A. S. Type Coll.) was found by Bennison at locality 30556 (C. A. S.) on Los Banos Creek, on the NE ¼ of NE ¼ of sec. 12, T. 11 S., R. 9 E. It has the following dimensions: maximum height, 45 mm; maximum width, 37 mm; height of aperture, 30 mm. Lower Maestrichtian.

Genus Ampullina Lamarck
Ampullina oviformis (Gabb)

Amauropsis oviformis GABB, Paleont. Calif. vol. 1, 1864, p. 109, Pl. 19, fig. 63; Tuscan Springs, Tehama County. . . . vol. 2, 1869, p. 223; locality as above; (probably Santonian).
Ampullina oviformis (Gabb), STEWART, Acad. Nat. Sci. Phila, Proc., vol. 78, 1926, p. 333, Pl. 21, Pl. 21, fig. 10 (not the holotype, but no. 4256 (Acad. Nat. Sci. Phila.). The holotype (Univ. Calif. Coll., no. 31391); height, 35.4 mm; width, 26.4 mm; locality as above.

Gabb's brief description reads as follows:

"Shell ovoid; spire rather elevated; whorls six, rounded; suture slightly channeled. Aperture moderate, acute posteriorly, expanded in advance; columella faintly incrusted; umbilicus imperforate. Surface marked by irregular and sometimes very distinct lines of growth."

Ampullina avellana (Gabb)
(Plate 4, figure 4)

Lunatia avellana GABB, Paleont. Calif., vol. 1, 1864, p. 106, Pl. 19, fig. 60; North Fork of Cottonwood Creek, Shasta County. . . . vol. 2, 1869, p. 222; locality as above. . . . STANTON, Geol. Soc. Am., Bull., vol. 4, 1893, p. 250, etc.; vol. 5, 1894, p. 439, 443, etc.; lower beds of Chico group, Elder Creek and North fork Cottonwood Creek, Shasta County. . . . ANDERSON, Proc. Calif. Acad. Sci., 3d ser., vol. 2, 1902, p. 38, 41, etc.; lower Chico beds, Cottonwood Creek.
Ampullina avellana (Gabb), STEWART, Acad. Nat. Sci. Phila., Proc. vol. 78, 1926, p. 333,

Pl. 21, fig. 9; example selected as the "lectotype." . . . ANDERSON, Geol. Soc. Am., Special Papers. No. 16, 1938, pp. 131, 132; Horsetown group, Shasta series, and lower Chico beds.

This species has often been referred to as pertaining to the Shasta "group," although it was found also in the basal beds of the Upper Cretaceous on the North fork of Cottonwood Creek, and on Hulen Creek. The "lectotype" was selected by Stewart from specimens in the Academy of Natural Sciences of Philadelphia. The present writer (1938) has shown that the range of the species is from the lower beds of the Horsetown group upward into the lower beds of the Upper Cretaceous

Ampullina packardi Popenoe

Ampullina Packardi POPENOE, Jour. Paleont., vol. 11, no. 5, 1937, p. 299, Pl. 49, figs. 4, 5; Holz shale member of the Ladd formation, Santa Ana Mountains, Orange County. . . . Am. Assn. Petrol. Geol., Bull., vol. 26, 1942, fig. 4; locality as given above.

Popenoe's description of this species reads in part as follows:

"Shell small to medium in size, robust; spire rather short; body whorl very large, about seven-eights the length of the shell; suture linear, bordered by a narrow sloping shoulder; whorl just below the shoulder markedly impressed by a shallow encircling sulcus; remainder of body whorl globular; . . . columella excavated anteriorly and covered with a smooth heavy callus that entirely conceals the umbilicus; anterior aperautral margin rather broadly rounded with a conspicuous fasciole; . . ."

Holotype (C. I. T.) has the following dimensions: length, 24.1 mm; diameter of last whorl, 20.8 mm; common in Holz shale member of the Ladd formation, Santa Ana Mountains, Orange County, California.

Family TURRITELLIDAE Gray

The Turritellas of the Upper Cretaceous on the West Coast, as reviewed by C. W. Merriam (1941) exhibit a succession of distinctive types in passing from the earlier part of the series to its top. Each of the recognizable stratigraphic units in the series has its own characteristic forms. It would be difficult to prove that any of the different types are genetically related inasmuch as they may have reached the West Coast with invasions from other regions following epochs of diastrophism and of readjustments of sea and shore lines. These several stocks of Turritellas and of their occurrence appear to correspond to diastrophic disturbances, and are useful in stratigraphic diagnosis. According to Merriam, the following groups of Turritellas are recognizable:

I,—Group of *Turritella tolenasensis* Merriam,—characteristic of the "Lower Chico,"— Cenomanian and Turonian—, including:
Turritella petersoni Anderson, and *Turritella hearni* Anderson.
II,—Group of *Turritella chicoensis* Gabb,—characteristic of the Chico formation—early-middle Campanian, including:
Turritella packardi Merriam, and *Turritella pescaderoensis* Arnold.
III,—Group of *Turritella peninsularis* Anderson and Hanna; characteristic of the early and middle Maestrichtian, including:
Turritella chaneyi Merriam, and an undescribed species (*T. "chicoensis"* Schenck)

To the foregoing groups others may be added, including:
Turritella ossa Popenoe, and *Turritella iota* Popenoe,[5] occurring in the Holz member of the Ladd formation; (?) Lower Senonian.

Genus Turritella Lamarck
Turritella chicoensis Gabb

Turritella chicoensis GABB, Paleont. Calif., vol. 1, 1864, p. 133, Pl. 21, fig. 91; Chico Creek, Butte County. . . . vol. 2, 1869, p. 228, locality as given above. . . . WARING, Proc. Calif. Acad. Sci., 4th ser., vol. 7, 1917, p. 69; Pl. 9, fig. 12; locality 2, (L. S. J. U.); Bell.
[5] By error *T. iota* Popenoe was compared with *T. "whiteavesi"* Anderson and Hanna, which is nonexistent; the only species described by Anderson and Hanna was *T. peninsularis,* from the Peninsula of Lower California.

Canyon; upper Senonian. . . . STEWART, Acad. Nat. Sci. Phila., Proc., vol. 78, 1926, p. 348, Pl. 21, fig. 1, Chico Creek, Butte County. . . . MERRIAM, Univ. Calif. Pub., Bull. Dept. Geol., Sci. vol. 26, 1941, p. 66, Pl. 2, figs. 9, 10, 11, 12; Pl. 3, figs. 1, 2, 3, 4, 9; holotype probably at Museum of Paleontology, University of California. Locality, Chico Creek, Butte County. Merriam recognizes two subspecies, *pescaderoensis* Arnold, and *perrini* Merriam.

Turritella petersoni Anderson
(Plate 21, figure 11)

Turritella petersoni (Anderson MS), MERRIAM, Univ. Calif. Publ. Bull. Dept. Geol. Sci., vol. 26, 1941, p. 64, Pl. 1, figs. 10, 11; Peterson ranch, 4 miles north of Sites, Colusa County.

Shell small or of moderate size, tapering rapidly to an accuminate point, sides flattened to an evenly sloping cone, with only slightly impressed sutural groove; surface of whorls marked by three prominent revolving cords, with a less prominent thread at top of whorl, two to three similar threads between each pair of cords, though not all of equal strength; all cords and threads showing a tendency to form beads, increasing with age; a few of the threads intervening between the cords have developed a strength almost equal to the major cords. The irregularities of sculpture increase with age.

Holotype No. 6854 (C. A. S. Type Coll.) has the following dimensions: length, 21 mm; greater width, 6 mm; length of largest example seen, 50 mm. The holotype and various incomplete examples were found at locality 1291 (C. A. S.), on the Peterson ranch, 4 miles north of Sites, Colusa County. Many examples of the same, or of a similar species, were found in somewhat later beds on Swede Creek, east of Millville, Shasta County; associated with *Romaniceras hesperium* n. sp. The holotype, found on the Peterson ranch, is regarded as Cenomanian.

Turritella packardi Merriam

Turritella packardi MERRIAM, Univ. Calif. Pub., Bull. Dept. Geol. Sci., vol. 26, 1941, p. 66, Pl. 3, figs. 5, 6, 7, 8, 10, 11; locality A-810 (Univ. Calif.), between Harding and Williams canyons, Santa Ana Mountains, Orange County.

Holotype No. 15362 (Univ. Calif. Paleont. Type Coll.) is small, having a length of about 38 mm and a diameter of body whorl near 11 mm. This species seems clearly to belong to the group of *Turritella chicoensis* Gabb, as was the view of Merriam.

Turritella hearni Anderson
(Plate 21, figures 10, 10a)

Turritella hearni (Anderson MS) MERRIAM, Univ. Calif. Pub. Bull. Dept. Geol. Sci., vol. 26, 1941, p. 64, Pl. 1, fig. 1–9 (fig. 9, holotype).

The holotype of this species No. 6855 (C. A. S. Type Coll.) was loaned to Merriam for study and illustration, and to him we are indebted for an excellent description and good illustrations.

The type locality is on the Hagerdorn ranch, 4 miles north of Montague, Siskiyou County, with middle Turonian beds in depositional contact with the older terrain.

Holotype (fig. 10) has the following dimensions: length, 29 mm; width, 7 mm.

Hypotype (fig. 10a) has the following dimensions: length, 30 mm; maximum diameter, 10.7 mm.

Turritella tolenasensis Merriam

Turritella seriatim-granulata GABB (not ROEMER), Paleont. Calif., vol. 1, 1864, p. 132, Pl. 20, fig. 88. . . . 1869, p. 227 (in part), STEWART, Acad. Nat. Sci. Phila., Proc., vol. 78, 1926, p. 348, 349; suggests a new name.
Turritella tolenasensis MERRIAM, Univ. Calif. Publ. Bull. Dept. Geol. Sci. vol. 26, 1941, p. 62, Pl. 1, fig. 12; Tolenas Grant, north of Fairfield, Solano County.

In Gabb's account of this species, he names three separate localities, Cottonwood Creek, Shasta County; Siskiyou Mountains, Siskiyou County; and Tuscan Springs, Tehama County, as places of its occurrence. In so doing, he suggests quite as many distinct horizons in which he thought it had been obtained, although he admitted considerable variation in its ornamentation. Forms similar to those figured by Merriam have been seen by the writer on the Cottonwood Creek, in beds correlative with those found on the Tolenas Grant, north of Fairfield. Probably Gabb's type came from the Cottonwood Creek, and it is correctly represented by Merriam's holotype Pl. 1, fig. 12.

Turritella peninsularis Anderson and Hanna
(Plate 64, figure 6)

Turritella peninsularis ANDERSON AND HANNA, Proc. Calif. Acad. Sci. 4th Ser., vol. 23,
    1935, p. 25, Pl. 10, fig. 5; Johnson's ranch, near San Antonio del Mar, Lower California.
Turritella chaneyi MERRIAM (in part), Univ. Calif. Pub., Bull. Dept. Geol. Sci., vol. 26, p. 71,
    Pl. 6, figs. 1, 2, 3, 5, 6; (not figs. 4, 7, 8).

The original description of this species (1935) reads as follows:

"Shell of medium size, robust; whorls subangular; sutural grooves impressed, deep and broad; sides of whorls flattened or slightly concave, surface almost smooth on the holotype, ornamented by faint revolving threads crossed by sinuous lines of growth; aperture subquadrate, spire high, tapering gradually to the apex; whorls rounded on the shoulders."

Many excellent examples of this species have been collected by Allan Bennison, and by J. J. Bryan from the upper beds of the Garzas member to the north and to the south of Garzas Creek, Stanislaus County, in the belt mapped as Moreno by Anderson and Pack (1915). Most of these differ in no essential detail from the holotype of the present species. It appears that *Turritella chaneyi* Merriam may in most part be regarded as a synonym of *Turritella peninsularis* Anderson and Hanna. It is evident from Merriam's account of *T. chaneyi* that the present species had not been called to his attention before the publication of his excellent contribution.

Turritella chaneyi Merriam

Turritella chaneyi MERRIAM (in part), Univ. Calif. Pub., Bull. Dept. of Geol. Sci., vol. 26,
    1941, p. 71, Pl. 6, figs. ? 4, 7, 8 (only). In the explanation of Plate 6, p. 143, figure 8 is
    named as the holotype of the species, to which figures 7, and perhaps 4, seem specifically
    identical. In his description this appears more clearly, as follows:

"Adult ornamentation: some ten or eleven rather broad but subdued spiral ribs, which tend to be irregularly spaced, some broadly, others closely set. Fine threads often lie on broader interspaces. When the median area is slightly concave, a low spiral swelling may be developed in the posterior quarter."

The two foregoing species seem to be related, and it may subsequently be shown that one of them is a subspecies of the other.

Merriam has indicated that "*T. chaneyi* is suggestive of *T. pachecoensis* Stanton, but appears to possess a distinct nuclear ornamentation," etc.

Genus **Nerinea** Defrance
Nerinea dispar Gabb

Nerinea dispar GABB, Paleont. Calif., vol. 1, 1864, p. 113, Pl. 19, figs. 66, 66a; North fork of
    Cottonwood Creek, Shasta County; "rare (Division B)." . . . vol. 2, 1869, p. 231; locality
    as above. . . . STEWART, Acad. Nat. Sci. Phila., Proc., vol. 78, 1926, p. 322; locality as
    above. . . . "*Nerinea*" *dispar* ANDERSON, Geol. Soc. Am. Special Papers, no. 16, 1938;
    p. 133.

The holotype (No. 11944) of this species is in the Meuseum of Paleontology, University of California, and consists chiefly of the cast—length, 55 mm; width, 13.5 mm. Gabb especially emphasized the feature seen in the collar-like band covering the whorl suture, as shown in his drawing, Pl. 19, figs. 66, 66a; this is not seen in the holotype, nor in his primary figure, and its importance is subject to question. No example conforming to his supplementary drawing has been found by the writer in the Shasta series at any place, although various types of *Nerinea* have been found in it, and also in the basal part of the Upper Cretaceous series. It is doubtful whether Gabb knew the boundaries between these series of sediments, and his assignment of the species to the "Shasta group" is doubtful, especially since he also added to his account of the species: "rare in Division B," a term often used by him for the Paleocene. The true position of the species is still in doubt.

Nerinea stewarti Anderson n. sp.
(Plate 30, figures 2, 3)

Shell very long and slender, possessing numerous whorls; holotype (incomplete) with 16 or more; taper extremely gentle and without either base or upper terminus; suture impressed and partly concealed by slight collar; surface of whorls ornamented by small vertical ribs, about 16 to the whorl; faint spiral lines can be seen on lower parts of whorls in the holotype, though not in figure; these cross the vertical ribs and interspaces, giving reticulated effect.

The holotype and paratype (C. A. S. Type Coll.) were found by Dana Russell, on the Hickman ranch, on the middle fork of the Cottonwood Creek, in the upper part of the Turonian. The holotype (fragment) has a length (incomplete) of 52 mm; the diameter of the largest whorl, 4 mm; total length of the paratype, 53 mm. Neither of these examples is complete.

The holotype and paratype were associated with *Prionotropis bakeri* Anderson, and *Eriphyla* aff. *E. umbonata* Gabb. This species, although having some resemblance to *Nerinea dispar* Gabb in form, has neither the size, nor whorl proportions of the latter, and lacks the thick sutural cover described by Gabb for his species.

Nerinea robertiana Anderson n. sp.
(Plate 66, figure 3)

Shell is of moderate size, with a slender elevated spire, consisting of many whorls and tapering gradually from a basal diameter of 16 mm to one of 3 mm or less near apex. On holotype, which is incomplete, 12 or more whorls present, all showing a uniform sculptural pattern, with three revolving zones on each whorl, of which the central zone is depressed, leaving the zone below and above in relief; thus each whorl is ornamented with 18 or more revolving, threadlike costae, though not of equal size and strength; on central zone, these threads are finer and more numerous, and on the lower and upper zones fewer and heavier; each zone on whorl carrying about three larger, and three smaller threads, alternating in strength. Internal structure of whorls is not yet known. Holotype has the following dimensions: height of spire (incomplete), 90 mm; basal diameter, (incomplete), 16 mm; maximum diameter (estimated) 20 mm; apical diameter (incomplete), 3 mm; the general taper, gradual. The holotype found by Robert Anderson and Robert W. Pack, bears No. 70009a (U. S. Nat. Mus. Coll.), from near the center of sec. 11, T. 12 S., R. 10 E., M. D. B. and M., at the head of the first arroyo south of 872-foot hill, in the upper part of the Moreno formation. The species is early Maestrichtian.

Nerinea parallela (Anderson and Hanna)

Turritella parallela ANDERSON AND HANNA, Proc. Calif. Acad. Sci., 4th ser., vol. 23, 1935, p. 26, Pl. 9, figs. 1, 2, 3; near Santa Catarina Landing, Lower California. (Not *Turritella seriatim-granulata* Gabb, 1864, p. 132; Tuscan Springs, etc. Not Stewart, 1926, p. 348; locality as above.)

The holotype of this species, and the fragments figured therewith, were found by Srs. Santillan and Barrera near the Arroyo Santa Catarina Landing, Lower California, and were given by them to the Museum of Paleontology, University of California.

The associated fauna indicates a Maestrichtian age.

Family ACTAEONIDAE d'Orbigny

Members of this family have hitherto not been well represented in the literature of the West Coast Upper Cretaceous, although they appear to have been overlooked rather than absent. Gabb (1864; 1869) was able to recognize only a few types among the genera known to him, namely, *Acteon* Montfort, *Acteonina* d'Orbigny, and *Acteonella* d'Orbigny, in all not exceeding five species.

It now appears that there are at least seven species of *Acteonina,* four of *Acteonella,* two of *Acteon,* and, according to Conrad (1860), one or more of *Tornatellaea,* to which Stewart doubtfully adds one of *Noetca,* and Stephenson (1941) one of *Nonacteonina.*

Genus **Acteon** Montfort
Acteon politus (Gabb)

Ringinella polita GABB, Paleont. Calif., vol. 2, 1869, p. 174, 175, 231; Pl. 28, fig. 60. . . . WHITE, U. S. Geol. Survey, Bull. 15, 1885, p. 20; "Horsetown beds, Shasta group." . . . STEWART, Acad. Nat. Sci. Phila. Proc., vol. 78, 1926, p. 431; horizon as given by White.

From a stratigraphic study of the area from which this species was described, it is evident that it is neither Knoxville, nor Shasta in age (Stanton, 1895, p. 19). This species and its associates "are suggestive of a much later age." Their occurrence is within the Coniacian.

Acteon inornata White

Acteon inornatus WHITE, U. S. Geol. Survey, Bull. 51, 1889, p. 15, 16, Pl. 4, figs. 15, 16; Pentz, Butte County, California.

This species was originally described from beds of the Chico formation, although it has also been listed from the middle part of the Elder Creek section by Diller and Stanton (1894, p. 439).

Stewart regarded this species (1926, p. 431) as "closely related" to the preceding; this would imply that the species ranged throughout the Senonian, but insofar as known to the writer, it has not been found in older beds.

Genus **Acteonina** d'Orbigny
Acteonina californica Gabb
(Plate 29, figure 1)

Acteonina californica GABB, Paleont. Calif., vol. 1, 1864, p. 114, Pl. 19, fig. 68; probably 2 miles north of Benicia, Solano County. . . . vol. 2, 1869, p. 231; locality as above. . . . STEWART, Acad. Nat. Sci. Phila. Proc. vol. 78, 1926, p. 433 (in part), (not Pl. 24, fig. 21). Locality uncertain.

The figure and description of this species given by Gabb have resulted in confusion and uncertainty from a lack of a recognizable holotype, and from a defective characterization. That a satisfactory holotype did not exist seems to have been admitted by Gabb himself, since his outline drawing was made from fragmentary material from two or more localities, and is admitted to be a "restoration." If a proper holotype ever existed it has been lost, and the figure given by Gabb does not conform to any known figure or example of the genus, though possibly to an approximation to it, as here suggested.

The example figured by Stewart (Pl. 24, fig. 21) exhibits neither the outline, the dimensions, nor the proportions of the figure given by Gabb. Since Gabb's figure (1864, Pl. 19, fig. 68) may be taken as an approximation to the fossil form, the example here figured may be offered as a neotype of the same (C. A. S. Type Coll.). This specimen (not wholly complete) has the following dimensions: length, 72 mm; maximum width, 39 mm; height of aperture, 32 mm. The specimen from which this figure was drawn was recently found by Wm. E. Kennett, at locality 31918 (C. A. S.) on Thompson Creek, a small tributary of Putah Creek, half a mile west of the Napa-Yolo county line, and about the same distance north of the main stream. Apex of spire is missing, including two upper whorls; complete length of shell could not have been less than shown in the drawing, was slightly higher than Gabb's figure, and had a more normal form of aperture. This example has the body whorl almost entire, most of the second, and a portion of the third whorl. Gabb states further, that: "The substance of the shell is thick, and that in all the specimens (examined) is so crystalline that not a specimen has been found sufficiently perfect to be drawn."

The present specimen resembles *"Euchrysalis" gigantea* Stoliczka very much. The relationship of this genus to *Acteonina* was not discussed, but the horizons of the fossils themselves appear to be the same. At the Thompson Creek locality, three or four fragmentary examples of the species were found associated with *Trigonarca excavata* Packard, *Trigonocallista nitida* (Gabb), a small prionotropid, and fragments of a rudistid (*Durania?*), and other Turonian types.

Acteonina berryessensis Anderson n. sp.
(Plate 29, figure 3)

This species occurs with the preceding, though more rarely found in a state of good preservation. In external form the shell is elongate-ovate, relatively high and narrow, and the aperture corresponds proportionally to the form. The body whorl makes up less than half the length of the entire shell. The aperture is relatively short and narrow, as compared to other species.

The holotype (C. A. S. Type Coll.), somewhat incomplete, has the following dimensions: height (incomplete), 60 mm; maximum width, 27 mm; height of spire, 30 mm; length of aperture, 25 mm; width of aperture, 9 mm. The surface of the shell is smooth, showing only lines of growth that curve backward behind the aperture, forming a shallow sinus; the sides of the spire slope evenly, with little impressed whorl sutures. The inner lip of the aperture is smooth, with a relatively narrow callous below showing no signs of plications on the columella. The completion of the spire, the apex of which is missing, would increase the complete length of the shell to 72 mm. The shell itself is heavy, having a thickness of at least 3 mm.

The holotype was found by Wm. E. Kennett, associated with *Acteonina californica* Gabb, and many other Mollusca, at locality 31920 (C. A. S.), on Thompson Creek, a small tributary of Putah Creek, Yolo County.

Acteonina bellavistana Anderson n. sp.
(Plate 29, figure 2)

Shell of medium height and width, narrowly ovate in outline, with a spire somewhat exceeding length of body whorl, narrowing a little roundly to apex; aperture relatively high and narrow; narrowly rounded at base; sutures little impressed; surface of shell smooth, marked only by lines of growth which curve backward behind aperture in a shallow sinus.

Holotype (C. A. S. Type Coll.) has the following dimensions: height, 51.6 mm; width, 25 mm; length of aperture (approximately) 27.5 mm. Found one mile north of Frazier Corners, by B. L. Cunningham, with others of the same species, at locality 1293A (C. A. S.). It differs from other members of the genus in its more oval outline, and in its narrow, elongated aperture. It has been found also in southern Oregon, at the old Clawson quarry, 4 miles south of Ashland, associated with many Mollusca, including *Pachydiscus ashlandicus* Anderson. Its horizon is Turonian.

Acteonina yrekensis Anderson n. sp.
(Plate 75, figure 2)

Acteonina californica GABB (in part), Paleont. Calif., vol. 1, 1864, p. 114, (not Pl. 19, fig. 68).
. . . vol. 2. in part, (not *"Acteonina californica* Gabb, eight miles north of Yreka"). STEWART, Acad. Nat. Sci. Phila., Proc. vol. 78, p. 433; *Acteonina californica* Gabb, in part; not "eight miles north of Yreka."

Gabb believed that *Acteonina californica* occurred in Siskiyou County, at a point referred to as "eight miles north of Yreka." This notation evidently referred to the Hagerdorn Ranch, 4 miles north of Montague, Siskiyou County, where Upper Cretaceous Mollusca are plentiful. Repeated visits to this place have resulted in finding a somewhat similar form, though not an example of *A. californica* Gabb. The species here described differs much from *A. californica* Gabb in size, form, and in horizon, and as it has also been recognized in other areas, it should be given a distinct name. This species is considerably smaller, though more rugged and robust in form than *A. californica,* and is found in a higher stratigraphic level, near the top of the Turonian, instead of its lower beds. Its lines of growth are more strongly recurved behind the aperture, its spire is less elevated and the body whorl is relatively broader than that of *A. californica* Gabb.

The holotype of the species (C. A. S. Type Coll.) is incomplete, with the apex of the spire missing, but with the body whorl and the second whorl complete, as shown in the figures; it has the following dimensions: Height, 47 mm; maximum width, 35 mm; height of spire (estimated), 15 mm; height of aperture, 32 mm; width of aperture, 10 mm.

Acteonina califia Stewart

?Acteonina pupoides Gabb, Paleont. Calif. vol. 1, 1864, p. 113, Pl. 19, fig. 67; Cottonwood
    Creek, Shasta County. . . . vol. 2, 1869, p. 173, 231, Pl. 28, fig. 57; locality as given above.
    Not *Acteonina pupoides* d'Orbigny, 1850.
"Acteonina" califia Stewart, Acad. Nat. Sci. Phila., Proc., vol. 78, 1926, p. 432; locality as
    above, "Shasta group."

This species is found on the North fork of Cottonwood Creek, at the base of the Upper Cretaceous and in about the same horizon at the Peterson ranch, 4 miles north of Sites, Colusa County, and at the base of the Upper Cretaceous 3 miles west of Phoenix, Oregon. Insofar as known, its horizon is Albian or Cenomanian in California and in southern Oregon, although it has usually been mistakenly reported in the Shasta series, Lower Cretaceous.

Acteonina colusaensis Anderson n. sp.
(Plate 21, figure 14)

Shell of moderate size, ovate in outline, with a moderately high spire, consisting of about four whorls above the body whorl; spire sloping evenly to apex; body whorl inflated; whorl sutures but little impressed; surface smooth, showing only lines of growth; aperture ovate, rounded below and acute above; outer lip simple; inner lip bordered by a slight callus, without an umbilical pit or performation; lines of growth faint, sinuous.

The holotype (C. A. S. Type Coll.) measures as follows: height of shell, entire, 35 mm; width of body whorl, 22 mm; height of spire, 8 mm; height of aperture, 18.4 mm. This example was found on the Peterson Ranch locality 1291 (C. A. S.), 4 miles north of Sites, Colusa County, associated with *Parapuzosia colusaensis* (Anderson), *Trigonia aequicostata* Gabb, *Turritella petersoni* Anderson, and fragments of *Durania*(?) *californica* n. sp. Its age cannot be regarded as younger than Lower Cenomanian.

Acteonina roguensis Anderson n. sp.
(Plate 30, figures 5, 5a)

Shell of medium size, or small, narrowly ovate, having a conical spire with acute apex; aperture narrowly ovate, rounded below, narrow or acute above, with strong outer lip; spire having five or six whorls, with distinct, but not deeply impressed whorl sutures; surface of shell marked only by sinuous lines of growth.

The holotype (C. A. S. Type Coll.) was found at locality 445 (C. A. S.) at the old "Forty-nine mine" 2 miles south of Phoenix, Oregon. It has the following dimensions: height, 28.4 mm; maximum width, 12.6 mm; height of aperture, 12.5 mm; surface smooth.

Except for its somewhat smaller size, this species appears to be represented by the specimen figured by Stewart (1926, Pl. 24, fig. 21), and thought by him to be the holotype of *Acteonina californica* Gabb. Its age is presumed to be Turonian.

Acteonina ursula Anderson n. sp.
(Plate 63, figure 4)

Shell ovate in outline, with a relatively large body whorl, and a short spire, terminating in a rather obtuse apical angle, and having a regularly rounded base; outer lip thin; inner lip rounded, smooth, bordered by a narrow callus; aperture rounded below, tapering rapidly to an acute angle behind, not channelled.

The holotype (C. A. S. Type Coll.) has the following dimensions: height (incomplete), 54 mm; width, 30 mm; length of aperture, 25 mm; width of aperture, 15 mm. The holotype was found at locality 31210 (C. A. S.) on Bear Creek, northeast Tehama County, by McCoy and Bennison, a little below the mouth of Snow Creek, west of the Aldrich home. It was associated with the following species.

Acteonina ursulagorda Anderson n. sp.
(Plate 63, figure 5)

Shell broadly ovate in outline, with a relatively short and broad body whorl, a short spire, terminating in an apex with an apical angle of about 86 degrees; the aperture is relatively large, broadly rounded below, and narrowing rapidly to an acute angle behind; outer lip thin; inner lip rounded, smooth, bearing a slightly thickened callus that extends more than half the length of the lip.

The holotype of the species (C. A. S. Type Coll.) has the following dimensions: height, 44 mm; width, 28 mm; aperture, having a length of 25 mm; width, 13 mm; enlarged.

The holotype was found with the preceding species, at locality 31210 (C. A. S.) by McCoy and Bennison. Turonian.

Genus Tornatellaea Conrad
Tornatellaea impressa (Gabb)

Acteon impressus GABB, Paleont. Calif., vol. 1, 1864, p. 142, Pl. 21, fig. 106. . . . vol. 2, 1869, p. 232; Cottonwood Creek, Shasta County. . . . DILLER AND STANTON, Geol. Soc. Am., Bull. vol. 5, 1894, p. 466; indirectly recorded as found in the lower part of the Horsetown group.
Tornatellaea impressa CONRAD, Smithson Inst. Misc. Coll., 200, 1866, p. 9. . . . STEWART Acad. Nat. Sci. Phila., Proc., vol. 78, 1926, p. 434; Horsetown group, Cretaceous; North fork of Cottonwood Creek(after Stanton).

Diller and Stanton list this species as found near the Wilcox ranch, in the Paskenta district, Tehama County, and indirectly also in the lower Horsetown group, on the North fork of Cottonwood Creek, Shasta County. The species is not included in the general list given by these writers from either district, and a careful search of both, and of the literature, by the present writer failed to discover it in any part of the Shasta series, though it may occur in the lower Upper Cretaceous beds on the North fork of Cottonwood Creek.

Genus Nonacteonina Stephenson
Nonacteonina stephensoni Anderson n. sp.
(Plate 19, figure 5)

The shell of this species is very similar, and clearly related to, the form described by Stephenson from the Nacatoch sand of the Navarro group, near Chatfield, Texas, having nearly the same dimensions and nearly identical surface ornamentation, although it is somewhat less oblique in its coiling and is slightly broader. The spirial lines occasionally show a disposition to become double, and the same appears to be true in the Texas species; the outer lip is usually arched, and distinctly calloused at the margin in mature stages of growth, and the inner, parietal wall appears to possess a callous that is only partially exposed near the base.

The holotype (C. A. S. Type Coll.), not wholly complete, consists of the body whorl, with the next above it, and an imperfect additional whorl, but without the apical part of the spire. The holotype has the following dimensions: length (incomplete), 24 mm; greatest breadth, 11 mm; if complete, the height would reach 30 mm.

The holotype was found by Bennison about 1350 feet west of the NE. corner of sec. 35, T. 10 S., R. 9 E., in the Volta quadrangle, in the upper part of the Garzas sandstone, associated with *Lytoceras epigonum* Kossmat and *Desmoceras* sp. Its age is later Maestrichtian.

Genus Acteonella d'Orbigny
Acteonella oviformis Gabb
(Plate 29, figure 6)

Actaeonella oviformis GABB, Paleont. Calif., vol. 2, 1869, p. 173, 232, Pl. 28, fig. 58; 'Chico group' (? Cottonwood Creek), Shasta County. . . . ANDERSON, Proc. Calif. Acad. Sci., 3d ser., vol. 2, 1902, p. 28, 34, etc.; 'Lower Chico', northern California. . . . PACKARD (in part ?) Univ. Calif. Publ. Bull. Dept. Geol., vol. 9, 1916, p. 144. . . . vol. 13, 1922 (in part ?), (not Pl. 36, fig. 4), Williams Creek, Orange County. . . . STEWART, Acad. Nat. Sci. Phila., Proc., vol. 78, p. 432, Pl. 21, fig. 13.

According to Gabb (p. 173), the type of this species came from the "Chico group," and probably from Cottonwood Creek, Shasta County. It appears to be nearly complete, lacking only the summit of the low rounded spire. Gabb's figure shows the species to belong to a group common in the Turonian of Shasta County, to the north and east of Redding, and on the Cottonwood Creek.

A number of examples that conform to the type figured by Gabb have been collected east and north of Redding. In the collections of the California Academy of Sciences there are many examples, including five collected by Taff, Hanna and Cross, at locality 27831 (C. A. S.), about 2 miles north of Frazier Corners, and others collected by the writer on Sand Flat, north of Redding.

A partial restoration of the most complete specimen from locality 27831, although small, is here figured for comparison, having a height of 35 mm, and a width of 18 mm. Gabb's example was somewhat larger; his figure indicates a specimen that should have a height of 50 mm and a width of 21.5 mm when complete. An example found by the writer a mile north of Frazier Corners, slightly incomplete, has a height of 41 mm and a width of 20 mm, and a low rounded summit, hardly to be called a spire. Gabb's name for this species has been variously interpreted by later writers without regard to the type most abundant in the areas of Gabb's work and his collections.

Acteonella packardi Anderson n. name
(Plate 29, figures 4, 4a, 4b)

Actaeonella oviformis Gabb, PACKARD, Univ. Calif. Pub. Bull. Dept. Geol., vol. 9, 1916, p. 144, 147 (?); . . . vol. 13, 1922, (in part), p. 458, Pl. 36, fig. 4; locality 2158 (Univ. Calif. Coll.) about half a mile NNE. of B. M. 1271, Corona Sheet. Right bank of Williams Creek, near Modjeska Springs, just above basal conglomerate.

The example figured by Packard in the University of California Museum of Paleontology has been examined by the writer, compared to examples found near the Klamath River 1½ miles south of Hornbrook, Siskiyou County. This species somewhat resembles *Acteonella oviformis* Gabb, but it is larger, and contrasts with it in form of the body whorl and apertural character, and in the relative height of its spire.

Packard (1922, Pl. 36, fig. 4) illustrated a specimen of this species, regarding it as a variety of *A. oviformis* Gabb, but this view can hardly be maintained. Packard states that the holotype was found near the base of the Cretaceous section in the Santiago district, Orange County. The same species occurs at this horizon on both sides of the Klamath River, as at Rocky Gulch, 2 miles southwest of Hornbrook, and on the east side of the river, 2 miles south of Hornbrook.

The figure given by Packard shows a height of 64 mm, and a width of 32 mm. The example from Rocky Gulch has a height of 66 mm and a maximum width of 32 mm; it is thus shown to be 40 to 50 per cent larger than the more abundant form figured and described by Gabb, but need not be confused with it.

Examples of *Acteonella packardi* in the California Academy of Sciences, collected in the Santiago district, Orange County, by Stephen Bowers, are much larger than the holotype, and may prove to be from a higher horizon, but at present it cannot be shown to differ specifically from it. It was *Acteonella packardi* n. sp. that was recorded as *"A. oviformis"* Gabb, from Silverado Creek, Orange County, by the writer (1902, p. 28).

Acteonella frazierensis Anderson n. sp.
(Plate 29, figures 7, 7a)

The mature shell is of moderate size, biconical in general aspect, spire of moderate height; body whorl of equal length sloping downward to columella; aperture nearly straight, narrow above, and expanded below; outer lip thin and nearly straight; inner lip converging gradually from outer lip above, expands suddenly below to anterior canal; columella carries three oblique plications, the anterior being reduced in size near anterior end of columella. Shoulders of whorls slightly rounded and tabular above, with a slight collar rising on the preceding whorl.

This species from the lower Turonian in Shasta County, east of Redding, is represented in the collections of the California Academy of Sciences by two examples of different stages of growth, collected by Taff, Hanna and Cross. The larger of these examples, incomplete below, is taken as the holotype and the smaller as the paratype of the species, though lacking the apex of the spire. The holotype has the following dimensions: height, 43 mm; maximum width of shell (including outer lip), 24 mm; restored length, 55 mm. The external surface of the shell is generally smooth, showing only vertical lines of growth, of faint revolving undulations. The paratype has the following dimensions: height, 27 mm; maximum width, 12 mm; the restoration of the length and general aspect of the holotype is based partly upon those of the paratype, which corresponds proportionally with the same features of the holotype itself.

This species is not abundant, though its congeners are more numerous. The holotype was found at locality 28103 (C. A. S.), in "Stinking Canyon," 1.5 miles north of Frazier Corners, and the paratype was found at locality 27831 (C. A. S.), 3 miles north of Bellavista, in beds of the same age.

Acteonella rustica Anderson n. sp.
(Plate 29, figure 5)

Shell similar to *Acteonella frazierensis* n. sp., although relatively stouter and more biconic in form, and distinct in most of its other external features. The holotype (C. A. S. Type Coll.) is a somewhat weathered example, though preserving most of its essential characters. It consists of the body whorl and five spiral whorls including apex, which is slightly reduced by weathering of shell substance. It has the following dimensions: total height, 53.8 mm; maximum width, 29.3 mm; length of aperture, 29 mm. The body whorl is a little inflated near its middle, thus modifying its conical form, and in some examples giving them a slightly barrel shape. The holotype and four additional examples were found by W. H. Ochsner, 2 miles above the Cawkins home on Little Cow Creek, Shasta County. Another example, somewhat more barrel shaped, and larger but incomplete, was found by the writer at locality 444 (C. A. S.), at "Rocky Gulch," near Hornbrook, Siskiyou County, in the lower Turonian (zone of *Acteonella oviformis* Gabb, var. *packardi* Anderson). It is not impossible that the species figured by Stewart (1926, Pl. 21, fig. 13) as *"Acteonella oviformis* Gabb" is a distorted example of the present species, although this cannot be proved. The type locality of the present species is on the opposite side of the Valley from that of the fragmentary example figured by Stewart.

Genus Trajanella Popovici-Hatzog
Trajanella acuminata Anderson n. sp.
(Plate 21, figure 5)

Shell relatively large, with a high spire, possessing about seven whorls, gradually narrowing to an apex of acute angle; sides sloping uniformly from near the middle of the body whorl; spire acuminate; involution of whorls, nearly one-half; whorl sutures deeply impressed; body whorl occupying more than half the length of shell; aperture elongate-ovate; surface of shell smooth, or showing only vertical lines of growth; shell thick. The dimensions of the holotype (incomplete) are as follows: length, 82 mm; maximum width, 32 mm.

The holotype (C. A. S. Type Coll.), the only example yet obtained, was found in the sandstones near the base of the Upper Cretaceous at Texas Springs, Shasta County, about

2 miles east of old Horsetown, where it was associated with a considerable fauna listed by Stanton (1893), but here supplemented by the following species: *Trigonia perrinsmithi* Anderson, *Terebratella densleonis* Anderson, *Sonneratia stantoni* Anderson, and *Neohibolites fontinalis* Anderson.

Nagao (1934, Pl. XVII; figs. 5, a, b) described and illustrated a related though smaller species, under the name *Trajanella japanica,* said to have come from strata of early Cenomanian age.

According to Nagao (1934, p. 240), the genotype also came "from the Lower Cenomanian of Rumania," and therefore, in point of age and of horizon, is approximately correlative with the present species from the Great Valley of California.

Genus Globiconcha d'Orbigny
Globiconcha remondii Gabb

Globiconcha (Phasianella ?) remondii GABB, Paleont. Calif., vol. 1, 1864, p. 114, Pl. 19, fig. 69; 2 miles north of Benicia, California. . . . vol. 2, 1869, p. 232; locality as above. . . . ANDERSON, Proc. Calif. Acad. Sci., 3rd ser., vol. 2, 1902, p. 29; locality, at the "Forty-nine" mine, southwest of Phoenix, Oregon; near Henley and Silverado, California. . . . STEWART, Acad. Nat. Sci. Phila., Proc., vol. 78, 1926, p. 433.

The holotype of this species, No. 11974, is in the Museum of Paleontology, University of California. There is no reason to doubt the record of its discovery, north of Benicia, where various other molluscan types are recorded. The examples of this species from northern California and southern Oregon, recorded by the writer (1902) were lost in the San Francisco fire of 1906. Stewart believed the species to be an Ampullinid, possibly *Pseudomaura,* and a comparison of the holotype with the figures of *Ampullina* given by Cossmann confirms this view. Few references to the species have been found in the literature of the West Coast Cretaceous, and for this reason it appears to be rare. The holotype was found with various other invertebrates, as shown in Gabb's synopsis (1864, p. 220–236), most of which seem referable to the Senonian. No record of its occurrence in older beds has been found.

Genus Phasianella Lamarck
Phasianella garzana Anderson n. sp
(Plate 73, figure 5)

Shell large and robust, with moderately elevated spire and broadly rounded body whorl and base, whorl occupying more than half its entire height. Aperture narrowly ovate, terminates below in slightly produced basal expansion of shell. Upper part of aperture slightly pinched due to depressed zone a little below whorl top, not shown in reduced figure. Surface of shell marked only by somewhat sinuous lines of growth, many of which produce varixlike effects, not carried to adjoining whorls. Holotype (C. A. S. Type Coll.) has following dimensions: height (incomplete), 80 mm; maximum breadth of whorl, 45 mm; width of aperture, 12 mm. This example was found by Bennison at locality 28311 (C. A. S.) on the SW ¼ of the NE ¼ sec. 12, T. 11 S., R. 9 E., M. D. B. and M., in the zone of *Glycymeris banosensis* n. sp., and *Opisoma pacifica* n. sp.

Shell resembles *Phasianella incerta* (Forbes) from India, as figured by Stoliczka. Its position is in the lower part of the Moreno formation.

Family CERITHIIDAE
Genus Cerithium Bruguiere
Cerithium (? Fibula) mustangense Anderson n. sp.
(Plate 71, figure 5)

Shell large, robust, with a high spire tapering uniformly to an acuminate point; whorl sutures impressed; sides of whorl slightly convex above middle; aperture ovate, narrowing to a point behind, but rounded before; inner lip bearing a slight callus, outer lip thin; surface apparently smooth, though showing remnants of a cordlike ridge at base of last whorl (laterobasal angle). Base terminates rather abruptly.

The holotype (C. A. S. Type Coll.) has the following dimensions: height (incomplete), 81 mm; greatest breadth, 34 mm; height of aperture, 23 mm. This example was found at locality 29120 (C. A. S.), 300 feet east, 1800 feet south of the NW. corner of sec. 27, T. 10 S., R. 9 E., M. D. B. and M., Volta quadrangle, California. The same species is represented in the collection of S. G. Clark by an example of the same size, though slightly incomplete, found near Gualala, southern Mendocino County, where it was associated with *Glycymeris* aff. *G. banosensis* n. sp.; *Baculites* sp., and *Coralliochama* sp. The holotype itself was found with a large fragment of *Baculites occidentalis* Meek, in the Garzas member of the Moreno Formation.

This species may be compared to *Cerithium* (*?Fibula*) *detectum* Stoliczka, from the Arrialoor group of southern India.

Cerithium clarki Anderson n. sp.
(Plate 59, figures 3, 3a)

In the collection assembled by S. G. Clark of Upper Cretaceous fossils from near Gualala, there is a large fragment of a *Cerithium* shell, of a distinct type that should not be overlooked. It is of unusual size, exposing base of body whorl, second whorl, and a small portion of a third whorl. It was found associated with a crushed fragment of another example, probably belonging to the same species. Maximum diameter of holotype is about 39.8 mm; its estimated height could hardly have been less than 140 mm; height of body whorl from end of columella to top of body whorl is about 47 mm, and total length of the fragment is 71 mm. Surface of the shell, best exposed on base of shell, is crossed obliquely by five oblique revolving cords, and traces of others are visible on higher whorls of the other example mentioned above. The holotype (C. A. S. Type Coll.) was found at locality 256 (S. G. Clark Coll.). This is the only example of the species known to the writer, sufficiently well preserved for a tentative description.

Cerithium aff. C. detectum Stolicizka

This species greatly resembles that described by Stoliczka from the Arrialoor group at Karapauda, southern India, although the whorls seem to be slightly more rounded than in the Indian species. The specimen consists of about three-fourths of the spire, with the larger part of the body-whorl, but is too poorly preserved for illustration. The four whorls constituting the example have the following dimensions: height, 60 mm; greater width, 28 mm; diameter at top, 15 mm.

This example was found by Bennison at locality 29120 (C. A. S.) 300 feet E., and 1800 feet S., of the NW corner of sec. 27, T. 10 S., R. 9 E., in the Garzas member of the Moreno formation, as nearly as can be determined.

The species is not wholly unlike *Cerithium mustangense* n. sp., with which it occurs, although it is somewhat slenderer, with more convex whorls than the latter.

Cerithium sp. indet.

An example of *Cerithium* having more rounded (inflated) whorls than the preceding was found by Taff, Hanna and Cross at locality 27853 (C. A. S.), associated with *Baculites occidentalis* Meek, on the E ½ sec. 31, T. 8 S., R. 8 E., on the east side of Mustang Gulch, Pacheco Pass quadrangle.

In this species, the whorls are more roundly inflated than in the preceding form. Its stratigraphic position is somewhat lower, and appears to be in the lower part of the Moreno formation.

Cerithium (?) suciaensis Packard

Cerithium (?) *suciaensis* PACKARD, Univ. Calif. Pub., Bull. Dept. Geol. Sci., vol. 13, no. 10, 1922, p. 430, Pl. 35, fig. 4; Sucia Island, San Juan County, Washington. Locality 2209 (Univ. Calif. Coll.).

The species described by Packard consists of portions of three whorls from the lower part of the holotype, of which he states:

"The whorls are markedly restricted at the sutures and slightly flattened midway between them; aperture apparently oval; columella smooth, without a sulcus probably imperforate; canal unknown; shell ornamented by about 22 axial ribs, being more prominent near the top and bottom of the whorl; each rib is deflected backward at the shoulder and joins the suture by a curved line; base of each whorl ornamented by several indistinct revolving ribs. Height of whorl 24 mm; diameter, 43 mm."

Cerithium pillingi White

Cerithium pillingi White, U. S. Geol. Survey, Bull. 22, 1885, p. 13, Pl. 5, figs. 3, 4, 5, 6; Todos Santos Bay, Lower California. . . . Fairbanks, Am. Jour. Sci., vol. 45, 1893, p. 474; locality as given above; "Wallala Beds."

Original description:

"Shell small, spire comparatively short; volutions four or five in number; each volution bearing four or five prominent longitudinal folds, which are usually so arranged upon the spire as to form continuous ridges along its whole length. These long ridges, together with the flattening of the sides of the volutions between them, give a distinctly angular aspect to the shell. Volutions marked by numerous revolving crenulated or tuberculated coarse lines or slender ridges, and the anterior side of the last one is marked in a similar manner; aperture . . . comparatively small; beaks short; canal narrow. (Height of largest example, 12 mm; greatest diameter, 7 mm).

"In general aspect, the shell resembles *C. sexangulatum* of Zekeli from the Gosau formation of Europe, but it differs from that species in being proportionally shorter, in the character of its revolving ridges, and in having the spaces between the longitudinal folds upon the spire more flattened."

Cerithium totium-sanctorum White

Certhium totium-sanctorum White, U. S. Geol. Survey, Bull. 22, 1885, p. 13, Pl. 5, figs. 12, 13; Shore of Todos Santos Bay, Lower California. "Wallala Group," Cretaceous. . . . Fairbanks, Am. Jour. Sci., vol. 45, 1893, p. 474; locality as given above.

Original description (in part):

"Shell small, slender; sides of spire straight or slightly concave; volutions eleven or twelve in number, not convex; each volution marked by four tuberculated revolving ridges, the anterior one being usually a little more prominent than the other three; at irregular and somewhat wide intervals upon the volutions there are moderately prominent longitudinal folds which are sometimes arranged approximately in rows along the spire, but they are not often scattered; suture impressed, . . . anterior side of the last volution marked by small revolving ridges, but they are crenulated and not tuberculate like those upon the side of the spire; beak moderately small; canal narrow. Length 20 mm; diameter of last volution, 7 mm." Todos Santos Bay.

Genus **Potamides** Brongniart
Potamides tenuis Gabb

Potamides tenuis Gabb, Paleont. Calif., vol. 1, 1864, p. 130, Pl. 20, fig. 86; Pentz (Pence's ranch), Butte County. . . . vol. 2, 1869, p. 227; locality as above. . . . Stewart, Acad. Nat. Sci., Philadelphia, Proc. vol. 78, 1926, p. 356, Pl. 23, figs. 8, 9; locality as given above.

Family Aporrhaidae Philippi
Genus **Anchura** Conrad
Anchura angulata (Gabb)

Aporrhais angulata Gabb, Paleont. Calif., vol. 1, 1864, p. 128, Pl. 20, fig. 84; Bull's Head Point, Contra Costa County, near Martinez.
Anchura angulata Gabb, Paleont. Calif., vol. 2, 1869, p. 165, 226; locality as above. . . . Stewart, Acad. Nat. Sci. Phila., Proc. vol. 78, 1926, p. 361, Pl. 22, fig. 4 (? fig. 5); locality not given.

The holotype is an incomplete cast, showing only some of the surface ornamentation on three upper whorls, consisting of uninterrupted revolving threads. Gabb seems to have confused this species from near Martinez, with another (*Anchura biangulata* Anderson) occurring on the North fork of Cottonwood Creek, Shasta County, in the lowest beds of the Upper Cretaceous series.

Stewart has figured an unidentified fragment, thought to be two whorls of an immature specimen of the same species, enlarged, though he does not give a locality.

Anchura biangulata Anderson

Anchura angulata GABB, 1864 (in part) ; "Huling Creek," collected by Brewer.
Anchura biangulata ANDERSON, Geol. Soc. Am., Special Papers, No. 16, 1938, p. 134, Pl. 9, figs. 4, 5, 6 ; North fork of Cottonwood Creek, Shasta County, locality 1546A (C. A. S.), at the base of the Upper Cretaceous.

Gabb (1864, p. 128) had evidently noted this species, stating that: "Mr. Brewer collected three specimens at Huling Creek, near the Cottonwood Creek locality, resembling the species (above described) in surface ornamentation and in the shape of the upper whorls, but in which the last whorl was distinctly bicarinate."

He did not show the aperture, the form of the outer lip expansion (wing), the outward form of the whorls, nor their surface ornamentation, supposing all of them to conform to his holotype from near Martinez, which they closely resemble.

Anchura falciformis (Gabb)

Aporrhais falciformis GABB, Paleont. Calif., vol. 1, 1864, p. 127, Pl. 20, fig. 83; Chico Creek, Butte County, California.
Anchura falciformis GABB, Am. Jour. Conch., 1868, p. 145. . . . Paleont. Calif., vol. 2, 1869, p. 165; locality, and other data as above. . . . STEWART, Acad. Nat. Sci. Phila., Proc., vol. 78, 1926, p. 360, Pl. 22, fig. 9; locality as given above. . . . TAFF, HANNA AND CROSS, Geol. Soc. Am., Bull. vol. 51, 1940, p. 1322, Pl. 2, figs. 7–9; Chico Creek, Butte County, California.

The identity of the species figured and described by Taff, Hanna and Cross with that described by Gabb is beyond question, although their figures stress the revolving cords in the ornamentation, whereas Gabb's figure emphasizes the vertical aspect of the same. The species is abundant in the type Chico formation on Chico and Butte Creeks, and occurs at various other places in strata of the same age, or in stratigraphically neighboring zones. It is associated with *Mortoniceras randalli* n. sp., and *M. chicoense* (Trask), and species of *Submortoniceras* of the type of *S. woodsi* Spath.

All of foregoing ammonites are here held to be close allies of *Mortoniceras delawarense* Morton, and of *Mortoniceras campaniense* Grossouvre, and to be of early Campanian age.

"Anchura" carinifera Gabb

? *Anchura carinifera* GABB, Paleont. Calif., vol. 2, 1869, p. 166, Pl. 28, fig. 46; near Martinez, Contra Costa County; horizon not clearly shown. . . . STEWART, Acad. Nat. Sci. Phila., Proc. vol. 78, 1926, p. 361, Pl. 22, fig. 6; locality as above.

The Cretaceous age of this species has been suggested by both Stanton (1896), and by Stewart (1926), and there is no reason for altering it. The species was not included in Merriam's list of type species in the Museum of Paleontology, University of California (1895), although Stewart found the holotype there. The photographic figure given by Stewart (Pl. 22, fig. 6) does not closely resemble Gabb's drawing, though probably there should be no doubt as to the identity of the holotype figured by Stewart. Stewart compares the species with one from the Maestrichtian of Europe (?).

Subgenus Arrhoges Beck
Anchura (Arrhoges) californica (Gabb) Stewart

Aporrhais californica GABB, Paleont. Calif. vol. 1, 1864, p. 128, Pl. 29, figs. 230, a, b; Orestimba and Puerto Canyons, Stanislaus County, and Siskiyou Mountains, northern California.
Anchura californica GABB, Paleont. Calif., vol. 2, 1869, p. 226; localities as above. . . . TURNER, Geol. Soc. Am., Bull. vol. 2, 1891, p. 395; Curry Canyon, Contra Costa County. . . .

STANTON, Geol. Soc. Am., Bull. vol. 4, 1893, p. 252; Elder Creek, Tehama County. . . .
  vol. 5, 1894, p. 439, 443; lower Chico beds, Elder Creek, and North fork of Cottonwood
  Creek, Shasta County. . . . ANDERSON, Proc. Calif. Acad. Sci., 3d ser., vol. 2, 1902, p. 28,
  34, 38, 93; "Forty-nine" mine, etc., southern Oregon.
Arrhoges californica STEWART, Acad. Nat. Sci. Phila., Proc. vol. 78, 1926, p. 363, Pl. 21, fig.
  15; locality (?), Siskiyou Mountains.

The type locality of this species is not definitely known, although it occurs in many places
in the Cenomanian of California. Its occurrence in later beds, except in transported boulders,
is doubtful.

Genus Drepanochilus Meek
Drepanochilus condoniana (Anderson)

Anchura Condoniana ANDERSON, Proc. Calif. Acad. Sci., 3d ser., vol. 2, 1902, p. 76, Pl. 8,
  fig. 179; lower Chico beds, at the "Forty-nine" mine, near Phoenix, Oregon.

The original description and figure of this species are given since much of the original
stock of the publication was lost in the San Francisco fire, and is out of print. The description of the species follows:

"Shell large, robust, with high spire; whorls about eight in number, moderately rounded,
surface of spire ornamented by twenty or more longitudinal ridges; body-whorl entirely
covered by longitudinal and revolving ridges equally developed; lip long and falcate, extending laterally, but bearing a spurlike process near the spire; lip strongly angled along the back,
with angle extending upon the body-whorl; lip also bearing an angle on the outer margin."

The species was found in the Lower Upper Cretaceous beds of the Forty-nine mine south
of the village of Phoenix, Oregon, where it was associated with many species of *Oregoniceras* and *Scaphites,* and many other Turonian species.

Drepanochilus (?) transversus (Gabb)

Anchura transversa GABB, Paleont. Calif., vol. 2, 1869, p. 165, Pl. 27, fig. 45; near Martinez,
  Contra Costa County. . . . STANTON, U. S. Geol. Survey, Ann. Rept., 17, p. 1029; regarded
  the species as of Upper Cretaceous age. . . . WARING, Proc. Calif. Acad. Sci., vol. 7, 1917,
  p. 65; refers to a species of *Anchura* from locality 1 (L. S. J. U.), that resembles the
  present form of Gabb.
Drepanochilus (?) *transversus* (Gabb), STEWART, Acad. Nat. Sci. Phila., Proc., vol. 78, 1926,
  p. 362; locality near Martinez.

This species appears to be from the upper part of the Upper Cretaceous, rather than the
lower Eocene, although its locality near Martinez is not very clear, except as given by
Stanton.

Genus Aporrhais Da Costa
Aporrhais vetus Packard

Aporrhais vetus PACKARD, Univ. Calif. Pub. Bull. Dept. Geol. Sci., vol. 13, 1922, p. 431, Pl.
  36, fig. 1; locality 2171 (Univ. Calif. Coll.), 4 miles southwest from Corona, Corona
  Quad., at clay pit; exact stratigraphic position not known.

The shell of this species is relatively small, and was described in part, as follows:

"Whorls six or seven; spire whorls convex, regularly curved above and below; suture rather
shallow; body-whorl large. . . . length of type 28 + mm; diameter of body whorl, 15 mm;
length from the middle of the body whorl, 18 mm."

The species has not been found since its original discovery.

Genus Alaria Morris and Lycett
Alaria nodosa Packard

Alaria nodosa PACKARD, Univ. Calif. Pub. Bull. Dept. Geol. Sci., vol. 13, 1922, p. 430, Pl. 36,
  figs. 5a, 5b; locality 2155 (Univ. Calif. Coll.), 3⅜ miles South 65° E. of B. M. 610, U. S.
  G. S., Corona Quad., half a mile from the mouth of Black Star Canyon, "float from Chico
  series."

The shell of this species is relatively small and is described in part as follows:

"spire high, eight whorls; spire whorls tumid, ornamented by about 14 slightly oblique transverse ribs, which do not reach the suture; region just below the suture on each whorl ornamented by several very fine spiral ridges (threads); body whorl large, canal long; . . ." "Height of type, 27 + mm. Zonal position unknown."

Since the species has been found near the mouth of Black Star Canyon, and near the locality from which the writer obtained a large fragment of a nostoceratid shell, and other Senonian forms, it seems certain that the stratigraphic position of the species described by Packard is not older than lower Senonian, and it probably represents a low Maestrichtian horizon.

"Alaria" fairbanksi Davis

Alaria fairbanksi DAVIS, Jour. Geol., vol. 21, 1913, p. 456, fig. 1.

The brief description of this species given by Davis (p. 455), reads:

"A single imperfect specimen is in the collection of the University of California, and was collected by H. W. Fairbanks. The expanded outer lip and turreted form suggests *Alaria,* a species of which occurs in the Vancouver Coal Measures."

The locality, near Slate's Springs, from which this species was obtained has been shown elsewhere to be Maestrichtian. Probably, all of the species discussed by Davis, as associated with the present species should be referred to this horizon.

Family STROMBIDAE d'Orbigny
Genus **Pugnellus** Conrad
Subgenus **Gymnarus** Gabb
Pugnellus (Gymnarus) manubriatus Gabb

Pugnellus manubriatus GABB, Paleont. Calif., vol. 1, 1864, p. 125, Pl. 29, figs. 229, 229a; Cottonwood Creek, Siskiyou County.
Pugnellus (Gymnarus) manubriatus GABB, Am. Jour. Conch, 1868, p. 139, Pl. 13, figs. 4, 5; locality as above. . . . Paleont. Calif. vol. 2, 1869, p. 163; data as before. . . . MERRIAM (1895), listed among type specimens found at the University of California. . . . ANDERSON, Jour. Geology, vol. 3, 1895; listed as found at an old quarry, near railway, 4 miles south of Ashland, Oregon. . . . STEWART, Acad. Nat. Sci. Phila., Proc., vol. 78, 1926, p. 358, Pl. 29, figs. 10–12; p. 359, states that:
"*Gymnarus* is closely related to *Pugnellus typicus* Gabb (= ? *P. densatus* Conrad), the type of *Pugnellus,* but may be distinguished by the hook-like development of the outer lip, and the axial ribs on the later whorls."

Gabb's figures of this species, which is taken as the subgenotype of *Gymnarus,* are of a shell at early maturity. In its older stages, the shell develops a thick callus or incrustation that begins on the inner lip, but later extends to the spire, and finally envelops the buccal side of the same, covering the apex entirely. On the extremity of the wing (outer lip), a similar incrustation is also developed, becoming enlarged in old age as a bulbous growth, though not equal in size to that on the spire, but roughly parallel to the axis of the shell.

Gabb's holotype was found near Cottonwood Creek, above Hornbrook, in beds of Turonian age, where similar examples have also been found by the writer. In the area north of Frazier Corners, numerous examples of the species have been collected by John Melhase, and also by the writer. These are at the California Academy of Sciences, and were found at locality 1293 and 1293-E (C. A. S.), 1.5 miles north of Frazier Corners, in a hard gray sandstone, on Dry Creek. The species is common in this area. The incrustations on the shell of this species are not mentioned by Gabb, nor are they shown on his figures, or on those of Stewart.

Concerning the canal, Gabb (1869, p. 163) states that 'it was not broken in the specimen figured,' and adds, regarding its terminus:

"I have never detected the slightest indication of a curve in this portion of the shell, where the specimens were perfect, or nearly so."

But such curve is often seen, when the terminus is exposed, and bears a narrow groove along the curve.

Pugnellus (Gymnarus) hamulus (Gabb)

Pugnellus hamulus GABB, Paleont. Calif. vol. 1, 1864, p. 124, 125, Pl. 20, fig. 81; Pl. 18, fig. 48, young example. . . . vol 2, 1869, p. 162, 163, 225, Pl. 27, figs. 42, 42a. . . . Am. Jour. Conch., vol. 2, 1866, p. 89. . . . vol. 4, 1868, p. 139, Pl. 13, figs. 1, 2, 3. . . . TRYON, MERRIAM, Jour. Struct. and System. Conch., vol. 2, 1883, p. 190, Pl. 60, figs. 71, 72. . . . Geol., vol. 5, 1897, p. 770; describes the type locality near Martinez.

Gabb (1869, Pl. 27, figs. 42, 42a) figured "A very old, but small individual, . . . so heavily incrusted that its original form is entirely lost," but which he identified as *P. hamulus*. Stewart makes no mention of this example in his text, and assigns the species to the genus *Conchothyra* "McCoy," Hutton, 1877, but gives little information as to his reasons for doing so.

In Gabb's view, this species, and *P. manubriatus* were regarded as belonging to the same genus, though he lacked the material for proving the same. A critical study of the younger stages of growth in the two forms clearly shows the basis of this opinion. Many good examples of *P. (Gymnarus) manubriatus* Gabb, have been collected by Melhase, and by the writer on Dry Creek, 1.5 miles north of Frazier Corners, at localities 1293, and 1923-A. Examples of *Pugnellus hamulus* Gabb, have been found at its type locality near Martinez, as shown by Merriam (1897, p. 768, and 770). Good examples of the same species have been found by Bennison and by others, in the Garzas member of the Moreno formation in the Pacheco Pass quadrangle. The Garzas has been shown by its invertebrate faunas to be Maestrichtian.

"Pugnellus" rotundus Waring

Pugnellus rotundus WARING, Proc. Calif. Acad. Sci., 4th Ser. vol. 7, No. 4, 1917, p. 67, Pl. 9, fig. 10; locality 3 (L. S. J. U), near Santa Monica, Los Angeles County.
The species though small, was described by Waring as follows:

"Shell robust, spire moderately high; whorls five, rounded, ornamented by fine spiral lines on the upper whorls; body-whorl ornamented by a row of small tubercules just above the center and by fine wavy spiral lines and fine lines of growth."

The specimen is thought to be a young one. The description is too incomplete for further comment. The horizon represented by the species is indefinite, but it is probably assignable to the lower Senonian.

Family MURICIDAE Tryon
Genus **Trophon** Montfort
Trophon condoni White

Trophon Condoni WHITE, U. S. Geol. Survey, Bull. 51, 1889, p. 21, Pl. 3, figs. 4, 5; Little Cow Creek Valley; J. S. Diller, Collector.

The description given by White reads (in part) as follows:

"Shell moderately small; spire low, the last volution constituting much of the greater part of the shell, its outer side convex above but becoming concave as it merges into the broad beak; the outer portion of the posterior side shouldered or abruptly rounded, and the inner portion appressed against the preceding volution, there being a revolving depression between the outer and inner portions; aperture broadly subovate; its two lips, meeting by the thickening of each, as the shell approaches maturity, extends back upon the penultimate volution; beak broad, rather short, and turned a little backward and to the left; . . .
Length of largest specimen in the collection, 30 mm; breadth of last volution, about 22 mm."

Position and locality.—Little Cow Creek, a mile or more east of Frazier Corners; Turonian.

This species has been found in considerable numbers by John Melhase, B. L. Cunningham, and others, and by the writer in the basal beds of the Turonian on Putah Creek, near the Napa-Yolo county line, a little north of the Creek, where it was associated with

Austiniceras sp., and *Prionotropis* (?), and other Turonian Mollusca. Age, probably middle Turonian.

Family FOSSARIIDAE Fischer
Genus **Lysis** Gabb
Lysis duplicosta Gabb

Lysis duplicosta GABB, Paleont. Calif., vol. 1, 1864, p. 138, Pl. 21, figs. 98 a, b, c; Texas Flat, Placer County. . . . vol. 2, 1869, p. 229; locality as above. . . . MERRIAM, 1895, Checklist of types at Mus. Paleont., University of California. . . . COSSMANN, Essais Paleont. Comp., vol. 5, 1903, p. 70; near to genus *Fossarus* Philippi.

Gabb's description of the type reads (in part) :

"Shell oblique; spire not very prominent; whorls three, rapidly increasing in size; suture impressed. Surface marked by from five to seven prominent ribs, each grooved along its whole length by sharp, deep channels; . . . Mouth very oblique, rounded posteriorly, and subacute in advance; outer lip simple; inner lip straight when viewed from the front; . . . Umbilical region broad, concave, especially above and toward the outer margin;" . . . Shell small, about 13 mm in length; 8 mm in width.

Locality and position.—Texas Flat, Placer County; at bottom of 40-foot shaft, now filled by caving. The horizon is probably Santonian.

Lysis oppanus White

Lysis oppanus WHITE, U. S. Geol. Survey, Bull. 51, 1889, p. 17, Pl. 4, figs. 14, 15; Pentz area, Butte County; (Chico formation, lower-middle Campanian, associated with *Mortoniceras chicoensis* (Trask)).

White's description of this species reads (in part) :

"the periphery of the last volution usually somewhat angulated, the spire small and slightly elevated, aperture large, inner lip broad, thickened by callus, and its surface and margin both concave. Surface marked by rounded, rugose, coarse, raised revolving striae or small ridges, every third or fourth one of which is larger than the others;" . . . (As compared to Gabb's species), "it differs materially in the angular character of the periphery and in the character of the surface markings, and it apparently reaches a considerably larger size."

As shown above it differs also in stratigraphic position, being younger.

Lysis californiensis Packard

Lysis californiensis PACKARD, Univ. Calif. Publ. Bull. Dept. Geol. Sci., vol. 13, 1922, p. 431; Pl. 37, figs. 2, 3; Santiago district, Orange County. . . . POPENOE, Am. Ass. Petrol. Geol., Bull., vol. 26, 1942, Figure 4; (probably referable to the Santonian).

Packard's brief description shows the species to be distinct from those described above, the shell being "imperforate; the surface apparently without ornamentation." . . . Height of the type, 27 mm; greatest width, nearly the same.

Lysis suciensis (Whiteaves)

Stomatia suciensis WHITEAVES, Meso. Foss., pt. 2, 1897, p. 128, Pl. 16, fig. 4; not fig. 5; Sucia Island.
Lysis suciensis WHITEAVES, Meso. Foss., pt. 5, 1903, p. 367, Pl. 45, fig. 3 only; not fig. 4: Sucia Island, western Washington.

Whiteaves appears to have had two distinct forms in view,—namely, the "Typical form," and another, described below. The "Typical form" he described (in part) as follows:

"Shell subovate, longer than wide, pointed above and more or less narrowly rounded below; spire short, about one-fifth the entire length. Whorls four, increasing very rapidly in size, convex, oblique; sutures distinct, Spire turbinate conical; body whorl very oblique, moderately inflated, devoid of any umbilicus, or umbilical depression, sometimes subangular near the base. Aperture ovate, longer than wide, pointed above, rounded below; outer lip thin, simple, gently convex; inner lip concave." Holotype, "probably two inches and a half in length."

This form was described from Sucia Island, but occurs also on Vancouver Island, and appears to be referable to the Coniacian.

Lysis carinifera (Whiteaves)

Stomatia suciensis, var. *carinifera* (WHITEAVES), Meso. Foss., vol. 1, pt. 2, 1879, Pl. 16, fig. 5; . . . pt. 5, 1903, p. 367, Pl. 45, fig. 4.

This species is described by Whiteaves, under *Lysis suciensis,* var. *carinifera,* p. 367, as follows:

"Brennan Creek, V. I.: two specimens, each with two spiral keels on the outer volution. One of these is a somewhat crushed specimen, some 18 mm high and 20.5 mm wide the original of figure 4 on Plate 45. Its two spiral keels are placed near to each other, just below the mid-height, but on the outer lip each keel, or ridge, is produced into a short, conical, slender spine. The other is a very small specimen, about five mm. high, with the two spiral keels also placed near each other, a little below the mid-height on the dorsal surface of the last volution. Texada Island, W. Harvey, 1901: three specimens, each with two spiral keels on the last volution."

Lysis intermedia (Cooper)

Stomatia intermedia COOPER, Calif. St. Min. Bur., Bull. No. 4, 1894, p. 46. Pl. 3, fig. 53; west base of Point Loma, San Diego County, Calif.

Cooper gave the following characterization of this shell:

"Shell haliotiform, whorls two or three, flattened, rapidly expanding, with four strongly carinate ribs revolving above the margin, and one or two below it; the outer ones sometimes forming an undulating margin toward the anterior end. Interspaces sub-equal, slightly concave, with revolving ridges near apex, crossed by irregular radiating lines of growth. The sculpture is sometimes scaly or imbricated. . . . Length, 1 inch or more; breadth, 0.90; height, 0.35."

Locality and position:—West base of Point Loma, San Diego County. The shell is said to resemble *"Stomatia" suciensis* Whiteaves, possibly forming a link between this species and "variety" *L. carinifera* Whiteaves.

Genus **Nonacteonina** Stephenson
Nonacteonina ? normalis (Cooper)

Tornatella normalis COOPER, Calif. State Min. Bur., Bull. No. 4, 1894, p. 46, Pl. 2, figs. 36, 37; west base of Point Loma, San Diego County.

Cooper's description of this species reads as follows:

"Shell oliviform, whorls six, apical subacute; next four gradually enlarging, with five to ten sharply impressed grooves parallel with the sutures, which are also rather deeply impressed; body whorl with about 50 similar grooves, crossed by irregular lines of growth, ending anteriorly in an obtuse point. Mouth subovate, acute posteriorly; columella with one basal plait."

Length, 0.65 inch (16.5 mm) ; breadth, 0.25 inch (6.3 mm) ; body whorl, 12.7 mm.

The locality of this species, at the west base of Point Loma, places it within the Maestrichtian.

This species closely resembles *Nonacteonina ? triticea* Stephenson (1941, p. 384, Pl. 73, figs. 20, 21) from the Nacatoch sand of the Navarro group, in east-central Texas, and is probably closely related to it, though of somewhat larger size.

Genus **Noetca** Stewart
Noetca gabbi Stewart

Cylindrites brevis GABB, Paleont. Calif., vol. 1, 1864, p. 115, Pl. 29, fig. 223; . . . vol. 2, 1869, p. 232; locality as above (not the Martinez group). . . . MERRIAM, Jour. Geol., vol. 5, no. 8, 1897, p. 770; "locality 1," southwest of Martinez . . . ANDERSON, Proc. Calif. Acad. Sci., 3d ser., vol. 2, 1902, p. 38, southwest of Martinez; "Upper Chico."

Gabb's description of this species reads as follows:

"Shell short, robust, ovoid; spire low; whorls four, rounded on the upper margin; suture deep. Aperture broad, produced and rounded in advance; outer lip simple; inner lip incrusted; the incrustation forming a large fold in advance. Sides of the body volution subflattened, approaching anteriorly. Surface marked only by a few indistinct lines of growth."

This locality was visited by the writer, in company with Merriam, in 1897, prior to the account referred to above, and from this point the beds were traced faunally and stratigraphically to the east and southeast, at intervals, for many miles.

Family FUSIDAE Tryon
Genus Fusus Lamarck

Members of this family are not abundant in the Upper Cretaceous of California and Oregon, although Gabb has enumerated at least three species, one of which was from the Turonian, and the others were from later beds. The following synopsis contains the species that were referred to the Upper Cretaceous by Gabb:

Fusus kingii Gabb

Fusus kingii GABB, Paleont. Calif., vol. 1, 1864, p. 85, Pl. 28, fig. 204; near Henley, Siskiyou County. Turonian. . . . MERRIAM, the species was included in a list of type specimens recognized in the collections at the University of California, in 1895. . . . STEWART, Acad. Nat. Sci. Phila., Proc. vol. 78, 1926, p. 409; thought the species may have been an example of *Volutoderma*. . . . WHITEAVES, Meso. Foss. vol. 1, pt. 2, 1879; believed he had recognized the species in a collection of fossils from Sucia Island, probably of lower Senonian age.

Fusus aratus Gabb

Fusus aratus GABB, Paleont. Calif., vol. 1, 1864, p. 84, Pl. 28, fig. 202; near Martinez, Contra Costa County. . . . STEWART, Acad. Nat. Sci., Phila., Proc., vol. 78, 1926, p. 290; type recognized by Stewart at the University of California, although its precise locality and horizon was held in doubt.

Fusus flexuosus Gabb

Fusus flexuosus GABB, Paleont. Calif., vol. 1, 1864, p. 85, Pl. 21, fig. 109; near Martinez. "*Fusus*" *flexuosus* Gabb, STEWART, Acad. Nat. Sci. Phila., Proc. vol. 78, 1926, p. 291; type material not found; the species seems not to have been recorded since by any writer.

Genus Serrifusus Meek
Serrifusus vancouverensis (Whiteaves)

Serrifusus Dakotensis var. *vancouverensis* WHITEAVES, Meso. Foss., vol. 1, pt. 2, 1879, p. 119, Pl. 15, fig. 5; Middle shales, Division D; northwest side of Hornby Island, B. C.

This form is specifically distinct from Meek's genotype, though congeneric with it, and may represent the same age, namely early Maestrichtian. It occurs on Hornby Island in the group containing *Parapachydiscus ootacodensis* (Stoliczka) as determined by Whiteaves, *Diplomoceras notabile* Whiteaves, *Bostrychoceras elongatum* (Whiteaves), and various types of nostoceratids.

Serrifusus joaquinensis Anderson n. sp.
(Plate 49, figure 3)

This species is undoubtedly closely related to the preceding, but it is smaller and as known from the shell, exhibits some features believed to have specific value. Shell is turreted, spire angular, of moderate height, possessing five or six whorls; whorls slightly convex on upper surface, more convex below; whorls bordered near middle by a prominent nodose keel; upper surface sloping outwardly, faintly ribbed by oblique undulation crossed by faint revolving threads; whorl sutures sharply defined, bordered below by a narrow collar-like zone; aperture ovate, angulate at its outer border, rounded below, base of body whorl sloping downward to an apparent short canal (not preserved).

Holotype (C. A. S. Type Coll.) has the following dimensions: height, 55 mm; greater width of whorl, 45 mm. Found by C. C. Church, at locality 2362 (C. A. S.), on Los Gatos Creek, 8 miles northwest of Coalinga, where it was associated with *Parapachydiscus catarinae* Anderson and Hanna, *Nostoceras fresnoense* n. sp., and *Baculites lomaensis* Anderson.

In general form and ornamentation it is a southern analogue of, and is correlative with its congener described above. Its stratigraphic position is the lowest member of the Moreno formation.

Family FASCIOLARIIDAE
Genus Eripachya Gabb
Eripachya hilgardi (White)

Fulgur Hilgardi WHITE, U. S. Geol. Survey, Bull. 51, 1889, p. 22, Pl. 3, figs. 2, 3; near Pentz, Butte County, California.
Eripachya hilgardi (White), COSSMANN, Essais Paleont. Comp., vol. 4, 1901, p. 147; . . . STEWART, Acad. Nat. Sci. Phila., Proc., vol. 78, 1926, p. 426; locality as above.

The characterization of this species by White is (in part) as follows:

"Shell small for a species of this genus (*Fulgur*); spire depressed—conical; volutions five in number; those of the spire so flattened upon their outer surface as to form an oblique cone, the sides of which are slightly concave, and the base of which is upon the periphery of the last volution; suture indistinct; last volution large, subangular at the periphery and convex below it; beak long, slender, and only slightly flexed; aperture suboval, angular behind and ending in a long, open, moderately narrow front; surface marked by numerous revolving raised coarse lines or slender ridges which disappear entirely upon the beak, and are often obscure on the spire above the periphery, especially in mature examples; . . ."

Locality and position,—near Pentz, Butte County, where it was associated with *Mortoniceras (Submortoniceras) chicoense* (Trask), *Trigonia evansana* Meek, and other species. It should be regarded as probably of lower—middle Senonian age.

Genus Eripachya Gabb
Eripachya ponderosa (Gabb)

Neptunea ponderosa GABB, Paleont. Calif., vol. 1, 1864, p. 88, Pl. 18, fig. 38; Tuscan Springs, Tehama County, California.
Eripachya ponderosa GABB, Paleont. Calif., vol. 2, 1869, p. 148, 149; locality as before. . . . COSSMANN, Essais Paleont. Comp., vol. 4, 1901, p. 147, Fig. 40, after Gabb; accepts this species as the genotype. . . . ANDERSON, Calif. Acad. Sci., Proc., 3d ser., vol. 2, 1902, p. 29, 34: Tuscan Springs, "Upper Chico" horizon. . . . STEWART, Acad. Nat. Sci. Phila., Proc., vol. 78, 1926, p. 425, Pl. 20, fig. 9; locality as above.

Gabb (1864, p. 88) described this species as follows:

"Thick, robust, spire high, whorls plane or slightly convex; four or five in number; suture linear, more distant as the shell increases in size; undulated. Surface marked by a few large ribs, varying in number and size on different specimens. These ribs are crossed by numerous revolving lines, all of the same size, on young specimens, but alternating irregularly on the larger whorls. Aperture broad, rounded subquadrate; columella slightly curved, outer lip straight, crenulate internally. Canal short, having at the extremity an oblique groove, indicating a rudimentary umbilicus, but entirely closed and very shallow."

Gabb's figure is natural size; length, 38 mm; maximum width, 20 mm; height of spire, 15 mm; length of aperture, 22 mm.

Locality and position.—The strata exposed at Tuscan Springs do not exceed 500 feet in thickness, and are confined to the upper part of the Coniacian. *"Fulgur" hilgardi* White is not a congeneric species.

Eripachya perforata (Gabb)

Neptunea perforata GABB, Paleont. Calif., vol. 1, 1864, p. 89, Pl. 18, fig. 39; North fork of Cottonwood Creek, Shasta County.

Eripachya perforata GABB, Paleont. Calif., vol. 2, 1869, p. 149; locality as given above. . . . COSSMANN, Essais Paleont. Comp., vol. 4, 1901, p. 147; (places this species doubtfully under *Eripachya* Gabb); . . . STEWART, Acad. Nat. Sci. Phila., Proc., vol. 78, 1926, p. 424; places the species under *Paladmete* Gardner, but accepting its occurrence on the North fork of Cottonwood Creek, Shasta County.

The species has not been recognized in this area by later writers, but should it be found there its horizon cannot be later than Upper Turonian.

Eripachya hoffmannii (Gabb)

Neptunea Hoffmannii GABB, Paleont. Calif., vol. 1, 1864, p. 90, Pl. 18, fig. 41; North fork of Cottonwood Creek, Shasta County.
Eripachya Hoffmannii GABB, Paleont. Calif., vol. 2, 1869, p. 149; locality as given above. . . . MERRIAM, 1895, recognized the type in the collections at the Museum of Paleontology, University of California. . . . COSSMANN, Essais Paleont. Comp., vol. 4, 1901, p. 147; placed the species only doubtfully under *Eripachya* Gabb. . . . STEWART, Acad. Nat. Sci. Phila., Proc., vol. 78, 1926, p. 425; appears to have recognized a part of the original material at the Museum of Paleontology, from the North fork of Cottonwood Creek, Shasta County, which he provisionally placed in *Paladmete* Gardner, and accordingly in strata not younger than Upper Turonian.

According to Stewart, (1926, p. 425): "The holotype of *Paladmete Hoffmannii* seems to be an unusually large specimen of the species." Height, 26.7 mm; width, 16 mm. It has 13 axial ribs on the body whorl and the spirals are more widely spaced than on the smaller specimens.

Family VOLUTIDAE Gray
Genus **Volutoderma** Gabb
Volutoderma californica Dall
(Plate 52, figures 1, 1a)

Volutilithes navarroensis GABB (not Shumard), Paleont. Calif., vol. 1, 1864, p. 102, Pl. 19, fig. 56; Tuscan Springs, Tehama County, California.
Volutoderma californica DALL, Smithson. Inst., Misc. Coll., vol. 50, 1903, p. 10. Not *"Volutoderma" averilli* (Gabb), Stewart, Acad. Nat. Sci. Phila., Proc., vol. 78, 1926, p. 409 (in part).

Stewart's (1926, p. 409) placing of *"Volutoderma" averillii* (Gabb) in the synonomy of the above species is subject to question, if not to serious objection, in that much is assumed that cannot be proved. He has assumed that the two specimens from Tuscan Springs in the collections at the Philadelphia Academy, figured by him (Pl. 22, figs. 10, 11) are specifically identical with the holotype of *"Volutoderma" averillii* (Gabb), which he himself refers to as only "an immature *Volutoderma.*" The larger of these specimens he states is the lectotype of *"Volutilithes navarroensis"* (Gabb), (not Shumard), which later was named *Volutoderma californica* by Dall.

In the collections of the California Academy of Sciences there are two excellent specimens of *Volutoderma* from Tuscan Springs. One, here figured, has the following dimensions: height (incomplete) 87 mm; maximum breadth, 32 mm; length of aperature, 62 mm. Locality 1125-B (C. A. S.), found at Tuscan Springs, Tehama County. This specimen agrees in all essential respects with the figures given by Stewart (Pl. 22, figs. 10, 11), but it cannot be identified with either Gabb's figure of *"Volutoderma" averillii* (Pl. 18, fig. 34), or with the type in the Museum of Paleontology.

Stewart (1926, p. 409) appears to have believed that the specimen of *Volutoderma* figured by White (1889, Pl. 3, fig. 1) also "seems to be this species," namely, *"Volutoderma" averillii* (Gabb). From the record *Volutoderma californica* Dall should be regarded as the genotype of *Volutoderma* Gabb, and an attempt to replace it with a doubtful or an unsettled example, even though it might belong to the genus, hardly appears to be logical.

Volutoderma gabbi White

Fulguraria Gabbi WHITE, U. S. Geol. Survey, Bull. 51, 1889, p. 23–25, Pl. 3, fig. 1;
  Centerville, Butte County. . . . DALL, Smithson. Inst. Misc. Coll. vol. 50, 1907, p. 10. . . .
  PACKARD, Univ. Calif. Pub. Bull. Dept. Geol. Sci., vol. 13, 1922, p. 432.
Volutoderma averillii, STEWART, in part, (not Gabb), Acad. Nat. Sci. Phila., Proc. vol. 78,
  1926, p. 409.

White's holotype was obtained by Turner from the Chico formation near Centerville,
Butte County. It was compared by White with the lectotype of *Volutilithes navarroensis*
Gabb, subsequently named *Volutoderma californica* by Dall, who regarded White's species
as distinct, being both larger and more robust.

A similar form was found by Sidney Richardson on his farm, 4 miles north of Montague,
Siskiyou County, and was sent by him to the California Academy of Sciences. It is from the
lower Senonian, as it was found near *Desmophyllites siskiyouensis* n. sp., *Prionocycloceras
crenulatum* (Anderson), and above the level of *Nowakites klamathonis* n. sp.

Whiteaves (1903, p. 356) reports this species from the Sucia Islands and from the coal-
bearing beds near Nanaimo, Vancouver Island. In both localities, the strata are correlative
with the lower Senonian beds at Richardson's ranch, also coal-bearing. These facts indicate
the stratigraphic range of the species as being from lower to upper Senonian.

Volutoderma jacksonensis Anderson n. sp.
(Plate 21, figure 1)

Shell of medium size, with an elevated spire, consisting of about seven whorls; aperture
of moderate length, about one-third length of shell; surface marked only by vertical folds,
or ribs, without visible revolving ridges, as in the preceding species. The number of vertical
ribs is about 18 to the whorl; the upper part of the whorl forms a flattened slope, terminating
above in an elevated collar, covering the whorl suture; aperture moderately broad, ratio of
height to breadth being about 33 to 15. The holotype (C. A. S. Type Coll.) has the following dimensions: length (incomplete), 85.4 mm; width (incomplete), 32 mm. It was found
at the "Forty-nine" mine, 2 miles southwest of Phoenix, Jackson County, Oregon. It was
associated with *Anchura condoniana* Anderson, species of *Oregoniceras,* and other Turonian
forms.

Volutoderma mitraeformis (Gabb)

Cordiera mitraeformis GABB, Paleont. Calif., vol. 2, 1869, p. 153, Pl. 28, fig. 32; "Shasta
  group, Colusa County, near Hot Sulphur Springs." . . . . STANTON, U. S. Geol. Survey,
  Bull. 133, 1895, p. 19; listed with other species from the same vicinity; locality not definitely known, and held in doubt.
Volutoderma mitraeformis (Gabb), STEWART, Acad. Nat. Sci. Phila., Proc., vol. 78, 1926,
  p. 410; quotes Gabb as to locality of discovery.

Both the locality and horizon of this species and its associates referred to by Gabb, have
been much misunderstood. The species occurring in Stanton's list (1895, p. 19), with the
exception of *Atresius liratus* Gabb, have all been found in Upper Cretaceous strata. From
Gabb's account it appears that all came from the same locality, which he described variously,
but which can only be understood by one familiar with the region, as being near the outer
foothills, east of Wilbur Springs, Colusa County, and south of the road then known, leading
from Williams to Wilbur Springs.

This horizon lies near the middle of the series, and probably in the lower part of the
Senonian. No species of *Volutoderma* has yet been seen or recognized in the Shasta series,
and most of the species of this genus known at present from the Cretaceous of California
are from Senonian beds. The genus ranges from upper Turonian to upper Campanian.

Volutoderma crossi Anderson n. sp.
(Plate 16, figures 3, 3a)

Shell small, as compared with others of the genus in California and Oregon. The spire
is moderately high, with relatively broad whorls, and it terminates in an acute apex, and

below in a narrow elongated columella. The surface is marked by broad vertical folds, or ribs, and by revolving ridges, somewhat flattened and separated by narrow grooves; aperture narrowly ovate, terminating in a short canal. The holotype (C. A. S. Type Coll.) has the following dimensions: length (incomplete), 33 mm; breadth of body whorl, 16 mm; height of aperture, 21 mm; greatest breadth, 8 mm. This specimen was found by Mr. C. M. Cross, at locality 1293-D (C. A. S.), on the SW ¼ sec. 4, T. 32 N., R., 3 W., M. D. M., near Frazier Corners, Shasta County. Its age is upper Turonian.

Volutoderma magna Packard

Volutoderma magna PACKARD, Univ. Calif. Pub. Bull. Dept. Geol. Sci. vol. 13, 1922, p. 432, Pl. 37, fig. 1; Santa Ana Mountains, Orange County; (? Campanian).

This species is said to resemble *Volutoderma gabbi* White, except in some details of sculpture; length of type, 95 mm; maximum width, 43 mm.

Volutoderma santana Packard

Volutoderma santana PACKARD, Univ. Calif. Pub. Bull. Dept. Geol. Sci., vol. 13, 1922, p. 432, Pl. 36, fig. 2; occurrence and horizon the same as foregoing species.

This species, like the preceding is said to have been found in the *"Turritella pescaderoensis* zone." As here interpreted, the position of both the foregoing species is above the base of the Senonian, but is probably within the lower part of the same.

Volutoderma suciana Dall

Volutilithes navarroensis, WHITEAVES (not Shumard), Meso. Foss., vol. 1, pt. 2, 1879, p. 117, Pl. 15, figs. 3, 3a; Sucia Islands, Strait of Georgia, western Washington.
Volutoderma suciana Dall, Smithson. Inst. Misc. Coll., vol. 50, 1907, p. 10, (Footnote); locality as given by Whiteaves (above).

According to Dall the species is most nearly related to *Volutoderma gabbi* (White), but possesses specific differences in its higher and more acute spire, as well as in its sculptural details. Good examples, obtained from the Upper Cretaceous beds on Sucia Island (locality 228, C. A. S.), are in the collections of the California Academy of Sciences; one of which is a well preserved fragment, having seven whorls and a high spire, that confrms to Dall's statement as to form and ornamentation. None of them, however, are as robust as the example figured by Whiteaves.

Volutoderma dilleri (White)

Scobinella Dilleri WHITE, U. S. Geol. Survey, Bull. 51, 1889, p. 25, Pl. 4, figs. 1, 2, 3; Chico group, Little Cow Creek, Shasta County. . . . STANTON, U. S. Geol. Surv., Bull. 133, 1895, p. 19.
Volutoderma (Rostellinda) Dilleri, DALL, Smithson. Inst. Misc. Coll., vol. 50, 1907, (new subgenus). . . . STEWART, Acad. Nat. Sci., Phila., Proc., vol. 78, 1926, p. 410.

Numerous examples of this species have been collected from the type locality. They do not support the suggestion of Stewart that they may be the adult form of *"Cordiera" mitraeformis* (Gabb), having fewer and much heavier varices, and a more pronounced spiral sculpture than the latter. On the other hand, from a critical study of the materials in the collection of the California Academy, it appears that White had only worn and imperfect examples of this species, in which sculpture of the spire had largely disappeared.

On the better preserved specimens the varices seen on the body whorl appear also upon the two lower whorls of the spire as well, not as a continuous ridge but with an offset at the sutural line.

Genus Gosavia Stoliczka
Gosavia biconica Anderson n. sp.
(Plate 75, figures 3, 3a)

Shell of medium size, biconic in general form, with a spire shorter than the body whorl, in the ratio of 26:31; total length of holotype, 44 mm; with an angle of about 135° between the spire and basal slopes; apical angle about 70°; surface generally smooth, marked by vertical lines of growth, with irregular varices, crossed by bearded spiral lines, not seen without a good lens, and not showing well in the figure. Aperture only moderately broad; outer lip thin, inner lip callused; columella bearing plications, only a few of which can be clearly seen on the posterior half of the aperture; canal short, slightly recurved, and partly lost. The general aspect of the shell is cone-like, although it is clearly a volutid, rather than a *Conus*.

The holotype (C. A. S. Type Coll.) has the following dimensions: height, 43 mm; greatest breadth, 25 mm; height of aperture, 29 mm.

The holotype was found by the writer at locality 1294A (C. A. S.), near the State highway, 4.6 miles north of Redding, Shasta County, on Sand Flat associated with *Trigonia* aff. *T. fitchi* Packard, *Acteonina* sp., and *Pachydiscus* aff. *P. ashlandicus* Anderson, in the lower part of the exposed Turonian.

Dall placed the genus among the Volutidae but assigns no definite age limits, except those given by Stoliczka. According to Stoliczka, the Indian species somewhat resembles *Gosavia squamosa* Zekete of the Upper Cretaceous of Europe. The Indian species appears to be younger than that of California.

Family CYPRAEIDAE Fleming
Genus **Cypraea** Linné
Cypraea berryessae Anderson n. sp.
(Plate 63, figures 2, 2a, 2b)

Shell is small, ovate in outline, highly arched, the maximum height being posterior to center; spire short, concealed at maturity; aperture narrow behind, expanding in anterior half of shell, denticulate on inner lip in its forward half; surface smooth, enamelled and polished beneath, and on lower borders, and only smooth in other parts of surface; general aspect exceptionally graceful.

The holotype of the species (C. A. S. Type Coll.) has the following dimensions: length, 18 mm; width, 13 mm; height, 9.8 mm; posterior end deeply notched by a narrow, slightly oblique sinus extending upward to one-third its height. The holotype of the species and three additional examples were collected by Wm. E. Kennett, at locality 31918 (C. A. S.) on Thompson Creek, in western Yolo County, near the Napa-Yolo county line, in the basal beds of the Turonian. They were found associated with *Acteonina californica* Gabb, *Acteonina* sp., *Trigonarca excavata* Packard, and (?) *Durania*.

Cypraea gualalaensis Anderson n. sp.
(Plate 62, figures 8, 8a)

This species may belong to the living genus *Mauritia* Troschel, but since the present species is from an Upper Cretaceous horizon, this generic name is not used. The form somewhat resembles that described by Stoliczka, from the Arrialoor group near Veraghoor, as *Cypraea cunliffei*.

Shell of moderate size, elongated, ovate in outline, inflated in posterior half of shell; spire short, hardly exceeding the terminus of the outer lip; aperture narrow, gently curved to the right near the posterior end, notched before and behind; surface smooth, but not polished in the holotype (C. A. S. Type Coll.).

The holotype, collected by S. G. Clark, has the following dimensions: total length, 50 mm; maximum width, 32 mm; height of shell, 23 mm; width of aperture in front, 4 mm.

This example was found by Clark near Gualala, on the coast of Mendocino County, associated with a form doubtfully regarded as *Ovula,* and with *Cerithium* sp., *Coralliochama* aff. *C. orcutti* White, *Glycymeris* aff. *G. veatchi* (Gabb), and a large species of *Inoceramus.* Its stratigraphic position is in the lower part of the "Wallala group" which, as indicated by the associated fauna, is lower Maestrichtian, correlative with the horizon exposed at Todos Santos Bay, Lower California.

Cypraea argonautica Anderson n. name
(Plate 21, figures 4, 4a)

Erato veraghoörensis (?) Stoliczka, Anderson, Proc. Calif. Acad. Sci., 3rd Ser., Vol. 2, 1902, p. 75, Pl. 9, figs. 181, 182; Fitch Ranch (formerly Smith), Jackson County, Oregon. Not *Erato veraghoörensis* Stoliczka, 1867.

The original description of this species reads (in part) :

"Shell ovate, more inflated posteriorly; spire low, though distinct, about one-eighth of the entire length of the shell; outer lip thickened and reflexed, broadly rounded, denticulate with fine ridges on the inner margin; aperture narrow, somewhat S-shape, a little wider at the anterior end; shell notched, both before and behind; inner lip rounded, not known to be toothed; surface smooth and polished. The outer lip is slightly expanded posterorly in an ear-like elevation that rises to a level with the low spire. The anterior end of the inner lip is bent a little downward just before reaching the forward notch. Both notches are somewhat shallow, the posterior one showing an upward curve, or groove, between the spire and the ear-like expansion of the outer lip."

A good specimen, found on the Fitch ranch, 3 miles west of Phoenix, Oregon, was damaged in the San Francisco fire, but it was recovered and is preserved as No. 42 C. A. S. Type Collection. No other example has since been found in Oregon or California. Its horizon was probably Turonian.

Cypraea fontana Anderson n. sp.
(Plate 21, figures 15, 16)

Shell of this species is small, oval in outline, but it is broader than high; shell more inflated in the posterior half of its length, sloping gracefully toward the front; surface smooth and polished.

The holotype (C. A. S. Type Coll.) has the following dimensions: length, 23.5 mm; width of shell, 17 mm; height, 11 mm; height of spire, 2 mm.

This shell was found by the writer at Texas Springs, Shasta County, associated with *Sonneratia stantoni* Anderson, *Beudanticeras haydeni* (Gabb), *Terebratella densleonis* Anderson, and *Neohibolites fontinalis* n. sp. and numerous pelecypod species, indicating a lower Cenomanian horizon.

Family CASSIDIDAE Adams
Genus **Haydenia** Gabb
Haydenia impressa Gabb

Haydenia impressa GABB, Paleont. Calif., vol. 1, 1864, p. 98, Pl. 18, fig. 51; Tuscan Springs, Tehama County. (? Pentz, Butte County). . . . vol. 2, 1869, p. 219; locality as above. . . . COSSMANN, Essais Paleont. Comp., vol. 4, 1901, pp. 155, 156; . . . . STEWART, Acad. Nat. Sci. Phila., Proc., vol. 78, 1926, p. 381, Pl. 20, figs. 5, 5a. The single specimen found in the collection at the Philadelphia Academy is doubtfully placed in Cassididae.

Although Gabb did not include the species in this family, it more likely belongs there than to the Buccinidae in which Gabb placed it, as Stewart doubtfully suggested. This assignment appears to be supported by Gabb's figure and description, and also by Stewarts comments, although they introduce an element of doubt.

Stewart's reference to three specimens of the species in the U. S. National Museum from Pentz, Butte County, raises a question as to their identity. The beds at Pentz are somewhat younger than the upper part of the sequence at Tuscan Springs.

Genus **Bullina** Férussac
Bullina yoloensis Anderson n. sp.
(Plate 18, figures 5, 6)

Shell small, subcylindrical or narrowly ovate, truncate behind, rounded in front, aperture expanded in front, extending backward as a narrow slit to posterior terminus; surface nearly smooth, or showing fine sculptural striae on its posterior half; anterior part of shell marked by fine lines of growth crossed by finer revolving threads, showing a tendency to doubling; on posterior half, the striae on mature and well-preserved shells often amount to vertical costae, separated by narrow impressed grooves. The holotype (C. A. S. Type Coll.) has the following dimensions: total length, 8:5 mm; greatest width, 3.5 mm. Paratype (C. A. S. Type Coll.) measures: length, 17 mm; greatest breadth, 7 mm. These and other specimens of the same were found with *Bullina nortonensis* n. sp., and other Mollusca, at locality 1467-A in Enos Canyon, 7 miles northwest of Winters, Yolo County. The species is not unlike *Bullina cretacea* (d'Orbigny) as illustrated by Kossmat (1897, Pl. 8), although it is relatively longer and less robust, and seems to occur at a somewhat lower horizon. The present species is found in the lower Senonian, associated with *Metaplacenticeras pacificum* Smith, *Metaplacenticeras californicum* Anderson, *Desmophyllites yoloensis* n. sp., *Tessarolax distorta* Gabb, and *Phylloceras ramosum* Meek.

Bullina nortonensis Anderson n. sp.
(Plate 21, figures 13, 13a)

This species is smaller than the preceding, is relatively more robust, and possesses no vertical ribbing, showing only faint lines of growth crossed by fine revolving lines somewhat oblique to the axis of the shell; posterior terminus rounded, only slightly narrower than the rounded anterior end; aperture wider than that of the preceding species, the body whorl terminating in a short canal; outer lip sharp.

The holotype (C. A. S. Type Coll.) has a maximum length of 5 mm; and a width of 3 mm. It was found with the preceding at locality 1467-A (C. A. S.) and with the associates already named.

The species recalls the second form described by Kossmat as occurring with *Bullina cretacea* (d'Orbigny), but it has no longitudinal sculpture (Kossmat, 1897, p. 91, Pl. 8, figs. 7a, 7b).

The occurrence of this and the preceding species, respectively resembling the two forms illustrated by Kossmat from the Valudayur beds of southern India, is taken as a mere coincidence, without stratigraphic significance.

Family MELANIDAE (Lamarck) Gray
Genus **Pseudomelania** Pictet and Campeche
Pseudomelania colusaensis Anderson n. sp.
(Plate 63, figure 3)

Shell turreted, spire high, whorls seven to ten, spire tapering moderately to an acute apex; whorls rounded, convex; sutures impressed; aperture elongated, ovate, terminating in a short canal, sculpture not clearly exposed in the holotype, but as seen in the rock-mold it is almost smooth, showing only lines of growth. The holotype (C. A. S. Type Coll.) consists of a rock-mold from which a plastotype has been made and figured. Its dimensions are as follows: length (incomplete), 70 mm; greatest width, 23 mm; height of aperture, 23 mm. The holotype and two or three fragmentary examples, including the two last whorls, were found at locality 25730 (C. A. S.) on Sand Creek, southwest Colusa County, at the north end of the Rumsey Hills, by Hugh L. Dobbins, near his ranch house. These were associated with *Nowakites dobbinsi* n. sp., *Eupachydiscus willgreeni* n. sp. *Parapuzosia* sp. and other cephalopod species, and with *Inoceramus* aff. *I. undulatoplicatus* (Roemer), and other species indicating a horizon much above the base of the Coniacian, as found in this area.

The species resembles *Pseudomelania elegantula* Nagao (1934, Pl. 37) from the Hiragia sandstone (? Aptian) of Hanshu, Japan, but it appears to have a closer analogue in *Pseudomelania southerlandi* Bailey.

The species has been found by Taff, Hanna, and Cross at locality 28323 (C. A. S.) on Puerto Creek, SW ¼ of sec. 35, T. 5 S., R. 6 E., also associated with *Inoceramus* aff. *I. undulatoplicatus* (Roemer), and *Canadoceras* aff. *C. multisulcatum* (Whiteaves).

Class CEPHALOPODA
Order NAUTILOIDEA Zittel
Family NAUTILIDAE d'Orbigny
Genus **Nautilus** Linné
Nautilus (Cymatoceras) charlottensis Whiteaves

Nautilus (sp. indet.) WHITEAVES, Meso. Foss., vol. 1, pt. 1, 1867, p. 14, 15, Queen Charlotte Islands, British Columbia.
Nautilus suciensis WHITEAVES, Meso. Foss. vol. 1, pt. 3, 1884, p. 197, 199, Pl. 21; Skidegate Inlet, Queen Charlotte Islands. (Not *Nautilus suciensis* Whiteaves, 1879, p. 97, 98; Sucia Islands, Strait of Georgia). . . . WHITEAVES, Meso. Foss., vol. 1, pt. 4, 1900, p. 269, Maple Island, Skidegate Inlet, Queen Charlotte Islands.

This species which represents a low position in the Upper Cretaceous (Cenomanian) of the Queen Charlotte series, has been found also in California and in Oregon, in strata of the same age. A well-preserved example, now in the collections of Stanford University, consisting of one-third of a whorl, was found at old Horsetown in 1894. A second example was found on Hulen Creek, Shasta County, in 1929, beneath the second conglomerate at the base of the Upper Cretaceous. A third example was later found by the writer at "Dark Hollow," on the old Pioneer Road, 4 miles southwest of Phoenix, Oregon. The last two specimens are in the collection of the Academy of Sciences.

Another example of the same species, more complete than either of the preceding, is in the collections of the Museum of Paleontology, University of California. It bears the label "No. 230, Pioche collection, *Nautilus Texanus*." Although the label is almost obliterated, and the locality is uncertain, the matrix adhering to it is similar to that at the mouth of Hulen Creek, Shasta County. It is not the specimen figured and described by Gabb (1864, p. 59, Pl. 9) as *Nautilus Texanus* ? Shumard (= *Nautilus gabbi* Anderson, 1938), from Alderson Creek, Shasta County.

Nautilus (Cymatoceras) hermosus Anderson n. sp.
(Plate 64, figure 5)

Shell large, a little inflated (not globose), slightly flattened on sides, abdominal zone more narrowly curved than in most West Coast forms; umbilicus narrow, walls sloping to broadly rounded sides; whorl expanding rapidly in diameter; surface of shell marked by numerous shallow, broadly curved, or semi-radial grooves curving gracefully backward from the umbilical pit; sutures roundly convex behind (concave at the front), meeting the external shell in a slightly curved line; position of siphuncle not shown.

The holotype (C. A. S. Type Coll.) measures: greatest diameter, 190 mm; height of last whorl, 100 mm; greatest thickness (near umbilical border), 70 mm; width of umbilicus 10 mm, slightly open. This example was found by G. D. Hanna at locality 2366 (C. A. S.), on the west side of sec. 25, T. 19 S., R. 14 E., M. D. B. M., at the top of the exposed part of the Panoche formation beneath the overlying Eocene shales.

Its nearest related species may be *Nautilus (Cymatoceras) pseudoatlas* Yabe and Shimizu, found in the Upper Cretaceous (? upper Senonian) on the island of Amakusa, Japan. It is also probably related to *N. suciaensis* Whiteaves.

Nautilus modestus Anderson n. sp.
(Plate 25, figures 9, 9a)

Nautilus danicus (?) Schlotheim, ANDERSON, Proc. Calif. Acad. Sci., 3d ser., vol. 2, 1902, p. 27; "Forty-nine" mine, Phoenix, Oregon.

Shell is small, sublenticular in section, compressed in outer half of sides, thickest in the umbilical area; umbilicus partly closed or showing only a slight depression; siphuncle subcentral; sutures falciform, curving sharply backward and upward near umbilical border, but below the middle of the side, curving strongly forward and crossing the ventral zone with a deep sinus; periphery slightly flattened near aperture.

The holotype (C. A. S. Type Coll.) was found by the writer near the old "Forty-nine" mine in the highest beds there exposed. The locality was a little to the east of the mine, above the horizon of the greater number of fossils found at this locality, and is thought to represent the lowest part of the Senonian.

The holotype has the following dimensions: greatest diameter, 44 mm; greatest breadth, 23 mm; height of outer whorl, 28 mm; shell wholly septate.

The shell differs much from the Indian species, *Nautilus danicus* Blanford, in many respects; it is thinner, has less sharply curved septa, and its forward curve is less prolonged, and its peripheral portion is narrower.

Order AMMONOIDEA Zittel

Family PHYLLOCERATIDAE Zittel

Genus **Phylloceras** Suess

Phylloceras gargantuum Anderson n. sp.

(Plate 53, figure 2)

This extraordinary species of *Phylloceras*, the largest found on the West Coast, was discovered by Donald R. Birch in western Fresno County, and was donated by him to the California Academy of Sciences. The holotype (C. A. S. Type Coll.) is a part of the living chamber of a mature shell, representing about a third of an entire whorl, and is accordingly quite incomplete. This fragment has the following dimensions: greatest length, 24 inches (609 mm); greatest breadth, partly crushed, 6 inches (152 mm); greatest height of whorl (slightly increased by pressure), 18 inches (457 mm). The original diameter of the whorl (estimated), not less than 29 inches (736 mm). The whorl section appears to have been narrowly ovate, but with a rounded periphery, giving the shell a general lenticular form; surface ornamented with coarse, radial ribs that crossed ventral zone, numbering 17 on the last 6 inches of periphery; ribs arising below umbilical border, curving sharply forward at lower extremity, rising vertically on sides, and describing a forward curve on approach to the ventral border.

The holotype was found at locality 28542 (C. A. S.), about 800 feet south of the center of sec. 15, T. 14 S., R. 11 E., M. D. B. M., in the zone of *Baculites inornatus* Meek, *Parapachydiscus panochensis* n. sp., and fragments of other species, but a few hundred feet above the zone with *Canadoceras* sp. indet. The horizon of this species is Senonian, probably near its summit, but about 7500 feet beneath the top of the Panoche formation in this section.

Phylloceras velledae Michelin

(Plate 16, figures 4, 4a)

Phylloceras Velledae PICTET AND CAMPECHE, Terr. Cret. de St. Croix, vol. 1, (1861–64), p. 268, Pl. 36, fig. 8. . . . STOLICZKA, Cret. Cephal., S. India, vol. 1, 1868, p. 116, Pl. 59, figs. 1-4; Ootatoor group. . . . Kossmat, Sudind. Kreideform., vol. 9, 1895, p. 108(12), Pl. 15, fig. 3 (suture line).

The species described and illustrated by Stoliczka from the Ootatoor group (lower Cenomanian) of Southern India has been found in California in at least three localities, and all at the same horizon, the lower part of the Upper Cretaceous series. It occurs at locality 31097 (C. A. S.), on Dry Creek, northern Tehama County, and at locality 2233 (C. A. S.), in a deep ravine about half a mile southeast of the mouth of the Hulen Creek, Shasta County, and also at Old Horsetown, on Clear Creek, Shasta County. At the first locality it occurs with *Desmoceras inane* Stoliczka, *Turrilites bergeri* Brongniart, and *Cyrtochilus stylus* n. sp., and at the second locality it occurs with *Puzosia (Parapuzosia) hindsi* n. sp., of the *Puzosia planulata* (Sowerby) group, and with forms of *Acanthoceras* aff. *A. newboldi* Kossmat. In all cases where the horizon of its occurence can be determined by stratigraphic evidence, it is at or near the local base of the series. At two localities it was found associated with *Desmoceras inane* Stoliczka. The following measurements are representative of the two better examples of the species from California: hypotype (C. A. S. Type Coll.) (Pl. 16, figs. 4, 4a) greatest diameter, 97 mm; width of umbilicus, 13 mm; breadth of shell, 25 mm; from locality 2233 (C. A. S.). Another specimen (not figured) from locality 31097 (C. A. S.) has the following dimensions: greatest diameter, 62 mm; width of umbilicus, 9.2 mm; breadth, 18 mm.

Phylloceras ramosum Meek
(Plate 40, figures 4, 4a)

Phylloceras (Scaphites) ramosum MEEK, Tr. Albany Inst., vol. 4, 1887, p. 45; Komox, Vancouver Island. . . . MEEK, U. S. Geol. and Geogr. Survey Terr., Bull. vol. 2, 1876, p. 371, Pl. 5, figs. 1, 1a, 1b; Komox, Vancouver Island. . . . ANDERSON, Proc. Calif. Acad. Sci., 3d ser., vol. 2, 1902, p. 58, 61, 86, 99; "Lower Chico" Oregon. . . . WHITEAVES, Meso. Foss. vol. 1, pt. 5, 1903, p. 327; Hornby Island, British Columbia.

According to Meek's figures and description, the shell is small, discoidal, compressed, thin and flat, with very small umbilicus, and with sides and periphery ornamented with fine, threadlike costae that arises on the umbilical border, cross the sides above and the ventral zone with a slight forward curvature. Meek's sectional figure shows the umbilicus to be narrow, funnel form above, with a flare not well shown in his lateral figure. The species is known by its small, but open umbilicus, the ratio of width to diameter of shell being about 1:20.

Few references to this species in the literature seem to correctly represent it. Gabb (1864, Pl. 10) erroneously figured a specimen from the north side of Mount Diablo as representing it, although the whorl section is more inflated. This specimen was identified by the writer (1902, p. 99), but in the light of more recent collections its identity is not now maintained. J. P. Smith collected fragmentary examples of *Phylloceras ramosum* Meek at Arroyo del Valle, associated with a considerable fauna. A later analysis of this fauna shows it to be of lower Senonian (Coniacian) age.

The species has since been found at Enos Canyon, locality 1467-A (C. A. S.), 7 miles northwest of Winters, Yolo County, where it is associated with a large fauna similar to that of Arroyo del Valle. It has been found also at the "Forty-nine" mine, near Phoenix, Oregon. As seen in examples from Enos Canyon, the species attained a considerable size; one of these indicates a diameter at the last septum of more than 56 mm, and a breadth of whorl exceeding 16 mm. Steinmann (1898, p. 80, Pl. 5) figured a form from Quiriquina Island (Chile), which seems to be closely akin to that of Meek, but its identity may be questioned. Whiteaves (1903) gives an excellent account of Meek's species, stating on the authority of Kossmat, to whom he had sent a specimen, that it is not identical with *Phylloceras velledae* of European authors, or with the Indian species; it may better be compared with *Phylloceras nera* Forbes.

Phylloceras vaculae Anderson n. sp.
(Plate 40, figures 3, 3a, 3b)

This species is intermediate in both form and in stratigraphical occurrence between *Phylloceras velledae* (upper Cenomanian), and *Phylloceras ramosum* Meek (zone of *Metaplacenticeras*). The holotype (C. I. T. Coll.) was found at locality 1346 (C. I. T.) on Little Cow Creek associated with *Kotóceras frazierense* n. sp., 1.5 miles east of Frazier Corners, Shasta County, in beds of lower Senonian age. The shell is discoidal, compressed, relatively thin in section, with flattened sides and a small umbilicus with funnel-form pit, of which the walls show an outward flare, less than in *P. velledae* but greater than in *P. ramosum,* and with flattened sides that do not converge rapidly toward the periphery, as in *P. velledae,* but more nearly resembling those of *P. ramosum;* ribs fine, and nearly straight. The holotype has the following dimensions: greatest diameter, 49 mm; width of umbilicus, 6 mm; height of whorl, 26 mm; breadth of whorl, 14 mm. In general aspect the mature shell resembles *P. ramosum* Meek, and many references to the latter may have been based upon specimens properly referred to the present species.

Phylloceras pachecoense Anderson n. sp.
(Plate 53, figures 1, 1a)

Shell is large, discoidal, compressed, flattened on sides, rounded, but not broad on abdomen, sides sloping toward periphery; umbilicus small, with steep walls; surface of sides crossed by numerous costal threads that arise on umbilical border, describing a sinuous curve outward to periphery; costae bundled on lower part of side, diverging slightly from a leading mid-rib, dispersing gradually in passing outward to periphery; outer third of side showing no bundling of costae, although the rib is continuous; suture lines not exposed. In section, the shell shows some resemblance to *Phylloceras velledae* Michelin, though it is much larger.

The holotype of the species (C. A. S. Type Coll.) consists of a large fragment (about one-third) of a whorl, having a peripheral length of 160 mm; a whorl height of 100 mm; and a maximum breadth of whorl 40 mm, measured a little above the umbilical border. The holotype was found by Allan Bennison at locality 29108 (C. A. S.) near the center of the west border of sec. 20, T. 11 S., R. 10 E., on a branch of Salt Creek, in the Moreno formation.

The horizon of the species is in the upper part of the Maestrichtian. It was found in the zone of *Lytoceras aureum* n. sp., *Diplomoceras mercedense* n. sp., and *Exicrioceras ortigalitense* n. sp.

Family LYTOCERATIDAE Neumayr
Genus **Lytoceras** Suess
Subgenus **Gaudryceras** Grossouvre
Lytoceras (Gaudryceras) kayei (Forbes)

Ammonites Kayei FORBES, Geol. Soc. London, Tr., vol. 7, 1856, p. 101, Pl. 8, figs. 3a, b, c; Pondicherri, south India. . . . STOLICZKA, Cret. Cephal. S. India, vol. 1, 1865, Pl. 77, figs. 1-2; Ootatoor group, southern India.
Lytoceras (Gaudryceras) Kayei, KOSSMAT, Sudind. Kreideform, vol. 9, 1875, p. 162, Pl. 16, figs. 5a, b; Pl. 17, figs. 2a, b; Valudayur Beds, Pondicherri, southern India.
Lytoceras Kayei, STEINMANN, Neues Jahrb. f. Min., Geol., etc., Beil. Bd. 10, 1895, '96, p. 86, pl. 5, figs. 5a, b; Quiriquina Island.
Lytoceras (Gaudryceras) kayei ANDERSON, Proc. Calif. Acad. Sci., 3d ser., vol. 2, 1902, p. 83; Chico beds, near Mount Diablo, California.

Shell of medium size, or small, little involute, discoidal, moderately compressed, whorls subcircular, broader than high, somewhat flattened on the ventral surface, and on the sides, ornamented with numerous fine, threadlike costae, with an occasional (about 6 in all) thickened varices, inclining strongly forward. Various accounts of this species have been found in the literature of the West Coast. The writer (1902, p. 83) mentioned its occurrence in the Upper Cretaceous near Mount Diablo, Contra Costa County, but its exact locality and horizon are not known.

Lytoceras (Gaudryceras) alamedense Smith
(Plate 41, figures 5, 5a)

Lytoceras alamedense SMITH, Proc. Calif. Acad. Sci., 3d ser., vol. 1, 1889, p. 136, Pl. 16, figs. 1-12; Pl. 17, figs. 1-6; Pl. 18; Jordan ranch, Arroyo del Valle, southeast of Livermore, California.

The original description of this species given by its author reads (in part):

"This species is evolute, with wide, shallow umbilicus and coils that increase very slowly in size, thus scarcely embracing the preceding. The shell is almost smooth, but has fine sinuous cross-striae of growth that bend forward on the abdomen, form a broad backward bend or lobe on the abdominal shoulders, and another forward sinus on the sides. These are exactly parallel to the mouth, which is marked by varices and constrictions. The growth lines scarcely show on internal casts, but the constrictions are quite distinct, showing them to have been formed by thickening the lip of the aperture during periodic cessations of growth."

The full-grown shell is of medium size, evolute and broadly umbilicate; section of whorl subcircular; umbilicus having steep walls, surface marked by about five forward curving varices and constrictions, between which are numerous costae that cross the ventral zone without interruption. An example of this species (C. A. S. Type Coll.) found at locality 1343 (C. A. S.) near the head of Pleasants' Valley, Yolo County, sec. 10, T. 7 N., R. 2 W., greatly resembles the figure of *Lytoceras (Gaudryceras) denmanense* Whiteaves. This example measures as follows: greatest diameter, 57 mm; width of umbilicus, 25 mm; height of whorl, 19 mm; width of whorl, 19 mm. In a later publication, Smith (1900, p. 203–209) includes among the associates of this species, *Lytoceras cala* Forbes (in Stoliczka), *Metaplacenticeras pacificum, M. californicum, Phylloceras ramosum* Meek, and other forms, not all of which he himself had found there.

Lytoceras (Gaudryceras) denmanense Whiteaves

Ammonites jukesi (Sharpe) WHITEAVES, Meso. Foss., vol. 1, pt. 2, 1878, p. 111, Pl. 13, figs. 3, a, b; Norris Rock, near Hornby Island, British Columbia. . . . ANDERSON, Proc. Calif. Acad. Sci., 3d ser., vol. 2, 1902, p. 58; Chico beds near Phoenix, Oregon.
Gaudryceras Denmanense WHITEAVES, Meso. Foss. vol. 1, pt. 5, 1903, p. 329; Denman Island, near east end of Vancouver Island, Brit. Columbia.

Only a single specimen found (Anderson, 1902, p. 58) seemed referable to the form originally identified by Whiteaves, and that example has been lost. It occurred in the "Chico beds" at the "Forty-nine mine," near Phoenix, Oregon. The species to which this name was applied by Whiteaves (1903) very greatly resembles *Lytoceras (Gaudryceras) alamedense* Smith (1898, p. 136), and may be identical with it. However, as here understood, the species described by Whiteaves should be referred to the lower part of the Conacian. If the species to which these names have been applied are subsequently shown to be specifically identical the name proposed by Whiteaves would be synonomous with *Lytoceras (Gaudryceras) alamedense* Smith, and should be discarded.

Lytoceras (Gaudryceras) delvallense Anderson n. sp.
(Plate 41, figures 4, 4a)

This species is large, evolute, with whorls of circular section, increasing rapidly, both of whorl and section with growth; in this respect it differs much from any other species known in the Upper Cretaceous on the West Coast. The surface is ornamented with strong costae, inclining strongly forward on the umbilical wall and on the lower part of the sides; in this respect also the shell contrasts much with the ornamentation of others, such as the two preceding forms.

The holotype (C. A. S., Type Coll.) is a rock mold, found in the making of the Aqueduct Tunnel, east of the Del Valle shaft, and was donated to the California Academy of Sciences by the courtesy of M. M. O'Shaughnessy. It was taken from the zone of *Placenticeras pacificum* and its associates, exposed half a mile to the north on the Arroyo del Valle, where a fragment of the same was found by the writer. It may have been this species that was taken for *Lytoceras batesi* Trask, in the lists of fossils published by Smith (1898, p. 138). *Lytoceras batesi* Trask belongs in the Alderson stage of the Horsetown group of the Shasta series.

Dimensions of holotype are as follows: greatest diameter, 112 mm; width of umbilicus, 62 mm; breadth of whorl, 37 mm. Lower Senonian.

Lytoceras (Gaudryceras) aff. L. tenuiliratum Yabe
(Plate 40, figure 1)

Gaudryceras tenuiliratum YABE, Jour. College of Sci., Imp. Univ. Tokyo, vol. 18, 1903, p. 19–29, Pl. 3, figs. 3, 4, sutures; var. *intermedium*, figs. 1a, 1b only; upper Ammonite beds, Hokkaido.

A well-preserved, but broken specimen of a lytoceratid species, closely related to the form figured and described by Yabe, was found by Popenoe and Findley at locality 1347 (C. I. T.) on Roaring River, Shasta County, above the junction of this stream with the North fork of Cottonwood Creek. This hypotype (C. I. T. Coll.) measures in greatest diameter, 160 mm;

its umbilical width is 50 mm; and has a breadth of 45 mm. Compared with the form figured by Yabe (pl. 3), it is thinner in section, and its umbilical ratio is a little greater than either types 1 or 2, but it is smaller than that of either 3 or 4 (Yabe). The surface features are indeed quite similar in all, consisting of primary ribs, about 36 in number on the mature whorl; upon and between these are numerous threadlike costae, concentric with the larger ribs, but 8 times as many. On the inner whorls no major ribs are visible below a diameter of 60 mm. Fragmentary examples of this species are found at locality 1690 (C. A. S.), 2 miles above Gas Point, in or near the zone of *Prionotropis bakeri* Anderson. With this species of *Lytoceras* were found fragments of *Acanthoceras* aff. *A. ornatissima* Stoliczka.

Regarding the stratigraphic position of Yabe's species in Japan, it appears that it is usually associated with *Parapachydiscus haradai* (Jimbo), *Peroniceras amakusense* Yabe, and *Mortoniceras fakazawai* Yabe and Shimizu. It occurs in the Akasaki beds, which are said to "rest on every possible horizon of the Himenaura group," (suggesting overlap).

Its occurrence in California in strata adjacent to those with *Prionotropis bakeri,* believed to mark the upper part of the Turonian, suggests the possibility that here, as in Japan, it may really represent a lower Senonian horizon.

Lytoceras (Gaudryceras) texanum Anderson n. sp.
(Plate 8, figures 3, 3a)

Shell small, discoidal, compressed, section of whorl narrowly elliptical, finely costate; surface marked by a few transverse grooves that cross the periphery; between these grooves are numerous fine costal lines; sides sloping toward venter and toward umbilicus. The holotype (C. A. S. Type Coll.) affords the following measurements: greater diameter, 25 mm; width of umbilicus, 10 mm; height of whorl, 10 mm; breadth of whorl, 8 mm.

The holotype was found at locality 465 (C. A. S.), Texas Springs, 3 miles east of old Horsetown, where it was associated with *Beudanticeras haydeni* (Gabb), *Sonneratia* aff. *stantoni* Anderson, *Terebratella densleonis* (Anderson), and *Neohibolites fontinalis* n. sp., and other species that characterize the lower beds of the Upper Cretaceous series.

Lytoceras (Gaudryceras) coalingense Anderson n. sp.
(Plate 68, figure 1)

Shell of medium size or large, discoidal, compressed, evolute, and broadly umbilicate; section of whorls semi-elliptical, thickest a little above umbilical border, sides sloping toward periphery; umbilicus broad, walls abrupt in young stages of growth, sloping more gently in mature and older stages; surface of whorls crossed by six or more oblique grooves, between which shell is almost smooth, or marked only by inconspicuous striae, becoming stronger with age.

Shell differs from all others yet described from the West Coast in its more elliptical section, in which the sides are not flattened but are gracefully rounded and convex. The holotype (C. A. S. Type Coll.) is the inner coil of a large shell, not so well preserved; it measures about as follows: greatest diameter, 71 mm; width of the umbilicus, 30 mm; height of whorl, 26 mm; breadth of whorl, 22 mm. Two incomplete examples were found 12 miles northwest of Coalinga, Fresno County, associated with *Parapachydiscus catarinae* Anderson and Hanna, *Neokotôceras fresnoense* Anderson, *Baculites occidentalis* Meek, and many other species. Its definite location was locality 2362 (C. A. S.) on Los Gatos Creek, in sec. 4, T. 20 S., R. 14 E. M. B. D. & M. Maestrictian.

Lytoceras (Gaudryceras) aureum Anderson n. sp.
(Plate 71, figures 1, 1a)

Large, lytoceratid in form and sutures, little involute, broadly umbilicate, with broadly oval section of whorl, increasing rapidly in size; surface of cast marked by faint costal lines, and crossed at intervals by thickened varices and shallow constrictions that curve gently forward on approach to periphery; in addition to these surface features, suture lines are lytoceratid with long plumose siphonal saddles, bipartite lateral lobes, with long, acute terminations, as shown in figure. The holotype (C. A. S. Type Coll.), wholly septate, has the following dimensions: greater diameter, 140 mm; width of umbilicus, 46 mm; height of whorl, 56 mm; breadth of whorl, 51 mm; surface of cast partly shown in the figure. The species is represented by a single example found by Allan Bennison, locality 29656 (C. A. S.), in coarse pebbly sandstone along canyon 1 mile south of Ortigalita Creek, which is about 2500′ north of the south corner of sec. 33, T. 11 S., R. 10 E., M. D. M., Charleston School Quad., in the Moreno formation. Its age should be lower Maestrichtian.

Lytoceras (Gaudryceras) birkhauseri Anderson n. sp.
(Plate 68, figures 4, 4a)

Moderate size, discoidal, with numerous coils, whorls involute, with broadly elliptical section; whorls crossed by six or more slightly sinuous, transverse, periodic constrictions, between which are numerous fine thread-like costal lines, arising near whorl suture, crossing umbilical wall with forward inclination, but curving backward on umbilical shoulder, and crossing the side normal to umbilical border, curving gently forward near periphery. The holotype (C. A. S. Type Coll.), has the following dimensions: greater diameter (est.) approximately, 108 mm; width of umbilicus (est.), 45 mm; maximum breadth of whorl, 35 mm. The species appears to belong to the group represented by *Lytoceras crassicostatum* Jimbo, from the Upper Cretaceous of Hokkaido, Japan, although having a greater umbilical ratio. The holotype was found by Max Birkhauser at locality 2361 (C. A. S.), about 2 miles northwest of "Oil City", or 11 miles northwesterly from Coalinga, Fresno County. The same species has been recognized by the writer at locality 2362 (C. A. S.), on Los Gatos Creek, 8 miles northwest of Coalinga. The species is named in honor of Dr. Birkhauser, to whom we are indebted for a stratigraphic column and section in the district of the Panoche Hills.

Subgenus Tetragonites Kossmat
Lytoceras (Tetragonites) henleyense Anderson n. sp.
(Plate 12, figures 5, 5a; Plate 41, figure 7)

Lytoceras (Tetragonites) cala (?) (Forbes), Stoliczka, ANDERSON, Proc. Calif. Acad. Sci., 3d ser., vol. 2, 1902, p. 84; Henley, California.

Kossmat has questioned the identity of Stoliczka's species with that of Forbes, described under the same name, and for the former has proposed the name *Lytoceras (Tetragonites) kingianum* Kossmat. It is still not possible to identify with confidence the California type with that of Stoliczka. No other example of the species has since been found. Forbes' species is listed with some doubt by Smith (1900, p. 203) among the fossils found by L. G. Yates on the Isabel Jordan ranch, on Arroyo del Valle. The original example of the present species, referred by the writer to Stoliczka's form, was found at Henley, Siskiyou County. The description of 1902 reads as follows:

"Shell discoidal, flattened on the sides, and of a diameter not exceeding 7.6 cm; umbilicus wide and shallow, with abrupt walls; involution very little, clasping little more than the flattened ventral surface; shell increasing slowly in size with growth; section of whorls tetragonal; suture consists of three lobes on each side, with auxiliary lobes much reduced, upon the umbilical surface. . . . The siphonal lobe is broad, divided by a denticulated tongue-shaped siphonal saddle."

The holotype (C. A. S. Type Coll.) measures as follows: greatest diameter, 44 mm; width of umbilicus, 18 mm; height of whorl, 18 mm; breadth of whorl, 16 mm. The horizon of this species is near that of *Metaplacenticeras pacificum* (Smith), and *M. californicum* (Anderson), and *Desmoceras (Kotoceras) richardsoni* Anderson in the lower part of the Coniacian.

Lytoceras (Tetragonites) jacksonense Anderson
(Plate 10, figures 2, 2a)

Lytoceras (Tetragonites) jacksonense ANDERSON, Proc. Calif. Acad. Sci., 3d ser., vol. 2, 1902, p. 82, Pl. 5, figs. 124, 125; "Forty-nine" Mine, near Phoenix, Jackson County, Oregon.

The original description of this species was based upon a single example in which the umbilical pit was not fully exposed, and its suture lines were not clearly shown. The holotype No. 44 (C. A. S. Type Coll.) was recovered from the ashes of the San Francisco fire, and other examples were later obtained at its type locality. A larger and more complete example was later found by the writer near Little Cow Creek, Shasta County, a few miles east of Frazier Corners, and a few hundred feet below the horizon of *Oregoniceras oregonense* (Anderson).

Another example from the same locality exposes an almost complete suture line. An emended description based upon the material now at hand follows:

Shell of medium size, discoidal, a little inflated, sides slightly flattened rounded on the periphery, section of whorl subelliptical; umbilicus moderate and deep, with steep walls, rounded above; surface crossed by faint grooves and lines of growth, but otherwise smooth; growth lines bending backward, and forming a moderate sinus on the ventral zone; suture line characterized by a long, narrow, lanceolate siphonal saddle, denticulate on its borders; the general aspect of the shell resembling *Lytoceras timotheanum*, as figured by Whiteaves (1884, Pl. 3).

Although the species somewhat resembles *Lytoceras timotheanum*, from the upper Horsetown beds, it is smaller, less quadrate in section, more rounded on the abdominal border, and shows distinctive sutural features not found in the former.

The horizon of this species is near the top of the Turonian. Dimensions of holotype No. 44 are as follows: maximum diameter, 52.8 mm; maximum breadth of body whorl, 22.7 mm; height of body whorl, 28 mm; width of umbilicus, approximately 13 mm.

Lytoceras (Tetragonites) timotheanum (Mayor)

Ammonites timotheanus (Mayor) WHITEAVES, Meso. Foss., vol. 1, pt. 1, 1876, p. 41, Pl. 3, figs. 2, 2a; Queen Charlotte Islands, British Columbia.
Lytoceras timotheanum WHITEAVES, Meso. Foss., vol. 1, pt. 3, 1884, p. 203; Bear Skin Bay, Skidegate, and Cumshewa Inlets, Queen Charlotte Islands. . . . ANDERSON, Proc. Calif. Acad. Sci., 3d ser., vol. 2, 1902, p. 41, 63; Pl. 7, figs. 146–148 (not 145); upper beds of the Horsetown group.

Collections of the California Academy of Sciences contain specimens of this species collected near the Indian village of Skidegate, Graham Island, by R. M. Kleinpell and E. W. Galliher. They were found associated with upper Horsetown species referred to by the writer (1938, p. 71).

The writer (1902) showed the occurrence of this species in the upper beds of the Horsetown group, and two distinct forms were figured. One of these (1902, Pl. 7, figs. 146–148) was found at old Horsetown, in the lowest beds exposed at this locality; the same species has since been found at locality 1659 (C. A. S.) in the Neptune zone of the Horsetown group. The other form (1902, Pl. 7, fig. 145) is more closely related to *Lytoceras jacksonese* Anderson, and is found only in the lowest beds of the Upper Cretaceous.

Lytoceras (Tetragonites) aff. L. jacksonense Anderson

Lytoceras timotheanum ANDERSON (in part), Proc. Calif. Acad. Sci., 3d ser., vol. 2, 1902, Pl. 7, fig. 145, only; "Forty-nine" mine, Jackson County, Oregon, associated with *L. jacksonense* Anderson.

This species was figured (1902, Pl. 7) in the belief that it represented *L. timotheanum* (Mayor), which, as understood by Kossmat (1894, p. 133), occurred in both Gault and Cenomanian strata. It has since been found that this is not the case in California. The present species has recently been found by the writer 2.5 miles northeast of Frazier Corners, Shasta County, California.

As compared to *Lytoceras timotheanum* (Mayor) Whiteaves (1876, p. 41, Pl. 3), *L.* aff. *L. jacksonense* has a more nearly circular section, a greater umbilical ratio, and a more graceful, less involute form. The figured specimen is in the collections of the University of California (No. 14854). The species is not abundant, but has been found occasionally in the lower part of this Upper Cretaceous. In addition to the discovery just noted, it has more recently been found in this group at locality 31097 (C. A. S.) on Dry Creek (Beegum road), associated with *Desmoceras inane* Stoliczka, *Turrilites bergeri* Brongniart, and *Cyrtochilus stylus* n. sp., and other lower Cenomanian species. It has not yet been reported from any horizon of the Horsetown group.

Lytoceras (Tetragonites) kernense Anderson n. sp.
(Plate 32, figure 4; Plate 73, figure 6)

Shell small, little involute, section of whorl quadrate, higher than broad; surface ornamented by lines of growth, and a few faint transverse grooves, inclined forward, crossing the ventral zone. In form and ornamentation, though not in breadth of whorl, the species resemble Kossmat's figure of *Lytoceras timotheanum* (Mayor) from the Ootatoor group of southern India. The resemblance is shown more clearly in the younger whorls, but it is somewhat changed in older stages of growth.

The holotype (C. A. S. Type Coll.) measures: maximum diameter, 34.8 mm; greatest width of umbilicus, 9 mm; maximum breadth of whorl, approximately 13 mm; paratype (C. A. S. Type Coll.) : maximum diameter, 17 mm; breadth of whorl, 7.4 mm.

Three examples of this species were found by G. D. Hanna at locality 1552 (C. A. S.) on the south border of the Antelope Valley, northern Kern County, associated with *Parapuzosia* (large species), *Kotôceras* aff. *K. selwynianum* Whiteaves, *Desmoceras yoloense* Anderson, *Baculites chicoensis* Trask, *Baculites inornatus* Meek, and various other species characteristic of the lower Senonian (Coniacian).

Lytoceras (Tetragonites) epigonum Kossmat
(Plate 65, figures 4, 5; Plate 67, figures 3, 3a)

Ammonites Timotheanus, STOLICZKA, Cret. Cephal. S. India, vol. 1, 1868, p. 146, Pl. 73, figs. 4, 5; near Odium, S. India.
Lytoceras (Tetragonites) epigonum KOSSMAT, Kriedeform India, 1897, p. 136, Pl. 17, figs. 4, 5; locality as above, "*Trigonarca* Beds," as described by Kossmat (upper part of Arrialoor group).

Numerous examples of this species, two hypotypes of which are figured here (Pl. 65, figs. 4, 5), and of closely related forms have been found by C. C. Church and by the writer, associated with *Parapachydiscus catarinae* Anderson and Hanna and with many other species at locality 2362 (C. A. S.), on Los Gatos Creek, on sec. 4, T. 20 S., R. 14 E., M. D. B. and M. Others have been collected by Church at locality 2361 (= locality 31593, C. A. S.) on the north slope of Joaquin Ridge, 11 miles north of Coalinga, Fresno County.

A single example (Pl. 67, figs. 3, 3a) of the same species was discovered by Bennison at locality 29102 (C. A. S.), in the Volta quadrangle, near the center of the S ½ of sec. 26, T. 10 S., R. 9 E., M. D. B. and M., Merced County, California.

This example closely resembles the type form figured and described by Kossmat, and it would be difficult to distinguish it from the same, in either form, surface features, or in sutures. At locality 31593 (C. A. S.), the species was found associated with *Didymoceras fresnoense* n. sp. and *Exiteloceras* aff. *E. vancouverense* (Gabb). All three figured specimens are in the California Academy Sciences Type Collection.

Family HAMITIDAE Hyatt emend. Spath

This family has been authoritatively regarded as typical of Aptian and Albian stages of the Lower Cretaceous, although some writers upon the later Cretaceous have described or mentioned types from post-Albian horizons thought to belong in this family. The generic groups that have been placed in this family by Spath (1922) include the following, of which few have been found on the West Coast:

Hamites Parkinson   type: *Hamites attenuatus* Sowerby (not d'Orbigny)
Torneutoceras Hyatt   type: "*Hamites*" *attenuatus* (d'Orbigny)
Helicoceras d'Orbigny   type: "*Hamites*" *annulatus* (d'Orbigny)
Lechites Nowak, (related to Hamites, not recognized here)
Turrilitoides Spath, (non-tuberculate forms, not recognized here)
Cyrtochilus Meek   type: *Baculites baculoides* (Mantell)

A partial account of the family was given by the writer (1938, p. 217), but few of the foregoing groups are represented in the Upper Cretaceous of the West Coast. The only genera thus far recognized as belonging in this family are *Cyrtochilus* Meek, and *Neocyrtochilus* n. gen. *Cyrtochilus* Meek is found in the lower Cenomanian and *Neocyrtochilus* n. gen., is found in the lower part of the Quinto shales on Los Banos Creek.

Genus **Cyrtochilus** Meek
Cyrtochilus stylus Anderson n. sp.
(Plate 11, figures 5, 5a)

The cone of this species is long and slender, tapering gradually to an unknown length; in section the shell is subcircular, the surface rather smooth, crossed by periodic, shallow, oblique grooves, and by numerous slight undulations, all of which are concentric with the grooves; suture lines rather widely separated, and in pattern greatly resemble those of the genotype, *B. baculoides* (Mantell), which according to Pervinquiere (1907, p. 92) occurs in upper Albian (Vraconian) strata in north Africa.

The holotype (C. A. S. Type Coll.) was found by Bennison, McCoy, and the writer at locality 31097 (C. A. S.) on Dry Creek (Redbluff—Beegum road), 4.6 miles west of Rosewood, northern Tehama County. The type specimen, incomplete at both ends, measures as follows: length, 95 mm; greater diameter, 9 mm; lesser diameter, 7 mm. When complete its length probably exceeded 190 mm. It was found associated with *Desmoceras inane* Stoliczka, and *Turrilites bergeri* Brongniart (Forbes), in beds of lower Cenomanian age, only a few hundred feet above the local base of Upper Cretaceous.

Fragments of the same species were found by Bennison, McCoy and the writer at locality 31131 (C. A. S.) on the NE ¼ SW ¼ of sec. 29, T. 8 S., R. 7 E., M. B. D. and M., associated with *Lyelliceras stanislausense* n. sp. *Desmoceras* aff. *D. inane* Stoliczka, and fragments of *Durania* sp.

Cyrtochilus glaber (Whiteaves)

Hamites glaber WHITEAVES, Meso. Foss., vol. 1, pt. 3, 1884, p. 218, Pl. 24, figs. 2, 2a, 2b, 2c; north shore of Cumshewa inlet, Queen Charlotte Islands, British Columbia.

Whiteaves has described and figured three fragmentary specimens of an ammonoid [shell] found on Cumshewa Inlet, that seem clearly to belong to the above genus, although it is not clear that all of them belonged to the same individual. According to Whiteaves,

"the outline of a transverse section of either (limb) would be elliptic ovate, the siphonal edge being slightly narrower than the antisiphonal. Surface apparently smooth, but marked at widely distant intervals by an occasional arrest of growth in the shape of a broad, but faint and shallow, flexuous and transverse constriction, which is obliquely ascending on the antisiphonal half of the limb and nearly straight on the siphonal half."

Whiteaves gives no information as to the size of his holotype, and it is assumed that his figures are of natural size. As to its chronological station nothing is said directly, although it is referred to "Division C," of the general section, and it is seen from its associated species (p. 254) that it represents a low horizon of the same (upper Albian, or lower Cenomanian, preferably the former).

Cyrtochilus major Anderson n. sp.
(Plate 38, figure 6)

This species is represented by only a fragmentary cast of the nonseptate portion, probably of the larger limb of the shell, but which retains sufficiently characteristic markings to establish its generic determination. In section the shell is subcylindrical, although slightly flattened on its dorsal side; sides crossed by strongly impressed, oblique grooves that continue across the dorsal and ventral areas; only a single groove is present on the fragmentary holotype. Concentric to this groove are clear traces of parallel ridges (ribs), all of which cross the shaft at an angle of about 45 degrees to the ventral border. The ribs continue entirely around the shaft, although they are less prominent on the ventral surface.

The holotype (C. A. S. Type Coll.) has the following dimensions: length, 60 mm; greater diameter, 18.4 mm; lesser diameter at larger end, 16.4 mm; greater diameter at smaller end, 16.6 mm; lesser diameter at smaller end, 14.4 mm. The shaft tapers gradually to an undetermined length. In size and surface markings, as far as they can be traced, the shell resembles *"Baculites" baculoides* (Mantell).

This specimen was found in the near-basal beds of the upper Cretaceous series, on Hayes gulch, 2 miles northwest of Gas Point, in the Cottonwood district of Shasta County. In general form, size, and surface markings it recalls the preceding, *Cyrtochilus glaber* (Whiteaves), from the Queen Charlotte series of Cumshewa Inlet, Queen Charlotte Islands.

Neocyrtochilus Anderson n. gen.
Genotype **Neocyrtochilus bryani** Anderson

This genus is here proposed for a group of small ammonoid forms of cyrtochiloid aspects found in the later Senonian (upper Campanian) strata in the San Joaquin Valley, California. Some of these, including the genotype, greatly resemble forms of *"Baculites"* (group of *B. baculoides* (Mantell)) described by Böse (1923, p. 156–157) from "Vraconian" strata of Zacatecas, Mexico. Usually these later forms are quite incomplete, and difficult to remove from the matrix, and might readily be mistaken for portions of *Ptychoceras* d'Orbigny, *Diptychoceras* Gabb, or *Cyrtochilus* Meek, but all these genera belong to earlier epochs of Cretaceous time, and may have no close relationship to the apparently similar types found in a later Senonian horizon, such as that of the genotype here described, whose stratigraphic position has been well determined. Further morphological features of the genus will be seen in the following notes upon the genotype, the type of which is a small but mature example. Its horizon is well marked as upper Campanian.

Neocyrtochilus bryani Anderson n. sp.
(Plate 72, figure 5)

Shell pearly, relatively thin, closely folded upon itself with parallel limbs; both limbs circular in section, without visible flattening on dorsal sides; each limb crossed by oblique lines of growth, which, on smaller limb are much more oblique than on buccal limb. The holotype (C. A. S. Type Coll.) was found by Hanna and Bryan at locality 30553 (C. A. S.) on Los Banos Creek, half a mile east of locality 29117 (C. A. S.). Both zones are in the upper part of the Campanian in the belt mapped as the Moreno formation by Anderson and Pack (1915). The point of discovery of the present species is given as "1200 feet E., and 1000 feet S. of the NW corner of sec. 7, T. 11 S., R. 10 E., M. D. B. and M." The holotype has the following dimensions: length of both limbs, 22 mm; width across both limbs, 4 mm; type almost without surface ornamentation, except as seen with a good lens. The species is named for Mr. Jos. J. Bryan of the Associated Oil Company, discoverer of the holotype.

Family Baculitidae Meek
Genus **Baculites Lamarck s. l.**

Many species of *Baculites* in its broader sense are found in the Upper Cretaceous in the Great Valley of California, and in other areas. Some of these species appear to have a relatively wide stratigraphic range; others are more restricted and few in number.

Baculites chicoensis Trask
(Plate, 48, figures 1, 1a, 1b, 1c, 1d; Plate 60, figures 3, 3a, 3b)

Baculites chicoensis TRASK, Proc. Calif. Acad. Sci., 1856, p. 92, Pl. 2, fig. 2; Chico Creek, Butte County. . . . GABB, Paleont. Calif., vol. 1, 1864, p. 80, Pl. 17, figs. 27, 27a: Pl. 14, fig. 27b; Chico Creek, Butte County; (not Pl. 17, figs. 28, 28a; not Pl. 14, figs. 29, 29a). . . . TAFF, HANNA, AND CROSS, Geol. Soc. Am., Bull. vol. 51, 1940, p. 1321, Pl. 1, figs. 3, 4; Chico Creek, Butte County.

Many examples of this species have been collected from the beds exposed on Chico Creek, at Pentz, and at other places in which the same formation is exposed. Much confusion has resulted from the early work of Gabb and others, in the identification of this species. Species is of only medium size, tapering gradually, and often reaching a length of 6 to 8 inches, although usually broken into smaller lengths; in section, as shown in Gabb's figure (1864, Pl. 17, fig. 27a) and by the figures given by Taff, Hanna and Cross, it is ovate, and slightly carinate, the ratio of greater to smaller diameter being about 15:12.

The species is found plentifully in the Chico formation, but it seems to have a stratigraphic range from early Coniacian to Santonian. Gabb has figured as many as three specific forms under this name, not all of which have been found in the Chico formation. Some of them occur in the Cottonwood district of Shasta County, and others at horizons below or above the Santonian.

Baculites fairbanksi Anderson
(Plate 48, figures 4, 4a, 4b; Plate 49, figures 4, 4a)

Baculites fairbanksi ANDERSON, Proc. Calif. Acad Sci., 3d ser., vol. 2, 1902, p. 92, Pl. 7, figs. 152, 153; Pl. 10, fig. 194; Santa Ana Mountains, Orange County, California; . . . (?) GABB, Paleont. Calif., vol. 1, 1864, Pl. 14, figs. 29, 29a; locality not known.

This species resembles the preceding, but it is more strongly costate, and more roundly ovate in section. The holotype (Univ. Calif. Type Coll.), (Pl. 48, figs. 4, 4a, 4b) measures: length, 115 mm; greatest diameter, 15 mm. It is noncarinate, and in this respect differs from *B. chicoensis* Trask, and from other species with which it may be confused. It is not known to occur with the latter, but is more often found in lower Senonian beds, associated with *Metaplacenticeras pacificum* (Smith) and with *Lytoceras (Gaudryceras) alamedense* Smith.

Hypotype (C. A. S. Type Coll.), (Pl. 49, figs. 4, 4a) measures as follows: length, 50 mm; greatest diameter, 17 mm. Found at locality 228 (C. A. S.), on Sucia Island, Strait of Georgia.

Baculites inornatus Meek
(Plate 48, figures 2, 2a, 3)

Baculites inornatus MEEK, Acad. Nat. Sci. Phila., Proc., vol. 13, 1861, p. 316; Sucia Islands, Strait of Georgia.
Baculites chicoensis MEEK, (in part), not Trask, U. S. Geol. and Geogr. Survey Terr. Bull., vol. 2, 1876, p. 364, Pl. 4, figs. 2, 2a, b, c; Upper Cretaceous, Sucia Islands.

In Meek's original description of this species he says (in part):

"The largest fragment of this species in the collection measures 1.49 inches in greater diameter, and 1.13 inches in its smaller, and judging from its very gradual taper, it appears to have been, when entire, as much as 15 or 16 inches in length."

The figures of this species later published by Meek (1876) as *"Baculites chicoensis* Trask" show it to be broadly ovate, and in cross-section more broadly rounded on the dorsal side than on the ventral. In the collections of the California Academy of Sciences from the Sucia Islands there are many fragments that conform to Meek's statement and with his figures. These are larger, however, than any examples found in correlative beds in the Great Valley of California.

The examples from the Great Valley that agree most closely with Meek's original description of the species are found in the Panoche formation, not in beds correlative with those of Sucia Islands or of Chico Creek, Butte County.

Baculites inornatus Meek occurs at locality 2908 (C. A. S.) on the north side of Kellogg Creek, on the NW ¼ of sec. 13, T. 1 S., R. 2 E., M. D. M. near the road from Byron Springs, where it was collected by Clark and his students. It is found here associated with *Parapachydiscus* sp., and *Lytoceras* aff. *L. kayei* Forbes.

It appears that no species closely related to *B. chicoensis* Trask has been recognized at the Sucia Islands, whereas, species either identical, or closely related to *Baculites inornatus* Meek occur in beds much higher in the section.

Dimensions of two hypotypes (C. A. S. Type Coll.) are as follows: (Pl. 48, figs. 2, 2a) : length, 102.6 mm; maximum diameter, approx. 23.5 mm; lesser diameter, 16 mm; (Pl. 48, fig. 3) : length, 52.8 mm; maximum diameter, approx. 34.8 mm; lesser diameter, 24.6 mm. Locality 228 (C. A. S.), Sucia Islands, Strait of Georgia.

Baculites buttensis Anderson n. sp.
(Plate 49, figures 6, 6a, 6b)

Moderately small, section roundly ovate; greatest diameter 8.4 mm, lesser diameter 6.4 mm; surface marked by moderately undulating ribs; suture distinctive with high multiple cleft saddles and narrow lobes. The holotype was found at locality 27835 (C. A. S.) on Chico Creek.

This species may be distinguished from *B. fairbanksi* Anderson, which has similiar undulating ribs, by its more rounded cross-section.

Baculites rex Anderson n. sp
(Plate 49, figure 2)

The cone of this species is very large, probably being the largest species yet described from the West Coast. The holotype (C. A. S. Type Coll.) has the following dimensions: length (incomplete), 240 mm; greatest diameter (approximately), 58.5 mm; lesser diameter (estimated), 48 mm; section roundly ovate; surface smooth, or marked only by lines of growth. The complete length appears to have exceeded 450 mm. The suture lines are distinctive, the successive septa being closely spaced, or crowded; the lobes are relatively short and bifid, the branches being separated by broadly rounded elements; the saddles, high, and deeply multiple-cleft. The holotype was found by Hanna, Taff and Cross at locality 28325 (C. A. S.) on the south side of Crow Creek, on the NE ¼ sec. 33, T. 6 S., R. 7 E., M. D. M., associated with *Inoceramus* sp., resembling *Inoceramus subundatus* Meek, though not identifiable with it.

Baculites vagina Forbes

Baculites vagina FORBES, Geol. Soc. London, Tr., 2d ser., vol. 7, 1846, p. 114, Pl. 10, figs. 4, 4a, 4b; Pondicherri, southern India. . . . STOLICZKA, Cret. Cephal. S. India, vol. 1, 1865, p. 198, Pl. 91, figs. 1–6; locality as above. . . var *simplex* KOSSMAT, Beitr. zur Paleont. Oest. Ungarns, vol. 9, 1895, p. 156, Pl. 19, figs. 13, 14; Upper Senonian.

According to Kossmat this species embraces many varieties besides its normal form, although some of them are subject to doubt. The type form (Kossmat, 1895, Pl. 6, figs. 4a, 4b, 4c) is carinate, and probably related to *Baculites lomaensis* n. sp. since their horizons are essentially the same. According to Kossmat (1897) *B. vagina* Forbes is characteristic of the upper Senonian (*Trigonarca* Beds), which are correlative with part of the Panoche formation.

Baculites lomaensis Anderson n. sp.
(Plate 48, figures 5, 5a, 6)

This species was first discovered at Point Loma, near San Diego, prior to 1892, by H. W. Fairbanks, and seems to have been the basis of Cooper's determination of *B. chicoensis* Trask, in the list published by Fairbanks (1893c, p. 476).

The species greatly resembles, and appears to belong to the group of *Baculites vagina* Forbes from Pondicherri, India.

The species was later figured by Stoliczka (1863–1866, p. 198, Pls. 90, 91). According to Stoliczka:

"The young shell is quite smooth, so as to give an ovate section; after the specimen has reached a certain stage of growth obliquely elongated tubercules begin to show in the middle of the sides, and generally at the same time on the margins of the ventral portion."

In all respects of outward form, section, and taper, the species conforms to the figures and description given by Stoliczka, but hardly with his figures of the sutures. The sutures of the California species are more like the figures given by Forbes, although the lobes and saddles are larger, and the sutures are less crowded than those given by Stoliczka. In *B. lomaensis* the lobes and saddles are more clearly cut and simple than those shown in Stoliczka's figures.

This species has also been found at locality 2361, and locality 2362 (C. A. S.) ; the former is on Joaquin Ridge, 9 miles to the northeast of the latter. The figured specimens are from locality 2361 (C. A. S.) on Joaquin Ridge.

The horizon of this species at its type locality, and at Point Loma is correlative to that of the Catarina formation at Arroyo Santa Catarina, Lower California, and is believed to be referable to upper Campanian or the Maestrichtian. This appears to be the species found near Slate's Hot Springs on the coast of Montery County, or closely related to it.

Dimensions of holotype (Pl. 48, fig. 5): length approximately, 35 mm; greater diameter, 13 mm; lesser diameter, 8.6 mm. Dimensions of paratype (Pl. 48, fig. 5a) : length approximately 33.4 mm; greater diameter, 10.3 mm. Dimensions of paratype (Pl. 48, fig. 6) : length approximately 66.9 mm; greater diameter, 8.7 mm; lesser diameter, 6 mm.

Baculites subcircularis Anderson n. sp.
(Plate 48, figure 7)

The present species is described from a fragment of the cone, (C. A. S. Type Coll.) having a length of about 36 mm and a maximum diameter of about 5 mm, showing but little taper, the smaller diameter being nearly 4 mm. The section of the whorl is nearly circular, or only slightly compressed on the sides; surface nearly smooth, or showing only oblique undulations. The holotype was found at locality 28442 (C. A. S.), at the mouth of Briones Creek, about 1250 feet southwest of the old John Marsh house, four miles south of Brentwood, Contra Costa County. The suture line is only partly exposed near the smaller end of the cone, showing only the central lobe, and two lateral saddles.

It is possible that this species belongs to the group represented by *Baculites teres* Forbes, illustrated by Stoliczka, from the Valudayur group of the Pondicherri district, although it should be younger, as illustrated by Kossmat (1897). The sutures are too immature to aid in closer comparison. The holotype was found associated with *Axonoceras* sp., *Lytoceras* sp., and *Bulla* sp., together with numerous types of foraminifera.

Baculites aff. B. capensis Woods
(Plate 48, figures 8, 8a)

Baculites capensis Woods, Ann. S. Afr. Mus., vol. 4, 1900, p. 342, Pl. 44, figs. 6, 7; Pondoland, South Africa. . . . Spath, Royal Soc. S. Africa, Tr., vol. 10, pt. 3, 1922, p. 46.

This species, not before recorded from the West Coast, has probably been observed in the lower part of the Panoche formation. Six or more fragmentary examples of the species were found at locality 31289 (C. A. S.) a little above the concrete bridge on Cache Creek, 3 miles northwest of Rumsey, Yolo County, but only four were obtained. Of these the largest and best preserved is the figured hypotype (C. A. S. Type Coll.). The most characteristic features of the species are the pronounced lateral grooves on the median line of the sides, and the tubercles below the dorso-lateral shoulders. Five such tubercles are seen on the anterior end of the shell between the lateral grooves and the dorsal border. These tubercles are set somewhat obliquely to the axis of the shell, but at a relatively small angle. The section of the cone is suboval, broader on the dorsal than on the ventral side of the grooves, the lower part of the sides sloping to a rather narrow ventral border. The suture lines are comparatively simple, consisting of lobes and short saddles; the narrow lateral lobe, with elongated divisions set unsymmetrical upon the stem is partly traceable; the saddles on either side of this lobe are short and but little divided. The species differs from *Baculites sulcatus* Baily from the Pondoland beds in the possession of the lateral grooves, and in the attitude of the tubercles. The species was found associated with species of *Inoceramus,* far beneath the zone of locality 31209 (C. A. S.), with *Nowakites dobbinsi* n. sp., and *Lytoceras* (*Gaudryceras*) *alamedense* Smith, near the big bend of Cache Creek.

Family TURRILITIDAE Hyatt (in part)
Genus **Turrilites** Lamarck
Turrilites bergeri Brongniart
(Plate 11, figure 2)

The species here figured is believed to be identical with the south Indian form described by Stoliczka from the Ootatoor group (1865 p. 185, Pl. 86, figs. 3–6). Stoliczka regarded his species as representing a horizon of the Gault, but this cannot be claimed for the present form, the type of which was found at locality 31097 (C. A. S.) on Dry Creek, northern Tehama County, a tenth of a mile east of the local base of the Upper Cretaceous series, associated with *Desmoceras inane* Stoliczka and *Phylloceras velledae* Michelin, believed to be of Cenomanian age. This example consists of two and a half whorls from the upper part of the spiral. It is ornamented with four distinct rows of small pointed tubercules on each whorl, the lower of which is almost concealed by the succeeding whorl; section of whorl subquadrate, ribs slightly oblique, tubercles almost equally spaced, and of nearly uniform size. The example figured (C. A. S. Type Coll.), has a total height of 43 mm, and a maximum width of about 33 mm. A larger fragment of apparently the same species was found showing its greatest diameter to be nearly 100 mm. In addition to the species noted above it was associated with *Cyrtochilus stylus* n. sp., and with species of *Acanthoceras.*

Turrilites pachecoensis Anderson n. sp.
(Plate 11, figure 4)

This species is founded upon a large fragment of a *Turrilites* consisting of parts of three closely contiguous whorls, two of which are fairly well preserved.

The shell is large, turreted, with coarse, oblique, slightly flexed ribs, separated by interspaces broader than the ribs; ribs possessing three or perhaps four elongated, rounded nodes, central two being more widely spaced than the others; suture line not clearly exposed, but crossing whorl obliquely, about 45 degrees from whorl border. The holotype (C. A. S., Type Coll.) was found in the basal beds of the Upper Cretaceous, on the north side of Quinto Creek, Stanislaus County, on the SE ¼ of sec. 3, T. 9 S., R. 7 E., M. D. M., by Taff, Hanna, and Cross.

Its dimensions are as follows: length of fragment, 75 mm; greatest width of whorl, 65 mm; height of whorl, 33 mm; number of ribs per whorl, about 24.

This species resembles and is probably related to *Turrilites bergeri* Brongniart, as figured by Stoliczka from the Ootatoor group near Odium, South India, which, according to Kossmat (1895, pp. 45, 142) occurs in the lower part of the group (upper Gault). The suture line is only partly exposed on the holotype, but insofar as it can be traced, it has broader elements than are shown in Stoliczka's figures. The whorls are stouter, and the ribs fewer and heavier. It is also related to *Turrilites oregonensis* Gabb, found at a somewhat higher horizon, and exhibits obvious differences in its ribbing and sculpture.

Turrilites petersoni Anderson n. sp.
(Plate 12, figure 6; Plate 75, figure 4)

Shell large, openly spiral, coiling dextrally; section of whorl nearly circular; surface almost smooth, or marked only by numerous oblique but inconspicuous costae, inclining backward on dorsal side of whorl, but slightly forward upon approach to the ventral zone of the shell; costae, 14 to an inch, narrow, separated by concave interspaces of twice their width; suture line lytoceratid, with lobes bearing two or more very unequal lateral branches; saddles indistinct on holotype; siphonal saddle long and narrow, with strong terminations, but otherwise not readily discerned. Diameter of coil, 100 mm; section of whorl, circular; diameter of larger end, 45.5 mm; diameter of smaller end, 35 mm. Holotype (C. A. S. Type Coll.) was found on the Peterson ranch, 4 miles north of Sites, Colusa County. It was found associated with *Parapuzosia colusaensis* (Anderson), *Beudanticeras alamoense* n. sp., and fragments of (?) *Durania californica* n. sp., *Trigonia aequicostata* Gabb, a species of *Pervinquieria,* and *Mantelliceras.* The horizon of the species is regarded as uppermost Albian or Cenomanian.

Turrilites oregonensis Gabb

Turrilites sp. indet., GABB, Paleont. Calif., vol. 1, 1864, p. 73, Pl. 28, fig. 102; near Jacksonville, Oregon.
Turrilites oregonensis GABB, Paleont. Calif., vol. 2, 1869, p. 138, 213; Crooked Creek, central Oregon.

Gabb's original type, consisting of a fragment of a whorl was found at a low horizon in the Upper Cretaceous, near Jacksonville, Oregon. He gave no detailed account of this fossil, saying only:

"The outer surface is marked by a series of regular, oblique, and slightly curved ribs, nearly obsolete in the middle, and each bearing four nodes, two above and two below. Under surface (dorsum) plain."

Later Gabb had opportunity of finding better preserved examples of the species from central Oregon, and gave it a name, saying (vol. 2, 1869, p. 138):

"The shell is very constant in sculpture, the spire elevated, and the whorls increase slowly in size. The longest spire I have seen is between two and three inches in length."

This species is not often found, although G. D. Hanna succeeded in finding a fragment somewhat larger than the holotype, but otherwise seemingly identical, about 6 miles southwest of Coalinga, Fresno County, sec. 16, T. 21 S., R. 14 E., associated with a fragment of *"Acanthoceras"* aff. *A. cunningtoni* (Sharpe). In southern India, the latter form, according to Kossmat (1895–1897) represents a Cenomanian horizon. In all cases in which its horizon is known in California and Oregon, it can be regarded as representing a horizon not younger than lower Cenomanian.

Turrilites excelsus Anderson n. sp.
(Plate 72, figure 4)

This species of *Turrilites* appears to belong to the group represented by *Turrilites costatus* Lamarck, figured by d'Orbigny (1840, Pl. 145), although its holotype shows neither its aperture nor its septation. Shell coils sinstrally in an elevated spiral, vertically costate, each whorl containing about 16 to 20 upright ribs, each bearing two or three tubercles on lower half; upper half a smooth vertical rib extending to upper suture. Turricone (incomplete) consists of five whorls, tapering uniformly toward apex.

The holotype (C. A. S. Type Coll.) was found by Allan Bennison at locality 29123 (C. A. S.) three-fourths of a mile south of Garzas Creek, east of the center of sec. 19, T. 8 S., R. 8 E., M. D. B. and M., 1800 feet west, and 2000 feet north of the SE corner of the section. It measures as follows: height of spire (incomplete), 72 mm; width at base (slightly flattened), 40 mm; number of ribs (near base), 20 to the whorl, whorl sutures deep. This example was found in the Moreno formation. It was associated with *Inoceramus* aff. *I. regularis* d'Orbigny, *Inoceramus* (*Endocostea*) *stanislausensis* n. sp., in the upper Campanian—"lower Danian."

Family Nostoceratidae Hyatt

In this family Hyatt placed a number of later Cretaceous phylogerontic ammonoid types, some of which had already been described under other names. The chief bases for discrimination were form, and ornamentation of shell, although others were perhaps used. The following list includes most genera referable to the family:

Nostoceras Hyatt type: *Nostoceras stantoni* Hyatt
Didymoceras Hyatt type: *"Heteroceras" nebrascense* Meek
Emperoceras Hyatt type: *Emperoceras beecheri* Hyatt
Diplomoceras Hyatt type: *"Hamites" cylindraceus* Defrance (in d'Orbigny)
Exiteloceras Hyatt type: *"Heteroceras" cheyennense* Meek
Bostrychoceras Hyatt type: *"Ptychoceras" crassum* Whitfield
Oxybeloceras Hyatt type: *"Heteroceras" polyplocum* Schleuter
Solenoceras Conrad type: *"Ptychoceras" annuliferum* Morton

The many variations in form, in spirals, in retroversal loops, and in ornamentation in West Coast types belonging to this family, afford many perplexing questions to students of cephalopod morphology. Spath (1921) has admitted difficulty concerning a certain turricone type with the apical portion missing, as to whether it should be referred to *Nostoceras* or to *Didymoceras* Hyatt. Similar difficulty is found in choosing between *Didymoceras* and *Emperoceras* Hyatt, and between other types for which only incomplete examples are known. Concerning the types last mentioned, Hyatt seems to have given only arbitrary bases for discrimination; it may be that one or the other should have only a subgeneric rank. Since *Didymoceras* has precedence in Hyatt's treatment, and is better illustrated, it may be given generic rank, and the other a sub-generic place, at least until the matter is further clarified. Whether the free early coils and depressed section in the type of *"Emperoceras"* are sufficiently important to distinguish it from *Bostrychoceras* Hyatt, on the one hand, and from *Didymoceras* Hyatt, on the other, is not clear, since both are marked by the same striking surface ornamentation in ribs and tubercles. In many cases at least the choice between the above types seems to have little more basis than personal preference.

Genus Nostoceras Hyatt
Nostoceras sternbergi Anderson and Hanna

Nostoceras sternbergi Anderson and Hanna, Proc. Calif. Acad. Sci., 4th ser., vol. 23, 1935, p. 22, Pl. 7, fig. 1, textfigure 2; Arroyo Santa Catarina, Lower California.

The holotype, No. 4254 (C. A. S., Type Coll.) is subcircular in section, with rounded, oblique, annular ribs, some of which are simple, and some branching, but all having little, if any, ornamentation, except at the top of the retroversal loop, and on the dorsal border of the buccal limb. The branching ribs are confined to the vicinity of the retroversal bend, and the dorsal border of the buccal limb, although a few prominent tubercles appear above the bend of the body chamber, as elongated nodes, but for the most part the ribs are without ornament; the spiral whorls are not yet known.

Nostoceras hornbyense (Whiteaves)

"Heteroceras" Hornbyense Whiteaves, Canad. Rec. Sci., vol. 6, 1895, p. 316; Hornby Island, B. C. (not *"Heteroceras" perversum* Whiteaves, 1895 p. 317) .... Meso. Foss., vol. 1, pt. 5, 1903, p. 332, Pl. 42, figs. 1 and perhaps 4; Hornby Island, British Columbia.

The original description of this species was based upon the dextral coil (Pl. 42, fig. 1), having a "Surface marked with simple and not very flexuous transverse ribs."

The illustrations given by Whiteaves (1903, Pl. 42) involve more than a single species, as may be seen in the manner of coiling, ribbing, and ornamentation. The small dextral coil (Pl. 42, fig. 1) is the holotype, and was the basis of the original description. It is hardly probable that the sinistrally coiled examples (Pl. 42, figs. 2 and 3) represent the same species, since their manner of coiling, the obliquity of the ribbing, and the tuberculate ornamentation are not the same as on the holotype of the species. It is not obvious that figure 4 represents either the species of figure 1, or that of figures 2 and 3, and it is possible that three species are illustrated on Plate 42.

Nostoceras mexicanum Anderson n. sp.
(Plate 58, figure 3)

This species is represented only by a single distorted spiral volution and an almost complete retroversal loop, a little compressed by rock pressure. The spiral is broken, but is capable of reconstruction by drawing; when so reconstructed it is seen to be openly helicoid.

The early whorls were circular in section, but with growth they assumed an elliptical or compressed ovate section. The nepionic and neanic stages seem to have been more nearly circular, but in the ephebic stage and later, the section became elliptical, and still later it flattened to a more compressed form; spiral and retroversal loop costate, with progressively changing obliquity, from simple, annular costae at right angles to the periphery, to oblique, and extended looplike costae, when viewed from above; ribs rarely dividing, except upon approach to the apex of the loop, where two or three ribs divide, either near the dorsal border, or at the ventro-lateral line; costae sparingly tuberculate, with two rows of small ventro-lateral nodes beginning on the neanic whorls, but traceable at intervals to the gerontic buccal limb of the loop; on this limb both dorsal and ventral zones are slightly flattened, giving the shell a somewhat quadrate section.

The holotype (C. A. S. Type Coll.) has the following dimensions: length of retroversal loop, 73 mm; normal width of same, 85 mm; maximum thickness of same 30 mm; maximum space between limbs, 21 mm; maximum width of normal spiral, 63 mm; diameter of neanic whorl-section, 17 mm.

The holotype was found by Arthur Bridge on Arroyo Santa Catarina, lower California, 2 or more miles above the coast line, and was presented by him to the California Academy of Sciences. Its horizon is that of *Parapachydiscus catarinae* Anderson and Hanna, and is Maestrichtian age.

Genus Didymoceras Hyatt
Didymoceras kernense Anderson n. sp.
(Plate 65, figures 1, 1a, 2)

This species is based upon a nearly complete and well-preserved retroversal body chamber differing specifically from the genotype, and from other members of the family. The holotype (Stanford Univ. Coll.) is large, strongly costate, and tuberculate; section of limbs subquadrate, or subcircular in different parts; ribs strong, elevated, branching irregularly, or single, and accordingly of two sorts;—on smaller limb, ribs are strongly oblique, extending sharply backward on approaching dorsal border, but suppressed on dorsum itself; on buccal limb ribs cross the sides nearly at right angles to its axis; ribs on the upper portion of the loop-like body chamber, branching into four smaller ribs, more or less tuberculate; the tubercles are in two rows on ventral border; through these ribs pass, branching from them in alternating manner, branches from each row crossing the ventral area obliquely. On the holotype only the last septum is visible, but not clearly. The single ribs rarely pass through more than one tubercle; the others pass through two.

The holotype is rather large, having the following dimensions: length of large limb, 112 mm; greatest width across the loop, 81 mm; greatest ventro-dorsal diameter of buccal limb, 38 mm; diameter of smaller limb, 32 mm. The holotype was loaned to the California Academy for study and description, and was from a deep well of the Honolulu Consolidated Oil Company in Kern County, the precise locality not known, apparently in T. 32 S., R. 24 E., M. D. B. and M., Honolulu Lease, Kern County, depth 2450 feet.

Didymoceras whiteavesi Anderson n. name

Anisoceras cooperi Gabb, Whiteaves, Meso. Foss. vol. 1, pt. 5, 1903, p. 336, Pl. 43, fig. 1; Hornby Island, British Columbia. (Not *Ammonites cooperii* Gabb, 1864, p. 69, Pl. 14, figs. 23, 23a; near San Diego).

This species is closely related to *Didymoceras kernense* n. sp., as may be seen in its form, the subcircular section of the smaller limb, the subquadrate section of its buccal limb, the sculpture and ornamentation of its ventral surface, and the branching of its ribs on the upper portion of its retroversal loop. It is in no way related to *Exiteloceras vancouverense* (Meek) nor to *Anisoceras vancouverense* Whiteaves.

Didymoceras perversum (Whiteaves)

"Heteroceras" hornbyense WHITEAVES (part),—*H. perversum* WHITEAVES, Meso. Foss. vol. 1, pt. 5, 1903, p. 332, Pl. 42, figs. 2, 3; Hornby Island, British Columbia.

Whiteaves figured under the name *Heteroceras hornbyense* two or more ammonoids that show opposite coiling (possibly not important), and also different types of coiling, ribbing, and ornamentation. He suspected this fact in his separation of his examples, referring those of figures 2 and 3 to *"Heteroceras" perversum,* but without explanation, or the recognition of a specific difference. The ornamentation shown in these figures conforms more nearly to that of *Didymoceras,* as illustrated in *D. whiteavesi* n. name.

Didymoceras californicum Anderson n. sp.
(Plate 72, figure 6)

Shell of moderate size, turreted in youth, coiling in a short dextral spiral, from which it departs at maturity, forming a retroversal loop. Spiral short and stout, composed of about three or four whorls; section of whorls subelliptical, a little flattened on dorsal side; whorls costate, with narrow, ridge-like ribs, with broader concave interspaces, rising to whorl suture; ribs sparingly tuberculate on spiral, smooth on reflexed portion; ribs on second and third whorls bearing two or more rows of tubercles, disappearing on body chamber; ribs dividing irregularly at the tubercles of the lower or upper row alternately, and rising to the whorl suture; sutures not known. The holotype (C. A. S. Type Coll.) was found by Allan Bennison, at locality 29664 (C. A. S.), on the NE ¼ NE. ¼ of sec. 30, T. 5 S., R. 7 E., on the south side of Puerto Creek, associated with *Exiteloceras bennisoni* n. sp., in the lower part of the Moreno formation. The holotype has the following dimensions: entire length (including spiral and reflexed portion), 105 mm; height of spiral (incomplete), 55 mm; breadth of spiral, 57 mm. The horizon of this species is Maestrichtian.

Didymoceras fresnoense Anderson n. sp.
(Plate 68, figure 2)

This species is probably closely related to *Didymoceras whiteavesi* n. name. The holotype of the present species (C. A. S. Type Coll.) consists of a retroversal loop, broken, but later restored. It has the following dimensions: total length of loop, about 57 mm; external width of loop, 73 mm; smaller limb, subcircular in section, slightly flattened on the dorsal side; maximum diameter, 28 mm; buccal limb, subquadrate in section, diameter, 26 mm. On larger limb of loop, the ribs for the most part are single, with little ornamentation, except by tubercles on either side of siphonal line, especially at summit of loop. On proximal end of smaller limb, the ribs are tuberculate, with elongated nodes on either side of this line, from which the ribs tend to divide alternately, forming the pattern frequent in *Didymoceras,* and indicating also the closing stage of the spiral, broken from the holotype. The holotype of the species was found at locality 29666 (C. A. S.) Orestimba Quad. Puerto Canyon ½ mile above the Panoche-Moreno contact. Stratigraphically in center of SW ¼ sec. 29, T. 5 S., R. 7 E. Maestrichtian.

Didymoceras orestimbense Anderson n. sp.
(Plate 45, figure 4)

Shell of moderate size, coiling sinistrally to an elevated spiral; whorls subquadrate in section, costate, with somewhat sinuous, semi-vertical ribs, tuberculate on a portion of the whorl; near or on the body chamber, and at irregular points on the spiral; ribs occasionally dividing at sporadic tubercles.

The holotype of the species (C. A. S. Type Coll.) was found by Hanna, Taff, and Cross, at locality 27854 (C. A. S.) on the east border of the SE ¼ of sec. 36, T. 7 S., R. 6 E., M.D.M., in a boulder in a conglomerate bed in the lower part of the Panoche Formation. It was found associated with various pelecypods and gastropods, including *Trigonia, Aphrodina, Tessarolax,* that indicate a lower Senonian horizon. The holotype has the following dimensions: greater diameter of coil, 45 mm; height of whorl (incomplete), 25 mm; maximum breadth of whorl section, 17 mm; width of umbilicus, 10 to 15 mm.

Genus **Emperoceras** Hyatt
Emperoceras cooperii (Gabb)

(?) *Ammonites Cooperii* GABB, Paleont. Calif., vol. 1, 1864, p. 69, Pl. 14, figs. 23, 23a; Point Loma, San Diego County, California. (Not *Anisoceras Cooperii* WHITEAVES, Meso. Foss., vol. 1, pt. 5, 1903, p. 336, Pl. 43, fig. 1; Hornby Island, Strait of Georgia. Not *"Hamites" vancouverensis* GABB, Paleont. Calif., vol. 1, 1864, p. 70, Pl. 13, fig. 18. Not *Heteroceras cooperii* MEEK, U. S. Geol. Surv. Terr., Bull. vol. 2, 1876, p. 367, Pl. 3, figs. 7, 7a.)

Gabb described this ammonid species from fragments "very much compressed," found at Point Loma, near San Diego, California, as doubtfully being an ammonite, since he had seen only fragments. The fragment figured by him as the holotype was evidently compressed and distorted by rock pressure, since Gabb mistook the ventral surface of the shell for the side. His figure has led to much confusion on the part of later writers who have endeavored to identify the species. Whiteaves supposed it to have been found on Hornby Island, although his figure (Pl. 43, fig. 1) illustrates a quite distinct form, with fewer ventral ribs per unit length, more prominent tubercles, and probably a more elevated section. Nevertheless, Whiteaves believed that he had definitely recognized Gabb's California species in the northern area. A careful study and comparison of the figures given by Whiteaves with that of Gabb supports the conviction that both represent forms of Hyatt's Nostoceratidae (1894), and possibly the same genus, but not the same species. Hyatt doubtfully regarded Gabb's species as belonging to his subgenus *Emperoceras,* and the writer knows no reason to suggest any other genus or subgenus for it.

Genus **Diplomoceras** Hyatt
Diplomoceras ellipticum (Anderson)
(Plate 39, figures 5, 5a)

Hamites ellipticus ANDERSON, Proc. Calif. Acad. Sci., 3d ser., vol. 2, 1902, p. 87, Pl. 3, figs. 102, 103; Pl. 10, fig. 191; "Forty-nine" Mine, southwest of Phoenix, Oregon.

The interpretation and the examples of *Diplomoceras* Hyatt, given by Spath (1921, p. 255) leave little doubt about the generic placement of this species. The holotype, No. 35 (C. A. S. Type Coll.), still nearly intact, is among the few that were recovered from the San Francisco fire. An abbreviated description of the species is here included.

Shell compressed, elliptical in section, more narrowly rounded upon the ventral side than on the dorsal; surface marked by simple, narrow, transverse costae, separated by spaces somewhat wider, and rounded, without tubercles or nodes; suture line complex, as shown in the figure.

It was stated that "a single constriction was visible on the holotype," but this seems to have been an accidental feature. The species seems to be related to *Diplomoceras* (?) *nereis* (Forbes), Stoliczka, which, according to the latter author, ranges from the Ootatoor to the Valudayr group in southern India.

The horizon of the present species appears to be upper Cenomanian, as judged by its associates, which include various species of *Scaphites* and *Acanthoceras.*

Dimensions of holotype No. 35 (C. A. S. Type Coll.) are as follows: length, 56 mm; greater diameter at larger end, 11 mm; lesser diameter at larger end, 10.5 mm; locality 445 (C. A. S.), "Forty-nine" Mine, southwest of Phoenix, Oregon.

Diplomoceras cascadense Anderson n. sp.
(Plate 55, figures 4, 4a; Plate 69, figures 2, 3)

This species is known only from internal casts of incomplete specimens, all in good state of preservation. The species appears to be closely related to *Diplomoceras obstrictum* (Jimbo) from the Upper Cretaceous of Hokkaido, Japan. The holotype and two paratypes (C. A. S. Type Coll.), including the retroversal body chamber, showing the smaller and larger limbs incomplete in their terminations, were found associated with *Scaphites condoni, Scaphites inermis* Anderson, various species of *Oregoniceras,* and other prionotropids at the old "Forty-nine mine" in southern Oregon. Dimensions of paratype (Pl. 55, figs. 4, 4a) are as follows: length (partly restored), 68 mm; greater breadth, 15 mm; paratype (Pl. 69, fig. 2) (incomplete), length, 46.4 mm; (fig. 3) holotype (incomplete); length, 66.9 mm; maximum diameter of whorl, 10.2 mm.

There is little difference in the form and the sculpture of these limbs, although they differ in size, diameter, and in the strength and obliquity of the ribbing; the section in both limbs is cylindrical. The sculpture consists of simple transverse, annular costae, thin and sharp at summit, separated by roundly concave interspaces, crossing the sides nearly at right angles to the axis.

The buccal limb shows a single transverse constriction, similar to that of *Diplomoceras obstrictum* (Jimbo) and to an allied species described by Whiteaves under the same name (1903, Pl. 44), although the obliquity of the ribs on the smaller limb is less. This species resembles more clearly the Indian form, *Diplomoceras nereis* (Forbes), Stoliczka.

The horizon of the species is that of *Oregoniceras* and other prionotropids, and is regarded as upper Turonian.

Diplomoceras phoenixense (Anderson)
(Plate 39, figure 8)

Hamites phoenixensis Anderson, Proc. Calif. Acad. Sci., 3d ser., vol. 2, 1902, p. 88, Pl. 3, fig. 104; "Forty-nine" mine, southwest of Phoenix, Oregon.

The form, section and ornamentation of this species place it in the group of the preceding two, although it is smaller in size. Its suture is not known. The species occurs with others in the upper part of the "Lower Chico" of earlier usage.

Shell small, subcylindrical in section, curved in one plane into a hooklike form; surface ornamented with slightly oblique, transverse annular costae, inclining slightly forward on the smaller limb. Its occurrence with the preceding forms, and with various types of *Scaphites, Oregoniceras,* and *Acanthoceras,* place it in the Turonian. Figure here shown was copied from original holotype, fig. 104, of 1902, slightly reduced. Holotype lost in 1906 fire.

Diplomoceras jimboi Anderson n. sp.
(Plate 68, figures 5, 5a)

The holotype of this species (C. A. S. Type Coll.) consists of a fragment of the proximal (smaller) limb of the shell, which is subcircular in section, slightly flattened on the dorsal side, having a length of about 33 mm; and maximum diameter of 24.6 mm; lesser diameter, 22.3 mm. The holotype, costate throughout, bears simple, narrow ribs, between which are concave interspaces, broader than the ribs, of which about 14 can be counted. The species appears to belong to the group of *Diplomoceras notabile* Whiteaves, although smaller in size, tapering gradually to an unknown length. The ribs are without nodes and are slightly oblique to the axis of the limb; suture lines as shown on the holotype are lytoceratid in character, with bifid lobes, much divided and somewhat crowded. This species greatly resembles *"Hamites"* sp. Jimbo (1894, p. 39(185), Pl. 7, figures 5, 5a) from the Upper Cretaceous of Hokkaido, Japan.

The holotype was found at locality 2362-A (C. A. S.) at or near the southeast corner of sec. 4, T. 20 S., R. 14 E., M. D. B. and M., a little below the zone of *Diplomoceras mercedense* n. sp., and of *Exicrioceras ortigalitoense* n. sp., in the Moreno formation of Anderson and Pack (1915).

Diplomoceras mercedense Anderson n. sp.
(Plate 64, figures 1, 1a, 2, 2a)

The larger fragments figured represent parts of the same individual (holotype) (C. A. S. Type Coll.), and the smaller fragment another of the same species (paratype) C. A. S. Type Coll.) from the same zone in the Moreno formation. Dimensions of holotype and paratype are as follows: holotype (Pl. 64, figs. 1, 1a), partly restored, slightly reduced; length, (large fragment), 50.5 mm; maximum diameter, 20.8 mm; lesser diameter, 17.7 mm; paratype (Pl. 68, figs. 2, 2a), fragment: length, 46.4 mm; lesser diameter, 11 mm; greater diameter, 13.3 mm; nearly circular, bearing U. S. Nat. Mus. No. 7006, from E. line of sec. 24, T. 12 S., R. 10 E., M. D. M. Maestrichtian. The holotype was found by Bennison at locality 29656 (C. A. S.) south of Ortigalita Creek, Merced County, in the upper part of the Moreno formation.

Shell of medium size, with a gently curving form, subelliptical in section, slightly compressed laterally, and costate, with numerous rounded ribs that extend around the cone almost at right angles to its axis. The species resembles, and is closely related to *"Anisoceras"* *subcompressum* (Forbes), as figured by Whiteaves (1903, Pl. 45), although it is less compressed. The paratype was found in the zone containing *Exicrioceras ortigalitense* n. sp., and *Lytoceras* (*Gaudryceras*) *aureum* n. sp., in the uppermost beds of the Moreno formation, near the E. line of sec. 24, T. 12 S., R. 10 E., M. D. B. and M.

Diplomoceras mustangense Anderson n. sp.
(Plate 65, figure 3)

This species is only imperfectly known from the holotype, which is a fragment of the smaller limb of the shell. It is elliptical in section, slightly flattened on dorsal side and rounded on abdominal; ribs numerous, narrow, with concave interspaces broader than ribs, which are oblique to axis of limb; ribs bearing no evidence of tubercles or other ornamentation, curving downward more sharply near dorsal border. The holotype (C. A. S. Type Coll.) consists of a fragment of a limb, to which is attached another, presumed to have been a part of the same example, or at least to the same species. Together these fragments have a length of 78 mm. They were found at locality 29118 (C. A. S.), half a mile south of Mustang Creek, on the east flank of the Panoche Hills, near the center of the south half of sec. 33, T. 8 S., R. 8 E., M. D. B. and M., in the lower part of the Moreno formation. The holotype was found in the zone containing *Parapachydiscus coalingensis* n. sp., *Didymoceras californicum* n. sp., and *Exiteloceras bennisoni* n. sp. A related species, here described as *Diplomoceras jimboi* n. sp., is somewhat more inflated in section and greater in diameter.

Diplomoceras aff. D. recticostatum (Seunes)
(Plate 62, figure 6)

Hammites recticostatus SEUNES, Geol. Rech. sur Les Terr. Secondaries, 1890, p. 186, Pl. 9, fig. 6; "Lower Danian."

This species is included by Seunes in a list of fossils that characterize the "Lower Danian" in southern and southwestern France, and its analogous species in the upper part of the Moreno formation of the Great Valley occurs at a stratigraphic level correlative with the "Lower Danian."

The present species has been found associated with *Diplomoceras vermiculare* n. sp. at locality 28441 (C. A. S.), on the west border of the NW ¼ of sec. 29, T. 1 N., R. 2 E., M. D. B. and M., by Church, Cross, and the writer, on the north border of Long Valley, Contra Costa County.

Dimensions of hypotype (C. A. S. Type Coll.) (Pl. 62, fig. 6) are as follows: length, 40 mm; height, 18 mm.

Diplomoceras o'shaughnessyi Anderson n. sp.
(Plate 56, figure 2)

Shell large, consisting of the two nearly parallel limbs with simple ribs, without ornamentation. Section in both limbs subelliptical, rounded on ventral border, narrowing toward dorsal border; costate, with nearly straight simple, rounded nontuberculate ribs that cross the sides obliquely, inclination on smaller limb being greater than on buccal limb; sutural features not known. The species resembles and is closely related to *Diplomoceras notabile* Whiteaves, found on Hornby Island, but it is smaller, with a more compressed section, and relatively heavier ribs, with broader interspaces, and a narrower section. The holotype (C. A. S. Type Coll.) has the following dimensions: length of smaller limb, 125 mm; width of loop, 114 mm; width between limbs, 20 mm. This example was found in the aqueduct tunnel, about 1.12 miles from the Tesla portal, by Mr. Gallager, foreman of construction, and sent by him to M. M. O'Shaughnessy, Chief Engineer. Its location, as determined on the surface, is probably near the center of the W ½ of sec. 6, T. 4 S., R. 5 E., San Joaquin County. It was found associated with *Parapachydiscus* sp., *Baculites occidentalis* Meek, *Exiteloceras vancouverense* (Gabb), and *Neokotoceras fresnoense* n. sp. Its horizon is in the Moreno formation of Maestrichtian age.

Diplomoceras vermiculare Anderson n. sp.
(Plate 62, figures 4, 5)

Shell small, coiling openly, as in *Exicrioceras,* but with section of whorl nearly circular, tapering gradually, and ornamented only with sharp annular ribs, slightly oblique to axis of shell and separated by concave interspaces somewhat broader than the ribs themselves.

This is represented by two similar examples found associated with *Diplomoceras* aff. *D. recticostatus* (Seunes), at locality 28441 (C. A. S.), on the west border of the NW ¼ of sec. 29, T. 1 N., R. 2 E., M. D. B. and M., on the north border of Long Valley, Contra Costa County. Its stratigraphical position is regarded as above, and its chronological level as Maestrichtian.

Dimensions of holotype (C. A. S. Type Coll.), (fig. 5) are as follows: length, 40 mm; width of whorl, 4 mm.

Genus Exiteloceras Hyatt

Hyatt included in this genus in addition to the type, the more regularly coiled symmetrical *"Ancyloceras" jenneyi* Whitfield, which is more complete and less eccentric in its form and ornamentation, and more correctly represents a number of species occuring in the Upper Cretaceous of California and Oregon.

Exiteloceras vancouverense (Gabb)

"Hamites" vancouverensis GABB, Paleont. Calif., vol. 1, 1864, p. 70, Pl. 13, fig. 18; Vancouver Island, British Columbia. . . . ANDERSON AND HANNA, Calif. Acad. Sci., Proc., 4th ser., vol. 23, 1935, p. 23, Pl. 7, figs. 2, 3, 4; Pl. 8, fig. 5; Catarina Landing, Lower California.

Gabb's figure of this species is defective, not showing the tubercles on the ventro-lateral angle, although he mentions them. These tubercles distinguish the shell from *Hamites* Parkinson, as interpreted by Spath (1921) and Whitehouse (1926). In the figures given by Anderson and Hanna (1935, Pl. 7) these tubercles are shown as they appear on the cast of the shell. Gabb does not give the horizon of its occurrence, but states that it occurs with *"Ammonites" newberryanus* (Meek), which is known only in lower Senonian horizons of the Nanaimo series.

Exiteloceras bennisoni Anderson n. sp.
(Plate 72, figure 7)

This species is related to *Exiteloceras* sp. found in the same formation and horizon farther south, but it is smaller, relatively more strongly, but less numerously costate, with simple or rarely branching ribs, although a few are intermediary, arising a little below ventral border; ribs mostly tuberculate, with small, inconspicuous tubercles on ventral borders, where they occur in parallel lines on either side of siphonal plane; limbs apparently parallel, forming a nearly symmetrical loop, as in other species of this genus; section of limbs subcircular, flattened on dorsal side; suture unknown.

The holotype (C. A. S. Type Coll.) consists of the upper part of the loop, which measures about as follows: peripheral measure of the loop, approximately 115 mm; transverse measure of loop, 75 mm; proximal end of smaller limb curving slightly downward toward the spiral. The holotype was found by Allan Bennison at locality 29664 (C. A. S.) on the northeast quarter of sec. 30, T. 5 S., R. 7 E. associated with *Didymoceras californicum,* in the central part of the Moreno formation, of Anderson and Pack (1915). Its chronological position is Maestrichtian.

Exiteloceras desertense Anderson n. sp.
(Plate 66, figures 2, 2a)

Holotype an incomplete retroversal loop, which includes a small terminal portion of the spiral of the living animal, although the spiral itself is missing; the spiral seems to have been one with a sinistral coil, from which the shell departed to form a short, stout loop; section of whorl subcircular, slightly flattened on ventral and dorsal zones; ribs numerous, strong, simple and tuberculate; tubercles occurring on ventral borders; ribs showing no tendency to divide, arising on dorsal side, passing outward on flanks almost at right angles to dorsal border of body-chamber; ribs on dorsal zone crowded and reduced in strength.

The holotype (C. A. S. Type Coll.) has the following dimensions: length on the periphery, 165 mm; distance between limbs, 24 mm; greatest ventro-dorsal diameter, 40 mm; greater transverse diameter, 40 mm. The simplicity of the sculpture and ornamentation distinguishes this species from others of the genus in California. The holotype was found by C. M. Cross in the north half of sec. 6, T. 19 S., R. 15 E., M. D. B. and M., on the northeast slope of Joaquin ridge, 3 miles or more northwest of "Oil City," Fresno County, at locality 28303 (C. A. S.).

Genus Oxybeloceras Hyatt

According to Spath's interpretation (1922, p. 145), the genus *Oxybeloceras* is represented by *"Hamites" amapondensis* v. Hoepen, *"Hamites" quadrinodosum* Jimbo (1894, Pl. 7, figs. 3, 4), and other ptychoceratid forms, and this seems to have been the intention of Hyatt himself. Hyatt doubtfully included (1893, p. 577) the California species, *"Ancyloceras" lineatum* Gabb, but he remarks that "it may be a fragment of *Ptychoceras.*"

In habit of growth, form and ornamentation, species of *Oxybeloceras* differ much from the three examples of *Exiteloceras* named by Hyatt, as for example the more regularly coiled form, *Exiteloceras ("Ancyloceras") jenneyi* Whitfield (1880). In the diagnosis of either genus, the other must be kept in mind. Following this interpretation the genus *Oxybeloceras* Hyatt will include the following species from the Upper Cretaceous series in California:

Oxybeloceras lineatum (Gabb)

Ancyloceras lineatum GABB, Paleont. Calif. vol. 2, 1869, p. 139, Pl. 23, figs. 18, a, b, c; probably from Texas Flat "Rock Coral," near Folsom, Placer County.

Similar species have been collected from this zone elsewhere, but there is little evidence that either this species, or its genus was ever found on Cottonwood Creek. Further information as to Texas Flat, Placer County, is found in Geology of California, vol. 1, p. 203. The horizon of the present species is probably near that found at Pentz, and within the range of the strata exposed on Chico Creek.

Oxybeloceras biconstrictum Anderson n. sp.
(Plate 31, figure 2)

Shell is laterally compressed, and moderately curved parallel to the plane of symmetry; transverse section narrowly elliptical; sides regularly costate, with thin elevated, oblique ribs, separated by broader interspaces; ribs crossing dorsal and ventral zones, each bearing small tubercles on ventro-lateral angles on either side of flattened venter; sides and ventral zone crossed at intervals by broad, double, periodic constrictions.

The shell of this species differs from that of *Oxybeloceras lineatum* (Gabb) in its curvature, in its oblique ribs and constrictions, and in its section, which is elliptical, rather than ovate. The holotype (C. A. S. Type Coll.) measures as follows: greatest length, 95 mm; greatest breadth, 20 mm; thickness, 10 mm.

The holotype was found at locality 31100 (C. A. S.) in the lower part of the zone with *Oregoniceras* sp., and *Prionotropis bakeri* Anderson, on Dry Creek, northern Tehama County, 1.8 miles west of Rosewood. A similar (or possibly the same) species occurs also with *Oregoniceras,* at locality 28571 (C. A. S.) on Quinto Creek, western Stanislaus County, and also on the North fork of Cottonwood Creek, Shasta County. In all cases the horizon is Turonian.

Oxybeloceras petrolense Anderson n. sp.
(Plate 56, figure 1)

This species appears to belong to the group of *"Hamites" quadrinodosus* Jimbo (1894), which Spath (1921; 1922) places with some doubt in the present genus. Jimbo's species, as implied in the name, has four rows of small tubercles, two on each side of the median plane, instead of one, and in this respect the present species conforms although the spread of the limbs is somewhat broader, and the section is more narrowly elliptical.

Shell of moderate size, section a little compressed, numerously costate, forming a loop with unequal limbs; ribs on earlier (smaller) limb, of medium breadth, slightly oblique to its axis; ribs on opposite (distal) limb, broader and flattened, extending at near right angles to dorsal border; but oblique on recurved portion of loop; ribs on smaller limb, somewhat finer, or of medium size, and more oblique than on the other; limbs uniting in a loop, but below this, extending in a parallel course; ribs tuberculate, with small tubercles in two or three rows; ventro-lateral row being the more persistent, the others appearing only on the upper part of the loop; a few of the ribs branch near the axis of the loop, but no branches are seen on other parts of the limbs.

The holotype (C. A. S. Type Coll.) has the following dimensions: peripheral length, 95 mm; greatest width of buccal limb, 29 mm; breadth across both limbs, 56 mm. The holotype was found at locality 31364 (C. A. S.) on Petroleum Creek, on the east slope of the Rumsey Hills, northwest Yolo County, in the upper part of the Coniacian.

Oxybeloceras taffi Anderson n. sp.
(Plate 51, figures 6, 6a)

This species is represented by a fragment of the smaller limb found by Taff, Hanna, and Cross on Chico Creek, Butte County. This specimen in section is subelliptical, slightly flattened on ventral zone, which is further set off by rows of small tubercles on its border. Surface of shell marked by numerous fine rounded costae, about 16 to the inch; costae entire, simple, bearing the small tubercles that border the ventral zone; otherwise the costae are unmarked; but are separated by concave interspaces, broader than the costae, which are uniformly parallel, set slightly oblique to axis of limb; holotype (C. A. S. Type Coll.) septate throughout, slightly curved at larger end, as if approaching the retroversal crook, has the following dimensions: greater diameter, 13 mm; smaller diameter at same point, 11 mm; total length, 55 mm; suture not shown.

This example was found at locality 27838 (C. A. S.), a little above the middle of the section exposed on Chico Creek, as shown by Taff, Hanna, and Cross (1940, p. 1316). A similar but small example of the same species and the same limb was recently found by McCoy north of "Brushy Knob" on the northeast dip of the Altamont anticline, Contra Costa County.

Genus Bostrychoceras Hyatt

Schleuter (1871-1872) illustrated various related types under the name *Heteroceras polyplocum* (Roemer), from which Hyatt (1894, p. 588) designated as the genotype of *Bostrychoceras* the form represented by his figure 4, of Plate 33, but without including any of the others figured by Schleuter. Spath (1921, p. 253) indicated another of Schleuter's figures (Pl. 35, fig. 8), perhaps as representing a form of Roemer's species better known to him, but without explanation. It is logical to assume that Hyatt's choice of the type, from the number illustrated by Schleuter, definitely fixed it as his genotype. In the Great Valley of California there are various types that conform well to the genotype chosen by Hyatt, not many that simulate the form favored by Spath.

According to Pervinquiere (1907, p. 104, 105), the range of Roemer's species is limited to upper Campanian, or Maestrichtian, although other species are found in Santonian, or even in Cenomanian horizons in north Africa.

In California the genus, as commonly interpreted, has a range from Turonian to Maestrichtian. Some of the West Coast types are ornamented with tuberculate ribs, and others are not so marked; in this respect they conform to Schleuter's interpretation of the morphological varieties of Roemer's species, which includes those with tubercules and those without.

Bostrychoceras puertoense Anderson n. sp.
(Plate 67, figure 4)

Shell very large, the spiral closely coiled, of sinistral habit, without ornamentation; only traces of growth lines visible on cast; whorls rounded in outline and in section; form of living chamber not known; suture not known. The holotype of this species (C. A. S. Type Coll.) is a cast of the lower portion of the spiral of a mature shell having the following dimensions: height (incomplete), 203 mm (8 inches); maximum diameter of base, 101.6 mm (4 inches); section of whorls, subcircular. This example was found by Mr. Jack Frame, of Patterson near "Swallow Rock" on Puerto Creek in the upper part of the Panoche formation, on the south side of the creek, in the zone of *Parapachydiscus coalingensis* n. sp., and *Exiteloceras bennisoni* n. sp. It was said to have had a total length of 12 inches when found, and a width of coil of more than 4 inches. It represents the largest species of this genus (and family) found in California, or on the West Coast.

Bostrychoceras serpiens Anderson n. name
(Plate 20, figures 3, 4, 7)

Helicoceras indicum (?) Stoliczka, ANDERSON, Proc. Calif. Acad. Sci., 3d ser., vol. 2, 1902, p. 91, Pl. 3, figs. 96, 97; Smith (now Fitch) ranch, 3 miles west of Phoenix, Oregon.

The generic determination of this species may be doubtful, although Collignon (1932, p. 40) suggested that it might be referable to *Bostrychoceras*. Its whorls do not resemble any of the types illustrated by Schleuter for *Bostrychoceras polyplocum* (Roemer), but this may be only negative evidence.

The spiral, at first coiling sinistrally, departs from this manner and assumes an opposite course, becoming in its neanic stage of growth a dextral spiral. The suture is unknown. The section of the whorls, at first nearly circular, later becomes somewhat elliptical; surface marked by oblique transverse, annular costae, not regularly spaced, among which are a few irregular periodic constrictions; greater diameter of spiral, 20 mm.

This example was found associated with *Oregoniceras* sp. and other prionotropids in the upper part of the Turonian (?), a few hundred feet above the zone of *Fagesia californica* Anderson.

Bostrychoceras elongatum (Whiteaves)

Heteroceras elongatum WHITEAVES (in part), Meso. Foss. vol. 1, pt. 5, 1903, p. 331, Pl. 44, fig. 2; Hornby Island, (not *H. conradi* MORTON, not *H. conradi* WHITEAVES).

As described and figured by Whiteaves, this species possesses a sinistrally coiled

"Shell composed of a calcareous tube, which is at first coiled in a regular elongated spiral as in *Turrilites,* but which is ultimately free and partially uncoiled. . . .

"This (spiral) feature is much better seen in two sinistral specimens from Hornby Island, collected by Mr. Harvey, in 1895, and especially in the one figured on Plate 44." . . .

This species was confused with one described earlier (pt. 2, 1879, p. 100, Pl. 12, figs. 1, 1a, 2, 2a, 3) as *H. conradi* Morton, which is coiled dextrally.

The assumption by Whiteaves that the "spiral portion (of this shell) is either dextral or sinistral," is questionable. From his illustrations and statements he was dealing with two distinct species. These species differ not only in their manner of coiling, but also in their ornamentation, and in the apical angles of their spirals, that of *B. elongatum* being little more than half that of the form figured on Plate 12, originally referred to *H. conradi* Morton. The form figured on Plate 12, is thus apparently unnamed, although it is probably congeneric with *H. elongatum* (Whiteaves).

Bostrychoceras columbianum Anderson n. name

Heteroceras conradi WHITEAVES (not Morton), Meso. Foss. vol. 1, pt. 2, 1879, p. 100, Pl. 12, figs. 1, 1a, 3; Maple Bay, Vancouver Island.
Heteroceras elongatum WHITEAVES (in part), Meso. Foss. vol. 1, pt. 5, 1903, p. 331 (not *H. conradi* Morton, not *H. conradi* Whiteaves).

It appears from the statement of Whiteaves (p. 100) that the holotype of this species was found at Maple Bay, Vancouver Island, according to the account given by Whiteaves:

"The surface is marked by rather distant, prominent and very acute, transverse ribs, which are much narrower than the rather deeply concave grooves between them."

There is nothing in either the text, or in the figures that justifies the identification of this species with *B. elongatum* Whiteaves, although both appear to be referable to the genus *Bostrychoceras* Hyatt.

Bostrychoceras occidentale Anderson n. sp.
(Plate 31, figures 4, 4a)

This species is represented by two supplementary fragments, one showing a helicoid spiral and the other a succeeding or terminal portion of the coil. It is not known that these fragments formed parts of the same shell, although they were found together. The following description is based chiefly upon the spiral coil, which is taken as the holotype.

Shell helicoid, whorls free, not contiguous, increasing rapidly in diameter, and in development of ribs; ribs narrow, elevated, and separated by concave interspaces, broader than ribs; on the smaller whorls these are occupied by numerous threads transverse to whorl; larger ribs occurring at slightly irregular intervals; without nodes; on later whorls, the ribs flatten somewhat on ventral side, showing a slight ventral angle on cast; ribs much reduced, or inconspicuous on dorsal side; suture line lytoceratid, with bifid lobes, having widely divergent branches, similar to those of *"Heteroceras" osukai* Yabe (1904, Pl. 6, figs. 7, 8), to which the present species appears to be related.

The figured fragments, holotype and paratype (C. A. S. Type Coll.) were found at locality 1293A (C. A. S.), 1 miles north of Frazier Corners, Shasta County, associated with *Scaphites pittensis* n. sp., *Scaphites condoni* Anderson, *Puzosia klamathonae* n. sp., *Gyrodes dowelli* White, and other species. The chronological position of the species is regarded as upper or middle Turonian.

Dimensions of holotype (Pl. 31, fig. 4) are as follows: width of larger coil, approximately 44.6 mm; greater diameter of whorl, 21 mm. Dimensions of paratype (Pl. 31, fig. 4a) are as follows: width of coil, 68 mm; greater diameter of whorl, 22 mm.

Bostrychoceras brewerii (Gabb)
(Plate 52, figure 7)

Helicoceras Brewerii GABB, Paleont. Calif., vol. 1, 1864, p. 72, Pl. 14, figs. 22, 22a; Pentz, Butte County, California.

Gabb's description of this species reads in part, as follows:

"Shell small, whorls slightly compressed, surface marked by small oblique ribs, encircling the whorls, faintest on the ventral (dorsal) side. At intervals of every four or five ribs there occurs a much larger one, faint on the ventral (dorsal) surface, but prominent on the sides and back (venter). These ribs bear a small tubercule on each side of the dorsum (venter)."

A fragmentary example of a young whorl of this species, hypotype (C. A. S. Type Coll.), length, 23.8 mm was found by the writer near Pentz, associated with *Canadoceras fraternum* (Gabb), and *Mortoniceras* (*Submortoniceras*) *pentzanum* n. sp. In most details of form and sculpture it agrees well with the description given by Gabb, although the tubercules described by him do not seem to be present. A slight angular bend is seen in a few of the ribs, accompanied by a slight flattening of the ventral surface, but this example shows no true tubercules, such as Gabb has described for the holotype. This fragment shows the sinistral coiling seen in the larger whorl fragment figured by Gabb.

Bostrychoceras aff. B. brewerii (Gabb)
(Plate 52, figures 5, 6)

A number of fragmentary examples of a closely related species with dextral coiling were collected by Popenoe at locality 85 (C. I. T.) on Trabuco Creek, Orange County, and were courteously sent to the writer for determination or description.

These fragments have the tuberculate ribs described by Gabb, although the ribs differ slightly in form. The larger fragment, hypotype (C. I. T. Type Coll.), consists of 1¼ whorls having a diameter of 18.6 mm, and a whorl diameter of 8 mm. It was found associated with other species of the same genus.

Bostrychoceras trabucoense Anderson n. sp.
(Plate 52, figures 8, 8a, 8b)

Eight fragmentary examples of this species were collected by W. P. Popenoe on Trabuco Creek, Orange County. Some of these fragments probably belonged to a single individual, but were not sufficiently well preserved to be fitted.

All show the shell to have formed an open helicoid spiral in which the section of the whorl was broadly elliptical, slightly flattened on dorsal side, and increasing gradually in diameter; costate with moderately thickened ribs extending singly entirely around the whorl; costae fine in the younger stages, but becoming gradually stouter with the growth of the shell, rounded and prominent; ribs neither branching nor bearing conspicuous tubercules at any stage of growth.

In general form, manner of coiling, and ornamentation, the shell resembles *Bostrychoceras otsukai* Yabe, as figured by Collignon (1938, Pl. 6, figs. 2, 2a, 2b), which appears to occur in both Japan and Madagascar.

On a few ribs only appears an eccentric swelling which disturbs the regularity of the coil and of the ribs themselves.

The holotype of the species (C. I. T. Type Coll.) has the following dimensions: maximum length, 52 mm; greater diameter of whorl, 14 mm; lesser diameter, 12.5 mm; other fragments have a maximum diameter of 16 mm. These examples were collected at locality 85 (C. I. T.) on the NE ¼ of sec. 13, T. 6 S., R. 7 W., S. B. B. and M., on the west flank of the Santa Ana Mountains, in the upper part of the section on Trabuco Creek, Orange County, California.

The species described by Yabe from Hokkaido is said to occur with *Parapachydiscus*, and in Andimaka, Madagascar, the species occurs with *Parapachydiscus colligatus, Mortoniceras delawarense*, and other species that indicate an upper or middle Campanian horizon.

Bostrychoceras sanctaeanae Anderson n. sp.
(Plate 52, figures 3, 4)

This species has been segregated from the total number of fragmentary examples of the genus collected by Popenoe at locality 85 (C. I. T.). The species is represented by two of three sinistrally coiled parts of a spire that in some respects resemble *Bostrychoceras brewerii* (Gabb), in its coiling, form and ornamentation, but it is more robust, is more closely coiled, and possesses heavier ribs and broader interspaces. The whorls are nearly circular in section and bear small tubercules on the ventral border at irregular intervals. The horizon of its occurrence is the same as that of the preceding species, and probably also of *Bostrychoceras brewerii* (Gabb).

Dimensions of holotype (C. I. T. Type Coll.) : width of coil, 23 mm; height of whorl, 11 mm.

Bostrychoceras declive (Gabb)
(Plate 52, figures 2, 2a)

Helicoceras declive GABB, Paleont. Calif., vol. 1, 1864, p. 73, Pl. 28, figs. 200, 200a; Pentz, Butte County, California.

Two incomplete examples of this species were found by the writer at its type locality, locality 1125 (C. A. S.) 1 mile west of Pentz, where it was associated with *Bostrychoceras brewrii* (Gabb), *Baculites chicoensis* Trask, *Mortoniceras* (*Submortoniceras*) *pentzanum* n. sp., and *Canadoceras* aff. *C. fraternum* (Gabb). The chronological position of the species, and of its associates, is that of the upper part of the section exposed on Chico Creek, and may be regarded as middle, or upper Campanian.

Dimensions of holotype (C. A. S. Type Coll.) : width of coil, 29 mm; greater diameter of whorl, 7 mm; lesser diameter 5 mm.

Bostrychoceras vermiculare (Gabb)

Helicoceras vermiculare GABB, Paleont. Calif., vol. 1, 1864, p. 71, Pl. 13, figs. 19, a, b; Upper Cretaceous, southwest of Martinez, Contra Costa County, California.

Gabb's original description of this species reads in part as follows:

"Shell small, subcompressed. Section elliptical; curve broad, regular. Surface marked by numerous small rounded ribs, regular in size, and extending completely around the shell, being slightly oblique and less distinct on the ventral (dorsal) side."

The septum is relatively simple, consisting of bifid lobes and saddles, with few elements. This species has been found only at its type locality, a mile or more southwest of Martinez, Contra Costa County, in a stratigraphic zone probably correlative with that of the preceding species.

Bostrychoceras buttense Anderson n. sp.
(Plate 51, figures 7, 7a)

Shell helicoid, coiling sinistrally, with open, but not a broad coil, section of whorls circular, increasing rather rapidly in diameter; surface ornamented with numerous transverse costal threads that encircle the whorl; a few periodic ribs, heavier than the others, increasing in strength toward the ventral zone, but not differing from the others on the dorsal side, bearing small tubercules on each side of the siphonal line; sutures only partly visible.

The species greatly resembles "*Helicoceras*" *venustum* Yabe (1904, Pls. 3, 5) to which it appears closely related, although more closely coiled, and increasing more rapidly in diameter with the growth of the shell.

The holotype (C. A. S. Type Coll.) has the following dimensions: length (fragment), 46.4 mm; maximum width, larger end, 13.5 mm. Found at locality 28173 (C. A. S.) by Taff, Hanna, and Cross, in the upper part of the Butte formation as exposed on Chico Creek, associated with *Baculites chicoensis* Trask, *Mortoniceras* (*Submortoniceras*) *randalli*, n. sp., *Mortoniceras* (*Submortoniceras*) *gabbi* n. sp., and *Mortoniceras* (*Submortoniceras*) *chicoense* (Trask), in beds regarded as middle Campanian.

Genus Exicrioceras Anderson n. gen.

Probably the latest crioceratid ammonoids that have been found on the West Coast, if not in the Upper Cretaceous of any country, occur in the closing stages of the series in the

Great Valley of California. In general aspect, if not in morphological features the group resembles *Shasticrioceras* Anderson (1938) found in the Barremian strata of the Shasta series in the Great Valley. In form, section of whorls, ribbing, and in its peripheral nodes, the members of the group are akin to the above genus, but without the support of sutural characters a lineal descent from it cannot be claimed. Type species *E. ortigalitense* Anderson, n. sp.

Exicrioceras ortigalitense Anderson n. sp.
(Plate 64, figures 4, 4a)

Shell large, coiling crioceratid, whorls not contiguous, tending to separate progressively with age; sides of whorl costate, ribs moderately heavy, slightly sinuous, terminating in small ventro-lateral nodes; sides marked by transverse periodic grooves, more frequent in younger whorls; section of whorls subquadrate (or subovate), flattened on the sides and on the dorsal zone, narrowly rounded on the ventral border; suture line not exposed. The holotype (C. A. S. Type Coll.) was found by Bennison at locality 29656 (C. A. S.), about 2500 feet north of the SE corner of sec. 33, T. 11 S., R. 10 E., M. D. B. and M., in pebbly sandstones of the Moreno formation.

The type was associated with *Lytoceras* (*Gaudryceras*) *aureum* n. sp., *Diplomoceras mercedense* n. sp., and species of pelecypods. Dimensions: length of outer whorl (fragment), 90 mm; height of outer whorl, 31 mm; breadth of outer whorl, 17 mm; height of inner whorl, 12 mm. The species may be compared to forms of *Phlychticrioceras* Spath from the Coniacian, but it can hardly be assigned to this or any other genus.

Exicrioceras diabloense Anderson n. sp.
(Plate 72, figures 1, 2, 3)

Shell small, coiling in one plane, at first with a nearly circular coil, but later assuming a looplike form; whorls compressed, or elliptical in section, increasing gradually from a greater diameter of 1 mm to more than 10 mm. The whorls are regularly costate, with costae slightly oblique, beginning as mere threads, but with growth attaining a width of 10 mm, separated by broader interspaces; costae bearing small nodes at their ventro-lateral terminations. This shell has the manner of coiling, the form and ornamentation of other members of the genus described above, and moreover is found in nearly the same stratigraphic and chronological position. The larger and more complete examples of the species, including the holotype, were found by Bennison, at locality 29123 (C. A. S.), a little east of the center of sec. 19, T. 8 S., R. 8 E., M. D. B. and M., in the belt mapped as Moreno formation by Anderson and Pack (1915).

The species has been found not only at its type locality, but also farther north in the Great Valley, as on Hospital Creek, and on Briones Creek, near the old John Marsh house, south of Brentwood. At the mouth of Hospital Creek, San Joaquin County, the species occurs with *Solenoceras* sp., and a diminutive species of *Lytoceras* (? *Gaudryceras*) and other cephalopods.

The holotype of the present species (C. A. S. Type Coll.) has the following dimensions: greatest diameter of coil (loop), 39 mm; width of same, 26 mm; greater diameter of whorl section, 9 mm; transverse section, 4 mm. Like its congeners, the species is found near the upper limit of the upper Campanian—Maestrichtian stage.

Family ANISOCERATIDAE Hyatt emend. Spath
Genus **Anisoceras** Pictet

According to Pictet this genus is characterized by a more irregular form than that of any other cephalopod. In young stages the shell is sinuous, forming an irregular heliciform spiral with disunited (free) volutions, having a double curvature, not included in one plane; later it straightens, and is (then) bent into a hook, as in *Ancyloceras*. The genus perhaps deserves better than any other, the characterization d'Orbigny gives to *Heteroceras,* by presenting the maximum of irregularity of form among cephalopods. It is more eccentric than any (other).

Anisoceras charlottense Anderson n. sp.
(Plate 11, figures 3, 3a, 3b)

Shell of moderate size, with long *Toxoceras*-like minor limb, subcircular in section, somewhat flattened on ventral side, costate, with oblique, annular ribs of two sorts; major limb not yet known; on smaller limb, the major ribs are tuberculate, with a row of thin elongated tubercules on either side of median plane, and a row of larger tumid tubercules on the side, elongated in the direction of the rib; the space between these major ribs occupied by three or four smaller rounded, cord-like costae tending to coalesce on the dorsal side of the limb.

The species appears to have some relationship to *Anisoceras armatum* (Sowerby) as illustrated by Stoliczka (in part), (1863–1866, p. 172–175, Pl. 82, figs. 1a, 1b, 1c) from the Ootatoor group of southern India.

The holotype (C. A. S. Type Coll.) was found by Kleinpell and Galliher on the southeast border of Graham Island, 2 miles or more north of the Indian village of Skidegate. It was found associated with *Lytoceras (Tetragonites) timotheanum* and various other species of upper Albian age.

The holotype has the following dimensions: total length, 82 mm; greater breadth of shell, near bend, 32 mm; transverse (dorso-ventral) measure, 25 mm; diameter at smaller end, 23 mm.

Anisoceras draconis Anderson n. sp.
(Plate 38, figures 8, 8a)

Hamites armatus ANDERSON, Proc. Calif. Acad. Sci., 3d ser., vol. 2, 1902, p. 89, Pl. 5, figs. 130–132; near Henley, Siskiyou County, California. Not *Hamites armatus* Sowerby.

This species is known from only a single example and is the straightened smaller limb of a gerontic loop of an ammonoid shell, showing at its larger end the beginning of the retroversal hook. The holotype No. 47 (C. A. S. Type Coll.) was recovered from the San Francisco fire of 1906, still in fairly good condition. It has the following dimensions: length of limb (incomplete), 80 mm; section of limb elliptical; greater diameter, 20 mm; lesser diameter, about 14.5 mm; surface ornamented with rounded ribs inclining obliquely forward toward the ventral border; limb crossed by 2 or 3 strong constrictions, about 30 mm apart, between which are 8 rounded ribs that cross both dorsal and ventral zones; ribs uniting at intervals with a loop-like connection across the ventral zone, forming on the ventro-lateral angles strong diverging spines at the point of juncture; spines attaining a length of 6 to 7 mm; ventral zone slightly flattened; suture lines not known.

The holotype (C. A. S. Type Coll.) was found associated with *Parapachydiscus henleyensis* (Anderson), 150 feet beneath the zone of *Metaplacenticeras pacificum* (Smith), and 200 feet beneath that of *Kôtoceras richardsoni* n. sp. and *Kôtoceras* sp., and 250 feet above the zone of *Fagesia siskiyouensis* Anderson and *Fagesia klamathensis* n. sp. The species is Turonian.

Genus Hyphantoceras Hyatt
Hyphantoceras ceratopse (Anderson)
(Plate 39, figures 6, 6a, 7)

Heteroceras ceratopse ANDERSON, Proc. Calif. Acad. Sci., 3d ser., vol. 2, 1902, p. 91, Pl. 3, figs. 100, 101; Pl. 10, fig. 201; Smith (now Fitch) ranch, 3 miles west of Phoenix, Oregon.

The generic determination of this species may be doubtful, but its resemblance to the genotype (*Heteroceras reussianum*) is striking.

Schleuter's species (1878, Pl. 32) is regarded as Senonian, whereas, the present species is clearly older. Yabe (1904, p. 11, 12) has described a very similar form under the name of *Helicoceras* (?) *venustum*, which later (1927, p. 42), together with *Hyphantoceras oshimai*, he placed in the "*Mammites* Beds," below the *Parapachydiscus* beds of Hokkaido. The horizon of *H. ceratopse* can hardly be younger than Turonian, since most of the species associated with it are of this age, or older. An abbreviated description of the present species follows:

Shell openly helicoid in form, section of whorl subcircular; surface ornamented with numerous transverse, annular costae of two sorts, major and minor; major ribs elevated and flange-like, rising abruptly at intervals of 5 to 10 mm; minor costae smaller, rounded, intervening between the others.

The holotype No. 37 (C. A. S. Type Coll.) of this species was partly destroyed in the San Francisco fire of 1906, but a portion was recovered; the original drawing is here reproduced. Other fragments of the species have since been found at its type locality, and at neighboring points.

Hyphantoceras irregulare Anderson n. sp.
(Plate 20, figures 5, 6)

The holotype (C. A. S. Type Coll.) consists of a looplike portion, or body chamber of a peculiarly coiled ammonoid shell, similar in general form to the preceding, but having different directional development and ornamentation. What the true course of the complete coil may have been is unknown, since only a terminal portion has been obtained. This example was found at the old "Forty-nine" mine, south of Phoenix, Oregon, associated with various species of *Scaphites* and other cephalopods such as usually characterize Turonian beds. Only a brief description is given here:

Shell of medium size, coiling eccentrically in later whorls; numerously costate, with two sorts of annular ribs, one high and thin, inclined strongly backward, separated by broad, concave interspaces, which are occupied by a few inconspicuous, thread-like wrinkles, not regularly spaced; suture line not known.

The horizon of this species is known only from its associated molluscan types, which indicate upper Turonian. Dimensions of holotype as follows: total length (on curve), 75 mm; breadth of whorl 18 mm.

Hyphantoceras laqueum Anderson n. sp.
(Plate 31, figure 3)

Shell coiling openly in approximately one plane, from which it departs, if at all, only at maturity; section of whorl, circular; shell costate, with two sorts of ribs, major and minor, extending obliquely forward; major ribs flange-like, the edges of which curve strongly forward on the ventral zone in mature stages of growth; between these major ribs are six to eight smooth, rounded, minor costae, increasing in number and strength with the growth of the shell. The holotype (C. A. S. Type Coll.) was found by Allan Bennison at locality 31115 (C. A. S.), an upper (southwestern) branch of Cortina Creek, 1 mile north of Rumsey, Colusa County. The exact age is not known. Most of the species on the West Coast are referable to Turonian horizons, and without contrary evidence, the present species should be considered this age. Dimensions of holotype are: width of outer coil, 82 mm; greater diameter of whorl, 15 mm; section of whorl, subcircular.

Genus Solenoceras Conrad
Solenoceras solanoënse (Anderson)

Hamites (Ptychoceras) solanoënse Anderson, Proc. Calif. Acad. Sci., 3d. ser., vol. 2, 1902, p. 90, Pl. 9, fig. 184; Upper Cretaceous, Solano County, California.

An abbreviated and emended description of this species follows:

Shell of moderate size, representing the smaller limb of a closely folded, ptychoceratid ammonoid, having the following dimensions: length of smaller limb (incomplete), 155 mm; section of limb transversely elliptical, average greater diameter, 14 mm; shell tapering gradually from the smaller end to the top of the recurved loop; surface marked by simple annular ribs; on the holotype are 75 ribs, gradually increasing in width and thickness.

The only ornamentation seen on the ribs are rows of minute tubercules on the borders of the ventral zone, most prominent at the top of the loop. On the dorsal side, which is flattened, the ribs are less prominent. The holotype is in the collections of the Museum of Paleontology, University of California, No. 12088. It was found by F. A. Steiger, in probable lower Senonian beds west of Vacaville, Solano County, California. It is the only example of this genus yet recognized in the Upper Cretaceous series of the Great Valley of California.

Spath (1926, p. 81) has given the chronological position of this genus as Campanian, but upon what basis is not stated. The holotype of the present species seems probably to have been found in a belt well marked by lower Senonian fossils along the west border of Pleasants Valley.

Solenoceras mexicanum Anderson n. sp.

(Plate 72, figure 8)

This species is small, its limbs are closely folded together, each circular in section, tapering slowly from its earliest stage, and in general form resembling *Ptychoceras*, with only a slight departure from actual contact near point of juncture; shell is costate throughout, but costae on buccal limb are relatively much heavier than on the other, and are less steeply inclined toward the line of contact. No sutural lines are visible in the holotype.

The holotype closely resembles *Solenoceras texanum* (Shumard) as described and figured by Stephenson (1941, p. 401, Pl. 79, figures 2, 3, 4) from the Nacatoch sand, Navarro County, Texas. The holotypes of the two species differ only in minor details of ornamentation that may have small significance. In the form here described, no evidence of periodic grooves are to be seen, as appear on *S. texanum* as figured by Stephenson (Pl. 79, figs. 3, 4). The dorsal nodes are concealed by the matrix.

The holotype (C. A. S. Type Coll.) was found by Hertlein and Jordan at locality 953 (C. A. S.), near the river crossing 9 miles north of Ensenada, Lower California. It was associated with *Parapachydiscus* sp. indet., *Baculites* aff. *B. vagina* Forbes, and *Diplomoceras o'shaughnessyi* n. sp. The beds exposed at locality 953 appear to be somewhat higher than these exposed on the south shore of Todos Santos Bay from which White obtained most of the fossils first described from the "Gualala group." Dimensions of holotype are as follows: length, 18.3 mm; width across both limbs, approximately 8 mm.

Family DESMOCERATIDAE Zittel emend. Spath 1921

A partial account of the desmoceratids in the Shasta series (Lower Cretaceous) in California was given by the writer (1938, p. 179, 180). Spath (1921; 1922) expressed some interesting views upon the taxonomic aspects of various generic groups within this family in the Upper Cretaceous, but with little reference to their development in the Indo-Pacific areas in which they are especially prominent. He offered only casual data as to their chronological sequence, and his views seem to have been based more upon morphological features than upon their stratigraphical occurrence. In the Great Valley of California, the records seem somewhat complete for various groups, providing essential historical rather than theoretical data pertaining to their sequential development. These groups include the desmoceratids and the pachydiscids.

The desmoceratids of the Shasta series ended with an association of puzosids with *Latidorsella* and *Beudanticeras,* each having definite characteristics.

In the Upper Cretaceous, a succession of desmoceratids and pachydiscids is well developed, although they are only partly similar to those in the Shasta series. Some stocks appear to be exotic, entering rather suddenly into the stratigraphic succession, in the early beds of the Cenomanian and Turonian, or at later stages, following upon an unconformity, or upon other evidences of diastrophism.

Some types of *Latidorsella* may be traceable from Albian-Shasta stocks into the Upper Cretaceous succession. Puzosids, forming a prominent group in the later Shasta series, continue into early Senonian time where they disappear. The genus *Hauericeras* first appears in early Senonian time, and continues to near its close.

The vertical distribution of the pachydiscids, and desmoceratids, exclusive of the *Puzosinae,* is illustrated in Table 7.

TABLE 7.—*Desmoceratidae in the Upper Cretaceous series*

UPPER ALBIAN, SHASTA SERIES

Desmoceras (Latidorsella) merriami (Anderson)
Beudanticeras brewerii (Gabb)   *Beudanticeras hulenense* Anderson

. . . . Unconformity . . . .

UPPER ALBIAN

Beudanticeras alamoense n. sp.   *Beudanticeras diabloense* n. name
Beudanticeras dawsoni (Whiteaves)   *Beudanticeras argonauticum* n. sp.

LOWER CENOMANIAN

Desmoceras (Latidorsella) inane (Stoliczka)
Beudanticeras haydenii (Gabb)   *Desmoceras (Latidorsella) barryae* n. sp.
Desmoceras (Latidorsella) jugale (Gabb)   *Beudanticeras* (small sp.)

UPPER TURONIAN

PACHYDISCINAE

Pachydiscus averilli n. sp.   *Pachydiscus ashlandicus* (Anderson)
Pachydiscus rosewoodensis n. sp.   *Pachydiscus oregonensis* n. sp.

SENONIAN

Eupachydiscus arbucklensis n. sp.   *Parapachydiscus cortinaensis* n. sp.
Eupachydiscus willgreeni n. sp.   *Parapachydiscus henleyensis* (Anderson)
Kotôceras richardsoni n. sp.   *Nowakites klamathonis* n. sp.
Kotôceras frazierense n. sp.   *Nowakites dobbinsi* n. sp.
Desmophyllites selwynianus (Whiteaves)   *Desmophyllites siskiyouensis* n. sp.
Desmophyllites yoloensis n. sp.   *Desmophyllites* aff. *D. crassus*
Hauericeras transitionale Waring   (v. Hoepen)
Canadoceras newberryanum (Meek)   *Hauericeras mickeyi* n. sp.
                                                  Hauericeras sp.
                                                  Canadoceras celeste n. sp.

MAESTRICHTIAN

Neokotôceras fresnoense n. sp.   *Neokotôceras* aff. *N. fresnoense* n. sp.
Parapachydiscus catarinae Anderson and   *Parapachydiscus peninsularis*
    Hanna   Anderson and Hanna
Parapachydiscus coalingensis n. sp.   *Canadoceras fraternus* (Gabb)

Genus **Beudanticeras** Hitzel
Beudanticeras haydenii (Gabb)
(Plate 8, figures 1, 1a)

Ammonites Haydenii GABB, Paleont. Calif., vol. 1, 1864, p. 62, Pl. 10, figs. 8, 8a; North fork of Cottonwood Creek, Shasta County.
Desmoceras (Puzosia) Haydeni, WHITEAVES, Geol. Survey Canada, Meso. Foss., vol. 1, pt. 4, 1900, p. 285; Maude Island, Queen Charlotte Islands. . . . ANDERSON, Proc. Calif. Acad. Sci., 3d ser., vol. 2, 1902, p. 41; "Horsetown beds," Shasta County. . . . 1938, Geol. Soc. Am., Special Paper, No. 16, p. 190, Pl. 48, figures 2, 3.
Desmoceras haydeni Gabb, HANNA AND HERTLEIN, Calif. Div. Mines, Bull. No. 118, 1941, p. 168, fig. 8 on p. 169. Horsetown, Shasta County, California.

This species has been found abundantly at Horsetown, Texas Springs, and at locality 1346B (C. A. S.), associated with *Pervinquieria inflata, Durania californica,* and *Beudanticeras alamoense* n. sp., in the Cenomanian. The specimen illustrated in the present paper, hypotype No. 5944 (C. A. S. Type Coll.) is from Horsetown, Shasta County, California.

Beudanticeras alamoense Anderson n. sp.
(Plate 5, figures 2, 2a)

Shell of medium size, sublenticular in section, somewhat compressed, involute, umbilicus small, sides sloping toward a narrowly rounded periphery; umbilicus deep, with abrupt walls, rounded above to convex sides; surface smooth, crossed by about nine sinuous periodic grooves and varices, curving strongly forward near periphery, and forming a moderate ventral sinus; between the periodic grooves, the ornamentation consists of fine flexuous growth lines that curve harmoniously with the grooves themselves. The species appears to be closely related to "*Desmoceras*" *dawsoni* Whiteaves, and is undoubtedly congeneric with it.

The holotype (C. A. S. Type Coll.) was found at locality 1346 (C. A. S.), in the second conglomerate, about 450 feet above the base of the Upper Cretaceous, associated with *Pervinquieria inflata* var., *Durania californica,* and *Beudanticeras argonauticum* n. sp. The dimensions of the holotype are as follows: greatest diameter, 103 mm; width of umbilicus, 19.5 mm; height of whorl, 49 mm; breadth of whorl, 36 mm. The holotype and the three species just named appear to have come from the sandy shales immediately underlying the second conglomerate in the Upper Cretaceous series.

Beudanticeras dawsoni (Whiteaves)

Haploceras beudanti WHITEAVES, Meso. Foss., vol. 1, pt. 3, 1884, p. 286, Pl. 26, fig. 1, Pl. 37, fig. 3; Bear Skin Bay, Queen Charlotte Islands.
Desmoceras (Puzosia) Dawsoni WHITEAVES, Meso. Foss., vol. 1, pt. 4, 1900, p. 286; Bear Skin Bay and Cumshewa Inlet, Queen Charlotte Islands.

Whiteaves gave no formal description of this species, although he compared it with the Indian species described by Stoliczka (1865), later named *Puzosia stoliczkai* by Kossmat (1895–1898). In size and form, the species is very similar to *Beudanticeras alamoense* n. sp., and undoubtedly is congeneric with it, having the sinuous transverse, periodic grooves bordered by varices, which curve definitely forward a little below middle of side, and more strongly forward upon approach to ventral border, forming a well-developed sinus upon the periphery; eleven transverse grooves and varices and a slightly broader umbilicus distinguish this species from the preceding. Whiteaves includes (Pl. 26) a partial suture line, that in its general features seem to resemble that of *Beudanticeras alamoense* n. sp. The locality is on the north shore of Cumshewa Inlet, where some 90 specimens were obtained. From the same area various other species, including *Lytoceras timotheanum* (Mayor), and *Cyrtochilus glaber* (Whiteaves) have been collected. All these species are here referred to the uppermost Albian or lowest Cenomanian.

Beudanticeras argonauticum Anderson n. sp.
(Plate 9, figures 1, 2)

This species is smaller than either of the preceding and has a smaller umbilical ratio. It differs from *Beudanticeras alamoense* in size, has a relatively smaller umbilical pit, and only faint periodic transverse grooves, with only inconspicuous varices, if any. In general aspect, the shell is discoidal, slightly inflated, with sides rounded, converging to the narrowly rounded periphery; suture lines similar to those of *Beudanticeras sphaerotum* (Seely), as figured by Spath (1921, Pl. 3, fig. 1e). Four examples of this species were found in concretionary boulders embedded in the second conglomerate near the base of the Upper Cretaceous, at the mouth of Hulen Creek, near where it enters the North fork of the Cottonwood Creek. The holotype (C. A. S. Type Coll.) has the following dimensions: greatest diameter, 71 mm; height of last whorl, 35 mm; width of umbilicus, 11 mm; thickness of last whorl, 26 mm. The horizon of its origin was apparently that of *B. alamoense,* and other species named above, namely, in the upper Albian or lower Cenomanian beds between the first and second conglomerate in the Hulen Creek district, Shasta County.

Beudanticeras diabloense (Anderson)
(Plate 10, figures 4, 4a)

(?) *Ammonites jugalis* GABB (in part), Paleont. Calif., vol. 2, 1869, p. 133, Pl. 22, figs. 13, 13a; locality not definitely known.
Schleuteria diabloensis ANDERSON, Proc. Calif. Acad. Sci., 3d ser., vol. 2, 1902, p. 80, Pl. 3, figs. 105, 106; Pl. 10, fig. 199; probably Curry Canyon, southeast of Mount Diablo.

The original description of this species, slightly emended, reads in part:

"The greatest diameter of the largest specimen is 25 mm; thickness near the umbilicus, 12 mm. The umbilicus is small, with sides abrupt at this diameter, though the younger whorls show more gentle slopes. The sides are apparently smooth, or marked only by a few faint transverse grooves and lines of growth, are flattened, converging gently toward the periphery. The fine lines of growth curve a little backward after crossing the umbilical border. The suture is that of *Desmoceras,* though in form the shell resembles that of *Phylloceras.*"

The specimen from which the figures were drawn was labelled "Mount Diablo," and being in a collection with others of the same species from Curry's is probably also from that locality. The type is in the collections of the University of California, and is among the number labelled by Gabb as *"Ammonites jugalis."*

Genus Desmoceras Zittel
Subgenus *Latidorsella* Jacob
Desmoceras (Latidorsella) jugale (Gabb)

Ammonites jugalis GABB (in part), Paleont. Calif., vol. 2, 1869, p. 133, Pl. 22, figs. 12, a, b (not 13, 13a); lower part of the Cretaceous series, near Benicia, California.
Desmoceras jugalis ANDERSON, Proc. Calif. Acad. Sci., 3d ser., vol. 2, 1902, p. 99.

Gabb's illustrations include two distinct, and apparently not closely related forms from different localities. The first of these should be regarded as the lectotype; it is said to have come from near Benicia, but the exact point is not known. According to Gabb's statement it attained a diameter of 2 inches. This statement serves to identify the holotype with the form represented by figure 12, Plate 22. This example has not yet been found, but as determined from the figures given by Gabb, it measured as follows: greater diameter, 50 mm; width of umbilicus, 7.1 mm; height of whorl, 25.4 mm; breadth of whorl, 24.4 mm. From these figures it is seen that the height and width of the whorl were about equal. The species has been found on the North fork of Cottonwood Creek, Shasta County, immediately beneath the second conglomerate, above the base of the Upper Cretaceous, half a mile above the mouth of Hulen Creek. The species is apparently closely related to *Desmoceras (Latidorsella) merriami* Anderson, occurring in the upper part of the Horsetown group, . . . that is, in the Neptune zone of the Hulen Beds. An example of the species has been found also 2 miles east of Frazier Corners, near Little Cow Creek, Shasta County.

Desmoceras (Latidorsella) barryae Anderson n. sp.
(Plate 12, figures 2, 2a)

Shell small, discoidal, compressed, umbilicus narrow, with abrupt walls, rounded above, curving quickly to the flattened sides; periphery rounded, or slightly flattened, also curving to the sides somewhat abruptly; surface nearly smooth, except for lines of growth, and some inconspicuous varieces near the periphery.

The holotype (C. A. S. Type Coll.) measures as follows: greatest diameter, 51 mm; width of umbilicus, 6.5 mm; height of whorl, 26 mm; thickness of whorl, 15 mm. The holotype resembles in some respects specimens of *Desmoceras alamoense* n. sp., but differs from it in having more compressed, flattened sides, a slightly flattened periphery, and a narrower umbilicus. It was found a little above the second conglomerate, in the lower beds of the Upper Cretaceous, near the mouth of Hulen Creek, Shasta County. The species is named in honor of the discoverer, Mrs. Teresa Barry Anderson, for her interest in the present work, and her helpfulness and cooperation.

Desmoceras (Latidorsella) inane (Stoliczka)
(Plate 10, figures 3, 3a)

Ammonites inanis STOLICZKA, Geol. Survey India, Mem., vol. 1, 1865, p. 121, Pl. 59, figs. 13, 14; Ootatoor group, near Odium, southern India.
Desmoceras inane (Stoliczka) SPATH, Paleont. Soc. London, vol. 75, 1921, p. 41; compared with *Desmoceras latidorsatum* (Michelin).

Many examples that are indistinguishable from the Indian form have been collected by Bennison, McCoy, and the writer at locality 31097 (C. A. S.) on Dry Creek, northern Tehama County, near the base of the Upper Cretaceous. They were found associated with *Turrilites* aff. *T. bergeri* Brongniart, *Cyrtochilus stylus*, n. sp., and *"Acanthoceras"* aff. *A. meridionale* (Stoliczka), about 0.1 mile east of the steeply dipping conglomerate at the base of the series. This species is closely related to *Desmoceras latidorsatum* (Michelin) from the upper Gault of Aube, France. The same species has been collected by the writer on the North fork of Cottonwood Creek, half a mile west of the mouth of Hulen Creek, Shasta County.

Genus Desmophyllites Spath

The generic name *Schleuteria* Grossouvre, was used by Spath (1921) for certain Senonian desmoceratids, for which *Schleuteria larteti* (Seunes) was proposed as an emended genolectotype. Later Spath (1929) replaced *"Schleuteria"* for these desmoceratids, by *Desmophyllites*, again using Seunes' species (*S. larteti*) as the genoholotype. By this proceeding the generic name *"Schleuteria"* seems to have been discarded, and for the type of desmoceratids which Spath had included under it, no better name has been proposed.

This generic name is accordingly used for the following Senonian desmoceratids, to which *"Schleuteria"* had been tentatively attached. On the West Coast various species which occur in the lower Senonian (Coniacian) fall readily into this generic group.

Desmophyllites selwynianus (Whiteaves)
(Plate 40, figure 2)

Ammonites Selwynianus WHITEAVES, Geol. Survey Canada, Meso. Foss., vol. 1, pt. 2, 1879, p. 104, Pl. 13, figs. 1, 1a; Sucia Islands, Strait of Georgia.
Desmoceras Selwynianum WHITEAVES, Meso. Foss., vol. 1, pt. 5, 1903, p. 351; locality as before.

This species has been found at various places in the Great Valley of California. It was recorded by Smith (1898; 1900) from the Arroyo del Valle, south of Livermore, associated with *Metaplacenticeras pacificum* (Smith), and other species. It has since been collected by Hanna and associates at locality 1552 (C. A. S.) on the south border of Antelope Valley, and on the west border of Mclure Valley, and also on the east border of Cedar Canyon, near Napolian Springs, western Kern County, in all cases in the lower part of the Coniacian. The figured example is from locality 1552 (C. A. S.). This specimen, hypotype (C. A. S. Type Coll.), measures: greatest diameter (incomplete), 60 mm; width of umbilicus, 5 mm; greatest breadth of whorl, 15 mm.

A smaller example has a diameter of 43 mm. As indicated by its form, ornamentation, elongated ventral sinus, and other features, the group to which this species belongs seems related to that included by Yabe (1927) under the name *Kotôceras*, although the latter possesses a keel.

Desmophyllites siskiyouensis Anderson n. sp.
(Plate 35, figures 3, 3a; Plate 41, figures 1, 2, 3, 3a)

Shell small, discoidal, flattened on the sides, rounded on the periphery, involute, with small umbilicus having rounded borders; surface smooth, though marked by three or more narrow periodic grooves, inclined forward on the sides, and more strongly flexed near the ventral zone, forming here a pronounced sinus; surface otherwise marked by numerous but obscure costal threads on the outer layer of the shell, curving with the periodic grooves;

suture lines having many narrow lobes and saddles (6 each), diminishing rapidly in size toward the dorsal borders.

The holotype (C. A. S. Type Coll.) (Pl. 41, fig. 1) measures: greater diameter, 47 mm; width of umbilicus, 4.6 mm; greatest thickness of whorl, 16 mm. Paratype (C. A. S. Type Coll.) (Pl. 41, fig. 2) measures as follows: maximum diameter, 25 mm; length of last whorl, 13.4 mm; maximum breadth of last whorl, 10.6 mm. Locality 455 (C. A. S.). Hypotype (C. A. S. Type Coll.) (Pl. 35, figs. 3, 3a) measures as follows: maximum height, last whorl, 18.9 mm; maximum breadth of last whorl, 15 mm. Locality 1467A (C. A. S.).

Holotype was found at locality 455a (C. A. S.) Richardson's Ranch, 4 miles north of Montague, Siskiyou County, associated with *Prionocycloceras crenulatum* (Anderson), a little above the horizon of *Metaplacenticeras pacificum* (Smith), and farther above that of *Prionotropis hiltensis* n. sp. The horizon of this species is lower Senonian (Coniacian).

Well preserved examples were found by Hanna at locality 1552 (C. A. S.), associated with the preceding and with *Paleotractus crassus* Gabb. At its type locality the present species occurs with *Kotôceras richardsoni* n. sp. about 400 feet above the horizon of *Nowakites klamathonis* n. sp., and 500 feet above that of *Puzosia* (*Parapuzosia*) *hearni* n. sp.

Desmophyllites yoloensis Anderson n. sp.
(Plate 41, figure 6)

This species is closely related to the preceding, but is stouter, and usually smaller. The section of the whorl is subelliptical, the umbilicus is relatively broader, and the ventral zone is more broadly rounded, upon which the periodic grooves are less prolonged into an abdominal sinus; surface of the shell smooth, or marked only by periodic constrictions and lines of growth with uniform concentric curvature; suture lines not unlike those of *Desmophyllites siskiyouensis*, having many elements, lobes and saddles; the summits of the saddles forming a nearly straight line from periphery to umbilicus. The holotype, No. 9816 (C. A. S. Type Coll.), and other examples were found at locality 1467A (C. A. S.) in Enos Canyon, 7 miles northwest from Winters, Yolo County, associated with *Metaplacenticeras californicum* (Anderson), *Tessarolax distorta* Gabb, *Bullina yoloensis* n. sp., and numerous other species. The holotype has the following dimensions: greater diameter, 34 mm; width of umbilicus, 3.5 mm. The horizon is regarded as low in the Coniacian, although not at its base.

Genus Kotôceras Yabe

Yabe has proposed the name *Kotôceras* (genotype *Desmoceras damesi* Jimbo) for a group of desmoceratid ammonites more or less strongly keeled, found in the Upper Cretaceous of southern India and Japan, and in related regions. Forms belonging in this group are found in the Coniacian of the Great Valley of California, and to the north of it in other basins of the Upper Cretaceous. None has yet been found in older beds, nor in strata younger than Coniacian. None of them is thought to be specifically identical with either the Indian or Japanese species. Forms that are possibly derivative occur in the upper Senonian, and are described here under another name. A small form belonging to this group was formerly thought (1902) by the writer to be identical with *Desmoceras sugatum* (Forbes) but this view cannot now be upheld, although the relationship is close. This species is here recognized, and renamed *Kotôceras subsugatum* n. name, although the type itself was much damaged in the San Francisco fire.

According to Jimbo (1894, p. 25, 26) *Desmoceras damesi* occurs with *Placenticeras subtilistriatum*, and on page 15, both these forms are included in a list with *Inoceramus digitatus* (locality 16). "*Placenticeras*" *subtilistriatum* Jimbo has the form and surface ornamentation of *Metaplacenticeras pacificum* (Smith), from the lower Senonian beds near Henley, Siskiyou County. *Inoceramus digitatus* Jimbo (not Sowerby) has an analogue in the lower Senonian (Coniacian) beds of locality 25730 (C. A. S.) in southwest Colusa County. It seems probable that the genus *Kotôceras* Yabe, will be found to be restricted to a lower Senonian horizon only.

Kotôceras richardsoni Anderson n. sp.
(Plate 36, figures 3, 3a)

Shell of moderate size, a little inflated, involute, umbilicus small but open, rounded on shoulders; surface smooth or marked only by curving transverse periodic grooves and threadlike costal lines, all of which curve strongly forward from umbilical border to periphery; all lines curving forward on ventral zone, forming here an elongated rostrum above aperture, as in other desmoceratid groups (group of *Desmophyllites selwynianus*), from which *Kotôceras* differs in possessing a keel.

The holotype (C. A. S. Type Coll.) was found at locality 455A (C. A. S.) on the Sidney Richardson ranch, 4 miles north of Montague, Siskiyou County, associated with *Desmophyllites siskiyouensis*. The holotype has the following dimensions: greater diameter, 61 mm; width of umbilicus, 10 mm; breadth of whorl, 25 mm. Its stratigraphical position is low in the Senonian (Coniacian), and is about 400 feet above the zone of *Nowakites klamathonis* n. sp., and higher above that of *Puzosia (Parapuzosia) hearni* n. sp.

The shell of this species is similar in form and surface features to *Kotôceras damesi* Yabe (not Jimbo), 1927, Pl. 7 (V).

Kotôceras frazierense Anderson n. sp.
(Plate 40, figures 5, 5a)

This species resembles the preceding, *Kotôceras richardsoni* in form and surface features, and in possessing a keel and an elongated sinus, forming a rostrum above the aperture; it is less robust, or relatively thinner, and its keel is more elevated; its periodic, transverse grooves are less flexuous, and its umbilicus relatively narrow. The holotype, No. 3724 (C. I. T. Type Coll.), measures as follows: greater diameter, 85 mm; width of umbilicus, 10 mm; breadth of whorl, 20 mm; suture line not exposed. Two examples of this species were found by W. P. Popenoe at locality 1347 (C. I. T.) on Little Cow Creek, 1.5 miles east of Frazier Corners, on the Meltin ranch, a quarter of a mile below the ranch house. A notable feature of the species is its prominent keel, which rises from its bevelled ventral zone; the sides are only moderately inflated, and are crossed by about seven flexuous grooves, bending strongly forward on the sloping ventral zone. The surface of the shell is ornamented also by fine thread-like costal lines that extend from the umbilicus to the keel. This species is the largest of the genus yet found in the lower Senonian of California, and may best represent the genus, although larger related forms are found near the top of the group in the Upper Senonian. The present species was found associated with *Phylloceras vaculae* n. sp., and other lower Senonian forms.

It may be noted here that *Ammonites obesus* Stoliczka (1865, Pl. 32, figs. 1, 1a) greatly resembles this form, and may be found to be a nearly related species.

Kotôceras subsugatum Anderson n. name
(Plate 35, figures 2, 2a)

Desmoceras sugatum Forbes, ANDERSON, Proc. Calif. Acad. Sci., 3d ser., vol. 2, 1902, p. 98, Pl. 3, figs. 98, 99; "lower Chico beds", Richardson Ranch and Henley, Siskiyou County.

Shell small, discoidal, involute, umbilicus small with steep walls, rounded on shoulder; sides a little inflated, flattened on median zone; ventral zone bearing a keel in mature stages of growth; keel not found on young whorls, becoming developed in older stages; surface smooth, or marked only by faint, flexuous periodic grooves, curving strongly forward on ventral zone; suture line consisting of many lobes and saddles, six of each appearing on holotype. On a portion of outer whorl on which the test is preserved are faint lines of growth, curving strongly forward near keel, indicating that an elongated rostrum had projected above the aperture.

The holotype of the species (C. A. S. Type Coll.), and most other examples, were lost in the San Francisco fire, and only imperfect examples have since been found.

The holotype was found on the Sidney Richardson ranch, 4 miles north of Montague, Siskiyou County, and four other examples were collected near Henley from beds of the same horizon, associated with *Parapachydiscus henleyensis, Metaplacenticeras pacificum* (Smith), *M. californicum* (Anderson), and other species that indicated a low position in the Coniacian. The holotype had the following dimensions: greater diameter, 27 mm; width of umbilicus, 4 mm; greatest breadth of whorl, 11 mm. The Henley examples were found about 250 feet above the zone of *Fagesia siskiyouensis,* and *F. klamathensis* Anderson.

Neokotôceras Anderson n. gen.
Genotype Neokotôceras fresnoense Anderson

The genus here described is proposed for a development of desmoceratids in the later Senonian beds in the Great Valley of California. The only species so far found occurs at the top of the Panoche formation. It possesses the general form and most of the surface features of *Kotôceras* Yabe, but differs from this genus not only in size, but in the absence of periodic grooves in its mature and older stages of growth. The suture line appears to be puzosid insofar as it can be traced.

Neokotôceras fresnoense Anderson n. sp.
(Plate 57, figures 1, 2, 3, 4, 5)

This species seems to be akin to *Kotôceras damesi* (Jimbo), and direct relationship between them may have existed. The holotype (C. A. S. Type Coll.) is a mature example, and is strongly keeled, and as seen in other examples, the keel becomes more prominent in older stages of growth. The keel begins to form at a diameter of 20 mm, and from this stage it develops regularly. The ornamentation of the shell is for the most part similar to that of *Kotôceras frazierense* n. sp., but its transverse periodic grooves are lost at an early stage of growth. The resemblance of the shell to *Kotôceras damesi* (Jimbo) is seen in the form and ornamentation, but it is less evident in older shells. The suture line can be traced inward from the siphonal zone for a limited distance, showing the saddles to be tripartite and deeply incised; the siphonal saddle is more symmetrical in this division, but the symmetry is lost in the lateral saddles; a trifid division of the strong lateral lobe is partly seen in the preceding minor lobe, but is not apparent in the next following; beyond this it cannot be traced. The general aspect of suture line suggests a puzosid pattern, but only in form, not in the number of its elements. Insofar as comparison can be made the line resembles that of *Kotôceras sugatum* (Forbes).

The holotype (C. A. S. Type Coll.) was found at locality 2362 (C. A. S.) on sec. 4, T. 19 S., R. 14 E. near the top of the Panoche formation as exposed in this district, and within 1000 feet of its summit. The holotype (Pl. 57, figs. 1, 2) has the following dimensions: maximum diameter, 105 mm; width of umbilicus, 9 mm; greatest breadth of whorl, 38 mm; suture line (Pl. 57, fig. 5) as shown in the figure. A larger example of the species, three-fourths septate, (paratype, C. A. S. Type Coll.), (Pl. 57, fig. 3), measures as follows: maximum diameter, 165 mm; width of umbilicus, approximately 12 mm; height of last whorl, 96.8 mm. Its greatest diameter, when complete, probably exceeded 200 mm. Another paratype (C. A. S. Type Coll.), (Pl. 57, fig. 4) has the following dimensions: maximum diameter, 31.8 mm; height of last whorl, 18.4 mm; breadth of last whorl, 14.6 mm.

Joaquinites Anderson n. gen.
Genotype Joaquinites fascicostatum Anderson

The Upper Cretaceous series on the West Coast, and especially the Senonian in the Great Valley of California, is rich in many known genera of Desmoceratidae, but it can hardly be supposed that all of them are now known. The present genus is proposed here for a small group of ammonites found in the upper part of the Panoche formation on the west border of the San Joaquin Valley, which in general aspect, form, section, and ornamentation are more closely connected with this family than with any other, although its sutural features are only partially known.

At least two species have been recognized, although only one of these can at present be described. The larger, and perhaps the major species of these, is known only from a single fragmentary example found in the uppermost beds of the Panoche formation, but its fragmentary condition does not permit a satisfactory reproduction or description. The smaller species, described below, may be regarded as the genotype, and is the only one sufficiently well preserved for diagnostic use. The suture line, although imperfectly exposed, is desmoceratid, recalling the septal features of *Desmoceras jugale* (Gabb, 1869, Pl. 23, figure 12).

Joaquinites fascicostatum Anderson n. sp.
(Plate 9, figures 3, 3a, 4)

Shell of medium size, discoidal, or somewhat lenticular in section, of desmoceratid aspect, having a moderately broad and deep umbilicus, neatly rounded on shoulder; sides but little inflated, sloping gently to periphery which is slightly flattened on ventral zone; sides of whorl marked by rather fine sinuous costal threads arising in small bullae on umbilical border, forming bundles of four or more, some of which subdivide near the middle of the side into minor groups, but tend to disappear before reaching ventral border; suture line showing only a strong lateral lobe and elevated saddles deeply cut by minor elements.

The holotype (C. A. S. Type Coll.) has the following dimensions: greater diameter, 58 mm; width of umbilicus, 12 mm; height of whorl, 28 mm; breadth of whorl, 20 mm. Two examples of the species were found at locality 31593 (C. A. S.), associated with *Parapachydiscus catarinae* Anderson & Hanna, *Kotôceras fresnoense* n. sp., and *Exiteloceras* aff. *E. vancouverense* (Gabb). This locality is about 1620 feet W., and 1400 feet S., of the NE corner of sec. 7, T. 19 S., R. 15 E., M. D. B. and M., Fresno County, California and its stratigraphic position in about 1700 feet beneath the top of the Panoche formation, in the uppermost part of the Campanian or Maestrichtian.

The second example of the species is somewhat larger than the holotype, having a diameter of 66 mm, but a similar section, and similar surface ornamentation.

Genus **Hauericeras** de Grossouvre
Hauericeras transitionale Waring

Hauericeras transitionale WARING, Proc. Calif. Acad. Sci., 4th ser., vol. 7, 1917, p. 69, Pl. 9, fig. 15; locality 2 (L. S. J. U.), in Bell Canyon, Los Angeles County.

According to Waring (1917, p. 56, 57), this species was found in "the upper shales of the Chico group," occurring at this locality. It was found associated with a considerable fauna, consisting of 16 other molluscan species, including *Turritella chicoensis* Gabb, and *Glycymeris veatchi* Gabb.

Hauericeras mickeyi Anderson n. sp.
(Plate 47, figures 2, 2a)

Shell of medium size, or small, discoidal, broadly umbilicate, sides flattened, crossed by about five shallow, curving, transverse periodic grooves, inclining forward near the periphery; section of whorl, narrow, lenticular, with ventral zone sloping to a narrow, almost acute periphery; umbilicus broad, with steep walls that unite with the flattened sides almost at right angles, forming an abrupt shoulder. The holotype (C. A. S. Type Coll.) was found by Taff, Hanna, and Cross at locality 27835 (C. A. S.), half a mile below Frank Mickey's house on Chico Creek, Butte County, near the middle of the Chico formation. It has the following dimensions: greater diameter, wholly septate, 62 mm; height of whorl, 22 mm; width of umbilicus, 25 mm; breadth of whorl, 12 mm. Its horizon is that of *Mortoniceras* (*Submortoniceras*) *randalli* n. sp., and *M. gabbi* (Anderson) (middle Campanian). The species resembles *Hauericeras welschi* Grossouvre, from the 'blue marls' of Aude, France, (? Senonian), although having a relatively broader umbilicus.

Hauericeras churchi Anderson n. sp.
(Plate 62, figures 2, 3)

Shell small, discoidal, thin and lenticular; surface smooth or marked only by four or five sinuous transverse grooves and faint lines of growth; umbilicus rather broad, walls low and sloping section of whorl narrowly ovate, with narrowly rounded periphery; involution slight, the ratio of diameter to the width of umbilicus being about 3:1. The critical measurements are: greater diameter of holotype (fig. 2), 30.5 mm; width of umbilicus, 10.25 mm; height of whorl, 10 mm; breadth of whorl, 6 mm; sutures not well exposed.

This species differs notably from the earlier forms of the genus, namely, *Hauericeras transitionale* Waring (Coniacian), and *H. mickeyi* n. sp. (middle Campanian) from the Chico Creek section, and also from its associated species, *H.* aff. *H. gardeni* (Baily). It more closely resembles *Hauericeras* sp. from the Cow Creek (Oak Run) section, of lower Senonian age, but it is smaller and has a different umbilical ratio.

The holotype and paratype of the species (C. A. S. Type Coll.) were found associated with *Parapachydiscus catarinae* and *Neokotôceras fresnoense* n. sp., at locality 2361 (C. A. S.) on Joaquin Ridge, northwest of "Oil City," by C. C. Church.

Hauericeras aff. H. gardeni (Baily)
(Plate 62, figures 1, 1a)

Ammonites gardeni BAILY, Quart. Jour. Geol. Soc. London, vol. 11, 1856, p. 456, Pl. 11, figs. 3a, b, c; near Natal, southeast Africa. . . . STOLICZKA, Cret. Cephal. S. India, 1865, p. 61, Pl. 33, figs. 4, a, b; Arrialoor group. . . . KOSSMAT, Beitr. zur Pal. und Geol., Oest. Ungarns u. d. Orients, Bd. 9, 1895, p. 188, Pl. 18, figs. 7a, b; Arrialoor group, India.

A large fragment of a body whorl of *Hauericeras* that appears to be referable to this species was found by Taff, Church, Cross, and Hanna at locality 2362 (C. A. S.), near the center of the E side of sec. 4, T. 20 S., R. 14 E., M. D. M. This fragment conforms in size, form, and all other visible characters to the original type found near Natal. The entire length of the fragment, hypotype (C. A. S. Type Coll.), is 117 mm; its maximum height of whorl is 40 mm; its breadth, 16 mm. It was found associated with *Parapachydiscus caterinae* Anderson and Hanna, *Baculites occidentalis* Meek, and many other species.

Family PACHYDISCIDAE Spath

Many genera of this family occur in the Upper Cretaceous of the West Coast, and their importance warrants more than a passing notice. The genera *Pachydiscus, Eupachydiscus, Canadoceras, Parapachydiscus,* and related types in these areas probably surpassed in numbers those of any other family, but their origin and relationships are not yet clear and seem likely to be more fruitful of speculation than of useful, conservative results, much needed at the present time. Collignon (1932) remarks with much justice, that *"Pachydiscus* is without dispute, the genus, or better the group, the least well defined of all the Ammonites of the Upper Cretaceous."

His remark applies more to the family than to the genus *Pachydiscus* in its restricted sense. Without attempting a discussion of their relationships, it seems more important at present to record their stratigraphic distribution.

Spath (1922, p. 120–126) has sought to distinguish a number of new genera (or subgenera), *i.e. Menuites, Nowakites, Eupachydiscus, Holcodiscoides,* etc., as occurring chronologically between the Turonian stock of *Pachydiscus* Zittel, and that of *Parapachydiscus* Hyatt, which latter he regards as being largely confined to Campanian and Maestrichtian stages. Some of these groups are well characterized, but others are not above question; others might be useful, if more precisely defined, but his treatment leaves much to be desired. In the following pages the writer has preferred to adopt usage of the older writers (Grossouvre, Hyatt, Pervinquiere, Kilian, *et al.*), rather than the thus far doubtfully understood names that lack definition, or whose characters are only suggested by examples selected from the literature, themselves not well defined, or well illustrated, and whose stratigraphical occurrence is only assumed, not proved.

Kossmaticeras Grossouvre forms a recognizable group in the Upper Cretaceous of the West Coast, related to the Puzosinae, as shown by Kilian and Reboul (1909), replacing *Holcodiscus* Uhlig in these stages, but at present few species have been found in California or in Oregon. The varied types illustrated by these authors, or mentioned by them, include forms much older than the Upper Cretaceous.

Spath (1922) has suggested a genetic relationship between *Puzosia* Bayle, *Nowakites* Spath, and *Parapachydiscus* Hyatt, but the basis for this view is not yet clear. The oldest group of the Pachydiscidae known in California and Oregon includes the Turonian forms, *Pachydiscus ashlandicus* (Anderson), *P. oregonensis* n. sp., and *P. rosewoodensis* n. sp., but they cannot be shown to have any relation to *Eupachydiscus* Spath. Certain Coniacian types, as *Nowakites klamathonis* n. sp., seem to have had puzosid ancestry, as seen on the inner coils, but a relationship with *Parapachydiscus* in the uppermost Senonian is not suggested in their later whorls.

Genus **Pachydiscus** Zittel
Pachydiscus ashlandicus (Anderson)
(Plate 27, figures 3, 3a, 4, 4a)

Desmoceras ashlandicum ANDERSON, Proc. Calif. Acad. Sci., 3d ser., vol. 2, 1902, p. 100, Pl. 4, figs. 107, 109; 4 miles southeast of Ashland, Oregon; "lower Chico" beds.

The holotype of this species (No. 33) was damaged in the San Francisco fire, but it is here illustrated, together with a smaller example (paratype 33a). Still others have been found at the old "Forty-nine" mine, and on the Fitch ranch, farther west.

An abbreviated description of the species is here given: Shell medium size, discoidal, a little compressed, moderately involute, umbilicus moderately broad, with abrupt walls; ribs about 40 in number near the periphery, are of two ranks, only about one-third reaching the umbilical border; all ribs crossing the ventral zone; in older stages of growth the ribs tend to become reduced in prominence, or to become obsolete, the exterior zone becoming almost smooth. The species appears to be related to *Pachydiscus vaju* Stoliczka, from the Trichinopoly group of south India, which, according to Pervinquiere (1907, p. 171) belongs to this genus. Others of the genus are known in the same horizon in Oregon and in the Great Valley of California.

The holotype No. 33 (C. A. S. Type Coll.) has the following dimensions: greater diameter, 77 mm; width of umbilicus, 23 mm; height of whorl, 31.5 mm; breadth of whorl, 25 mm. Dimensions of paratype No. 33a (C. A. S. Type Coll.) are as follows: greater diameter, 12 mm; width of umbilicus, 10 mm; breadth of whorl, 10 mm. The species is found associated with the following form, and with *Pugnellus manubriatus* Gabb, and with species of *Oregoniceras* and other cephalopods regarded as Turonian in age. The largest specimen measured 250 mm in greater diameter, and was almost smooth.

Pachydiscus oregonensis Anderson n. sp.
(Plate 27, figures 2, 2a)

This species is nearly related to the preceding, and occurs with it at the old "Forty-nine" mine, near Phoenix, Oregon, and farther west. In general form, ribbing, and sutural features, it shows the characters of *P. ashlandicus,* but differs from it in section, being more lenticular, and in detailed ribbing. The umbilicus is more sharply defined, its walls are more abrupt, and the ribs do not reach its borders, nor develop so strongly upon its sides. The ribs are of two ranks, only a few reaching the borders of the umbilicus; other ribs arise on the outer part of the sides, some of them but little below the ventral border; all cross the periphery, as in the preceding species. The holotype (C. A. S. Type Coll.) has the following dimensions: greater diameter, 101.4 mm; width of umbilicus, 26 mm; height of whorl, 46.7 mm; breadth of whorl near the umbilical border, 33 mm.

The holotype is wholly septate, indicating that it may have had a diameter of 160 mm, or more, which is less than that of the preceding form. The suture line follows the pattern of

Pachydiscus ashlandicus, both of which seem to retain characters of *Puzosia,* as seen in *P. subquadrata* Anderson. This species has a near ally in *Pachydiscus averilli* n. sp., and in an undescribed form found a few miles north of Redding.

Pachydiscus rosewoodensis Anderson n. sp.
(Plate 31, figure 1)

Shell large, discoidal, moderately inflated, moderately umbilicate, section of whorl narrowly ovate, rounded on the periphery, sides sloping regularly to the ventral border, crossed by about 60 rounded, gently curving ribs, and by five or more periodic constrictions, accompanied by 'bourrelets,' all of which curve forward more sharply upon approach to the periphery, forming on the ventral zone a slight sinus; ribs on the mature whorls without prominent nodes on the umbilical borders; umbilicus moderately broad and shallow; suture lines pachydiscoid, with broad saddles and relatively narrow lobes, having digitoid divisions and terminations. The holotype (C. A. S. Type Coll.) consists of a fairly well preserved coil, 5.5 inches in diameter, and fragments of an outer whorl, showing the original diameter to have been 10 inches or more; ribs on outer whorl almost obsolete, reduced to broad undulations, separated by half-inch broad spaces.

The better preserved portion of the coil has the following dimensions: greater diameter, 140 mm; width of umbilicus, 35 mm; height of whorl, 55 mm; breadth of whorl, 40 mm. The holotype has the general aspect of *"Pachydiscus" denisonianus* Stoliczka, although a slightly thicker section and more numerous primary and secondary ribs. This example was found at locality 31102 (C. A. S.) on Dry Creek, northern Tehama County, near the eastern limit of the exposed shales, before they pass beneath the cover of the Tehama formation. The species marks the highest known fossil horizon of this section. The shell possesses some of the features of *Canadoceras,* as described by Spath, but it lacks the umbilical nodes that characterize the genotype of this group.

Pachydiscus averilli Anderson n. sp.
(Plate 7, figures 4, 4a)

Shell small, discoidal, or lenticular, compressed, with moderately broad umbilicus; section of whorl sphenoidal, thickest a little above umbilical border; sides slightly inflated, sloping toward narrow periphery; surface of shell nearly smooth, showing but little ornamentation, chiefly on lower part of sides, where lines of growth are more pronounced; outer part of sides somewhat costate, with low, inconspicuous ribs, curving forward, and crossing ventral zone with a slight sinus; suture line pachydiscid, with deeply cut lobes and saddles. The species is related to *Pachydiscus oregonensis,* but is smaller, has a more wedge-shaped section of whorl, and a more intricate sutural pattern. The holotype (C. A. S. Type Coll.) has the following dimensions: greater diameter of a partly septate whorl, 85 mm; width of umbilicus, 23 mm; height of whorl, 40 mm; greatest breadth of whorl, 18 mm. This example was found by Charles V. Averill, on the left (north) bank of the Sacramento River at Redding. It is upper Turonian in age.

Genus **Eupachydiscus** Spath

Spath mentions as representative of this genus, *Eupachydiscus levyi* (Grossouvre), *E. grossouvrei* (Kossmat), *E. jeani* (Grossouvre), and *E. teshionensis* (Jimbo).

Most of the forms referable to this genus in California resemble the genotype, *Eupachydiscus levyi* (Grossouvre), although they are found here associated with *Parapuzosia, Nowakites,* and *Inoceramus undulatoplicatus* Roemer, and represents only strata of early Senonian age.

According to Collignon (1932, p. 49), these are the "true *Pachydiscus,*" with sutural saddles whose summits are arranged in a line descending toward the dorsal border of the whorl.

Eupachydiscus arbucklensis Anderson n. sp.
(Plate 44, figures 1, 1a; Plate 45, figure 1)

This species belongs to the group of *Eupachydiscus jeani* (Groussouvre), but certain features distinguish it from all others. It is believed to best represent the stock of *Eupachydiscus* in California. The species attained a diameter of as much as 12 inches. Shell discoidal, moderately inflated, moderately involute, whorls embracing more than half the preceding volution; whorls semi-elliptical in section, costate, with ribs arising on the umbilical border in low, tumid bullae, from which, in younger stages of growth, they branch into two, three, or more fine costal lines that flatten on middle of sides and tend to disappear near periphery; suture lines as in *Parapachydiscus,* with elongated lobes and broader saddles, deeply cleft, but with summits arranged in a descending line; siphonal saddle distinctly headshaped, flattened at summit, and having long, digitoid divisions; umbilical walls abrupt, sides sloping convexly toward periphery; sutures as shown in the figures.

The holotype (C. A. S. Type Coll.) (Pl. 44, figs. 1, 1a) has the following dimensions: greater diameter (wholly septate), 132 mm; width of umbilicus, 40 mm; height of whorl, 54 mm; greater breadth, 43 mm.

The paratype (C. A. S. Type Coll.) (Pl. 45, fig. 1) has the following dimensions: greater diameter (three-fourths costate), 200 mm; width of umbilicus, 75 mm; height of whorl, 70 mm; breadth of whorl, 60 mm.

The largest complete example of the species found was about 200 mm in diameter. Five or more examples were found at locality 25730 (C. A. S.), on Sand Creek, Colusa County, on the L. L. Dobbins ranch, 10 miles southwest of Arbuckle. They were associated with others of the genus, and with species of *Parapuzosia, Nowakites,* and *Inoceramus undulatoplicatus* Roemer. The stratigraphic horizon of these species is lower Senonian, but above the horizon of *Metaplacenticeras pacificum* (Smith), and of *Peroniceras tehamaense* (Gabb).

Eupachydiscus willgreeni Anderson n. sp.
(Plate 46, figure 2)

Shell large, robust, a little flattened on sides, section of whorl sub-quadrate, somewhat narrowly rounded on periphery; umbilicus comparatively narrow, with steep walls, rounded above to the moderately flattened sides; surface numerously costate, with low rounded, and almost straight, or only slightly curved ribs, about 64 in number (est.), arising in pairs from low umbilical nodes, or from no nodes, all crossing the sides with a slight forward curve upon approach to periphery; sides crossed by six or more broad and shallow periodic grooves which become obsolete with age. The holotype (Calif. Acad. Sci. Type Coll.) consists of a large fragment representing a part of a living chamber, found at locality 25730 (C. A. S.) on Sand Creek, southwest Colusa County. It has the following dimensions: greater diameter, 186 mm; width of umbilicus, 34 mm; greatest breadth of whorl, 56 mm; height of whorl, 70 mm.

The species appears to belong to the group of *Eupachydiscus jeani* (Grossouvre), and tends to lose its costal ornamentation in old age, but in young adult stages of growth it possesses numerous rounded ribs.

The holotype and other examples were found by H. L. Dobbins, associated with other forms of the genus, and with *Nowakites dobbinsi* n. sp., *Puzosia (Parapuzosia) arenaica* n. sp., and with *Inoceramus* aff. *I. undulatoplicatus* Roemer.

The holotype has some resemblance to *"Ammonites newberryanus"* Gabb (not Meek), (1864, Pl. 27, figs. 199, 199b, c; Pl. 28, fig. 199a), from Vancouver Island, British Columbia.

Its stratigraphic position is in the middle Coniacian-Emscherian. The species is named in honor of William S. Green, pioneer resident of Colusa County.

Eupachydiscus (?) suciensis (Meek)

Ammonites complexus ? var. *suciensis* MEEK, Acad. Nat. Sci. Phila., Proc., vol. 13, 1861, p. 317 (not figured). . . . U. S. Geol. and Geogr. Survey Terr., Bull. vol. 2, 1876, p. 369, Pl. 5, figs. 2b, 2c, lectotype; Sucia Island (not figs. 2, 2a); Comox, Vancouver Island.

Pachydiscus suciensis (Meek) WHITEAVES (in part). Meso. Foss., vol. 1, pt. 2, 1879, p. 106, 107, No. 1, only; Sucia Island (not No. 2); Northwest Bay, Vancouver Island; (not GABB, Paleont. Calif., vol. 2, 1869, p. 133, Pl. 21, fig. 11; near Mount Diablo, California.)

The exact generic relationship of this species is not yet known. Its nearest ally in the Upper Cretaceous of California seems to be *Parapachydiscus cortinaensis* n. sp. from the upper part of the Coniacian near Rumsey. A partial discussion of Gabb's interpretation of this species is given under *Parapachydiscus diabloensis* n. name.

Genus **Parapachydiscus** Hyatt
Parapachydiscus catarinae (Anderson and Hanna)
(Plate 58, figure 2)

Pachydiscus catarinae ANDERSON AND HANNA, Pan-Am. Geol., vol. 50, 1928, p. 238, Pl. 9; photograph only, without description.
Parapachydiscus catarinae ANDERSON AND HANNA, Proc. Calif. Acad. Sci., 4th ser., vol. 28, 1935, p. 19, Pl. 1, fig. 1; Pl. 2, fig. 1; Pl. 3, figs. 1–5; Arroyo Santa Catarina, Lower California.

Shell very large, moderately inflated, sides flattened, narrowly umbilicate; shell with little ornamentation, almost smooth, ribs low, nearly obsolete, or reduced to mere undulations on the sides, curving slightly forward; sutures as shown in the figure, elements finely divided, with long lobes and saddles, the latter having summits arranged in a nearly horizontal line.

The holotype No. 4245 (C. A. S. Type Coll.) was found at locality 1431 (C. A. S.), near Catarina Landing, Lower California, associated with other species of the same genus. The species is almost the largest of the genus known from the Pacific Coast. The holotype, wholly septate, has the following dimensions: greatest diameter, 503 mm; width of umbilicus, 74 mm; height of whorl, 216 mm; breadth of whorl, 170 mm. The maximum diameter of the mature shell cannot be accurately given; if the living chamber has occupied only half a whorl, the diameter of the whorl would have been 711 mm.

The species occurs in central California near Coalinga, at locality 2362 (C. A. S.) and fragmentary examples have been found along the east flank of the Diablo Range at other localities as far north as Puerto Creek. The species is found with *Parapachydiscus* aff. *P. peninsularis* Anderson and Hanna, *Parapachydiscus coalingensis* n. sp., *Neokotôceras fresnoense* n. sp., *Baculites occidentalis* Meek, *Baculites inornatus* Meek, *Lytoceras (Gaudryceras) coalingense* n. sp., and other species. These species characterize the upper part of the Senonian and the Maestrichtian.

Parapachydiscus henleyensis (Anderson)
(Plate 36, figures 2, 2a, 2b)

Pachydiscus henleyensis ANDERSON, Proc. Calif. Acad. Sci., 3d ser., vol. 2, 1902, p. 104, Pl. 8, figs. 165, 166; near Henley, Siskiyou County, California (not *Ammonites newberryanus* Meek, GABB, Paleont. Calif., vol. 1, 1864, Pl. 27; Pl. 28, fig. 199a; Vancouver Island, British Columbia).

This species has been misunderstood by some writers, partly because of its incomplete description, and partly to editorial errors, which the author had no opportunity to correct before publication. The holotype of the species was almost destroyed in the San Francisco fire; only the inner whorls of the two examples found were recovered; these and an additional fragmentary example since found at the type locality permit a partially corrected description, with notes as to its stratigraphical occurrence and its associates. In young stages of growth the shell is robust, inflated, having a whorl section broader than high; at a diameter of 89 mm the ratio of breadth to height of whorl was as 9:5; with growth this ratio was changed, the height increasing more rapidly than the breadth; at a diameter of 14 inches (355.6 mm), this ratio became as 1:1.24. The sides of the whorl sloped rapidly toward the periphery, and the latter became more narrowly rounded. The umbilicus was narrow, with rounded borders; ribs numerous, low and rounded, in two ranks, major and minor; all were flattened upon approach to the periphery; major ribs arising on the umbilical border, the minor ribs higher on the side of the whorl.

The holotype No. 22 (C. A. S. Type Coll.)* and one other example of the species, Syntype 22a (C. A. S. Type Coll.) were found near the village of Henley, about 300 feet stratigraphically above the horizon of *Fagesia siskiyouensis,* and *Fagesia klamathensis* n. sp., and 150 feet beneath the zone of *Metaplacenticeras pacificum* (Smith) *Lytoceras (Tetragonites) henleyense* n. name, and *Kotôceras richardsoni* n. sp., all of which latter represent a lower Senonian horizon, whereas the species of *Fagesia* represent an upper Turonian horizon.

This species appears to belong to the group of *Parapachydiscus quiriquinae* Philippi, which has been assigned by Collignon (1932) to a special branch of *Parapachydiscus.*

Parapachydiscus peninsularis Anderson and Hanna

Parapachydiscus peninsularis ANDERSON AND HANNA, Proc. Calif. Acad. Sci., 4th ser., vol. 23, 1935, p. 20, Pl. 4, fig. 1 on p. 21; Pl. 5, figs. 1, 2; Pl. 6, figs. 3, 4; Pl. 7, fig. 5; textfigure 1; Arroyo Santa Catarina, Lower California.

Shell large, roundly inflated, moderately involute, and costate, with numerous rounded, but not prominent ribs; section of whorl semicircular in young stages of growth, becoming more nearly circular at maturity; umbilicus small, rounded on borders, curve merging gradually with that of rounded sides; ribs low and rounded in young stages become less prominent with age, arising in low bullae on umbilical slope, curving gently forward on approach to periphery, crossing ventral zone with a slight forward curve. The ribs, 56 in number, appear in two alternate ranks, major ribs arising on umbilical slope, others arising higher on sides of whorl, all extending across periphery.

The holotype No. 4248 (C. A. S. Type Coll.) was found at locality 1431 (C. A. S.), near Santa Catarina Landing, Lower California, associated with *Parapachydiscus catarinae* (Anderson and Hanna), *P. ootacodensis* Stoliczka, and *"Nostoceras" sternbergi* Anderson and Hanna. The holotype, wholly septate, has the following dimensions: greatest diameter, 355 mm; breadth of umbilicus, 87 mm; height of whorl, 155 mm; breadth of whorl, 144 mm. The species appears to belong to the group of *Parapachydiscus colligatus* Binckhorst, found in the upper Senonian beds of Limbourg. A closely related species has been found near Coalinga, Fresno County, at locality 2362 (C. A. S.). The species is characteristic of the Maestrichtian on the Pacific Coast.

Parapachydiscus princeps Anderson n. sp.
(Plate 66, figure 1)

Shell of this magnificent species is very large, thick and heavy, exceeding in thickness and weight, if not in diameter, mature examples of *Parapachydiscus catarinae.* The holotype (Univ. Calif. Mus. Paleo. Type Coll.), from locality A-3100 (Univ. Calif.), has the following dimensions: diameter, 20 inches (508 mm); height of whorl, 240 mm; breadth of whorl, 233.7 mm; width of umbilicus, 96.5 mm. The whorl, wholly septate, if extended half a whorl, as representing the living chamber, would attain a diameter of about 29 inches (727 mm). In young shells, the ribs develop in two ranks, major and minor alternating; former arising in slight bullae on umbilical border; in old age, shell becoming smooth, or showing only faint undulations on surface, scarcely extending across ventral zone.

This species appears to be closely related to *Parapachydiscus peninsularis,* but it has a relatively broader umbilicus, less nearly circular section, and a smoother surface in old age. The holotype was found by Mr. Arthur Bridge of Ontario, California, on Arroyo Catarina, Lower California, not far from locality 1431 (C. A. S.) described above. The photograph of the holotype has also been supplied by Mr. Bridge.

* Dimensions of holotype as follows: maximum diameter 90 mm; maximum breadth last whorl approximately 53 mm.

Parapachydiscus gabbi Anderson n. name
(Plate 54, figures 3, 3a, 3b, 3c)

Ammonites Newberryanus GABB (not Meek), Paleont. Calif. vol. 1, 1864, p. 61, Pl. 27, figs. 199, b, c; Pl. 28, fig. 199a; Comox, Vancouver Island, (not *Pachydiscus henleyensis* ANDERSON, Proc. Calif. Acad. Sci., 3d ser., vol. 2, 1902, p. 104.)

The exact locality and stratigraphic position of the holotype of this species is not known, since Gabb did not give them. Only its form, surface features, and relationships indicate its position in the column of the Nanaimo series. According to Gabb's notes (1864, p. 61), the holotype was found at or near Comox, and had a diameter of nearly 7 inches. It is not known that the holotype is preserved, but, like other examples collected by Gabb, it may have been lost. It was formerly thought by the writer that Gabb's figure might represent *Parapachydiscus henleyensis* (Anderson), from the lower Senonian of northern California, but the material now at hand, including a portion of the holotype shows that although the latter somewhat resembles Gabb's figure in form and size, it cannot be shown to be identical with it, and appears to represent a distinctly lower horizon. *P. gabbi* has some resemblance to *Parapachydiscus bidwelli* n. sp., but it is broader in section, and has more regularly spaced ribs. Smaller examples of a more closely related species were found by Taff, Hanna, and Cross at locality 27838 (C. A. S.) on Chico Creek, that may later prove to be identical with the form from Comox, Vancouver Island, but this cannot now be determined.

Parapachydiscus aff. P. gabbi Anderson
(Plate 54, figures 2, 2a)

The two figured hypotypes (C. A. S. Type Coll.) apparently represent small immature forms of the early whorls of an adult. This form seems to be closely related to *Parapachydiscus gabbi*. Young example (Pl. 54, fig. 2): greater diameter, 19.7 mm; breadth of whorl, 10.4 mm; width of umbilicus, approximately 4.5 mm. Somewhat older example (Pl. 54, fig. 2a): height of whorl, 17 mm; breadth of largest whorl, 18 mm. The figured examples were found by Taff, Hanna, and Cross at locality 27838 (C. A. S.) on Chico Creek.

Parapachydiscus cortinaensis Anderson n. sp.
(Plate 45, figures 2, 2a)

Shell of medium size, discoidal in young stages of growth, at which the section of the whorl is narrowly elliptical; umbilicus of moderate width, bordered with steep walls, rounded above to moderately inflated sides; ornamentation simple, or only slight; whorls increasing rapidly in height and breadth, after attaining a diameter of 70 mm; increment of growth rapid and continuing to old age, with loss of ornamentation. The holotype (C. A. S. Type Coll.) has the following dimensions: greater diameter, 131 mm; width of umbilicus, 27 mm; height of whorl, 55 mm; greatest width of whorl, 47 mm; sutures not exposed.

The holotype was found at locality 25730 (C. A. S.) on Sand Creek, southwest Colusa County, associated with *Eupachydiscus willgreeni* n. sp., *Nowakites dobbinsi* n. sp., *Puzosia (Parapuzosia) arenaica* n. sp., and *Inoceramus undulatoplicatus* Roemer, and various other species. Its stratigraphic position represents a Coniacian-Emscherian horizon.

Parapachydiscus panochensis Anderson n. sp.
(Plate 67, figures 1, 1a, 2)

Shell large and thick at maturity, but in young stages of growth inflated, broader than high, becoming relatively narrower in old age; section of whorl subcircular in youth, but in older stages narrowing near periphery; umbilicus moderate, walls at first steep, but rounded above to convex sides; sides of whorl crossed by about 40 narrow, rounded ribs, arising from slightly elevated bullae on umbilical border, curving strongly forward above middle of side, and crossing ventral zone with a shallow sinus; suture lines not well shown in younger stages, but at an older age becoming broad and deeply cleft. The holotype (C. A. S. Type Coll.) is a large fragment of a mature shell, wholly septate, and a well preserved portion of an inner whorl (here figured), and one-third of an outer whorl (not figured). These fragments permit the drawing of an outline for an estimate of its original form and dimensions. From these drawings the following figures have been obtained: greater diameter, 356 mm (14 inches); width of umbilicus, 85 mm; height of whorl, 165 mm; breadth of whorl, 120 mm; inner whorl only is shown in the figure, with dimensions as follows: (Pl. 67, figs. 1, 1a, 2) portion of inner whorl, length, approximately 143 mm; height, 73 mm; breadth, approximately 62.5 mm.

The species may belong to the group of *Parapachydiscus henleyensis* (Anderson), but to a higher horizon. The holotype was found in the zone of locality 28542 (C. A. S.) in the Panoche Hills, 800 feet due south of the center of sec. 15, T. 14 S., R. 11 E., by Hanna and Church, 6800 feet stratigraphically below the top of the Panoche formation. A fragment of *Canadoceras* found a little lower in the section indicates that this horizon is no older than Campanian. In form and ornamentation this type resembles the figure given by Gabb (1864, Pl. 27) of an example from Vancouver Island, and determined by him as *Ammonites newberryanus* (Meek), which it does not resemble. Fragments of a species having the form and ornamentation of *P. panochensis* have been found by Hanna on Crow Creek, on the east half of sec. 5, T. 7 S., R. 7 E., M. D. B. and M., and also by the writer in 'Round Valley' near the Murphy ranch, east of Mount Diablo.

Parapachydiscus coalingensis Anderson n. sp.
(Plate 65, figures 6, 6a)

Shell of medium size, moderately inflated, strongly costate, bearing ribs of two ranks, major and minor; major ribs, 16 in number, arising on umbilical wall, at first slanting backward, but on umbilical border forming inconspicuous bullae, from which they cross the sides almost vertically, with a slight forward curve on approach to ventral border; minor ribs, 24 in number, arising a little below middle of side, crossing side and ventral zone in the manner of the others; umbilicus rather small, section of whorl moderately inflated.

The holotype (C. A. S. Type Coll.), measures as follows: greater diameter, 117 mm; width of umbilicus, 32 mm; height of base whorl, 54 mm; the holotype, septate throughout, if entire, with body chamber, would exceed 176 mm in diameter. This example has been compared with the figures and description of *Parapachydiscus colligatus* Binckhorst, which it resembles, and with others. It seems to be more closely related to *P. subrobustus* Suenes, than to any other, having 38 or more ventral ribs to fewer umbilical ribs, (the ratio being about 3:1).

The holotype was found by C. C. Church, at locality 2362 (C. A. S.), 8 miles northwest of Coalinga (sec. 4, T. 20 S., R. 14 E.), associated with *Parapachydiscus catarinae* (Anderson and Hanna), *Neokotoceras fresnoense* n. sp., and many other cephalopod species characteristic of the lower beds of the Maestrichtian.

Other examples of this species have been found north of Los Banos Creek, one by Bennison on the E ½ of sec. 2, T. 11 S., R. 9 E., in the area mapped as "Moreno," and another, partly crushed but recognizable example was also found by Bennison on the SW ¼ of sec. 29, T. 5 S., R. 7 E., near Puerto Creek.

Parapachydiscus stanislausensis Anderson n. sp.
(Plate 67, figures 5, 5a)

Shell large at maturity, moderately inflated, section of whorl narrowly elliptical; umbilicus narrow, walls steep in young stages, more sloping in older stages, borders gently rounded to slightly convex sides; involution covering about half or more of preceding whorl; section of whorl subquadrate; sides crossed by about 44 moderately prominent ribs that arise near umbilical border, straight on lower half of side, curving gently forward near periphery, but flattened to undulations on ventral zone, crossing it with a small sinus.

The holotype (C. A. S. Type Coll.) consists of a large fragment of an outer whorl, wholly septate, and half of an inner whorl, which is removable. From these the following approximate measurements have been made: greatest diameter, 285 mm; width of umbilicus, 66 mm; height of whorl, 127 mm; breadth of whorl, 74 mm; sutures not well exposed. This example was found near the NE corner of sec. 30, T. 5 S., R. 7 E., M. D. M., on Puerto Creek, by Allan Bennison.

On the younger whorl (diameter, 104 mm), the ribbing differs from that of other California types, in that its ribs are of two sorts, major and minor, but all arise on the umbilical border and extend upward to the ventral border, crossing the periphery in a slight forward curve. Between the major ribs the surface is occupied by finer threadlike ribs, all of which cross the sides and ventral zone.

This species is known only from the holotype, which seems to resemble in section "*Pachydiscus*" *neevesi* Whiteaves, but differs from it in costal ornamentation, possessing major ribs at unequal intervals, between which are the threadlike costae.

Parapachydiscus californicus Yabe

Parapachydiscus fascicostatus Yabe, var. *californicus* YABE, Science Reports, Tohoku Imper. Univ. (Japan), 2d ser., vol. 5, 1921, p. 58 (6), Pl. 8, fig. 4, and textfigure 5; Santa Ana Mountains, Orange County, California.

Yabe figured and described a *Parapachydiscus* obtained from the district of Santiago Creek, which he doubtfully regarded as a variety of his *Parapachydiscus fascicostatus,* from the province of Teshio, Hokkaido, Japan.

Some features of resemblance seem to exist between the Japanese and California forms, although a comparison of the sections illustrated by him hardly supports the view that they are specifically identical. The costal features of these shells show some resemblance, but a close inspection of them discovers other points of difference that should not be overlooked. In *Parapachydiscus fascicostatus* Yabe the walls of the umbilicus are smooth, the ribs seem to arise in pairs and trios, from elongated swellings on the outer border of the umbilicus, or singly on the lower part of the side; in *P. californicus* Yabe, the umbilical border is not marked in this manner, but it appears to possess broad swellings on the wall itself, from which 6 or more ribs take their rise. The locality of discovery of *P. californicus* Yabe, as given by E. L. Packard, is on a north tributary of Black Star Canyon, and its horizon appears to be at or near that of *Metaplacenticeras pacificum* (Smith), and therefore to be lower Senonian (Emscherian), as may be that of *P. fascicostatus* Yabe, which is said by Yabe (p. 58) to have come from the "*Placenticeras* Bed." The umbilical ratios of the two are not the same; that of *P. fascicostatus* is about 0.333; that of *P. californicus* Yabe is 0.233, or less.

Parapachydiscus californicus resembles, and appears to be more closely related to *Eupachydiscus willgreeni* n. sp., or to *Parapachydiscus quiriquinae* Philippi, from the west coast of Chile.

Parapachydiscus bidwelli Anderson n. sp.
(Plate 51, figures 5, 5a; Plate 54, figure 1)

This species resembles *Parapachydiscus gabbi,* but is thinner in section, and the ribs are finer and less regularly spaced. The figured examples were found at locality 27838 (C. A. S.) on Chico Creek, Butte County, associated with smaller examples of a species still more closely resembling *P. gabbi;* with *Mortoniceras randalli;* and with other species characteristic of the Chico formation in its type area on the east side of the Sacramento Valley. The holotype (C. A. S. Type Coll.) (Pl. 54, fig. 1) represents only the body chamber of a young but adult shell, measuring as follows: greater diameter, 150 mm; width of umbilicus, 36.4 mm; height of whorl, 60 mm; breadth of whorl, slightly reduced by pressure, 47.8 mm; number of ribs per whorl (est.) 68. The suture line is not exposed. The holotype and its smaller companion (C. A. S. Type Coll.) (Pl. 51, figs. 5, 5a) were found by Taff, Hanna, and Cross. The holotype has been compared with *Parapachydiscus panochensis* n. sp., from locality 28542 (C. A. S.) near Moreno Gulch, Panoche Hills, Fresno County, from which it can readily be distinguished by its thinner section, its more numerous and slender ribs, and a relatively smaller umbilicus. The species is named in honor of Col. John Bidwell, early pioneer of California.

Dimensions of paratype (Pl. 51, figs. 5, 5a) are as follows: greater diameter, 125 mm; width of umbilicus, 29.6 mm; breadth of whorl, 45.5 mm.

Parapachydiscus diabloensis Anderson n. name
(Plate 56, figures 3, 4, 4a)

Ammonites suciaensis Meek, GABB, Paleont. Calif., vol. 2, 1869, p. 133, Pl. 21, figs. 11, a, b; "near Mount Diablo". Not Meek, 1861.

The exact locality of the holotype was not given by Gabb. The holotype, No. 12111 in the type collection of the University of California, was identified by Merriam (1895) and is here illustrated. As shown in the two figures, it does not closely resemble the figure (Pl. 21) given by Gabb. It may be supposed that it was found either east or southeast of Mount Diablo, since beds that might have yielded it are exposed only in these directions. In any case, the locality of its discovery could hardly have been very near to the mountain itself. In "Round Valley," about 5 miles east of the mountain, at locality 29084 (C. A. S.), fragments of a *Parapachydiscus* sp. have been found that resemble the holotype. The holotype appears to be related to *Parapachydiscus panochensis* n. sp.

Spath (1922, p. 125) has stated that this form may belong to his genus *Canadoceras,* but the basis for this view was not given, and the figure given by Gabb is too imperfect and misleading for its proper determination. It seems preferable to regard it as belonging to *Parapachydiscus* until more definite evidence has been gathered.

Parapachydiscus ootacodensis (Stoliczka)

Ammonites ootacodensis STOLICZKA (in part), Cret. Cephal. So. India, vol. 1, 1865, p. 109, Pl. 54, figs. 3, 4, not Pl. 57), *Fide* KOSSMAT.

Pachydiscus ootacodensis KOSSMAT, Sud. Ind. Kreideform., vol. 9, 1897, p. 98, Pls. 16, 17, figs. 1a, 1b; southern India. . . . WHITEAVES, Meso. Foss., vol. 1, pt. 5, 1903, p. 340, Pl. 46, fig. 1; Hornby Island, British Columbia. . . . ANDERSON AND HANNA, Proc. Calif. Acad. Sci., 4th ser., vol. 23, 1935, p. 20, Pl. 6, figs. 1, 2: Arroyo Santa Catarina, Lower California.

This species has not yet been recorded or recognized in California or Oregon, although it has been found on the Peninsula of Lower California and on Vancouver Island; it seems probable that it will be found in California also. Collignon (1938, p. 49–51) records its occurrence in southern Madagascar, and expresses the belief that it is closely related to *P. catarinae* Anderson and Hanna, and to the similar form figured by Whiteaves, under the name *P. ootacodensis.*

The stratigraphic occurrence of these forms is perhaps about the same, although they differ much in form and ornamentation. The horizon of the species is regarded as upper Campanian as was thought by Collignon, or Maestrichtian.

Parapachydiscus abbotti Anderson n. sp.
(Plate 58, figures 1, 1a)

Shell very large, robust, involute, with a relatively small umbilicus, having sloping walls, curving roundly to meet the moderately inflated sides; sides costate, with low, rounded, rather straight ribs that radiate from umbilical border, without nodes or noticeable swellings, and appearing to cross ventral zone; section of whorls semi-elliptical, rounded on periphery, and sloping to umbilical pit. The holotype (San Diego Soc. Nat. Hist. Coll.), has the following dimensions: greater diameter, 520 mm; height of whorl, 220 mm; breadth of whorl, 205 mm. The holotype was obtained from the zone containing *Parapachydiscus catarinae* Anderson and Hanna, *P. peninsularis* Anderson and Hanna, *Baculites occidentalis* Meek, and many other species, near the mouth of Arroyo Catarina, Lower California.

The species is named in honor of Clinton G. Abbott, of San Diego, California, Director of the San Diego Society of Natural History, by whose courtesy the photographs, and the above data were obtained.

Parapachydiscus aff. P. ganesa Forbes
(Plate 71, figures 4, 4a)

Shell small, roundly inflated, section of whorl as broad as high, nearly circular; surface generally smooth, but having six short radial riblike varices on each side, disappearing upon approach to the periphery.

A single example (hypotype, C. A. S. Type Coll.) was found at locality 29121 (C. A. S.), on the south side of Ortigalita Creek, in the NE ¼, SW ¼ of sec. 28, T. 11 S., R. 10 E., M. D. B. and M., in gray pebbly shale, in the zone containing *Diplomoceras mercedense,* in the Moreno formation.

The figured example measures as follows: greater diameter, 24 mm; width of umbilicus, 6 mm; height of whorl, 12 mm; breadth of whorl, 12 mm.

This species aids in the correlation of the beds in which it was found with the Valudu-dayur group in India.

Genus **Nowakites** Spath
Genotype "**Pachydiscus**" carezi Grossouvre (1903, p. 190, Pl. 25)

Spath has proposed this name for a group of puzosid ammonite forms intermediate between *Puzosia* Bayle and certain types of *Parapachydiscus* Hyatt. According to Spath the genotype "attaches itself to such contemporaneous (Coniacian-Emscherian) forms as '*Puzosia' le marchandi* Grossouvre," and he includes as examples, *Nowakites draschei* (Red-tenbacher), *Nowakites yokoyami* (Jimbo), *Nowakites linderi* (Grossouvre), and others, and as a lateral offshoot of the stock, *Nowakites savini* (Grossouvre).

Some forms of the genus are said to resemble *Canadoceras* Spath. It seems probable that some of the California types once thought to be varieties of "*Pachydiscus*" *newberryanus* (Meek) would be better included under *Nowakites.* For the most part, they differ from the genotype of *Canadoceras,* being relatively thinner in section, having more frequent trans-verse periodic grooves, and occur at different horizons.

Nowakites klamathonis Anderson n. sp.
(Plate 35, figures 1, 1a, 1b)

This species is distinct from any hitherto recorded from the West Coast, or other Ameri-can province. Its morphological position between *Puzosia* and *Parapachydiscus* is readily seen in the figures. The mature shell is large, with a broad umbilicus and moderately inflated whorls. In its younger stages of growth the shell is *Puzosia*-like, with finer costae crossing the sides and periphery of the whorls, and it also exhibits periodic transverse grooves, as in *Puzosia.* At a diameter of about 40 mm, the costae begin to increase in thickness and to separate; at this stage the section of the whorl is elliptical, the umbilical walls are abrupt, and are surmounted by umbilical bullae on its borders. On more mature whorls each sec-ond or third rib is heavier than the others, and is accompanied by a slight transverse groove; intervening costae are smaller, and all cross the ventral zone with a slight ventral sinus; whorls crossed by about seven grooves and about 50 ribs, as estimated upon the last whorl; ribs mostly single, curving strongly forward near the periphery. This species is represented by two well-preserved fragments, each showing the same characters in form and ornamen-tation, the developmental changes toward maturity and old age. The holotype (C. A. S. Type Coll.), (Pl. 35, fig. 1) measures as follows: greater diameter, 170 mm; width of umbilicus, 61 mm; height of outer whorl, 58 mm; breadth of same, 58 mm; section of whorl nearly circular. Paratype (C. A. S. Type Coll.), (Pl. 35, figs. 1a, 1b) measures: length, 104 mm; height of whorl, 48 mm; breadth of whorl, 42 mm.

The two examples were found about 400 feet beneath the zone of *Desmophyllites siskiyou-ensis* n. sp., *Kotôceras richardsoni* n. sp., and *Prionocycloceras crenulatum* (Anderson) on the Sidney Richardson ranch, 4 miles north of Montague, Siskiyou County. Their age is Coniacian-Emscherian.

Nowakites dobbinsi Anderson n. sp.
(Plate 44, figures 2, 2a)

Shell of moderate size, discoidal, somewhat compressed, flattened on sides, costate and moderately umbilicate; umbilicus with steep walls, rounded above to slightly flattened sides; ribs low and rounded, rising on umbilical walls, or on its border in inconspicuous bullae, nearly straight, crossing the sides with a slight forward inclination, but curving more sharply forward near the ventral border; sides also crossed by about five shallow transverse grooves.

In young examples, the aspect of the shell is more rugged, resembling the young of *Nowakites rumseyensis* n. sp., although with growth the ribs become flattened and the sides more nearly smooth, and the constrictions become almost obsolete.

This species appears to fall within the group of *Nowakites savini* (Grossouvre), which occurs in beds with *Placenticeras syrtale* Morton. The holotype (C. A. S. Type Coll.) was found by H. L. Dobbins at locality 25730 (C. A. S.) on Sand Creek, Colusa County. The holotype of the species has the following dimensions: greatest diameter, 87 mm; width of umbilicus, 24 mm; breadth of whorl, 32 mm; suture line not well exposed; number of ribs to the whorl, about 48.

The precise stratigraphical position, as determined by measurements and by its faunal associates is in the lower middle part of the Coniacian. Its associated fauna includes *Eupachydiscus willgreeni, Eupachydiscus arbucklensis, Puzosia (Parapuzosia) arenaica, Inoceramus undulatoplicatus* Roemer and *Inoceramus subundatus* Meek. This horizon is about 800 feet above that with *Metaplacenticeras pacificum* (Smith), and *Lytoceras (Gaudryceras) alamedense* Smith.

Nowakites rumseyensis Anderson n. sp.
(Plate 45, figure 3)

This species is closely related to the preceding, but differs from it in its more robust form, smaller umbilicus, more elevated and sharper ribs, in its more rugged character, and also in the number of its transverse constrictions. It appears to be closely akin to *Nowakites savini* (Grossouvre). The holotype (C. A. S. Type Coll.) was found by H. L. Dobbins at locality 25730 (C. A. S.) on Sand Creek, southwest Colusa County.

The holotype and two additional specimens vary in size from 60 mm to 100 mm in diameter. The holotype has the following dimensions: greatest diameter, 75 mm; width of umbilicus, 21 mm; greatest breadth of whorl, 30 mm; height of whorl, 34 mm; number of ribs, about 44; transverse constrictions about 7 on a complete whorl. Its associated species are those of the preceding form. It occurs in beds of approximately Coniacian age.

Nowakites (?) puertoensis Anderson n. sp.
(Plate 35, figure 4)

Shell incomplete, section of the whorl higher than broad; sides moderately inflated; umbilicus moderate, with steep walls and rounded border; border surmounted by elongated nodes, from which many of the ribs arise, branching into two, or occasionally into three costal divisions; ribs about 30 in number on a single whorl, rounded, with broad interspaces, curving forward upon approach to the periphery; inner whorls not shown; on the outer whorl, containing the living chamber, are three well-developed constrictions that indicate the total number to have been about six. These features are sufficiently well preserved to indicate the characters of either *Canadoceras* Spath or *Nowakites,* more probably the latter. It seems to belong to the group of *Nowakites klamathonis* n. sp., although this cannot now be positively determined. The diameter of the outer whorl is about 140 mm; that of the umbilicus probably about 55 mm; breadth of whorl about 42 mm.

The holotype (C. A. S. Type Coll.) was associated with various other types usually found in the lower beds of the Panoche formation, including: *Baculites inornatus* Meek, *Pseudomelania* sp., *Inoceramus undulatoplicatus* Roemer, var., *Inoceramus* aff. *I. aduncus* Anderson.

By its field and stratigraphical position, as well as by its character and by its associated species, a lower Coniacian horizon is indicated. This example was found by Taff, Hanna, and Cross, at locality 28323 (C. A. S.), on the SW ¼ of sec. 35, T. 5 S., R. 6 E., M. D. B. and M., on Puerto Creek.

Genus **Canadoceras** Spath

Spath (1922) proposed this generic name for a group of pachydiscid ammonites occurring in the Upper Cretaceous of the West Coast, and in other Indo-Pacific regions, including Japan, south Patagonia, Southeast Africa and other areas. The genotype is *Ammonites newberryanus* Meek, from the lower part of the Nanaimo series, near Comox, Vancouver Island. In addition to this form Spath named a considerable number of other species, the figures and descriptions of which were found in the literature, as belonging to this group.

Some resemblances are to be seen in the outward forms of many of these, especially in their periodic constrictions and the parallel transverse ridges ("bourrelets"), in their manner of development, and perhaps in their sutures, although few of the latter are well illustrated or known. It would have been helpful if he had indicated in his account some of the more important external and internal features of the genotype, and its position in the stratigraphic series. It is regrettable also that he had no authentic example of the species selected for his genotype. Meek's holotype is in the National Museum at Washington, D. C. It is a well-preserved specimen. Examples of various types included by Spath in the genus are in the collections at the California Academy of Sciences, at the University of California, at Stanford University, and in other West Coast collections, with notes as to their locality and stratigraphical positions, associated species, and other data. These show the genus *Canadoceras* to have a very considerable stratigraphic range, for the most part within the Senonian. However, there are records of its occurrence even in the middle Turonian.

C. H. Clapp (1911–1912) divided the Nanaimo series of Vancouver and neighboring islands into eight formations, having an aggregate thickness of 6785 feet. The holotype of *Canadoceras* has been recorded wrongly or rightly from lower one-third of the series, through a stratigraphic range of 2000 feet or more, within which as many as six species of the genus seem to be recognizable.

However, it appears that Meek's holotype—*Ammonites newberryanus*—was found in the "Productive Coal Measures" that form the lower part of the Nanaimo series of Clapp, probably of Coniacian age. The holotype of *Canadoceras fraternum* (Gabb) came from strata that appear to be lower Campanian, or later.

Canadoceras newberryanum (Meek)
(Plate 42, figures 1, 1a, 1b, 2)

Ammonites Newberryanus MEEK, Tr. Albany Inst., vol. 4, 1857, p. 47. . . . U. S. Geol. and Geogr. Survey Terr. vol. 2, 1856, p. 367, Pl. 4, figs. 3, 3a, 3b; Comox, Vancouver Island; (not WHITEAVES, Meso. Foss. vol. 1, pt. 2, 1879, p. 109, Pl. 14, figs. 1, 1a; locality not definitely given).

This species was described by Meek from an immature example, 58.5 mm in diameter, but clearly indicating its characters. Some confusion has arisen, and still exists in the literature regarding this species, due in part to the not fully grown holotype, and in part to the fact that as many as four species of the genus have been collected from Vancouver and neighboring islands, that resemble it. Whiteaves' account (1879, p. 109–111; 1903, p. 348, 349) illustrates the confused state of the subject at the time, and that has since existed. Meek's figures were much reduced in size, but as here given, his holotype better illustrates the species. As stated by Whiteaves, the species grew to a larger size.

In form the holotype (U. S. Nat. Mus. Coll.) is a robust shell, having the following dimensions: greater diameter, 58.5 mm; height of whorl, 26 mm; width of umbilicus, 18 mm; breadth of whorl, 23 mm; umbilical ratio, 0.327.

Section of whorl semi-elliptical, with abrupt umbilical walls, and with sides converging toward a narrowly rounded periphery; sides crossed by six or more transverse, periodic constrictions and "bourrelets," with intervening ribs, all with a forward curvature; eight to ten ribs intervening between constrictions; shell marked by prominent umbilical tubercules on the "bourrelets" preceding the constrictions, and at other points on umbilical border; ribs arising on umbilical border, either branching from tubercules, or arising singly, all ribs curving forward and crossing periphery with a forward sinus. Suture line as shown in Meek's figure.

Stratigraphic occurrence.—Whiteaves (1879, p. 109) indicates a stratigraphic range of 2000 feet or more. But briefly, of the 21 examples of *"Ammonites newberryanus"* collected by Richardson from this region, ten were from the "Productive Coal Measures," Division A, in the lower beds of the section, and six were from Sucia Islands, from strata correlative with the "Coal Measures." Others were from higher parts of the section.

Canadoceras fraternum (Gabb)
(Plate 50, figure 1)

Ammonites fraternus GABB, Paleont. Calif., vol. 2, 1869, p. 137, Pl. 23, figs. 15, a, b; near Benicia, Solano County. . . . STANTON, U. S. Geol. Survey, 17th Ann. Rept., 1896, p. 1029; . . . (?) SPATH, Royal Soc. So. Africa, Tr., vol. 10, 1922, p. 125, Pl. 7, fig. 5; Pl. 8, fig. 4. Locality not definitely stated.

Gabb's description of this species, based upon an immature, fragmentary example, leaves much to be desired. His description, in part, follows:

"Shell small, whorls rounded, deeply enveloping; sides rounded and converging toward the dorsum (venter), which is regularly convex; umbilicus deep, moderate in size; umbilical margin rounded. Surface marked by slightly sinuous ribs, nearly straight, arising on the umbilical margin, and continuing over the dorsum (venter); every fourth or fifth of these ribs is a little larger than the others, and bears a prominent flattened tubercule on the border of the umbilicus. An occasional constriction exists between the ribs. . . . "

In the light of Gabb's figures and description of related species and of the associates of his holotype (1864, p. 220–236), it seems evident that his species is correctly assigned to *Canadoceras* Spath, although it represents a type distinct from *C. newberryanum* (Meek). Well-preserved examples of both types are in the collections of the California Academy of Sciences, and in other available collections. Three fairly good examples in the Academy are from Chico Creek, and a fourth, larger specimen found at the same place by C. K. Studley is at the University of California.

Others have been found by the writer, and by earlier collectors at Pentz. All of these are from strata of upper Senonian age, and apparently from beds that on the basis of the associated fauna may be correlated with those containing the holotype of *Canadoceras fraternum* (Gabb). In brief, all of them represent the type of Gabb's species, rather than *Canadoceras newberryanum* (Meek). To the group of *C. fraternum* (Gabb) probably belongs the example figured by Spath (1922, Pls. 7 and 8), and thought by him to be *Canadoceras newberryanum* (Meek).

In all examples of *C. fraternum* (Gabb) examined by the writer, the whorl section in younger stages of growth is nearly circular, up to a diameter of 25 mm, and in these stages only, the shell resembles that of *C. newberryanum* (Meek). In later stages, the ratio of height to breadth of whorl increases more rapidly than in other types, the shell loses much of its rugged aspect, and the strongly developed constrictions, of youthful stages, as seen in the figured example, are lost.

A similar example of Gabb's species examined by the writer is in a private collection in Oroville, Butte County. The exact stratigraphic range of this species is not yet known.

A specimen in the collections of the University of California, found on Chico Creek, Butte County, California, is shown on Plate 50, figure 1.

Canadoceras whiteavesi Anderson, n. name

Ammonites Newberryanus, WHITEAVES (not Meek), Meso. Foss. vol. 1, pt. 2, 1879, p. 109–111 (in part), Pl. 14, figs. 1, 1a; Vancouver Island, or vicinity.

A comparison of the figures given by Whiteaves with those of Meek, or better, with the type of *Canadoceras newberryanum* (Meek) shows some striking differences. In

Meek's holotype, here figured (Plate 42, figures 1, 1a, 1b, 2), the ribs arise in part in umbilical bullae, from which they divide into three or more diverging branches, instead of singly from the umbilical wall near the whorl suture, as do the ribs of the species figured by Whiteaves (Pl. 14). The umbilical ratio as determined from this figure is 0.277, instead of 0.327, as obtained from Meek's holotype.

In the collections of the University of California there is a *Canadoceras* from Nanaimo that conforms in great measure to Whiteaves' figure 1, Pl. 14, indicating that this figure is a correct representation of a type distinct from *C. newberryanum* (Meek), although probably belonging to its group. The examples mentioned by Whiteaves (p. 110, lines 21–26) may well refer to mature examples of *C. newberryanum* (Meek).

Whiteaves gives no definite locality or stratigraphic position for the form that he figured, but it probably came from the "Productive Coal Measures" or from the Sucia Islands, and in either case its stratigraphic position would have been that of the coal measures.

Canadoceras georgianum Anderson, n. sp.
(Plate 32, figures 3, 3a)

The holotype is in the collections of Stanford University. It is well-preserved, slightly distorted by rock pressure, but none the less showing clearly its characteristic features and its relationship to the sub-group of *Canadoceras newberryanum* (Meek). It has the following dimensions: greatest diameter, 135 mm; width of umbilicus, 41 mm; height of whorl, 58 mm; breadth of whorl, 44 mm. The relatively thin form, its smaller number of ribs, and its larger umbilical ratio distinguish it from other types of the genus. The sides of the whorl are flattened, section of whorl subquadrate, higher than broad, the ribs broader than in *C. newberryanum* (Meek), and fewer in number to the whorl. The umbilical walls are rounded or sloping, rather than abrupt, the ribs arise low on the umbilical slope, and only occasionally spring from umbilical tubercules, of which there are few; sides crossed by about seven periodic transverse constrictions to the whorl, each preceded by a rounded and slightly thickened rib ("bourrelet"), between the pairs of which are five to eight rounded ribs all of which cross the ventral zone with a slight forward curve.

The holotype is said to have been found on the Sucia Islands, where it was associated with *Placenticeras vancouverense* Whiteaves, *"Desmoceras" selwynianum* Whiteaves, and *Inoceramus digitatus* (Sowerby) (? = *Inoceramus undulatoplicatus* Roemer).

All these species appear to represent a lower Senonian (Coniacian) horizon showing the strata to be correlative with beds containing a similar fauna in the Great Valley of California, as in the Rumsey Hills, Yolo County.

Canadoceras celeste Anderson n. sp.
(Plate 42, figures 3, 3a)

The holotype of this species belongs to the subgroup of *Canadoceras* represented by the genotype, *C. newberryanum* (Meek), but it differs from this species in some notable characters. It is more robust and rugged, with fewer and thicker ribs and a greater umbilical ratio. The sides are crossed by about six periodic transverse constrictions and "bourrelets" per whorl; the number of ribs between the successive constrictions, about four or five; ribs branching from bullae on the umbilical border, or in part arising singly on the umbilical wall near the whorl suture. The holotype (C. A. S. Type Coll.) has the following dimensions: greatest diameter, 108 mm; width of umbilicus, 31 mm; greatest breadth of whorl, 28 mm; umbilical ratio, 0.375. This example was found at locality 31208 (C. A. S.), in the brown shales on the east border of the "Nigger Heaven" basin in the Rumsey Hills, Yolo County, on the west half of sec. 23, T. 12 N., R. 3 W., M. D. M. It was found associated with *Inoceramus vancouverensis* Shumard, *Puzosia* (*Parapuzosia*) sp., and *Eupachydiscus* sp. Fragmentary examples of *Canadoceras* of another type were found at the same stratigraphic level on Petroleum Creek, on the east flank of the Rumsey Hills.

The stratigraphic level of these species is a few hundred feet above that of locality 25730 (C. A. S.) on Sand Creek, Colusa County, containing *Nowakites dobbinsi* n. sp., *Eupachy-*

discus arbucklensis n. sp., and *Inoceramus undulatoplicatus* Roemer var., here regarded as representing a lower Senonian (Coniacian) stage.

Family PUZOSIDAE Spath

Genus **Puzosia** Bayle

Subgenus *Parapuzosia* Nowak

Nowak (1913) sought to differentiate from the Albian types of *Puzosia* Bayle, a generic group of puzosids of post-Albian age, for which he proposed the name *Parapuzosia,* giving as the genotype *Ammonites denisonianus* Stoliczka, from the Ootatoor group of India, mentioning other species as examples, and in addition figuring *"Parapuzosia" daubreei* (Grossouvre) as an illustration of the genus.

Spath (1922) regarded Nowak's group as a subgenus, proposing *"Parapuzosia" daubreei* (Grossouvre) as its type, and selecting *Ammonites denisonianus* Stoliczka as the genotype of his proposed new genus, *"Pachydesmoceras,"* which would thus be synonomous with *Parapuzosia* Nowak.

M. Collignon (1932) has challenged with much justice the procedure of Spath, as being arbitrary, and his generic groups (p. 126–128) as being insufficiently defined, and, in brief, does not recognize all his groups as having generic validity. It appears to be better to adopt the term proposed by Nowak. In Collington's view the genus *Puzosia* Bayle maintains an exceptional longevity, without important modifications. This view may well be adopted, but with the recognition of subgeneric groups within it.

Spath has proposed (1922, p. 124) for a group of ammonites stemming from *Puzosia,* and contemporary in part with *Parapuzosia* Nowak, the genus *Holcidiscoides.* He named as the genotype, *Ammonites cliveanus* Stoliczka. The genus was not clearly defined, although it is well illustrated by the genotype and the forms referred to it. However, it would be convenient to include the group here as a subgenus, since it may embrace a few related types whose forms and positions approach those of the proposed genotype, differing from it chiefly in size or horizon.

In the sense of Nowak, *Parapuzosia* appears suddenly in the Upper Cretaceous succession, following the wide-spread late Albian-Cenomanian transgressive overlap in the Great Valley, the Coast Ranges, and Oregon. Among its earliest species is *Parapuzosia colusaensis* (Anderson), first described (1902) as *Desmoceras.* Its relationship to *Puzosia dilleri* (Anderson), as well as its departure from it, in size, form, and sutural details, may be seen in the original illustrations (1902).

The Puzosinae of the California Upper Cretaceous and their stratigraphic succession are summarized in the following table.

TABLE 8.—*Puzosinae of the California Upper Cretaceous*

UPPER ALBIAN (SHASTA SERIES)

Puzosia hoffmannii (Gabb)	*Puzosia dilleri* Anderson
Puzosia subquadrata Anderson	*Puzosia buenaventura* Anderson
Puzosia (Parapuzosia) onona (Anderson)	

LOWER CENOMANIAN

Puzosia (Parapuzosia) colusaensis (Anderson)
Puzosia (Parapuzosia) waringi n. name

UPPER CENOMANIAN

Puzosia (Parapuzosia) hindsi n. sp.	*Puzosia (Parapuzosia)* aff. *P. planulata* (Sowerby)

LOWER, OR MIDDLE TURONIAN

Puzosia (Parapuzosia) klamathonae n. sp.	*P. (Holcodiscoides) weaveri* (Anderson)
P. (Austiniceras) giganteum n. sp.	*P. (Eocanadoceras) hannai* n. sp.

UPPER TURONIAN

Puzosia (Parapuzosia) hearni n. sp.

LOWER SENONIAN

Puzosia (Holcodiscoides) gorrilli n. sp.	*P. (Parapuzosia) arenaica* n. sp.

Puzosia (Parapuzosia) colusaënsis (Anderson)
(Plate 10, figure 1)

Desmoceras colusaënse ANDERSON, Proc. Calif. Acad. Sci., 3d ser., vol. 2, 1902, p. 96, Pl. 5, figs. 128, 129; Pl. 10, fig. 200; near Sites, Colusa County.

This species appears to belong to the group represented by *Ammonites denisonianus* Stoliczka. A brief emended description of the species follows.

Shell large, discoidal, somewhat compressed in younger stages, increasing rapidly in thickness with the growth of the same; section of older whorls ovate, higher than broad; sides crossed by 10 or more transverse periodic grooves, between which are numerous rounded, somewhat flexuous costae, more strongly inclined forward in the ventral zone; involution covering more than one-half the preceding whorl; suture line imperfectly shown in the drawing; sides sloping toward the relatively narrow periphery.

The puzosid character of the suture line as seen in the holotype differs somewhat from the figure, the summits of the saddles descending in a curved line more steeply than shown, the species occupies a stratigraphic position in the Cenomanian intermediate between the Albian puzosids (*P. hoffmanni* (Gabb), *P. subquadrata* Anderson) and the Turonian *Puzosia (Parapuzosia) hearni* n. sp.

The holotype No. 4283 (C. A. S. Type Coll.) has the following dimensions: greatest diameter, 239 mm; width of umbilicus, 76 mm; height of whorl, 106.5 mm; maximum breadth of body whorl, 83.3 mm. This specimen was found on the Petersen ranch, 4 miles north of Sites, Colusa County, in a stratigraphic position a little below the base of the Venado formation. The example here figured, hypotype (C. A. S. Type Coll.), has the following dimensions: maximum diameter, 176 mm; width of umbilicus, 46 mm; breadth of whorl, 68 mm. Found on the North fork of Cottonwood Creek, immediately beneath the second conglomerate bed, half a mile west of the mouth of Hulen Creek. Its age is probably late Albian or early Cenomanian.

Puzosia (Parapuzosia) waringi Anderson n. name
(Plate 12, figures 3, 3a, 4)

Desmoceras hoffmanni Gabb, ANDERSON, (in part), Proc. Calif. Acad. Sci., 3d ser., vol. 2, 1902, p. 27 only; "Forty-nine" mine, southern Oregon.
Desmoceras ishikawai, SMITH (not Jimbo), Calif. State Min. Bur., Folio accompanying Bull. 69, 1914, P. 1, fig. 6; near Horsetown, Shasta County (= *Puzosia Jimboi*, Anderson (name preoccupied), Geol. Soc. Am., Special Paper. No. 16, 1938, p. 188, Pl. 42).

The shell of this species is small, no example exceeding a diameter of 40 mm. It belongs to the group of *Parapuzosia bhavani* (Stoliczka), which Kilian and Reboul (1909, p. 25, etc.) place incorrectly in *Kossmaticeras*. The example figured by Waring came from the same locality and zone as that here figured, namely, from Jackass Flat, between old Horsetown and Texas Springs, Shasta County.

A large number of well-preserved specimens were obtained here by the writer prior to 1902, and some of these are now in the collections of the California Academy of Sciences. The holotype, No. 8819 (C. A. S. Type Coll.), has the following dimensions: greatest diameter, 23 mm; width of umbilicus, 7 mm; height of whorl, 10 mm; breadth of whorl, 9 mm.* The umbilical ratio of the Japanese form is much greater, being 0.368: 1, and other features show similar differences.

In the holotype the last whorl is crossed by about eight flexuous, forward curving grooves, between which are six to nine evenly spaced costae, all of which cross the ventral zone. The zone of this species was first thought to be in the upper part of the Shasta series, but later investigation has shown that its true position is at the base of the overlap preceding the widespread transgression of the Turonian. The species has been found at the "Forty-nine" mine, near the old Pioneer road, southern Oregon, and in the basal part of the Turonian at the head of Garzas Creek, Stanislaus County, California.

* Dimensions of Paratype 8820 (C. A. S. Type Coll.) are as follows: greatest diameter, 19 mm; breadth of whorl, 7 mm.

Puzosia (Parapuzosia) onona Anderson
(Plate 13, figure 4)

Puzosia onona ANDERSON, Geol. Soc. Am., Special Paper, No. 16, 1938, p. 188, Pl. 42, fig. 8; Jackass Flat, Shasta County.

This species occurs with the preceding at its type locality, with others of the genus not described here. The shell is small, discoidal, compressed, flattened on the sides, numerously costate; umbilicus small, walls abrupt, rounded on the borders; surface marked by five or more faint sinuous grooves that cross the ventral zone with a distinct forward sinus; interspaces occupied by eight or more fairly well marked, rounded costae; suture lines not exposed. The holotype No. 8821 (C. A. S. Type Coll.), almost wholly septate, has the following dimensions: greater diameter, 30 mm; width of umbilicus, 8 mm; height of whorl, 12 mm; breadth of whorl, 10 mm.

As in the preceding, this species was first thought to occur in the upper beds of the Shasta series, but later investigation has shown that its zone should be assigned to the lower part of the Turonian, since it is found only in its wide overlap, resting upon the Shasta series.

Puzosia (Parapuzosia) hindsi Anderson n. sp.
(Plate 8, figure 2)

Shell of moderate size, moderately compressed, discoidal; involution moderate; transverse section elliptical, narrowing toward periphery; umbilicus moderately wide, with abrupt walls, rounded above to flattened sides; sides crossed by flexuous periodic grooves and inconspicuous costal lines that bend sharply forward near the ventral border; ventral zone narrow, but rounded; surface of shell almost smooth, or showing only costal lines between periodic grooves; suture lines puzosid but not wholly exposed.

This shell bears some resemblance to *"Ammonites" bhima* Stoliczka, although it is probably distinct. The holotype (C. A. S. Type Coll.) has the following dimensions: greatest diameter, 50 mm; width of umbilicus, 13 mm; height of whorl, 23 mm; breadth of whorl, 13 mm. This example was found at locality 2233 (C. A. S.), about half a mile southeast of the mouth of Hulen Creek, where it was associated with *Phylloceras velledae* var., *Puzosia* aff. *P. planulata* (Sowerby), and (?) *Forbesiceras* sp. This locality is about 300 feet above that of *Calycoceras newboldi* (Kossmat), near the central part of the Upper Cenomanian in the Cottonwood district.

The species is named in honor of the discoverer, N. E. A. Hinds, University of California.

Puzosia (Parapuzosia) aff. P. planulata (Sowerby)

Ammonites planulatus SOWERBY, Min. Conch., vol. 6, 1829, p. 136, Pl. 570, fig. 5; Mantell Collection, England. . . . SHARPE, Tr. Paleont. Soc. Lond., vol. 4, 1854, p. 29, Pl. 12, fig. 3; Gray Chalk, near Lewes, England. . . . STOLICZKA, Cret. Cephal. So. India, vol. 1, 1865, p. 134, Pls. 67, 68.

Desmoceras planulatum (Sowerby) ANDERSON, Proc. Calif. Acad. Sci., 3d ser., vol. 2, 1902, p. 63, etc., middle Cretaceous of California. According to Kossmat (1898, p. 112, 177) the species occurs in the Ootatoor group in southern India.

Species belonging to the group of *Puzosia planulata* (Sowerby) are not unknown in the middle Cretaceous of California and Oregon, and in other parts of the West Coast, as has been noted by other writers. The forms most nearly related to *Puzosia planulata* (Sowerby) are found in the upper part of the Shasta series as already noted by the writer (1938, p. 69), and others are found in the upper part of the lower Upper Cretaceous. The form most nearly related to the Indian type has been found at locality 2233 (C. A. S.), half a mile east of the mouth of Hulen Creek, where it is associated with *Phylloceras velledae*, *Puzosia (Parapuzosia) hindsi*, and *Forbesiceras* (?) sp.

Puzosia (Parapuzosia) klamathonae Anderson n. sp.
(Plate 5, figures 1, 1a)

This species appears to belong to the group of *Puzosia crebrisulcata* Kossmat (1898, p. 116, Pl. 17) of southern India. Shell of medium size, discoidal, a little compressed, involution moderate, section of whorl subelliptical, sides sloping to a narrow periphery; umbilicus moderate, with abrupt walls; sides costate, with numerous rounded ribs, and characterized by six transverse periodic constrictions; suture distinguished by elongated trifid lobes, broad saddles and subdivisions; siphonal saddle broad and deeply cleft at the summit.

In form and ornamentation, the shell resembles some forms included by Spath in his proposed genus, *Holcodiscoides,* but in sutural features it differs notably, in its more elongated lobes and smaller elements, and in its broader saddles. The holotype (C. A. S. Type Coll.) has the following dimensions: greatest diameter, 92 mm; width of umbilicus, 28 mm; height of whorl, 32 mm; breadth of whorl, 25 mm; shell wholly septate.

The holotype was found on Roaring River, Shasta County, in the Cottonwood district, not far above the Thompson ranch house, and 1.5 miles east of the basal conglomerate of the Upper Cretaceous, within the Turonian. The species was found also in this horizon one mile north of Frazier Corners, 10 miles east of Redding, in beds regarded as middle Turonian, and also in beds of correlative age near the "Forty-nine" Mine, south of Phoenix, Oregon.

Puzosia (Parapuzosia) hearni Anderson n. sp.
(Plate 38, figures 1, 1a, 1b)

This species appears to be related to *"Puzosia" planulata* (Sowerby) as figured by Stoliczka (1868, Pl. 47), from the Trichinopoly group of Anapauda, southern India. According to Stoliczka the species has a considerable stratigraphic range, beginning in the Ootatoor group (Cenomanian) and extending into the Turonian.

The form here figured is of moderate size, discoidal, compressed, costate, with moderate involution; sides sloping from near their middle to a narrowly rounded periphery, crossed by about five rounded ridges ("bourrelets") and shallow grooves, between which are numerous costae, all curving more sharply forward near the periphery; walls of umbilicus abrupt, rounded above, sides flattened; section of whorl semielliptical, broadest a little below the middle of the side.

The holotype (C. A. S. Type Coll.) has the following dimensions: greatest diameter, 90 mm; width of umbilicus, 27 mm; height of whorl, 36 mm; breadth of whorl, 27 mm. This specimen was found by F. G. Hearn, early pioneer of Yreka, Siskiyou County, and was donated to the Academy of Sciences by his daughter, Miss Minnie Hearn. The specimen was found on the old Hagerdorn ranch, 8 miles northeast of Yreka, Siskiyou County, about 400 feet beneath the horizon of *Nowakites klamathonis* n. sp., in the upper part of the Turonian, in soft gray sandstone.

The species is related to *"Puzosia" gaudama* (Forbes), as figured by Kossmat (1895, Pl. 16, figs. 2a, 2b, 3; Pl. 17, figs. 3a, 3b, 3c), from the Trichinopoly group of southern India. In the present species the costae arise within the umbilical border, whereas in the figure of the Indian form they arise above it, and the constrictions and intervening costae are not so regularly curved.

Puzosia (Parapuzosia) arenaica Anderson n. sp.
(Plate 46, figures 4, 4a)

Shell resembles figures of *Puzosia gaudama* (Forbes) in its outward form, its reduced ornamentation and section, although the chronological occurrence of the two can hardly be the same. Shell small, discoidal, compressed, and with a moderately broad umbilicus and a narrowly lenticular section; the surface of the whorl is crossed by five or six transverse periodic grooves that curve gently forward, between which are finer costal lines not readily counted; shell soon loses its early ornamentation, and becomes nearly smooth. The holotype (C. A. S. Type Coll.) has the following dimensions: greatest diameter, 65 mm; width of umbilicus, 22 mm; greatest thickness of whorl, 15 mm; sides sloping to a narrowly rounded periphery. The holotype was found at locality 25730 (C. A. S.) on Sand Creek, southwestern Colusa County, associated with *Nowakites dobbinsi, Eupachydiscus arbucklensis,* and *Eupachydiscus willgreeni,* in the zone of *Inoceramus* aff. *I. undulatoplicatus.* Its stratigraphic level is near the middle of the Coniacian.

Subgenus **Eocanadoceras** n. subg.

Adults generally similar to adults of *Canadoceras* Spath, but with more numerous ribs and lacking umbilical nodes. In young below a diameter of 25 mm with five costae and periodic grooves similar to *Puzosia*. Slightly larger juveniles very similar to *Canadoceros* but losing this character in adults. Type *Puzosia (Eocanadoceras) hannai* n. sp.

Puzosia (Eocanadoceras) hannai n. sp.
(Plate 30, figures 6, 6a, 6b, 6c)

This species was undoubtedly large when fully grown, robustly discoidal, section of whorl ovate, sides convex, sloping toward periphery; umbilicus relatively broad, with nearly vertical walls, meeting the sides at nearly right angles, a little rounded on shoulder; shell costate, with about 90 or more rounded ribs of two ranks, major and minor; major ribs arising in slight bullae, or swellings on the umbilical border, from which they sometimes divide into two or three branches, curving roundly forward, notably upon approach to ventral border; minor ribs arising at or a little above middle of side, curving forward concentrically with others, and all crossing ventral zone with a slight forward sinus; sides crossed also by about six broad and deep periodic constrictions, nearly concentric with ribs, also crossing ventral zone in the manner of the ribs.

In young whorls below a diameter of 25 mm, the coils and their ornamentation are *Puzosia*-like, with fine costae and a few periodic grooves, but later they soon become *Canadoceras*-like, with inflated form and tuberculate ornamentation, resembling the young of *Ammonites newberryanus* Meek, the section being as broad as high, but later differing from this type in section of whorl, and in retaining a greater number of ribs, and in the loss of umbilical nodes. In general aspect the shell is *Canadoceras*-like, resembling that of *Canadoceras multicostatum* (Whiteaves), but it is less robust and is characterized by about twice the number of ribs.

The holotype (C. A. S. Type Coll.) consists of a large fragment containing a complete inner whorl, and about two-fifths of two outer whorls, the larger being wholly septate, with *Canadoceras*-like sutures, having the following whorl dimensions: peripheral length, 160 mm; greater height of whorl, 50 mm; width of umbilicus, 48 mm; greater breadth of whorl, 40 mm; general form, quasi-lenticular.

The holotype was found associated with *Puzosia (Austiniceras) giganteum* n. sp., *Coelopoceras hyatti* n. sp., and *Acanthoceras* sp., in the middle or lower part of the Turonian. Its occurrence at this horizon may be taken as an explanation of the record by Stanton (1894, p. 439), of *Ammonites (Pachydiscus) newberryanus* Meek, in beds of Turonian age in the Elder Creek section. The horizon of the genotype of *Canadoceras* Spath, and of other West Coast species of the genus, is lower Senonian, and no strata of this age are exposed in the Elder Creek section. Found at locality 2245 (C. A. S.), 15.1 miles southeast of Beegum, Tehama County, on road to Rosewood, across Dry Creek from Ranch House.

Subgenus *Austiniceras* Spath
Puzosia (Austiniceras) giganteum Anderson n. sp.
(Plate 16, figures 1, 1a, 2)

Holotype very large, somewhat inflated, rounded on the periphery, and having a rather broad umbilicus; sides and ventral surface costate, with numerous rounded ribs, some of which on older whorls divide into two or more branches, all crossing the periphery with a forward curve; surface of sides smooth on older whorls, and crossed by six or more shallow periodic constrictions curving forward, concentric to the ribs; sides sloping toward the periphery. In young stages of growth, below a diameter of 136 mm, the ribs, 56 in number, are rather prominent, and not often divided, but with growth division occurs more frequently. The holotype (C. A. S. Type Coll.) (Pl. 13, figs. 1, 1a) was found by Hanna, Taff, and Cross at locality 2245 = 28179 (C. A. S.), about 15.1 miles southeast of Beegum, near the Rosewood road, across Dry Creek from Ranch House, Tehama County. It has the following dimensions: greater diameter, 17.5 inches (446 mm), almost wholly septate; width of umbilicus, 146 mm; height of whorl, 184 mm; breadth of whorl, 132 mm. The holotype was associated with *Puzosia (Eocanadoceras) hannai* n. sp., and *Coelopoceras hyatti* n. sp., about 2800 feet beneath the zone of *Prionotropis bakeri* and *Oregoniceras* sp., on Dry Creek, and a paratype, (C. A. S. Type Coll.) (Pl. 13, fig. 2) was collected at nearly the same stratigraphic level on the Middle fork of Cotton wood Creek, Shasta County, in both places in the lower part of the Turonian.

Subgenus **Holcodiscoides** Spath

Puzosia (Holcodiscoides) gorrilli Anderson n. sp.

(Plate 46, figure 3)

Shell large, when fully grown, discoidal, compressed, with relatively broad umbilicus; section narrowly ovate, numerously costate, with low, rounded ribs that curve forward at a progressive angle on nearing ventral border; sides crossed five or six shallow transverse, periodic constrictions; some of the ribs are tuberculate on the umbilical border.

The holotype (C. A. S. Type Coll.) appears to belong in the group of *Puzosia (Holcodiscoides) moraviatoorensis* (Stoliczka) from the Trichinopoly group of southern India. It has the following dimensions: inner whorl: greater diameter, 102 mm; width of umbilicus, 38 mm; breadth of whorl, 24 mm; outer whorl (incomplete): greater diameter, 204 mm; width of umbilicus, 70 mm; height of whorl, 76 mm; breadth of whorl, 62 mm.

Costae on the inner coil, 54 to the whorl, narrow but rounded, and are separated by interspaces of nearly the same width; on the outer whorl the ribs are broader, flattened, and smooth, with shallow interspaces, and are 48 in number, and of unequal strength. The suture line consists of one strong median lobe, and two smaller inner lobes nearer the umbilicus; in general features the suture line is not unlike that of *Kossmaticeras voyanum* n. sp., although larger, with narrow and finely dissected saddles.

The holotype was found at locality 25730 (C. A. S.), on Sand Creek, southwestern Colusa County, near the old Gorrill well, sec. 7, T. 13 N., R. 3 W., M. D. M., where it was associated with *Nowakites dobbinsi* n. sp., *Inoceramus* aff. *I. undulatoplicatus* Roemer, and other species that characterize the "Forbes shale," as found in the Rumsey Hills district. Coniacian.

Puzosia (Holcodiscoides) weaveri Anderson

(Plate 13, figure 3)

Puzosia weaveri ANDERSON, Geol. Soc. Am., Special Paper No. 16, 1938, p. 189, Pl. 42, fig. 4; horizon not definitely known.

Shell relatively small, discoidal, compressed, and numerously costate; umbilicus relatively broad, walls not abrupt, but rounded on border, curving to slightly convex sides; sides crossed by about five transverse, shallow periodic constrictions, inclining forward and crossing ventral area with a forward sinus; interspaces between grooves occupied by 8 to 10 rounded costae, separated by equally broad, rounded hollows; section of whorl narrowly elliptical; suture line desmoceratid, although not completely exposed.

The holotype, No. 14930, of the species is in the Museum of Paleontology, University of California. It is in part well preserved, and has the following dimensions: greater diameter, 55 mm; width of umbilicus, 19 mm; breadth of whorl, 20 mm. The holotype was found at the Fernandez tunnel on the Sante Fe Railroad, about 3 miles east of Rodeo, Contra Costa County. The beds here appear to be nearly on the zone of those southeast of Crockett, from which the large fragment of *Acanthoceras lecontei* was obtained, formerly referred to as "*Acanthoplites.*" Further study of the holotype, and a comparison with other types now in the California Academy of Sciences shows it to be related to *Puzosia (Holcodiscoides)* sp., recently obtained from the Turonian of western Tehama County, and to *Puzosia (Holcodiscoides) gorrilli.*

Family KOSSMATICERATIDAE Spath

Few representatives of this family are now known in California or Oregon, or on the West Coast. In the restricted sense employed by Spath and by other contemporary writers, only a few species belonging to the group of *Kossmaticeras* (*Madrasites*) *bhavani* Stoliczka have been recognized on the West Coast, all of which occur in upper Albian or lower Cenomian strata.

Genus Kossmaticeras Grossouvre
Subgenus *Madrasites* Kilian and Reboul
Kossmaticeras (Madrasites) cumshewaense (Whiteaves)

Haploceras cumshewaense WHITEAVES, Meso. Foss., vol. 1, pt. 3, 1884, p. 208, Pl. 24, fig. 1: north shore of Cumshewa Inlet, Queen Charlotte Islands, British Columbia.

Holcodiscus cumshewaensis WHITEAVES, Meso. Foss., vol 1, pt. 4, 1900, p. 278; locality as above.

From Whiteaves' accounts at least six specimens of this species had been found, of which the largest was 4.5 inches in diameter.

This species was regarded by the writer (1902) as a close ally of *Holcodiscus theobaldianus* Stoliczka with which was compared *Holcodiscus* cf. *H. theobaldianus* (= *K.* (*Madrasites*) *voyanum* Anderson n. name) from the Cottonwood district in Shasta County, California.

Kilian and Reboul (1909, p. 29) stated that both these forms belong to the group of *Kossmaticeras* (*Madrasites*) *bhavani* Stoliczka, from the Senonian of southern India.

This assignment was based primarily upon morphological considerations, rather than upon the stratigraphical occurrence of the two forms. However, the chronological position of the present species may be recognized as established, not only from its stratigraphical occurrence, but from its associated species as given by Whiteaves (1884, p. 254).

There can be no doubt that the species are not younger than early Cenomian, and in part they are probably of late Albian age, and are correlative with a similar fauna in the Cottonwood district on the west border of the Sacremento Valley, at the base of the Upper Cretaceous series.

Kossmaticeras (Madrasites) voyanum Anderson n. name
(Plate 37, figures 5, 5a, 5b)

Holcodiscus cf. *H. theobaldianus* Stoliczka ANDERSON, Proc. Calif. Acad. Sci., 3d ser., vol. 2, 1902, p. 101, Pl. 5, figs. 126, 127; Pl. 10, fig. 197; locality not definitely known.

In the collections of the University of California there is a small, well-preserved specimen of an ammonite that was figured by the writer (1902, Pl. 5, figs. 126, 127; Pl. 10, fig. 197; locality not definitely known). This specimen was compared by the writer (1902, p. 101) to *Holcodiscus theobaldianus* Stoliczka (1865, Pl. 78, fig. 1), and also with *Holcodiscus cumshewaensis* Whiteaves (1900, p. 278, Pl. 24, fig. 1), from Cumshewa Inlet, Queen Charlotte Islands. Kilian and Reboul (1907, p. 29) have referred both these forms to the group of *Kossmaticeras* (*Madrasites*) *bhavani* Stoliczka, from the Arrialoor group (Senonian) of southern India.

The holotype of this species, No. 12115 (Univ. Calif. Coll. Invert. Paleont.) is small, discoidal, a little inflated, finely costate, having the following dimensions: greater diameter, 60 mm; width of umbilicus, 18 mm; height of whorl, 25 mm; breadth of whorl, 22 mm. The precise locality of discovery of this species is not known, although it is certain that no strata later than Turonian outcrop in the Cottonwood district. Evidently suggestions of its Senonian age by Kilian and Reboul (1909) must be regarded as misleading. The Indian allies of the California and Queen Charlotte Island species are to be found in the lower part of the Ootatoor group, not in Senonian strata.

Family ACANTHOCERATIDAE Douvillé
Genus **Acanthoceras** Neumayr
Acanthoceras shastense Reagan
(Plate 20, figures 1, 2; Plate 60, figure 5)

Acanthoceras shastense REAGAN, Pan-Am. Geol., vol. 41, 1924, p. 179, Pl. 18, fig. 1; Shasta County, California.

Little information concerning the stratigraphic position of this species was given by its author. The holotype is in the collections of Stanford University. The following notes and measurements are added:

Shell of medium size, moderately inflated, sides convex, strongly costate; ribs rectiradiate, are in two ranks, major and minor, crossing ventral zone, and on periphery bearing three rows of small tubercules; one on median plane and one on either side of it, and others on ventrolateral angle, slightly elongated parallel to ventral border; ribs about 10 in number, narrow and ridgelike, separated by broad, concave interspaces; younger whorls bearing faint nodes near umbilical border; section of whorls subelliptical, higher than broad; umbilicus moderately broad, walls abrupt; ventral zone slightly arched or rounded; suture line of normal form for the genus *Acanthoceras*. This species was said to be closely related to *Acanthoceras rhotomagense,* var. *compressum,* but a comparison of the holotype with Stoliczka's figure can hardly support this view. The California form has a considerably greater umbilical ratio, and the periphery is more strongly arched, rather than flattened, as in *Acanthoceras rhotomagense* var. *compressum* Stoliczka. The holotype (L.S.J.U. Type Coll.) has the following dimensions: greater diameter, 120 mm; width of umbilicus, 43 mm; height of whorl, 45 mm; breadth of whorl, 41 mm. Reportedly the holotype was found in "Horsetown beds" in the Cottonwood district, but this may be corrected to read, in the lower beds of the Upper Cretaceous series, where it was found by J. A. Taff. An imperfect example was found by the writer on an upper branch of Willow Creek, Glenn County, in the middle, or possibly in the lower part of the Cenomanian, rather than in the Shasta series; the Willow Creek example was found below the zone of *Inoceramus glennensis* n. sp., believed to be lower Turonian, from stratigraphic evidence.

Acanthoceras lecontei Anderson n. sp.
(Plate 13, figures 1, 1a)

Shell large, discoidal, flattened on sides, with broad umbilicus, involution little more than a fifth; costate, with about 50 ribs to a complete whorl, as indicated on the fragmentary holotype; ribs of two ranks, alternating; primary ribs extending from umbilical border to perimeter, intermediary ribs arising near middle of side, and all crossing ventral zone as short, stout ridges; ribs tuberculate, major ribs with two median and two terminal rows of tubercules; shorter ribs with only two, lower belonging to outer lateral row; all tubercules rather prominent, and elongated in direction of ribs themselves.

The holotype No. 32858 (Univ. Calif. Mus. Paleont.) is a large fragment, consisting of a 50-degree segment of a body chamber, without septa; section of whorl flatly elliptical, when drawn in the inter-costal spaces, but subquadrate when drawn upon the ribs. The holotype (fragment) has the following dimensions: peripheral length, 73 mm; maximum height of whorl, 62 mm; breadth of whorl (rib section), 37 mm; maximum space between ribs, 15 mm; maximum diameter of complete whorl (est.), 155 mm.

The holotype was found 1 mile southeast of the town of Crockett, Contra Costa County. Its horizon is nearly that of *Puzosia weaveri* Anderson (1938 p. 189, Pl. 42) from a point 3 miles east of Rodeo, probably early Cenomanian.

Genus **Calycoceras** Hyatt
Subgenus **Eucalycoceras** Spath
Calycoceras (Eucalycoceras) newboldi (Kossmat)
(Plate 7, figures 1, 1a)

Acanthoceras newboldi KOSSMAT, Sudind. Kreideform. 1898, p. 5 (112), Pl. 1 (12), figs. 2, a, b; 3, a, b, c; Pl. 3 (14), fig. 2; Ootatoor group, south India. . . . PERVINQUIERE,

Etude Paleont. Tunis, Paris, 1907, p. 264, Pl. 13, figs. 1, a, b; 2, a, b; Cenomanian, Tunis, Madagascar.

This widely distributed species is represented in California only by fragmentary specimens. One was found in the upper part of the Cenomanian, half a mile southeast of the mouth of Hulen Creek, Cottonwood district, and another in the same zone on the Middle fork of Cottonwood Creek, a mile west of the old Foster ranch house. A comparison of these fragments with the figures given by Kossmat leave little doubt as to their identity. An example of the same, or a closely related species, was found by the writer at the narrows in "Jasper Canyon," on the West branch of the Jacalitos Creek, south of Coalinga, western Fresno County, but it was lost in the San Francisco fire.

Calycoceras (Eucalycoceras) turneri (White)

Ammonites Turneri WHITE, U. S. Geol. Survey, Bull. 51, 1889, p. 26, Pl. 5, figs. 1, 2; Curry Canyon, south of Mount Diablo, Contra Costa County, California.

Kossmat has figured and described (1895–1898, pt. 2, p. 2 (109)) a specimen found in the Ootaoor group, near Odium, south India, that he believed to be identical with that of White. A detailed comparison of the figures and descriptions is not too assuring, although their near relationship can hardly be questioned. Kossmat believed that both forms were very closely related to *"Acanthoceras" rhotomagense* DeFrance. However, all of these forms represent the same stratigraphical horizon, Cenomanian.

White's species may be described . . . . in part as follows:

"Shell of moderate size, robust, with inflated whorls; section of whorls subcircular; umbilicus moderate, with rounded borders; sides strongly costate, ribs at first narrow, numerous and tuberculate, becoming more widely spaced and more narrowly ridge-like at maturity; tubercules in seven rows during youth, whereas in older stages these are lost, and on the periphery the ribs tend to subside, or disappear, leaving the ventral areas rounded and smooth," as is shown in White's figures.

Calycoceras (Eucalycoceras) diabluense Anderson n. sp.
(Plate 23, figures 4, 5)

This species belongs to the group of C. (*Eucalycoceras*) *newboldi* (Kossmat), and of C. (*Eucalycoceras*) *gothicum* (Kossmat). It was found by the writer in Curry Canyon, on the SE ¼ sec. 8, T. 1 S., R. 1 E., at the horizon of *Eucalycoceras turneri* (White).

Shell of moderate size, discoidal, little inflated, having fine, elevated costae of two ranks, major and intermediate, not strongly tuberculate, and having a moderately broad umbilicus; primary ribs arising on umbilical border in elevated bullae, nearly straight; minor ribs arising near middle of sides, all crossing periphery; three rows of inconspicuous nodes appearing on ventral surface, one in median plane, and another on each ventro-lateral angle; ventral zone flattened, showing median tubercules only on younger whorls; section of whorl quadrate, rounded at angles.

The holotype (C. A. S. Type Coll.) has the following dimensions: greatest diameter, 93 mm; width of umbilicus, 28 mm; height of whorl, 44 mm; breadth of whorl, 45 mm. This form resembles C. (*Eucalycoceras*) *choffati* (Kossmat), as figured by Collignon (1937, Pl. 4, figs. 1, 1a) from the Cenomanian of Ramonda, southwest Madagascar.

Subgenus *Metacalycoceras* Spath
Calycoceras (Metacalycoceras) auspicium Anderson n. sp.
(Plate 20, figures 8, 9)

This species is closely related to C. (*Metacalycoceras*) *boulei* Collignon, from the Cenomanian of Madagascar (Collignon, 1937, Pl. 5, figs. 4, 5a). The holotype from University of Oregon Coll. was found by E. L. Packard at the old "Forty-nine" mine, a few miles southwest of Phoenix, Oregon.

The shell is large, section of whorl semi-circular, numerously costate, with simple narrow ribs of two ranks, alternating; major ribs arising on the umbilical border in elevated narrow bullae, crossing the sides and ventral zone in a slightly sinuous course, showing only obscure traces of tubercules; umbilicus not large, but deep, and having abrupt walls. The holotype (C. A. S. Type Coll.), (fig. 8), septate throughout, has the following dimensions: greater diameter, 110 mm; width of umbilicus, about 36 mm; height of whorl, 46 mm; greatest width of whorl, 65 mm. The suture line as far as shown, resembles that of *"Acanthoceras"* *rhotomagense* DeFrance, as illustrated by d'Orbigny, but the form of the whorl and its costation prevent its inclusion in this group. Paratype (C. A. S. Type Coll.) (Pl. 20, fig. 9), natural size, marked from locality 465 (C. A. S.).

Family MANTELLICERATIDAE Hyatt emend. Spath

Genus **Mantelliceras** Hyatt

Mantelliceras oregonense Anderson n. sp.

(Plate 8, figures 4, 4a; Plate 14, figures 1, 1a)

A single complete and well preserved example was found at the old "Forty-nine" mine, southwest of Phoenix, Oregon, by E. L. Packard, and was sent to the writer for study and description from the University of Oregon. Its specific description follows: Shell of moderate size, inflated, or subglobose, heavily costate, narrowly umbilicate, the umbilicus having steep walls, rounded above; ribs numerous, rounded, elevated, separated by interspaces equal in width to the ribs; ribs of two kinds, single and branching; branching ribs more numerous than the single, arising in inflated bullae on the borders of the umbilicus, whence they divide, spreading at an angle of about 12°, crossing the ventral zone as rounded ridges; ribs bearing only inconspicuous nodes near the ventral zone; sutures not exposed.

The holotype (Pl. 14, figs. 1, 1a) has the following dimensions: greatest diameter, 78 mm; width of umbilicus, 28 mm; height of whorl, 35 mm; breadth of whorl, 55 mm; the two last measurements require slight corrections, since the buccal part of the whorl is a little depressed by rock pressure. This species was found in the horizon of the following, associated with other cephalopods, all indicating a Cenomanian horizon. Incomplete and fragmentary examples of the species have also been found at "Dark Hollow," a locality 3 miles to the west on the old Pioneer Road. One such fragment is the hypotype (C. A. S. Type Coll.) (Pl. 8, figs. 4, 4a), which has the following dimensions: length, 68 mm; height of whorl, 25 mm.

A large fragment representing the living chamber was found in the lower part of the series on the Cow Creek highway, east of Frazier Corner near the Cawkins ranch house, Shasta County, California.

Mantelliceras phoenixense Anderson n. sp.

(Plate 13, figures 2, 2a)

Complete examples have not yet been found, and only the holotype and various fragmentary specimens have been obtained, but these exhibit characters that distinguish the species from its associated congeners. It has been found only at the old "Forty-nine" mine, a few miles southwest of Phoenix, Oregon.

Only a partial description can be given at this time:

Shell of moderate size, a little inflated, costate, broadly umbilicate; ribs about 36 in number, straight, of two ranks; primary ribs bearing tubercules on the umbilical border, and two rows on the ventro-lateral angle, all of which are elongated in the direction of the ribs themselves; walls of the umbilicus steep; suture lines not exposed.

The species belongs to the group represented by *Mantelliceras cottreaui* Collignon (1937, p. 33) found on the upper Manombo River, western Madagascar; and perhaps also by the group of *Mantelliceras cantianum* Spath, from the Cenomanian of England. The holotype of the present species (C. A. S. Type Coll.) has the following dimensions: greater diameter, 100 mm; width of umbilicus, 40 mm; height of whorl, 37 mm; thickness of whorl (est.), 33 mm. The holotype was found associated with *Mantelliceras oregonense, Scaphites condoni, Oregoniceras siskiyouense,* and *Puzosia (Parapuzosia) klamathonae.*

Mantelliceras conquistador Anderson, n. sp.
(Plate 15, figure 2)

This species is closely related to *Mantelliceras mantelli* (Sowerby) taken by Hyatt (1903) as the genotype. Shell large, thick, subcircular in section, broader than high, with thick rounded ribs separated by broader interspaces, all of which continue across ventral surface; ribs numerous, tuberculate, bearing five to seven rows of tubercules during youth and middle stages of growth; tubercules in young stages somewhat acute, becoming more rounded with age, and almost obsolete at senility. The holotype (C. A. S. Type Coll.) is a large fragment of the body whorl, measuring as follows: length, 185 mm; breadth of whorl, 85 mm; height on median line, 75 mm.

The holotype was found by Mrs. Melton, Jr., on the Redding-Alturas highway, east of the Calkins ranch on Little Cow Creek, and was donated by her to the California Academy of Sciences. Its stratigraphic position was in the upper part of the Cenomanian. A closely related species was found by the writer a little west of the Calkins house, and is described below.

Mantelliceras aff. M. conquistador Anderson
(Plate 14, figure 2)

Shell large, heavily costate, tuberculate in young stages of growth, tubercules becoming obsolete in age; section of whorl subquadrate, a little broader than high; umbilicus broad and but little involute; ribs occurring in two ranks, alternately major and minor, the former arising on umbilical border, the latter arising higher on the side, all crossing the ventral surface as simple rounded ridges.

The hypotype (C. A. S. Type Coll.), representing about one-third of a whorl, has the following dimensions: length, 150 mm; height of whorl, 64 mm; breadth of whorl, 80.5 mm; umbilicus deep, with steep walls.

The stratigraphic position of the species is somewhat higher than the preceding, being a little beneath the horizon of *Lytoceras jacksonense* Anderson, found on the highway 1000 feet to the west. The stratigraphic position of the present species, as determined by the three successive species, is uppermost Cenomanian and beneath the level of *Lytoceras jacksonense,* regarded as marking the lower part of the Turonian.

Genus **Cunningtoniceras** Collignon
Cunningtoniceras aff. C. **cunningtoni** (Sharpe)

Ammonites cunningtoni SHARPE, Paleont. Soc. London, Trans., vol 4, 1853, Pl. 15, fig. 2; Gray Chalk, England.
Acanthoceras cunningtoni KOSSMAT, Mitt. Pal. Inst., Univ. Wien, Bd. 11, 1898, p. 18 (125), Pl. 5 (16), figs. 1, a, b, c; middle part of Ootatoor group, near Odium, southern India.

Among the more diagnostic species in the lower beds of the Cenomanian in the Great Valley of California is one nearly related to, if not identical with, the Indian form described by Kossmat. It clearly belongs to this group, and probably occurs in the same horizon in California.

The species is represented by a large fragment of a whorl, showing septa, and two prominent spines and ribs, with a mold of the ventral surface of an inner whorl. The Indian species is characterized by such prominent surface features, but our fragment is scarcely sufficient for a positive determination. This example was found by G. D. Hanna, and C. C. Church, about 6 miles southwest of Coalinga, western Fresno County, on sec. 16, T. 21 S., R. 14 E., M. D. B. M. It was found associated with a large fragment of *Turrilites oregonensis* Gabb, closely related to *T. brazosensis* Roemer, occurring in the Del Rio clay of southern Texas.

The Cenomanian age of the strata from which these species came is established by much paleontological evidence. Böse (1927, Pls. 1–3) illustrates both *C. cunningtoni,* and *T. brazosensis* from the upper Georgetown beds (lower Cenomanian) of northern Mexico and southern Texas.

Cunningtoniceras roguense Anderson n. name
(Plate 15, figures 1, 1a)

Acanthoceras rhotomagnense REAGAN (not Defrance), Pan-Am. Geologist, vol. 41, 1924, p. 180, Pl. 18, fig. 2; "Forty-nine" mine, Jackson County, Oregon.

No detailed description was given by Reagan. The specimen figured by him is in the Stanford University collection. It may be described as follows: Shell large, with depressed, subquatrate section, broader than high, and with thick lateral ribs, separated by equally broad interspaces; ribs armed with stout spines on the ventrolateral angle, extending laterally, and with others less prominent a little below the middle of the side; interspaces occupied by vertical wrinkles or lines of growth, passing upward and across the ventral area; umbilicus broad, with steep walls; ventral surface crossed by broad undulations upon which are numerous wrinkles (lines of growth), but otherwise smooth, without nodes or other ornament; sutures not known.

This species seems nearly related to "*Acanthoceras*" *aberrans* Kossmat (1895, p. 202, Pl. 24 (10), figs. 4a, 4b, 4c), from the Ootatoor group near Odium, southern India, but it is much larger, more robust, has less prominent ribs, stouter and more blunt tubercules, and a relatively broader umbilicus. The holotype (L. S. J. U. Type Coll.) consists of a large fragment of an outer whorl, having the following dimensions: length, 165 mm; width, 100 mm; height of whorl, 60 mm; width of umbilicus (est.), 95 mm; complete diameter of whorl (est.), 216 mm. Its age is Cenomian.

Genus **Stoliczkaia** Neumayr
Stoliczkaia praecursor Anderson n. sp.
(Plate 12, figures 1, 1a)

Stoliczkaia dispar ANDERSON, Proc. Calif. Acad. Sci., 3d ser., vol. 2, 1902, p. 63, 106; "upper Horsetown" beds; Cottonwood district; (not *S. dispar* (d'Orbigny) KOSSMAT, Sud. Ind. Kreideform., vol. 9, 1895, p. 194, Pl. 24); lower part of Ootatoor group, southern India.

In most of the references to *Stoliczkaia dispar* (d'Orbigny), the first Indian form described by Stoliczka under this name has been regarded as correctly representing it. Doubtless Kossmat recognized its distinctness from that of d'Orbigny, but did not separate them. Neumayr had already done this, and had noted that Stoliczka had included two species, neither of which was identical with d'Orbigny's species.

These forms were described by Neumayr (1875, p. 935) as *S. tetragona* and *S. clavigera*. The California species is nearly related to the latter, but it is here regarded as not identical. It is represented by a single incomplete example from the Cottonwood district, Shasta County. This was first thought to have come from upper Horsetown strata, but later investigation proves that it was associated with *Pervinquieria tehamaensis* (Reagan), and that it properly belongs in the lowest beds of the Upper Cretaceous:

Shell of medium size, strongly costate in young stages, becoming nearly smooth in old age; the whorls increasing rapidly with age; umbilicus small, walls sloping, border somewhat tuberculate; suture only imperfectly shown.

The holotype (Univ. Calif. Mus. Paleont. Coll.) has the following dimensions: greatest diameter, 84 mm; width of umbilicus, 20 mm; height of whorl, 40. 6 mm; breadth of whorl, 30.5 mm. The stratigraphic horizon of the species is near the top of the Albian, but within the Upper Cretaceous series.

Genus **Romaniceras** Spath
Romaniceras hesperium Anderson n. sp.
(Plate 23, figures 1, 1a)

Shell of moderate size, robust, whorls moderately inflated, heavily costate, with about 16 thick and elevated ribs, spinose, with nine strong spine-like tubercules on most of ribs in adult stages of growth; section of whorls circular between ribs (subquadrate in rib sections); ribs straight, or curving gently backward; surface of shell between ribs costate on sides and ventral surface with transverse cordlike costae that extend from sides across ventral area; umbilicus large, with vertical or rounded walls, which merge between ribs to the rounded sides.

The holotype (C. I. T. Type Coll.) was found by W. P. Popenoe on Swede Creek, an eastern branch of Cow Creek, on the S ½ sec. 4, T. 32 N., R. 3 W. The holotype has the following dimensions: greater diameter, 160 mm; width of umbilicus, 55 mm; greatest breadth of whorl (between ribs), 63 mm.

The species is believed to represent a lower Turonian horizon.

Family LYELLICERATIDAE Spath

Genus **Lyelliceras** Spath

Lyelliceras stanislausense Anderson n. sp.

(Plate 8, figures 5, 5a)

Shell small, as seen in the holotype (C. A. S. Type Coll.). It was found at locality 31131 (C. A. S.), on the NE ¼ of the SW ¼ of sec. 29, T. 8 S., R. 7 E., M. D. M., on an upper branch of Garzas Creek. It was associated with many other invertebrates, including *Puzosia waringi* n. sp., *Cyrtochilus* aff. *C. stylus* n. sp., a fragment of rudistid (? *Durania*), and *Turrilites* sp.

In section, whorl is somewhat depressed, broader than high, heavily costate, with three rows of tubercules upon ribs, in addition to ventral nodes, which form a bead-like row upon median plane; umbilicus broad and deep, showing ventro-lateral spines arising within umbilical wall, against outer whorl; ribs curving forward upon periphery, forming chevron-like undulations. The holotype has the following dimensions: greater diameter, about 30 mm; breadth of whorl, 13 mm; height of whorl, 10 mm. This is the only known occurrence of the genus in the Cretaceous of California. It seems to mark the lower part of the Cenomanian in the Pacheco Pass quadrangle.

Family MAMMITIDAE Hyatt

Genus **Mammites** Laube and Bruder

The genus *Mammites* has not hitherto been reported from the Upper Cretaceous of California and Oregon, and is rare on the Pacific Coast. It appears to be more common in the Cretaceous of other countries. Pervinquiere (1907) has described four or more species from the Cretaceous of North Africa, to some of which he gives the subgeneric name of *Pseudaspidoceras*.

In the Turonian north of the Klamath River, fragmentary examples of an ammonite have been found that seem referable to this genus, and possibly to the subgenus proposed by Pervinquiere.

Mammites rancheriae Anderson n. sp.

(Plate 49, figure 1)

Shell large, discoidal, heavily costate, little involute, with broad umbilicus; section of whorl somewhat inflated, walls of umbilicus sloping from whorl suture to rounded sides; ribs arising on umbilical wall, curving gently forward, each rib bearing a strong, blunt spine below middle, and apparently a second at ventrolateral angle; surface between ribs crossed by three to five minor costal ridges, some of which appear on flanks of major ribs.

The holotype (C. A. S. Type Coll.) is a rock mold in a block of sandstone, from which a plaster cast was made; this has the following dimensions: greatest diameter (incomplete), 200 mm; width of umbilicus, 105 mm; greatest breadth of whorl (est.), 38 mm; greatest height of whorl (est.), 72 mm. This example was found half a mile west of Henley, Siskiyou County, at locality 455 (C. A. S.). The holotype resembles *Mammites* (*Pseudaspidoceras*) *salmuriensis* (Courtiller) from the lower Turonian of Tunis, as figured by Pervinquiere (1907, Pl. 19, figs. 1a, 1b), and may belong to the same subgenus.

This species occurs in the middle part of the Turonian stage west of Henley, midway between the zone of *Oregoniceras siskiyouense* and that of *Fagesia siskiyouensis* Anderson.

Family VASCOCERATIDAE H. Douvillé
Genus **Fagesia** Pervinquiere

The genus *Fagesia* had been known in some countries of South America prior to 1920, but in that year Böse described two species from the lower Turonian in north-central Mexico. Representatives of the genus were recognized on the West Coast by the writer as early as 1900, but no species were described. In northern California and in southern Oregon, the genus occurred only in middle and upper Turonian beds. Species of *Fagesia* and their stratigraphic positions were described by the writer (1932).

Fagesia californica Anderson
(Plate 39, figures 1, 2)

Fagesia californica ANDERSON, Jour. Paleont., vol. 5, 1932, p. 123, Pl. 15, fig. 1; Pl. 16, figs. 1, 2; Pl. 17, fig. 1; text-fig. A.

This species is the largest known on the West Coast, having a diameter of 250 mm; and a width of umbilicus of 122 mm; found near the north fork of the Cottonwood Creek, Shasta County, California. The same species, paratype No. 4685, (C. A. S. Type Coll.) has been found near Phoenix, Oregon, associated with *Prionotropis branneri* Anderson, and with *Prionotropis casperi* n. sp., in the upper part of the Turonian.

Fagesia siskiyouensis Anderson
(Plate 28, figures 1, 2)

Fagesia siskiyouensis ANDERSON, Jour. Paleont., vol. 5, 1932, p. 125, Pl. 17, figs. 2, 3; near Henley, Siskiyou County, California.

The holotype, No. 4689 (C. A. S. Type Coll.), was found in the upper beds of the Turonian, associated with *F. klamathensis* n. sp., about 250 feet below the horizon of *Parapachydiscus henleyensis* Anderson, and 400 feet beneath the horizon of *Metaplacenticeras pacificum* (Smith), *M. califoricum* Anderson, and *Kotôceras richardsoni* n. sp.

Fagesia klamathensis Anderson n. sp.
(Plate 28, figures 3, 3a)

Shell large, robust, deeply umbilicate, heavily costate, rounded on periphery; section of whorl broader than high; ribs coarse, rounded, curving slightly forward, especially on approach to periphery; ribs arising on umbilical wall as slight undulations, developing prominent bullae on the umbilical border, from which they often branch; secondary ribs arising at intervals, either near umbilical border or near middle of side, all crossing ventral area of shell.

This species appears to be closely related to *Fagesia thevestensis* (Peron) from the lower Turonian of Algeria. A similar but thicker species has been figured by Yabe (1904, Pl. 16) from Hokkaido, Japan, under the name of *Ammonites kotoi,* precise horizon not known.

The holotype (C. A. S. Type Coll.) was found at locality 455 (C. A. S.), half a mile west of Henley, Siskiyou County, at the horizon of *Fagesia siskiyouensis*. It has the following dimensions: greatest diameter, 130 mm; width of umbilicus, 35 mm; height of whorl, 55 mm; breadth of whorl, 65 mm; suture line only imperfectly exposed.

The horizon of these species is high in the Turonian.

Genus **Vascoceras** Choffat
Vascoceras shastense (Anderson)

Fagesia shastensis ANDERSON, Jour. Paleont., vol. 5, 1932, p. 124, Pl. 16, fig. 3; middle fork of Cottonwood Creek, Shasta County, California.

Shell of medium size, broadly umbilicate; section of whorl roundly reniform; whorls rounded, outer one bearing about 12 low rounded nodes, which in its younger stages give rise to broad and flattened ribs which incline forward; in younger stages, whorls become relatively broader, nodes are less prominent, and general aspect of shell is smooth or undulating. Suture line only partly visible. The holotype No. 4690 (C. A. S. Type Coll.) has the following dimensions: greatest diameter, 137 mm; width of umbilicus, 62 mm; height of whorl, 42 mm; breadth of whorl, 51 mm. The horizon of this species is perhaps middle Turonian, as determined from recently collected species in its zone of occurrence. This is the only example of *Vascoceras* known from the Upper Cretaceous of California or Oregon.

Family COELOPOCERATIDAE Hyatt
Genus **Coelopoceras** Hyatt
Coelopoceras hyatti Anderson n. sp.
(Plate 19, figures 1, 1a, 1b, 1c)

The species appears to be closely related to the genotype and is the first record of the genus in the Upper Cretaceous of California. Whiteaves (1884, p. 200) describes and illustrates a form from Maud Island that may belong in this group, but this cannot now be confirmed. The holotype (C. A. S. Type Coll.) is of moderate size, lenticular in form, with small umbilicus, periphery bevelled, surmounted by an acute keel; surface almost smooth, bearing only faint traces of flattened costae; umbilical pit funnel-shaped; whorl section a little inflated above umbilical border, narrowing rapidly toward periphery; ventral zone acute; suture only partially shown. The holotype was found by Hanna at locality 2245 (C. A. S.), about 15.1 miles by road, southeast of Beegum, on the road to Rosewood. It has the following dimensions: greater diameter (incomplete), 95 mm; width of umbilicus, 10 mm; height of whorl, 58 mm; breadth of whorl, 22 mm; if complete, its diameter would be 105 mm. It was associated with *Puzosia (Parapuzosia) sp.*, in a stratigraphic position that could hardly be older than middle Turonian, about 1500 feet below the horizon of *Oregoniceras sp.*, and *Prionotropis bakeri* Anderson.

Family SCAPHITIDAE Meek
Genus **Scaphites** Parkinson

Few species of the genus *Scaphites* have been recorded from the West Coast, although it is well represented in the Upper Cretaceous of India and Japan, and in the Rocky Mountain regions of the American Interior. Reeside (1927) has reviewed the *Scaphites* and summarizes the views of earlier writers—J. Perrin Smith, Pervinquiere, Nowak, Spath, and others. Of the nine generic groups that had been proposed, at least four are believed to be valid. All that have been described from the West Coast, and perhaps most of those from Indo-Pacific areas, come within the subfamily *Scaphitinae* Meek, and possibly within the generic group represented by *Scaphites aequalis* Sowerby. Most of those that have been recorded from California and Oregon have come from the Turonian, although their range extends from the upper Cenomanian to lower Senonian.

A comparative study of the several forms from California and Oregon suggests that they have not all been derived from the same ancestral stock, but have arrived at some semblance of relationship under the influence of environmental, or ecological conditions. From their ontogenic development, we are led to the belief that some of them have descended from lytoceratid stocks, whereas others have features suggestive of other sources.

Seven species have been recognized in the Upper Cretaceous of the Great Valley, and in the Rogue River Valley of southern Oregon, but still others are indicated by fragmentary examples that do not permit description.

Scaphites condoni Anderson
(Plate 24, figures 6, 6a, 6b, 6c, 6d, 6e)

Scaphites condoni ANDERSON, Proc. Calif. Acad. Sci., 3d ser., vol. 2, 1902, p. 111, Pl. 2, figs. 58–63; "Forty nine" mine, near Phoenix, Jackson County, Oregon. . . . W. D. SMITH, Jour. Geol., vol. 13, 1905, pp. 637, 644, 649, etc. . . . REESIDE, U. S. Geol. Survey, Prof. Ppr. 150B, 1927, p. 22, 27, 28, etc.; locality as above; (? upper) Cenomanian.

The holotype No. 34 and paratype No. 34a (C. A. S. Type Coll.), (figs. 6, 6a, 6b) were among the types recovered from the ashes of the San Francisco fire. An abbreviated description of the species follows: Shell small, a little compressed, coiling at first discoidal, costate, the costae numerous, rounded, regular; section of coil elliptical, section of body chamber nearly circular; outline of shell subquadrate, inclining to oval; length of shell, 25 mm; width of shell, 16 mm; moderately inflated, especially at the recurved hook, where the section of the cone is nearly circular; body chamber crossed by thick transverse ribs and intervening hollows on the side of the shell; after part of body chamber flattened on the sides, forming dorsal expansions that almost closes the umbilicus; ribs on the coil branching, each branch terminating in a ventro-lateral node from which arise two or more finer costae which extend across the ventral zone; suture line simple, consisting of a few bifid lobes and saddles, as shown in the figure.

The species belongs to the group represented by *Scaphites aequalis* Sowerby, from the Cenomanian of England and western Europe. Although Nowak regarded these species as possibly identical, their identity has not been proved, and specific differences are readily seen. The horizon of the species is probably upper Cenomanian.

The species is named in honor of Thomas Condon, formerly of the University of Oregon.

Scaphites condoni var. appressus Anderson

Scaphites condoni, var. *appressus* ANDERSON, Proc. Calif. Acad. Sci., 3d ser., vol. 2, 1902, p. 112, Pl. 2, figs. 64–66; "Forty-nine" mine, near Phoenix, Oregon. . . . REESIDE, U. S. Geol. Survey, Prof. Paper 150B, p. 28; locality as above.

This form differs from the preceding in accord with the following description: The shell has a thinner and more compressed form than the normal type; the transverse ribs and constrictions on the body chamber are farther forward, and have a more oblique direction; costae upon coil are obscure; the suture line is a little more developed and more complex in details, but in most other features it conforms to those of the typical form.

The holotype of the variety was lost in the San Francisco fire, but paratype No. 28 (C. A. S. Type Coll.) was recovered and similar examples have since been found at the type locality, and at other places in the Great Valley of California. It is regarded as representing an upper Cenomanian horizon.

Scaphites roguensis Anderson
(Plate 19, figures 3, 3a)

Scaphites roguensis ANDERSON, Proc. Calif. Acad. Sci., 3d ser., vol. 2, 1902, p. 112, Pl. 2, figs. 67–70; "Forty-nine" mine, southwest of Phoenix, Oregon. . . . REESIDE, U. S. Geol. Survey, Prof. Paper 150B, 1927, p. 27, 34; locality as above.

This species is apparently related to *Scaphites condoni,* with which it occurs, although it has not the constrictions characteristic of that species, is more flattened on the sides, and the ribs on the body chamber are less developed. The holotype and paratype were lost in the San Francisco fire, copies of the figures are reproduced here. Good examples of the species have not since been found. The young exhibit lytoceratid features, but its origin is probably that of the preceding types. An abbreviated description of the species follows: Shell small, coil discoidal, body chamber flattened on the sides, section of shell quadrate; umbilicus small in adult stages, relatively broader in young stages; surface of shell nearly smooth on the body chamber, except near the periphery; coil costate, having many transverse oblique ribs; ventro-lateral angles on the body chamber bearing small oblique nodes; dorsal border of same expanded, covering most of the umbilicus; length of holotype, 20 mm; width of same, 15 mm; greatest breadth, 6 mm; septation not known.

This species occurs with the preceding, and is regarded as being upper Cenomanian in age.

Scaphites aff. S. roguensis Anderson
(Plate 9, figure 5)

The form here figured, hypotype (C. I. T. Type Coll.), appears to be closely related to *Scaphites roguensis* Anderson, but it differs in number and prominence of the ribs.

Type here figured was found by Popenoe at locality 1010 (C. I. T.) on Salt Creek, north of the Alturas-Redding Highway, in the SW. corner of SE ¼ sec. 34, T. 33 N., R. 3 W., Redding quadrangle, Shasta County, California.

Dimensions of figured hypotype are as follows: greater diameter, 20.9 mm; lesser diameter, including body whorl, 18.3 mm.

Scaphites inermis Anderson
(Plate 27, figures 1, 1a, 1b, 1c)

Scaphites inermis ANDERSON, Proc. Calif. Acad. Sci., 3d ser., vol. 2, 1902, p. 113, Pl. 3, figs. 74–77; "Forty-nine" mine, near Phoenix, Oregon. . . . W. D. SMITH, Jour. Geol., vol. 13, 1905, pp. 637, 644, 649, etc. . . . REESIDE, U. S. Geol. Survey, Prof. Paper 150B, 1927, pp. 27, 30, 36; locality and position as above.

It was noted that in one specimen of this species that had been broken, the dorsal border bore a distinct groove, showing the amount of involution. This feature indicated lytocerid origin, and this view seems to be supported in the younger whorls. An abbreviated description is here given: Shell small, compressed, elliptical in outline of coil, surface smooth, almost without ornamentation; umbilicus open in young whorls, little involute, showing lytoceratid characters; body chamber deeper than wide, with quadrate section, truncated on the dorsal side; sides of living chamber crossed by faint oblique lines and obscure ribs that seem to bifurcate, but to continue across the ventral surface; shell without conspicuous nodes, although on the dorsal and ventral borders of the body chamber are seen faint linear markings that may be thought to be such; aperture surrounded by a buccal ridge, behind which there is a slight constriction. On the dorsal edge of the aperture are small auricular expansions of the shell, of triangular shape, showing faint concentric striae.

This species is abundant at the Fitch ranch, and at the old "Forty-nine" mine, and has also been found north of Frazier Corners, Shasta County, California. The holotype was destroyed in the San Francisco fire, but a neotype (C. I. T. Type Coll.) is here figured, with two paratypes, all of which were found by Popenoe, at locality 1010 (C. I T.), in the SW corner of the SE ¼ sec. 34, T. 33 N., R. 3 W., M. D. M., Redding Quadrangle, Shasta County, California. Dimensions of neotype are as follows: greater diameter, 14.6 mm; lesser diameter, 13 mm; breadth of whorl, 5 mm.

Scaphites klamathensis Anderson
(Plate 19, figures 2, 2a, 2b)

Scaphites klamathensis ANDERSON, Proc. Calif. Acad. Sci., 3d ser., vol. 2, 1902, p. 115, Pl. 3, figs. 78–81; Upper Cretaceous of Shasta Valley, Siskiyou County, California. . . . REESIDE, U. S. Geol. Survey, Prof. Paper 150–B, 1927, p. 27, 30; locality and position as given above. ? Turonian.

The following abbreviated account is taken from the original description:

"Shell small, compressed, ovate in outline of whorl; umbilicus small, whorl involute, clasping about half the preceding whorl in young stages, but concealing it in older stages; section of younger whorls subcircular, of lytoceratid form, body whorl flattened on the sides, but a little inflated at the bend; surface ornamented by fine costae that cross the ventral surface, converging to small nodes near the umbilical margin; costae seen only upon the body chamber, the nodes only upon its last two-thirds. Suture simple, consisting of a large siphonal lobe and smaller lateral lobes, with secondary branches. The aperture is bordered by a distinct lip, preceded by a broad and shallow constriction extending upward toward the dorsal side, without reaching it. From the side of the aperture wing-like expansions of the shell (lappets) extend to the preceding whorl, against which it rests; surface of lappets ornamented by concentric undulations."

The holotype and paratype (C. A. S. Type Coll.) were lost in the San Francisco fire. Copies of the figures are here reproduced. The holotype had the following dimensions: length of whorl, 13 mm; width of whorl, 9 mm; greatest breadth of shell, 3.5 mm. In form and surface features this species resembles *Scaphites larvaeformis* Meek (1876). It is also apparently related to *Scaphites inermis* n. sp. It was found associated with *Scaphites gillisi* Anderson, on the north border of Shasta Valley.

Scaphites pittensis Anderson n. sp.
(Plate 19, figures 4, 4a)

This species belongs to the group of *Scaphites condoni* Anderson, and accordingly also to the group of *Scaphites aequalis* Sowerby. It differs from the former in size, ornamentation, and to some extent in sutural character. It is about two-thirds the size of *S. condoni,* has a narrower buccal limb and aperture, is costate on the ventral zone of the living chamber, but is without ventro-lateral nodes; suture has more broadly rounded terminations on ultimate divisions of the saddles. Shell oval in outline, a little inflated, costate on the body chamber with four thickened ribs crossing the sides, separated by interspaces of nearly the same width; most of the abdominal costae branching at the ventrolateral angles and crossing the periphery without tubercules; but showing a few faint nodes; suture line resembling that of *S. condoni* only in general, differing in its minor features, and in the terminations of the lobes and saddles.

The holotype (C. A. S. Type Coll.) measures as follows: total length, 19 mm; width of shell, 16 mm; thickness of body chamber, 5 mm. This specimen was found by the writer at locality 1293-A (C. A. S.) 1 mile north of Frazier Corners, Shasta County, 9 miles east of Redding, where it was associated with *Scaphites inermis, S.* aff. *S. roguensis, Puzosia (Parapuzosia) klamathonae,* and many other species characteristic of the Turonian.

Scaphites hippocrepis (DeKay)

Ammonites hippocrepis DeKay, N. Y. Lyceum Nat. Hist. Ann., vol. 2, 1827, p. 273–277, Pl. 5, fig. 2.

Five fragmentary examples were collected by McCoy and the writer in the Coniacian at locality 31209 (C. A. S.), on Cache Creek, 2 miles above Rumsey. In form, ornamentation, size, and perhaps in age, these examples conform to those found in the Western Interior. They were found in a thin argillaceous shale intercalated in massive sandstone.

The better preserved of these examples consists of the coiled portions of three individuals, two of which have a diameter of 14 mm and an umbilical diameter of 2.5 mm.

No comparison of these can be made with the European examples, but they resemble closely those described by Reeside (1927b, Pl. 16), especially figures 1, 11, and 16, although they are somewhat smaller and relatively more compressed, the whorl being flatly elliptical.

Ornamentation of about 18 low, rounded primary ribs arising at umbilical border, with a forward slant, changing to a backward curve near middle of side, where they branch alternately into two and three minor rounded ribs, curving more sharply backward. At beginning of straightened living chamber, secondary ribs disappear, and only the primary ribs continue, which broaden perceptibly, rising at right angles to margin of umbilical curve, to near the ventral border, where a few low, rounded tubercules occur. Ventral surface is not well exposed on body chamber, though it is relatively narrower than in forms occurring in the Western Interior, and also they appear to occur at a somewhat lower horizon, although here it occurs with *Peroniceras* aff. *P. leei* Reeside, *Scaphites* (? *Discosaphites*) sp., and other fragmentary species of *Scaphites.*

They occur at locality 31209 (C. A. S.) beneath the zone of *Inoceramus* sp., *Inoceramus undulatoplicatus* Roemer, and of *Eupachydiscus arbucklensis* n. sp.

Subgenus "Yezoites" Yabe
Scaphites ("Yezoites") perrini Anderson
(Plate 25, figures 6, 6a, 6b)

Scaphites Perrini Anderson, Proc. Calif. Acad. Sci., 3d ser., vol. 2, 1902, p. 114, Pl. 2, figs. 71–73; Fitch (formerly Smith) ranch, 3 miles west of Phoenix, Oregon. . . . W. D. Smith, Jour. Geol., vol. 13, 1905, p. 653 . . . Reeside, U. S. Geol. Surv., Prof. Paper 150-B, 1927, pp. 27, 33; locality and position as indicated below; ? Upper Cenomanian.

This species is known from only a single nearly perfect example, the holotype, found on the Fitch ranch by J. Perrin Smith, formerly of Stanford University, to which institution the specimen belongs. An abbreviated description is here given:

Unlike other known types of the genus, this species possesses whorls that are broader than high, the section being transversely elliptical, with lateral angles, that form the margins of a funnel-form umbilicus. The ventral surface is broad, rounded, and nearly smooth; the aperture is reduced by a strong, rounded lip and constriction, extending a little beyond the lateral angles; large lappets extending forward from the anterior dorsal area, further reducing the aperture to a subquadrate form; the dorsal margins of the body chamber ornamented by small, oblique, simple ribs, not crossing the ventral surface; suture line traceable only in part upon the ventral surface, consisting of broad saddles and narrow lobes, bifid in their subdivisions; siphonal lobe simple, almost as broad as long, having one terminal and two lateral branches.

This species is included by Yabe in his subgenus *"Yezoites."* The whorl form, development, and ornamentation of the holotype suggests an origin in an olcostephanid stock, and this accords with the view of a polyphyletic origin for the genus *Scaphites* held by some authors.

Family PLACENTICERATIDAE Hyatt

Representatives of this family, even in its broadest sense, are not abundant in the Upper Cretaceous of the West Coast, and the known species are limited to seven or eight, most of which may be included in a single genus. The genus *Forbesiceras* Kossmat (1898) sometimes placed in this family is represented in California by only a single fragmentary example found in the middle part of the upper Cenomanian in the Cottonwood district, Shasta County, but it is omitted from the present synopsis as being somewhat doubtful. The earliest species definitely recognized appear in the lower Senonian (Coniacian) beds, and are here included in the genus *Metaplacenticeras* Spath.

Concerning the stratigraphic range of *Placenticeras* J. Perrin Smith (1900, p. 196) states: "The earliest known species of *Placenticeras* occurs along with *Sphenodiscus* in the zone of '*Schloenbachia*' (= *Pervinquieria*) *inflata,* in the upper Gault, top of the Lower Cretaceous." As a result of an extended study of the phylogentic aspects of the two species best known in California, Smith reached the conclusion (p. 204) that:—"it is fair to assume that *Placenticeras californicum* is characteristic of the lower Chico, or Cenomanian portion of the formation." Smith seems to have been influenced in this statement by his own list of species (p. 203) which were alleged to have been found on the Isabel Jordan ranch, Arroyo del Valle.

This list included both *Placenticeras californicum* Anderson, and *Placenticeras pacificum* Smith, both of which have since been found there, although a part of the assemblage contained in the list could not have been obtained at this place.

Without questioning the authenticity and soundness of Smith's analytical study and conclusions as to the origin and relationships of *"Placenticeras,"* it should be pointed out that the chronological position of the species associated with it should be the same, and since the type is new, or quite unusual, its position is best determined by its associates, or by stratigraphical evidence.

Genus **Metaplacenticeras** Spath

Spath proposed this name for a group of West Coast species and selected *Placenticeras pacificum* Smith as the genotype. The group includes also *Placenticeras californicum* Anderson, and *Placenticeras sanctaemonicae* Waring (1917), and probably others.

E. W. Fredenburg (1907) had grouped the first two with *Placenticeras prudhommei* Peron, and had assigned them to a lower Senonian horizon. He also included in the group *Placenticeras tamulicum* Kossmat, of lower Senonian age, and *Placenticeras fritsche* Grossouvre, as he understood it. It is difficult to determine from Spath's meager statement concerning *Metaplacenticeras* just what relationship should exist between his group and other members of the family, although he made the species *P. fritschi* Grossouvre the type of his *Proplacenticeras.* As here understood, the group to which *Metaplacenticeras* was applied cannot be restricted to the West Coast species known to Spath, and since in size, form, and sutures, *Placenticeras vancouverense* Meek conforms to his genotype, this also should be included with it. Whiteaves states (1903, p. 339) that . . . "a few specimens of this shell were collected at Sucia Islands by Newcombe (1894; 1896)." In the California Academy of

Sciences are good examples of this species obtained from these islands, showing both surface and sutural features. For the latter the pronounced expansion of the central lobes and saddles, and the weakening of the auxiliaries form striking evidences of near relationship, and furthermore, the two occur at correlative stratigraphic levels. In both, the associated faunas include species characteristic of lower Senonian horizons on the West Coast, although *P. californicum* was at first thought to be older.

The holotypes of the California species were obtained at locality 444 (C. A. S.) near Henley, Siskiyou County. At the locality of these types other cephalopods were found associated with them, and still others occur immediately below and also above their zone. The position of both *pacificum* (Smith) and *californicum* (Anderson) is early Senonian (Coniacian), rather than Cenomanian, as thought by Smith.

Metaplacenticeras pacificum (Smith)
(Plate 37, figures 1, 2, 3, 4, 4a)

Placenticeras pacificum SMITH, Proc. Calif. Acad. Sci., 3d ser., vol. 1, 1900, p. 207–210, Pls. 26–28; near Henley, Siskiyou County, California. . . . ANDERSON, Proc. Calif. Sci., 3d ser., vol. 2, 1902, p. 79, Pl. 8, figs. 162–164; Pl. 9, fig. 180; Henley, California, (lower Senonian).

Smith's description reads in part as follows:

(This species) "is large, discoidal, involute, and laterally compressed, having the typical plate shape of the genus. At maturity the whorl embraces somewhat more than one-half of the preceding; the breadth of the whorl is one-fifth of the diameter, the height of the whorl is three-sevenths, and the width of the umbilicus, one-fifth. The body chamber is about two-thirds of a revolution in length. The abdomen is narrow, flattened, slightly concave, bounded by a row of elongated knots, forming rough keels, . . . The umbilicus is moderately narrow, and the shoulders angular, becoming more so as age advances. . . . The sides are ornamented with rather coarse sigmoidal ribs, bundling in umbilical knots; . . . The septa consist of an abdominial lobe with a pair of long branches, and seven lateral lobes, all finely digitate, and rather narrow. The saddles are broader and deeply divided by narrow secondary lobes.". . .

This species was found abundantly in the upper part of a sandy facies forming the lower part of the Coniacian half a mile west of Henley at locality 444 (C. A. S.) ; the holotype was in a hard calcareous concretion. Most of the examples were smaller, having only half the diameter of the holotype. Along the strike and half a mile south of the Klamath river, the same species is abundant, but it is smaller here. The species has been found also at the Arroyo del Valle, Alameda County, and at Enos Canyon, Yolo County, but at few other places in the Great Valley. Outside the Great Valley, it has been found at the old "Forty-nine" mine, in southern Oregon, and farther south in Orange County, where Popenoe has obtained excellent examples of this and the following species, in the Santiago district (Popenoe, 1942, fig. 4), and also in the Simi Hills, Los Angeles County.

A fragment of *Placenticeras* recovered from the fire of 1906, which may be a portion of the holotype, is No. 29 in the type series of the Department of Paleontology of the California Academy of Sciences.

Metaplacenticeras californicum (Anderson)
(Plate 36, figure 1)

Placenticeras californicum ANDERSON, Proc. Calif. Acad. Sci., 3d ser., vol. 2, 1902, p. 78, Pl. 8, figs. 173-177; half a mile west of Henley, Siskiyou County; found with the preceding species.

This species is related to the preceding, but differs from it in ornamentation and in sutural features, although the two are often found in the same beds.

The following description is taken from the original notes:

"Shell discoidal, involute, compressed, narrowing regularly from the umbilical region outward to the periphery; the shell is more rugged in form and ornamentation and has coarser ribs than the preceding; costae flexuous, extending to the umbilical border, and terminating outwardly in tubercules upon the peripheral angles; tubercules elongated and narrow, standing in single rows upon either side of the ventral area, and opposite one another. The ribs are low and rounded, and about equal in width to the intervening furrows. . . . Upon the periphery the space between the rows of ventro-lateral tubercules is flattened and bandlike, being equal in width to one-third the thickness of the shell.". . .

The largest specimen has the following dimensions: greater diameter, 120 mm; height of last whorl, 58 mm; width of same, 30.5 mm; width of umbilicus, 23 mm. The holotype was destroyed in the San Francisco fire. The neotype, No. 23B (C. A. S. Type Coll.), has the following dimensions: greater diameter, 86 mm; width of umbilicus, 18 mm; height of whorl, 41 mm. Found at the original locality half a mile west of Henley. The species has been found at many localities in California, and also in Oregon, as at the old "Forty-nine" mine southwest of Phoenix. It was associated with *Metaplacenticeras pacificum* (Smith) at the following places: "Forty-nine" mine, 2 miles southwest of Phoenix, Oregon; Enos Canyon, Yolo County, California, 7 miles northwest of Winters; Arroyo del Valle, Alameda County, 8 miles south of Livermore, California; "Windmill Canyon," on south border of Antelope Valley, northwest Kern County; and at locality 3, (L. S. J. U.), near Santa Monica, and also at the same horizon on the west slope of the Santa Ana Mountains, Orange County, California. In all these localities, the species may be regarded as marking a zone of Coniacian age.

Metaplacenticeras sanctaemonicae (Waring)

Placenticeras sanctaemonicae WARING, Proc. Calif. Acad. Sci., 4th ser., vol. 7, 1917, p. 70, Pl. 9, figs. 20, 21; locality 3, (L. S. J. U.), near Santa Monica, California.

According to Waring's description this species is intermediate between the two preceding forms in many of its features, but differs from both. Following is his description, in part:

"The external surface is ornamented by sickle-shaped ribs, which are separated by deeply channeled interspaces; ends of ribs abruptly terminated at outer edge and forming a chain of elongated tubercules on either edge of the squared back, as keels; thus differing from *Placenticeras pacificum,* which has only faint keels, and only slightly channeled interspaces between the ribs, None of these tubercules is developed on the sides as in *Placenticeras californicum. Placenticeras santaemonicae* has fine ribs with deeply impressed interspaces," etc.

As shown by its character, its associated species, and its stratigraphic position, the species marks the same horizon as the preceding.

Metaplacenticeras ? bowersi Anderson, n. name
(Plate 70, figures 3, 4, 4a)

"Acanthoceras compressum" ANDERSON (in part), Proc. Calif. Acad. Sci., 3d ser., vol. 2, 1902, p. 107, Pl. 9, fig. 187; Bowers Canyon, Los Angeles County (not from the Santa Ana Mountains, Orange County).

In original description the example illustrated was from Bowers Canyon, (probably Dayton Canyon, of the Calabasas quadrangle), a few miles southwest of Chatsworth. The example was partly covered by the matrix. Later work has uncovered the umbilical pit, showing the true form, and the umbilical margin, and a comparison of the same with other material from the same locality, shows the specimen to be referable to *Placenticeras* (s. 1.), and possibly to *Metaplacenticeras,* though it differs notably from other members of this genus as known in California and Oregon. The holotype, (Univ. Calif. Mus. Paleont. Type Coll.) (Pl. 70, fig. 3) is here figured together with a better preserved, but smaller example, paratype, (C. I. T. Type Coll. bearing No. 3907). Dimensions of the paratype (Pl. 70, figs. 4, 4a) are as follows: maximum diameter, 35.5; minimum diameter, 29.2 mm; maximum height body whorl, 15.3 mm; maximum breadth body whorl, 12 mm. Found at locality 1159 (C. I. T.), from Dayton Canyon, Calabasas quadrangle, Los Angeles County. In some respects the species resembles *Metaplacenticeras califoricum* (Anderson) described from near Henley, Siskiyou County, but is relatively more robust, has stouter ribs, marked by pronounced nodes below the ventro-lateral angle, at which point the rib bends sharply forward, in a manner not seen in any example of *Metaplacenticeras californicum.* This feature gives it a submarginal slope downward and outward, unlike the curving borders of any known types of *Metaplacenticeras* Spath. The ribs arise on the umbilical border from nodes, in pairs, or in trios. The species is named in honor of Stephan Bowers (deceased) who discovered the type near his property.

In the possession of the sub-marginal nodes, in the sharp bending of the ribs at them and in other details, the species shows some resemblance to *"Hoplites" plasticus-semicostatus* Paulcke although in other respects the ribs are different.

Genus **Placenticeras** Meek

Placenticeras vancouverense (Meek)

(Plate 32, figures 1, 2)

Ammonites vancouverensis MEEK, Acad. Nat. Sci. Phila., Proc., vol. 13, 1861, p. 317, Vancouver Island, B. C.

Placenticeras ? vancouverense MEEK, Geol. and Geogr. Survey Terr., Bull., vol. 2, 1876, p. 370, Pl. 6, figs. 1, 1a, 3; 'Komooks,' Vancouver Island, British Columbia.

Hoplites vancouverensis, WHITEAVES, Royal Soc. Canada, Trans., vol. 10, 1892, sec. 4, p. 116. . . . Meso. Foss. vol. 1, pt. 5, 1903, p. 339.

Whiteaves states (1903, p. 339) that "a few specimens of this shell were collected at the Sucia Islands by Dr. C. F. Newcombe in 1894 and 1896."

Meek had figured a fragment of an immature shell, with a suture line from a more mature example, but characteristic of the genus *Placenticeras.*

In the California Academy of Sciences are large collections of Upper Cretaceous fossils from the Sucia Islands, including good examples of this species. The figured specimen, hypotype, (C. A. S. Type Coll.) is somewhat larger than Meek's holotype. It still retains much of the shell, but otherwise it is clearly representative of his species. On a companion specimen somewhat larger, the suture line is well exposed and conforms well to the pattern illustrated by Meek. The dimensions of this specimen are as follows: greatest diameter (incomplete), 90 mm; width of umbilicus, 20 mm; greatest breadth of whorl, 28 mm. The young whorls of the species (diameter, 25–30 mm) have some resemblance to *"Hoplitoplacenticeras"* Paulcke, from southern Patagonia, and this fact may have led Whiteaves to assign the species to *Hoplites,* rather than to *Placenticeras,* as suggested by Meek.

In older shells, umbilical nodes number about 16–18 and are strongly inclined forward, from which ribs (costal threads) are bundled and diverge, curving a little backward and later forward near ventral border. In young stages (diameter, 20–40 mm), they are more strongly costate, simple ribs arising singly, or in pairs, crossing sides and periphery, bearing small, transverse tubercules a little above middle of sides, and at their terminations on ventral border; with growth of shell, the median row of tubercules is lost, and the ribs assume the bundled character, with nodes at umbilical and ventral borders only; suture line is that of *Placenticeras,* resembling that of *Placenticeras stantoni,* var. *boli* Hyatt, although the ventral lobe conforms more closely to that of Meek's figure, and in external features it also does the same, suggesting genetic relationship in the two species.

Placenticeras ? yakounense (Whiteaves)

Hoplites yakounensis WHITEAVES, Meso. Foss., vol. 1, pt. 4, 1900, p. 280, Pl. 36, figs. 1, 1a-1b; east end of Maud Island, British Columbia.

The meager description of this species, based on a single specimen, 40 mm in diameter, and a similar but smaller specimen, found south of Yakoun Lake, afford only a small basic for generic determination, but since Whiteaves regarded it as congeneric with *Placenticeras vancouverense* (Meek), it also may be included in the present synopsis of the genius on the West Coast. It differs in various details, as in the umbilical ratio, curvature of the ribs, position and obliquity of the abdominal nodes, etc., and probably also in the horizon of its occurrence. The species seems also to have some resemblance to the smoother types of *"Hoplitoplacenticeras"* Paulcke, from southern Patagonia.

Family PERVINQUIERIDAE Spath

Genus **Pervinquieria** J. Boehm

Many references to *"Schloenbachia" inflata* (Sowerby) are in the Upper Cretaceous literature of the West Coast, probably not all referring to the same variety or species. More than five distinct species of the genus are known from the well preserved but fragmentary specimens found in the Upper Cretaceous of California and Oregon. One of these was figured and described by the writer (1938, p. 198, Pl. 82), and four others are now known from fragmentary examples. Various related types have been described from contemporary beds in Texas and Mexico, some of which have been discussed by Böse (1927, p. 146–148), who regarded them as representing late Albian horizons. The several forms found in California appear to belong to the same age except for the form already referred to from the uppermost Horsetown group, which is clearly distinct from any of the others. Most of the species have been found between the first and second conglomerate beds in the lower part of the Upper Cretaceous series in the Cottonwood district of Shasta County, or in the second conglomerate bed, in reworked conceretionary boulders. This conglomerate has also supplied a considerable fauna of other types that may represent Albian horizons.

Pervinquieria tehamaense (Reagan)
(Plate 3, figure 1)

Schloenbachia tehamaensis REAGAN, Pan-Am. Geologist, vol. 41, 1924, p. 182, Pl. 19, fig. 3; "Chico beds," 30 miles west of Red Bluff, western Tehama County.

The holotype now in the collections of Standford University, consists of a fragment of an internal cast of less than a fourth of a whorl. Its exact point of discovery was not given in the description. The example here figured was found in place near the north fork of Cottonwood Creek, in western Shasta County. The shell is large, discoidal, and somewhat compressed; the umbilicus is broad, the whorls having but little involution; sides heavily costate in the adult stages of growth. In this example, which is almost entire, a part of the shell still remains. The specimen here figured is in the Museum of Paleontology, University of California; the figure is about three-fourths actual size. The zone of the figured specimen crosses the north fork of Cottonwood Creek half a mile above the mouth of Hulen Creek, near the lower limit of the Upper Cretaceous series, from here it extends south through western Tehama County, crossing the south fork of Cottonwood Creek, about 30 miles west of Red Bluff. The holotype may have been discovered in this vicinity.

Two fragments of a similar species have been found south of Los Vallecitos, in San Benito County, one of which is in the collections of the California Academy of Sciences. This species is not to be confused with *Peroniceras tehamaense* (Gabb), the holotype of which was found on the east side of the Sacramento Valley, in a much higher horizon.

Pervinquieria gainesana Anderson n. sp.
(Plate 4, figures 1, 1a)

Shell large, discoidal, flattened on sides, keeled, numerously costate; broadly umbilicate, ventral zone flattened but convex; section of whorl subquadrate, narrowing a little toward periphery; keel not greatly elevated, rounded, entire, bordered by distinctly impressed grooves; umbilicus broad, walls steep, border rounded, surmounted by elongated nodes (bullae); ribs mostly branching from the bullae, rarely single, noded; nodes of three types— (a) umbilical bullae; (b) small tubercules, occurring on the ribs above the middle of the side; (c) multiple nodes on the ventral zone, narrow and elongated in the direction of the siphonal plane, six to eight upon each rib, increasing in number with growth of the shell. The holotype, No. 14940 (Univ. Calif. Mus. Paleon. Type Coll.), measures as follows: greatest diameter, 120 mm; width of umbilicus, 45 mm; height of whorl, 45 mm; greatest thickness of whorl, 38 mm. This example has much resemblance to *"Inflaticeras" robustum* Spath (1921, p. 129, Pl. 4), except that it sides show less convergence, and it possesses a relatively broader ventral zone. It was found on the north fork of Cottonwood Creek, in the lower part of the Upper Cretaceous series, associated with *P. tehamaense* (Reagan), and with an intermediate form described below, and with various other cephalopods and pelecypods, including *Durania california*.

Pervinquieria sylvana Anderson n. sp.
(Plate 4, figures 2, 3; Plate 7, figure 2)

This species has some resemblance to the preceding, with which it is found, but it differs in its more rounded ventral border, its more prominent keel, and a somewhat greater umbilical ratio. Most of the ribs branch a little above umbilical bullae, have elongated nodes above middle of the sides, from which zone the sides converge more rapidly toward the ventral border; this feature is more prominent in the older stages of growth.

The holotype (C. A. S. Type Coll.) was found in the shales between the first and second conglomerate, on the south side of the north fork, a mile above the mouth of Hulen Creek. Dimensions: greater diameter, 110.5 mm; width of umbilicus, 38 mm; height of whorl, 46.8 mm. This appears to be the more common species found in the basal beds of the Upper Cretaceous series in the district of the north fork of the Cottonwood Creek.

Pervinquieria furberi Anderson n. sp.
(Plate 9, figures 6, 6a; Plate 11, figure 1)

The holotype is somewhat flattened by rock pressure, and is slightly distorted and fragmentary, although a portion of the outer and of an inner whorl are sufficiently well preserved for generic determination, and for a partial specific description. A part of the inner whorl is fairly well preserved, showing it to be costate and trinodose, the nodes appearing on the ribs in three distinct zones; the inner row is on the umbilical border, the nodes being elongated on the rib, and from these the ribs usually divide, although some are single. In size, form, and ornamentation, the holotype resembles "Pervinquieria n. sp." illustrated by Adkins (1928, Pl. 10, fig. 1) by an example from near Fort Stockton, Texas.

On outer whorl of holotype, dorsolateral nodes tend to disappear in older stages, ribs crossing this zone as thin elevated ridges, with a slight forward flexure on umbilical border; middle row becomes more prominent and elongated, although on some ribs the nodes are obsolete; the outer tubercules become elevated, or prominent and rounded. Keel was evidently high and continuous, with sides sloping toward ventro-lateral angle. Whorl section was ovate; sides a little inflated, but sloping toward periphery with gentle curvature; ventral zone was not broad, concave on either side of keel. The holotype (C. A. S. Type Coll.) was found by G. D. Hanna, at locality 28180 (C. A. S.), on the Dry Creek (Beegum) road, about 100 feet beneath the coarse conglomerate in this section, where it was associated with Parahoplites aff. P. sjogreni Anthula.

The direct comparison of the holotype (Pl. 11, fig. 1) with a representative of "Pervinquieria n. sp." (Adkins) shows little differences, and indicates that the horizon of the Dry Creek specimen is approximately correlative with that of the Duck Creek beds near Fort Stockton, Texas.

Dimensions of holotype are as follows: maximum diameter, approximately 180 mm; height of last whorl, 63 mm; breadth of last whorl, approximately 43 mm; width of umbilicus, 71.5 mm.

Pervinquieria aff. P. inflata (Sowerby)
(Plate 7, figure 3; Plate 8, figure 6)

A large fragment of a Pervinquieria, similar to but not identical with the preceding, differing from it chiefly in possessing intermediary ribs on outer half of sides, was found by Hanna in the lower part of the Upper Cretaceous on the north side of the Waltham Creek valley, locality 2324 (C. A. S.)

The form differs from the holotype of Pervinquieria furberi n. sp., in having more prominent nodes in the median row, and in both the ventro-lateral and dorso-lateral zones. The present note is here added only for the purpose of supplying evidence as to Albian age of the lowest part of the Upper Cretaceous on the border of the Great Valley, and to stimulate search for further data in this area.

Hypotype no. 14943 (Univ. Calif. Mus. Paleo. Type Coll.) (Pl. 7, fig. 3) and hypotype (C. A. S. Type Coll.) (Pl. 8, fig. 6) approximate dimensions of which are: greatest diameter, 139 mm; height of whorl, 55 mm.

Family BRANCOCERATIDAE Spath
Genus **Brancoceras** Steinmann

According to Pervinquiere (1907, p. 225): "The genus *Brancoceras* was proposed by Steinmann (1881, p. 133) for a group of ammonites from the Albian of Europe and Peru, including *Ammonites varicosus* Sowerby, *A. aegoceratoides*, etc. These ammonites are characterized by the fact that the keel, when it exists, disappears quite completely, and that the ribs cross the ventral region, thickening there, and sometimes becoming 'chevrons,' as in certain ammonites of the Lias. The sutures are always very simple."

Steinmann included as typical of his genus—*Brancoceras varicosum* (Sowerby), *Brancoceras seniquieri* (d'Orbigny), and adds also, *Brancoceras aegoceratoides*.

Hyatt later proposed the name *Hystatoceras* for the ammonites included by Steinmann in *Brancoceras*, giving as the type of the proposed genus *Ammonites seniquieri* d'Orbigny. An adequate justification for this procedure has not yet been found by the writer, or by others. Böse (1923, p. 175–180) has reviewed the subject and expressed essentially the same view.

Brancoceras parvum (Anderson)
(Plate 3, figures 2, 2a, 3, 3a, 3b, 4, 4a, 5)

Hoplites parva ANDERSON, Proc. Calif. Acad. Sci., 3d ser., vol. 2, 1902, Pl. 3, figs. 82–84; "Forty-nine" mine, near Phoenix, Jackson County, Oregon; lower Chico beds.

This species is represented by a single specimen, holotype No. 31 (C. A. S. Type Coll.), from the lower beds of the Upper Cretaceous on the south border of the Rogue River Valley, Oregon. This specimen was figured (1902) but without a description, because of lack of sufficent data as to its character and relationship. In the San Francisco fire, a portion of the outer whorl was detached, but it was otherwise undamaged and now forms the basis of an emended description. The removal of a portion of the outer whorl disclosed a distinct keel on the next inner whorl, showing its identity with the genus *Brancoceras* Steinmann. The emended description follows:

Shell small, discoidal, compressed, broadly umbilicate, costate on the outer whorl, but in younger stages of growth it is quite smooth, moderately inflated, with an elliptical section; keel acute, appearing on the periphery of the whorl next the last; keel entire, smooth, bordered on both sides by a flattened zone; keel disappearing at a diameter of about 7 mm; costae first showing at a diameter of 5 mm as thin elevated ridges radiating from the umbilical border, increasing in height and strength with growth; at a diameter of 10 mm the rudimentary ribs become divided into two, three, or more costae, some of which subdivide; all costae crossing the ventral zone without forming nodes, but showing a slight angle in the ventral zone.

This species was found associated with *Dipoloceras* n. sp., *Puzosia* aff. *P. waringi* n. name, manian of Tunis, although thinner in its mature form. It also greatly resembles in size, form, and simple ornamentation, *Brancoceras* aff. *B. varicosum* (Sowerby) figured by Böse (1923, Pl. 11) from near Comancho, Zacatacas, Mexico.

This species was found associated with *Diploloceras* n. sp., *Puzosia* aff. *P. waringi* n. name, and *Pervinquieria* sp., indicating a low position in the upper Albian. Its greatest diameter is 15 mm; width of umbilicus, 6 mm; thickness of whorl, 3 mm; suture as shown in the figure.

Family PRIONOTROPIDAE Hyatt

Meek (1876) described two related types of keeled ammonites both of which are now included in this family, the genotypes being respectively *Prionocyclus wyomingensis* Meek and *Prionotropis woolgari* (Mantell). Various American and foreign species have since been included under one or another of these genera, and the names now have wide acceptance. To these genera Spath (1926) has added *Prionocycloceras*, the genotype being *"Prionocyclus" guyabanus* (Steinmann) from near Cerro Pelado, southern Colombia, S. A. The West Coast *Oregoniceras*, n. gen. should also be included in the same family.

In *Prionocyclus* Meek the keel in younger stages is either crenulated, or is finely serrated; in *Prionotropis* Meek the early stages have a continuous and smooth keel, which becomes serrated in mature stages, but may finally become obsolete. In most respects, *Oregoniceras* follows the development of *Prionotropis,* but usually has double nodes at the rib terminals, and the highly serrated keel is finally lost, the keel becoming reduced to a bevelled ridge, forming an angular periphery, the ribs on opposite sides becoming united in a chevronlike manner.

Genus **Peroniceras** Grossouvre
Peroniceras tehamaense (Gabb)
(Plate 62, figures 7, 7a)

Ammonites subtricarinatus GABB (not d'Orbigny), Paleont. Calif., vol. 1, 1864, p. 60, Pl. 10, figs. 4, 4a; Battle Creek, Tehama County.
Ammonites tehamaensis GABB, Paleont. Calif., vol. 2, 1869, p. 132, new name; locality as above.
Peroniceras tehamaense GROSSOUVRE, Mem. Expl. de la Carte Geol. de France, Paleont., p. 104.

The original material includes five fragments of which two representing about half a whorl are here figured. Possibly more than one individual is represented. These specimens are now in the Museum of Paleontology, University of California. No other examples of the species have since been found. As most members of this genus are regarded by Grossouvre as belonging in the lowest Senonian (Coniacian) stage, it is assumed that this species represents the same in California.

The exact original locality is not definitely known, but it appears to have been on the east side of the Sacramento Valley on Battle Creek, in eastern Tehama County. The two fragments here figured (Pl. 62, fig. 7) fit together precisely. The larger is the original of Gabb's Figure 4. The cross section (Pl. 62, fig. 7a) is the adapical end of the larger fragment. The original of Gabb's Figure 4a appears to represent about half a volution earlier.

Peroniceras quintoense Anderson n. sp.
(Plate 47, figures 1, 1a)

Shell very large, discoidal, broadly umbilicate, little involute, heavily ribbed in older stages of growth, tricarinate, central carina being higher than lateral, all smooth and elevated. In younger stages of growth, ribs are slender but more conspicuously noded, with two rows of tubercules of little prominence; outer row near ventro-lateral angle rounded, inner row near umbilical border elongated radially and slightly more prominent; on older whorls, ribs become stronger, inner row of nodes tend to disappear, and ribs are more strongly curved, especially on approach to periphery. The holotype (C. A. S. Type Coll.) consists of a broken example, the original septate diameter of which had been (est.) not less than 200 mm; height of whorl (detached), 62 mm; breadth of same, 45 mm; septa as shown in the figure. This example was found by Allen P. Bennison, at locality 29596 (C. A. S.), on Quinto Creek, Stanislaus County, on the NW ¼ of NE ¼ sec. 7, T. 9 S., R. 8 E., M. D. M. This example represents the largest species of *Peroniceras* known in the Upper Cretaceous of California. When complete, its greatest diameter (est.) was not less than 12 inches (305 mm). It was found a little above a thick bed of conglomerate which seems to mark the base of the Panoche formation in the Quinto Creek district. Its occurrence here, a little above the horizon of *Prionotropis bakeri* Anderson, and of many species of *Oregoniceras,* conforms to the view that it marks the base of the Senonian strata in this district.

Peroniceras shastense Anderson n. sp
(Plate 69, figures 5, 5a, 5b, 5c)

The holotype of this species was found by Popenoe and Findley on Oak Run Creek, eastern Shasta County, about four-tenths of a mile north of the Hathaway Home, at locality 1034 (C. I. T.). The type of this species is quite unlike any before found in California, or on the West Coast, or from any part of the American Cretaceous, as far as known. It differs much from *Peroniceras tehamaense* (Gabb), although apparently found in nearly the same stratigraphic horizon. It was found associated with, or a little below, *Prionocyclus californicus* n. sp.

The shell is relatively small, having a diameter of less than 55 mm, a maximum width of about 19 mm, height of 15 mm, and an umbilical ratio of about 1 :40.

The section of the whorl is broader than high, with a periphery marked by three low and rounded keels, separated by slightly broader grooves. Keels are slightly undulating, but continuous; lateral keels are flanked by prominent tubercules, flattened on peripheral surface. Sides of shell are marked by about 15 stout ribs, separated by broader interspaces, each of which bears two stout tubercules, outer row closely bordering outer keels; these tubercules are marked by a flattened, triangular slope above, though rounded beneath; inner row of tubercules is near umbilical border and are slightly elongated in the direction of the rib itself.

Should this species be taken as marking the lower part of the Coniacian, as apparently it does, the Coniacian at this place rest directly upon the basement rocks (greenstones), although Turonian deposits are well exposed 3 miles to the north and a few miles to the south.

Genus **Prionotropis** Meek
Prionotropis bakeri (Anderson)
(Plate 38, figures 2, 3, 4, 5, 5a)

Schloenbachia bakeri ANDERSON, Proc. Calif. Acad. Sci., 3d ser., vol. 2, 1902, p. 121, Pl. 2, figs. 26–33; Lower Chico beds, "Forty-nine" mine, near Phoenix, Jackson County, Oregon.

Shell small, discoidal, compressed, narrowly quadrate in section; umbilicus rather broad, with rounded borders; shell carinate, keel beginning to appear on third whorl, at a diameter of 3 mm; keel prominent and entire in young stages of growth, becoming serrated in older stages, having slightly impressed grooves at sides; involution covering about a third of preceding whorl; sides of whorl crossed by about 28 to 40 simple and narrow ribs inclining forward, and more strongly curved near ventral border; ribs bearing only small nodes on umbilical border, but a double row of small tubercules at outer end. In earlier whorls, shell is smooth, and without a keel, and with a broadly elliptical section; ribs are thin in young stages, increasing regularly in thickness up to a diameter of about 30 mm, at which point they rapidly become thicker, and more widely spaced; shell thus develops in the manner of its congener, *Prionotropis woolgari* (Mantell), as illustrated by Stanton (1893, Pl. 42).

This species was found plentifully on the Fitch (Smith) ranch, a little west of the locality of the old Fort Baker, and at the "Forty-nine" mine, southwest of Phoenix, Oregon. Here and in various places in the Great Valley of California, the species marks the upper limit of the Turonian.

The holotype No. 39 (C. A. S. Type Coll.) from locality 445 (C. A. S.), "Forty-nine" mine near Phoenix, Oregon, is shown on Plate 38, figure 3, also 3 hypotypes (Pl. 38, figs. 2, 4, 5, 5a) from locality 445-A (C. A. S.) Fitch's ranch, 2 miles southwest of Phoenix, Oregon.

This species is found on the north and middle forks of the Cottonwood Creek, and on Dry Creek, Tehama County, and on Quinto Creek, western Merced County.

Prionotropis branneri Anderson
(Plate 34, figures 1, 2, 3, 3a)

Prionotropis branneri ANDERSON, Proc. Calif. Acad. Sci., 3d ser., vol. 2, 1902, p. 125, Pl. 1, figs. 11–16; Fitch (Smith) Ranch, 2 miles west of Phoenix, Oregon.

The holotype of this species, No. 48 (C. A. S. Type Coll.), was partly destroyed in the San Francisco fire. Two other smaller examples of the species were found at the type locality but were lost in the fire. The original figures (Anderson, 1902, Pl. 1, figs. 13, 15, 16) are here reproduced as figures 1–3 of Plate 34. The original description of the species follows (in part) :

"Shell more or less discoidal, but compressed; greatest diameter of largest specimen found, 12 cm, though fragments of larger specimens were collected; thickness at this diameter 35 mm; keel simple at first, appearing at a diameter of 2 mm, showing faint undulations at 10 mm, and in old age breaking up into a median row of nodes with rounded outline and with rounded intervening depressions; umbilicus relatively wide, equal to about three-eighths of entire diameter of coil, having abrupt walls, especially at a diameter of 30 to 40 mm; ribs 25 in number, simple at first, appearing at a diameter of 2 mm or earlier. At 50 mm tubercules begin to develop upon the (ventral border) of the whorl in a double row; those of the inner row have a greater lateral prominence, while the outer incline more toward the plane of the keel. . . . The suture line is simple; siphonal lobe long and relatively narrow, with short, narrow (spurs) upon the side, parallel and equal; . . . The furrows along the keel . . . comparatively shallow, as seen upon the casts. . . ."

The holotype and other examples were found on the Fitch (formerly Smith) Ranch, 2 miles west of Phoenix, Oregon. It represents a horizon near the upper limit of the Turonian.

Prionotropis casperi Anderson n. sp.
(Plate 34, figure 6; Plate 39, figures 3, 4)

Shell of medium size, discoidal, flattened on the sides, section of whorl quadrate, strongly costate, with moderately broad umbilicus; ribs broad, arising on the umbilical border in elongated bullae, depressed near the middle of the sides, bearing two distinct rows of nodes near the ventral border; ribs strongly flexed forward beyond the outer row of tubercules; keel high, narrow, serrated, the segments standing in quite definite relation to the termini of the ribs, a little in advance of the outer tubercules.

The holotype (C. A. S. Type Coll.) (Pl. 34, fig. 6; Pl. 39, fig. 3) was found on the Fitch Ranch, 2 miles west of Phoenix, Oregon, a little above the zone of *P. branneri,* and 200 to 300 feet above the horizon of *Fagesia californica.* It has the following dimensions: greater diameter, 93 mm; width of umbilicus, 33 mm; height of whorl, 36 mm; thickness of whorl, 26 mm. The species is named for the late John Casper Branner of Stanford University, California.

Dimensions of paratype (C. A. S. Type Coll.) (Pl. 39, fig. 4), (young shell): greater diameter, 40 mm; width of umbilicus, 15 mm locality 445A (C. A. S.).

Prionotropis hiltensis Anderson n. sp.
(Plate 63, figure 1)

Shell of medium size in most examples seen, and is disclike, with flattened sides, broad umbilicus having steep walls, little rounded on shoulders, crossed by umbilical ribs that curve forward, and rise on umbilical border in sharp, vertically elongated nodes without spines; ribs crossing sides with a slightly forward slant, and near the ventrolateral angle bear a rather prominent, elongated node that also slants strongly forward on peripheral surface; keel continuous, thin, and a little elevated.

The holotype (C. A. S. Type Coll.) was found about 3 miles north of Henley, Siskiyou County, in the lower part of a narrow shale belt which traverses the west border of the Cottonwood Valley. Its dimensions are: greatest diameter, 81 mm; width of umbilicus, 30 mm; height of whorl, 28 mm; breadth of whorl, 16 mm. The species appears to have attained a much greater size, one example found had a diameter of 178 mm. The horizon of this species is the upper part of the Turonian.

Genus Prionocyclus Meek
Prionocyclus californicus Anderson n. sp.
(Plate 69, figures 4, 4a, 4b)

This species is the first known representative of the genus to be reported from the West Coast.

Undoubtedly this form is related to the genotype, and also to *Prionocyclus macombi* Meek, as figured by Stanton (1893, Pl. XLI, figs. 1, 2) from the Western Interior. Its general features conform to those of the genotype, though having a somewhat broader umbilical ratio, a relatively thicker whorl section, and fewer and heavier ribs. The holotype (C. I. T. Type Coll.) is a fragmentary example of a young adult shell, representing about five-twelfths of a whorl. Apparent diameter of the holotype had been at least 34.9 mm; width of the umbilicus, 16 mm; maximum height of whorl, 8 mm; keel thin, moderately high, not rising to the level of the summit of the rib terminals, and slightly undulating, undulations rising to their maximum near the chevronlike juncture of opposite ribs; ribs strong and single, widely spaced, and nearly straight on sides, though curving strongly forward near peripheral border to meet opposing ribs on opposite side of shell, and a slight backward curve, or none, on umbilical border, but not reaching the whorl suture; interspaces between ribs, rounded, broader than the ribs. Sutures not exposed.

The holotype was found by Popenoe and Findley at locality 1034 (C. I. T.), on Oak Run Creek, Shasta County, associated with *Peroniceras shastense* n. sp., about four-tenths of a mile north of the Hathaway home, and about 800 feet above the base of the Coniacian in this area. Only the holotype and a fragment of another individual were collected.

Genus Prionocycloceras Spath
Prionocycloceras crenulatum (Anderson)
(Plate 34, figures 4, 4a, 5, 5a)

Mortoniceras crenulatum ANDERSON, Proc. Calif. Acad. Sci., 3d ser., vol. 2, 1902, p. 125, Pl. 1, figs. 17, 18; Richardson's ranch, 4 miles north of Montague, Siskiyou County, California. Lower Senonian.

The holotype was lost in the San Francisco fire. The following description is based upon a neotype (C. A. S. Type Coll.), found at the same locality, on the Richardson ranch, and representing a more mature stage of growth. An abbreviated description is given:

Shell of moderate size, discoidal, flattened on the sides, broadly umbilicate, heavily costate, with stout ribs at mature stages; ventral zone flattened, giving the whorl section a narrowly quadrate form; keel well developed, bearing numerous crenulations, separated by broader interspaces, more closely spaced in younger whorls; in young stages of growth the ribs are more slender, arising in bullae on the umbilical border, curving slightly forward, depressed near the middle, but terminating in elongated tubercules which incline forward; in young stages of growth the major ribs bear elevated, sharp spines (Pl. 34, fig. 4a), up to a diameter of 50 mm, not seen in older stages of growth. Keel well developed and crenulated (Pl. 34, fig. 5a); crenulations becoming obsolete in old age.

The neotype (Pl. 34, figs. 5, 5a) has the following dimensions: greater diameter, 110 mm; width of umbilicus, 41 mm; height of whorl, 38 mm; breadth of whorl, 30 mm; number of ribs on last whorl, 25 or more. This species is more closely related to *Prionocyclus macombi* Meek, than to *Prionocyclus wyomingensis* Meek, as is seen in its spines and its crenulated keel, especially in the early stages of growth in both species. In neither case do crenulations appear to have close spatial relations to the ribs; the spines appearing at widely spaced intervals on young, but mature shells. The species appears to be related to *Prionocyclus medio-tuberculatim* Gerhardt, from southern Colombia.

Genus Oregoniceras Anderson n. gen.*
Genotype Schloenbachia oregonensis Anderson

The genus *Oregoniceras* n. gen. exhibits characters belonging to both *Schloenbachia* Neumayr, and *Prionotropis* Meek, and may be regarded as being intermediate between them as it appears to be stratigraphically. Its earliest appearance is in the early or middle Turonian stages in California and Oregon.

In early stages of growth there is a simple continuous keel, which later breaks up into undulations, and still later into a succession of high, thin nodes that resemble those of *Priono-*

---

* *Oregoniceras* first appeared (as a *nomen nudem*) on page 185 of Bull. 118, Calif. State Div. Mines (preprint, 1941). *Subprionocyclus* Shimizu, 1932, type species *Prionocyclus hitchinensis* Billinghurst, is a subjective senior synonym (see Wright and Matsumoto, Mem. Fac. Sci., Kyushu Univ., Ser. D, Geol., vol. 4, p. 129–130, 1954). J. Wyatt Durham, July 15, 1956.

tropis, but in older stages of growth these are lost, the keel becoming reduced to a bevelled ridge with an undulating summit, the ribs uniting on the median plane in chevronlike manner. The ribs, at first like those of *Schloenbachia,* grow a double row of nodes at their outer terminations, but later this feature is also lost. At some stages of growth, the ribs show a disposition to divide in the manner seen in the genotypes of both *Prionotropis* and *Prionocyclus* Meek. Smith (1899), in his phylogenetic study of *Oregoniceras oregonense* (Anderson) and related types has traced the development of its several features, especially of its septation, and has compared them with those of other types dating back to early Mesozoic times. In the same manner he has partially traced the ontogeny of *Mortoniceras (Submortoniceras) gabbi* (Anderson) (= *A. chicoensis* Gabb, not Trask). Smith suggests (1899, p. 248) a common ancestry for both *Oregoniceras oregonense* (Anderson) and *Mortoniceras (Submortoniceras) gabbi* (Anderson), and the descent of the latter from a stock of the former; this suggestion accords well with their stratigraphic relations.

The Turonian age of *Oregoniceras* is shown by the association of its several species with, or preceding the occurrence of *Prionotropis bakeri, Prionotropis branneri, Mammites* and *Scaphites,* and also with *Inoceramus* aff. *I. labiatus* (Auct.)

Oregoniceras oregonense (Anderson)
(Plate 24, figures 4, 4a, 4b)

Schloenbachia oregonensis ANDERSON (M. S.), J. Perrin SMITH, Jour. Morph., vol. 16, 1899, p. 247, Pls. A-E. . . . Anderson, Proc. Calif. Acad. Sci., 3d ser., vol. 2, 1902, p. 122, Pl. 2, figs. 48–57; Pl. 6, fig. 144; Pl. 7, figs. 149, 150.

The first published description of any species belonging to this genus was by Smith (1899), and fortunately the form selected by him for phylogenetic study and illustration is well suited to serve as the genotype.

Following is a brief account and characterization of this species as it is now known, but taken partly from that of 1902, p. 122: Shell discoidal, compressed, increasing in thickness with age and growth; involution about two-fifths; umbilicus broad and shallow, walls not often steep; keel reduced, but distinct, and in mature examples usually reduced; periphery bevelled, and forming an obtusely angled ridge; in youth the keel begins as a low thin, and continuous ridge, which with growth breaks up into undulations, which become more prominent with growth, but which finally become less acute, and at length is reduced to a bevelled, angulated ridge, as shown in the present illustrations. In the earlier account the later stages of growth were not well known, but later search has shown that tubercules continue in reduced form into old age, and examples have been found that indicate the attainment of a diameter of more than 140 mm, in which the ribs become coarse, but still retain their characteristic form and ornamentation, as shown in the figures, with a bevelled but noded periphery. The usual number of ribs is about 48 or 50, and the greater number mentioned in the early account (1902, p. 122) appears to represent another species (? *O. multicostum* Anderson).

This species is most closely related to *O. knighteni, O. condoni,* and perhaps *O. argonautarum.* Representative species were abundant at the old Smith ranch (now Fitch ranch), and have since been collected from the Turonian, near Frazier Corners, east of Redding, on the west side of the Valley near the North Fork of Cottonwood Creek, on Dry Creek, Tehama County, and on Quinto Creek, in the Pacheo quadrangle, and in the Santiago district, Orange County, California. The holotype is No. 36 (C. A. S. Type Coll.) (Pl. 24, figs. 4, 4a); hypotype (C. A. S. Type Coll.) (Pl. 24, fig. 4b).

Oregoniceras knighteni (Anderson)
(Plate 24, figures 5, 5a, 5b; Plate 33, figures 1, 1a, 2, 3)

Schloenbachia knighteni ANDERSON, Proc. Calif. Acad. Sci., 3d ser., vol. 2, 1902, p. 119, Pl. 1, figs. 1–4; Pl. 2, figs. 39, 40; "Forty-nine" mine, southwest of Phoenix, Oregon.

Most of the original material of this species was destroyed in the San Francisco fire though a part was recovered, one of which is figured; other examples have since been found at the type locality, some are also figured. An abbreviated description of the species follows:

Shell discoidal, compressed, sides flattened in youth and in young adult stages, becoming more inflated in older stages, attaining a diameter of 100 mm or more; sides characterized by about 30–32 simple and slightly curved ribs, the curves becoming more pronounced near the periphery; ribs arising in vertically elongated nodes near the umbilicus from which they branch in pairs or trios; others arise a little above this level, singly, but they all extend to the ventral border where they terminate in tubercules, which are more distinct in younger shells, as seen on Plate 24, figures 2 and 3; this tendency is seen in most shells of the species below a diameter of 40 mm, and many below a diameter of 60 mm. The ribs bend more strongly forward at the lower marginal nodes, which are less prominent than the outer row. The ventral and dorsal margins of the whorl are usually abruptly truncated in youth and at maturity, but later become more rounded, or in old age, bevelled. The keel, at first smooth, begins to show undulations at a diameter of 15 or 20 mm; these gradually increase in prominence until maturity; soon after, these begin to decline, finally are lost.

The following specimens are all in the California Academy Sciences Type Collection: holotype (Pl. 24, fig. 5); paratype No. 49 (Pl. 33, fig. 3); hypotype No. 30 (Pl. 33, figs. 1, 1a); additional hypotype (Pl. 33, fig. 2); and large fragment of outer whorl of another hypotype (Pl. 24, figs. 5a, 5b).

The holotype originally described was rather large. A hypotype (No. 30) (Pl. 33, figs. 1, 1a) has the following dimensions: greater diameter, 75 mm; width of umbilicus, 22 mm; height of whorl, 32 mm; breadth of whorl, 18 mm. It was found associated with species of *Scaphites, Mantelliceras,* and other cephalopods characteristic of lower Turonian age, or older.

The name *Oregoniceras knighteni* was given this species in remembrance of the interest taken in the local geology, and in the study of these forms which was first begun by Mr. E. Knighten Anderson, pioneer settler in southern Oregon (1852), to whom the writer is indebted for first calling his attention to this rich locality, and for much aid and encouragement in the study of the region and its faunas.

Oregoniceras condoni Anderson n. sp.
(Plate 14, figures 3, 4, 4a, 5, 6)

This species is small, and belongs to the group of *Oregoniceras oregonense* and *O. knighteni.* In young stages of growth, below a diameter of 30 mm the whorls possess a thin, high keel, which becomes progressively reduced with growth, and disappears at a diameter of 40 mm. Ribs for the most part arise in oblique umbilical bullae, either singly, or in pairs, although others seem to arise near middle of side as intermediary ribs.

This species has been found at the old "Forty-nine" mine, and also farther west near the old Pioneer road on the south border of the Rogue River Valley, Oregon, near the Fitch ranch. The species occurs with other congeners beneath the zone of *Fagesia californica,* and *F. klamathensis.* It belongs to an upper Turonian horizon.

Oregoniceras multicostum (Anderson)
(Plate 28, figures 4, 4a, 4b)

Schloenbachia multicosta ANDERSON, Proc. Calif. Acad. Sci., 3d ser., vol. 2, 1902, p. 120, Pl. 2, figs. 41–47; Fitch (Smith) ranch and the "Forty-nine" mine, near Phoenix, Oregon.

The holotype and other materials upon which this species was based were lost in the San Francisco fire but additional examples were later found at the type locality, and are here illustrated. The species belongs to the group of *Oregoniceras oregonense,* but it is readily distinguished by its finer ribs and other distinctive marks. An abbreviated description follows:

Shell discoidal, compressed, narrowly quadrate in section; umbilicus broad, shallow, and bordered by steep walls; involution moderate, the outer whorls embracing about one-third of the preceding; sides of whorl flattened, cross by about 50 oblique, flexuous ribs, which often bifurcate from the elongated umbilical nodes. The ribs curve forward on approaching the ventral border, as in *O. knighteni,* and at their termini form a double row of tubercules along the ventral border in mature examples. The ribs are generally rounded; the keel, which in young stages is smooth and entire, lacks the parallel grooves noted in other species. In some features, this species is intermediate between *O. oregonense* and *O. knighteni,* but in good examples they are readily distinguished.

The species occurs abundantly at the Fitch ranch (formerly Smith), two miles west of Phoenix, and at the "Forty-nine" mine, where it is associated with other species of the genus, and with other forms which characterize Turonian and older horizons. It has also been found on the west border of the San Joaquin Valley, near Quinto Creek, western Merced County.

Neotype No. 32 (C. A. S. Type Coll.) (Pl. 28, figs. 4, 4a) has the following dimensions: maximum diameter, 23.6 mm; width of umbilicus, 8.5 mm; height of whorl, 9.3 mm; breadth of whorl, 5.9 mm. Hypotype No. 32a (C. A. S. Type Coll.) (Pl. 28, fig. 4b) has the following dimensions: maximum diameter, 18.5 mm; width of umbilicus, 5.8 mm; height of whorl, 8 mm; breadth of whorl, 5 mm.

Oregoniceras siskiyouense (Anderson)
(Plate 23, figures 2, 3; Plate 24, figures 1, 1a, 2, 3)

Schloenbachia siskiyouensis ANDERSON, Proc. Calif. Acad. Sci., 3d ser., vol. 2, 1902, p. 119, Pl. 1, figs. 19, 20; "Forty-nine" mine, near Phoenix, Oregon.

In the original description, the form was said to be "compressed," but later collections of better examples from its type locality show that the shell is more inflated than was the holotype, which was lost in the San Francisco fire. An abbreviated description of the species, based upon better examples, including the Neotype No. 25 (C. A. S. Type Coll.), follows:

Shell discoidal, slightly inflated, with a small umbilicus; keel, at first simple, smooth and thin, begins to break up into nodes at a diameter of 30 mm; which soon become separated by moderately wide intervals; in older stages the segments of the keel become high and narrow, and have a definite spatial relation to the ribs, standing a little in advance of their terminal nodes. The ribs are simple, about 25 in number, and are of two ranks; the first arise in prominent nodes on the umbilical margin, from which they branch, and terminate in the outer row of nodes which diverge slightly from the plane of symmetry. The ribs of the second rank appear first between the pairs of the first; thus each third rib arises a little above the middle of the side, and terminates, as do the others in the external row of tubercules at the ventral border. A little below the inner row of these the ribs develop a distinct swelling which forms the thickest part of the same, separated from the marginal nodes by a shallow but distinct depression.

Spath (1921) has referred to this species under the name *Barroisiceras* ? *siskiyouense* (Anderson), placing it in an upper Chico horizon, but this is clearly an error, since the species is a prionotropid, and its horizon is not above that of its several congeners of Turonian age.

Dimensions of two hypotypes (C. I. T. Type Coll.) (Pl. 23, fig. 2): greater diameter, 31 mm; width of umbilicus 8.2 mm; breadth of whorl, 11 mm; height of whorl, 14.5 mm (Pl. 23, fig. 3); greater diameter, 40 mm; width of umbilicus, 11 mm; breadth of whorl, 11 mm. Locality 1042 (C. I. T.), Rancheria Creek, near Henley, Siskiyou County.

Dimensions (C. A. S. Type Coll.). Hypotype (Pl. 24, figs. 1, 1a) greater diameter, 58 mm; width of umbilicus, 15 mm; height of whorl, 27 mm; maximum breadth of whorl near ventral zone, 20 mm; minimum, 12 mm. Hypotype (Pl. 24, fig. 2); maximum diameter, 33 mm. Neotype No. 25 (Pl. 24, fig. 3); maximum diameter, 48 mm; maximum height, 23 mm; maximum breadth, 14.5 mm. These examples found at locality 445 (C. A. S.), "Forty-nine" mine, 2 miles south of Phoenix, Oregon. Upper Turonian.

Oregoniceras phoenixense Anderson n. sp.
(Plate 25, figures 7, 7a; Plate 33, figures 6, 6a)

Schloenbachia propinque ANDERSON (not Stoliczka), Proc. Calif. Acad. Sci. 3d ser., vol. 2, 1902, p. 123, Pl. 2, figs. 34-38; "Forty-nine" mine, near Phoenix, Oregon.

An abbreviated description from the original text is as follows:

Shell discoidal, compressed, flattened in early stages, more inflated in older whorls; section of whorl at 40 mm diameter, elliptical; ribs, 40–44, showing a tendency to branch near the umbilical border; keel at first simple, smooth and continuous, becomes broken up into undulations at about 20 mm diameter.

The species differs from *O. oregonense* not only in its smaller number of ribs, but in other minor, but important features, as seen in its original description. The sides are more flattened, its keel less conspicuous in both young, and in older stages of growth, and the abdominal area is more angular. The suture lines show important differences, more apparent in direct comparisons of example, than in figures. In *O. oregonense* the ventral lobe has only slight subdivisions, if any; the lateral saddles are simple and rounded, the smaller divisions forming only shallow scallops; the lateral lobe shows a corresponding simplicity. This feature contrasts considerably with the more deeply cut lobes and saddles of *"Schloenbachia" propinqua* (Stoliczka).

This species occurs with other forms of the genus at the "Forty-nine" mine, near Phoenix, Oregon, and also a little to the south of the Fitch ranch in beds that are some 500 feet beneath the horizon of *Fagesia californica* Anderson, and *Prionotropis bakeri* Anderson, which are regarded as being nearly that far beneath the top of the Turonian in this locality.

Dimensions of holotype (C. A. S. Type Coll.) (Pl. 25, figs. 7, 7a) : greater diameter, 39.8 mm; width of umbilicus, 10 mm; maximum breadth of whorl, 8 mm; height of whorl, 18 mm. Paratype (C.A.S. Type Coll.) (Pl. 33, figs. 6, 6a).

Oregoniceras jacksonense Anderson n. sp.
(Plate 25, figures 1, 1a, 2, 2a, 3, 3a, 4, 4a, 4b, 5)

Schloenbachia blanfordiana Stoliczka (?), ANDERSON, Proc. Calif. Acad. Sci., 3d ser., vol. 2, 1902, p. 124, Pl. 1, figs. 5–10; old "Forty-nine" mine, Jackson County, Oregon. (Not *Ammonites blanfordianus* Stoliczka).

In the light of newer collections of fossils from the type locality, this species cannot be regarded as identical with the form described by Stoliczka from southern India. An abbreviated description follows:

Shell discoidal, flat, with moderately wide umbilicus and thin section; umbilicus bordered by abrupt walls, surmounted by about 14 elevated nodes; sides of shell bearing about 40 flat and broad ribs, as seen in shell of 30 mm diameter, becoming obsolete in older shells; sides smooth, except for nodes bordering the umbilicus, and on the ventral margin. In smaller shells the sides are usually smooth, the ribs appearing on the ventral and dorsal borders, extending with the growth of the shell to near the middle of the sides; whorls becoming gradually more involute with age, and finally clasping about half the preceding whorl.

The keel is never prominent, and at a diameter of 30 mm shows undulations; at 45 mm it is reduced to an obtuse ventral angle. The ribs are obsolete at an earlier stage than in others of its congeners.

The dimensions of the holotype (C. A. S. Type Coll.) (Pl. 25, figs. 1, 1a) (1902, Pl. 1, figs. 5, 6) : greater diameter of 48 mm; width of umbilicus, 10 mm; height of whorl, 23 mm; breadth of whorl, 10 mm. Dimensions of paratypes (Pl. 25, figs. 2, 2a) maximum diameter, 26 mm; (Pl. 25, figs. 3, 3a), maximum diameter, 20.8 mm; (Pl. 25, figs. 4, 4a, 4b, 5), maximum length of fragment of whorl, 72.4 mm.

This species has recently been found on Quinto Creek, western Merced County, by Allan Bennison, associated with other species of the genus.

Oregoniceras jillsoni Anderson n. sp.
(Plate 19, figures 6, 6a)

This species is relatively large, thick, and rugged, and is characterized by a broad ventral zone, bearing a moderately prominent keel, having rounded nodes of two ranks, occurring alternately; sides costate, ribs arising singly at umbilical border, crossing sides at nearly right angles to latter, and occasionly dividing a little below ventral border; ribs bearing at outer end a double row of nodes, somewhat reduced in older stages of growth; ribs crossing ventral area, much reduced in prominence, having a forward curve, and meeting in larger nodes of keel; umbilicus broad. The species is related to *Oregoniceras siskiyouense* Anderson, although illustrating an extreme development of the genus in thickness, and in breadth of the ventral zone.

The Holotype (C. A. S. Type Coll.) consists of about one-fifth of a non-septate outer whorl, showing only traces of its umbilical border. It has the following dimensions: Total diameter (est.), 90 mm; umbilicus, 23 mm; height of whorl, 45 mm; breadth of whorl, 32 mm. It was found at the old "Forty-nine" mine, 2 miles south of Phoenix, Oregon. Many fragmentary examples of the species have also been found at a low horizon at loc. 444-A (C.A.S.) at "Rocky Gulch," near the old Jillson (Hazel) mine, 1.5 miles southwest of Henley, Siskiyou County, California. The species is named in honor of C. B. Jillson.

Oregoniceras argonautarum Anderson n. sp.
(Plate 33, figures 4, 4a, 4b, 4c)

Schloenbachia chicoensis ANDERSON (not Trask, not Gabb), Proc. Calif. Acad. Sci. 3d ser., Geol., vol. 2, 1902, p. 116, Pl. 1, figs. 21, 22; Pl. 2, figs. 23-25; "Forty-nine" mine, Jackson County, Oregon.

The early whorls of this species so greatly resemble the figure originally given by Trask (1856, Pl. 2, fig. 1) as to mislead the writer, but later study of localities from which these types were obtained, and also of developments in growth stages of each, led to the corrections here given. The mature stages of the two species have little in common, as has long been recognized, and they are not closely related, though both bear keels, one smooth and entire, the other broken into prominent undulations as shown in the figures. The stratigraphic horizons of the two forms are also far apart, as will be shown. The following notes pertain to the present species.

Shell discoidal, slightly flattened on the sides, umbilicus moderate, walls sloping up to the shoulder; involution about half; walls of the umbilicus surmounted by about 10 or 12 rounded nodes from which ribs arise singly at times, but usually in pairs; intermediary ribs also arise above the umbilicus; ribs about 25-27 in number, broad and nearly straight, terminating in rounded, slightly prominent nodes at the ventral border; ribs rather broad and flat; ventral zone bevelled, and supporting an undulating, or noded keel.

The holotype was destroyed in the San Francisco fire, but it had the following dimensions: greater diameter, 40 mm; width of umbilicus, 10 mm; height of whorl, 16 mm; breadth of whorl, 11 mm. The maximum growth limits are not known.

This species was found associated with others of the genus at the old "Forty-nine" mine, southwest of Phoenix, Oregon, and with species of *Scaphites, Hyphantoceras,* and *Acanthoceras,* showing its age to be early Turonian or older.

The name is suggested in recognition and honor of the early settlers of southern Oregon, and of northern California (1850-1860), and of the pioneers throughout the West.

Oregoniceras normale Anderson n. sp.
(Plate 25, figures 8, 8a)

Shell of medium size, umbilicus moderate, involution normal, and sculpture moderate though distinct, somewhat compressed. Number of ribs per whorl is about 30-32; ribs nearly straight, curving forward near periphery; moderately noded; keel moderate, periphery bevelled in mature and older stages of growth.

The shell is noted chiefly for its lack of pronounced features, and its narrowly quadrate form. The holotype (C. A. S. Type Coll.) has the following dimensions: greater diameter, 44 mm; width of umbilicus, 10 mm; height of whorl, 22 mm; breadth of whorl, 12 mm. This species is apparently rare and was found only at the "Forty-nine" mine, southwest of Phoenix, Oregon.

Family MORTONICERATIDAE Spath
Genus **Mortoniceras** Meek

As now interpreted the genus *Mortoniceras* Meek includes a considerable number of keeled types occurring in Europe and America. Among these are *Mortoniceras (Texanites) texanum* (Roemer), *Mortoniceras delawarense* (Morton), *Mortoniceras vespertinum* (Morton), *Mortoniceras campaniense* Grossouvre, *Mortoniceras falloti* Collignon, *Mortoniceras (Submortoniceras) woodsi* Spath, and many others.

Keeled forms coming within the limits of this genus (s. 1.), occur in considerable numbers and varieties in some districts in the Great Valley of California. These types have not yet been recorded from other areas on the West Coast, although they are known elsewhere in the greater Indo-Pacific basin, in southeast Africa, and in Madagascar. In California types are found that seem to be closely related to some known on the Atlantic Coast, namely, *Mortoniceras delawarense* (Morton), but they seem less closely akin to those of Texas, namely, *M. (Texanites) texanum* (Roemer), and to similar species in north Africa, and Europe. No exhaustive study of these types is attempted here.

A study of an unusually large collection of keeled ammonites from the Chico formation in Butte County, and from other areas, greatly enlarges our knowledge of this formation and its fauna.

On the west border of the Sacramento Valley, no species of *Mortoniceras* have been found north of Carquinez Strait, although types of *Mortoniceras* and other faunal elements occur south of Mount Diablo, on the east flank of the Diablo Range, showing the presence of equivalents of the Chico formation on the west side of the Great Valley.

Subgenus SUBMORTONICERAS Spath
Mortoniceras (Submortoniceras) randalli Anderson n. sp.
(Plate 46, figures 1, 1a; Plate 50, figures 2, 2a, 3)

Submortoniceras chicoensis HANNA and HERTLEIN, (not Trask, not Taff, Hanna and Cross), Calif. Dept. of Nat. Res., Division of Mines, Bull. 118, 1941, p. 168, Pl. 61, figs. 13, 14; locality 27838 (C. A. S.), Chico Creek, Butte County, California.

The holotype (C. A. S. Type Coll.) (Pl. 50, figs. 2, 2a) has the following dimensions: greater diameter, 87 mm; width of umbilicus, 30 mm; height of whorl, 37 mm; breadth of whorl, 26 mm. Shell is discoidal, a little inflated in inner half of whorl; umbilicus moderately broad, sides a little convex, curving abruptly to umbilicus; section of whorl subquadrate, broadest near umbilicus, narrowing toward periphery; sides strongly costate, ribs arising on umbilical border in elongated nodes, separated by equally broad, concave interspaces; ribs slightly sigmoidal, some of them dividing a little below outer row of tubercules, or near median row; ribs bearing five rows of tubercules in all; keel entire, low and rounded, up to a diameter of 90 mm, or more; tubercules elongated parallel to periphery. The figured hypotype No. 5952 (C. A. S. Type Coll.) (Pl. 46, figs. 1, 1a) is somewhat smaller than the holotype. A fragment (Pl. 50, fig. 3), nearly one-fourth of a whorl, resembling part of the hypotype, is in the collections of Stanford University. It was found at the "Redmond Cut," on the Western Pacific R. R., 3 miles east of Altamont, Alameda County.

By analogy, *Mortoniceras randalli* should be regarded as representing a lower-middle Campanian horizon in its type area on the east border of the Sacramento Valley, and at all other places where it may be found.

Mortoniceras (Submortoniceras) chicoense (Trask)
(Plate 60, figures 1, 2)

Ammonites chicoensis TRASK, Calif. Acad. Nat. Sci. Proc., vol. 1, 1856, p. 92, Pl. 2, figs. 1, 1a; Chico Creek, Butte County. (Not *Ammonites chicoensis* Gabb, Paleont. Calif. vol. 1, 1864, p. 68, Pl. 13, figs. 17, 17a, b).
Schloenbachia chicoensis ANDERSON (in part), Proc. Calif. Acad. Sci., 3d ser., vol. 2, 1902, p. 116 (not Pl. 1, figs. 21, 22; not Pl. 2, figs. 23, 25), Oregon and California.
Ammonites chicoensis TAFF, HANNA, AND CROSS, Geol. Soc. Am., Bull., vol. 51, 1940, p. 1320, Pl. 1, figs. 1, 2; Chico Creek, Butte County.

The holotype of this species was the property of the California Academy of Sciences, and was well known to the writer prior to 1906, when it was lost in the San Francisco fire. It was a small, immature specimen, not fully representative of the species or of the generic group to which it belonged, and was poorly figured. It probably belonged to the genus *Mortoniceras* Meek, since most of the keeled ammonites since collected in this area are so assignable. Many later attempts have been made to obtain a representative of the species in its more mature stages of growth, and to ascertain its true stratigraphic position in the Upper Cretaceous of the Great Valley, but hitherto without much success. From the more recent collections made on Chico Creek by Taff, Hanna and Cross, a neotype has been selected, and was figured by these writers, and it appears to correctly represent the species first described by Trask. The neotype is No. 5785 (C. A. S. Type Coll.), and was found at locality 27838 (C. A. S.) on Chico Creek, 3.1 miles south of the Frank Mickey ranch house. Examination of the neotype show it to be referable to the genus *Mortoniceras* Meek, and of the group of *Mortoniceras delawarense* (Morton). It has the following dimensions: greater diameter, 79.8 mm; width of umbilicus, 20 mm; height of whorl, 37 mm; breadth of whorl, 26 mm. As determined from the faunal assemblage, and its stratigraphic relations to other faunal zones its age is not younger than lower-middle Campanian, even though some of its congeners in other areas may be assigned to somewhat higher or lower horizons. It was thought earlier that its age might be Santonian.

Mortoniceras (Submortoniceras) buttense (Anderson)
(Plate 33, figures 5, 5a)

Schloenbachia buttensis ANDERSON, Proc. Calif. Acad. Sci., 3d ser., vol. 2, 1902, p. 118, Pl. 4, figs. 110, 111; Pentz, Butte County, California.

An abbreviated description of this species is here taken from the original account:

This species is related to *Mortoniceras (Submortoniceras) gabbi* (Anderson). The ribs of the present species, about 16 in number, counted on the umbilical border, are branching and noded; the nodes being in five rows on the several ribs; umbilical row more elevated and narrow; ribs branching at either of the median rows; node on the outer row sharp and ridge-like on both sides of the venter, forming between them a flattened ventral zone; keel low and entire, rounded; suture line not clearly exposed.

The holotype No. 12096 is in the Museum of Paleontology, University of California, from which were obtained the following measurements: greater diameter, 64 mm; width of umbilicus, 16 mm; height of whorl, 30 mm; breadth of whorl, 16 mm. The species occurs with *M. (Submortoniceras) pentzanum* n. sp., and *M. (Submortoniceras) gabbi* (Anderson) at locality 1125 (C. A. S.) a mile west of Pentz, in the upper portion of the Chico formation. It was associated with *Canadoceras* aff. *C. fraternum* (Gabb), *Butticeras buttense* n. sp., and many species of pelecypods and gastropods. This species and its associated fauna here mark a lower-middle Campanian stage.

Mortoniceras (Submortoniceras) pentzanum Anderson n. sp.
(Plate 51, figures 1, 1a, 2, 2a)

This species is similar to *M. (Submortoniceras) gabbi* (Anderson) in having a thin, discoidal form, a narrow umbilicus, and a large number of ribs (50-60) which are almost without nodes. In the present species, the ribs are only faintly noded, and are more numerous, and also more flattened than in other species. The umbilicus is exceptionally narrow, and in these features it differs from other species of *Mortoniceras* and might be given subgeneric rank. The holotype and paratype (C. A. S. Type Coll.) were found by the writer at locality 27838 (C. A. S.), associated with *M. (Submortoniceras) gabbi* (Anderson), *Butticeras buttense* n. sp., *Canadoceras* aff. *C. fraternum* (Gabb), *Baculites chicoensis* Trask, and with numerous pelecypods and gastropods. The holotype, septate throughout, has the following dimensions: greater diameter, 89 mm; width of umbilicus, 9.5 mm; height of whorl, 45.2 mm; breadth of whorl, 24 mm. Paratype has a maximum diameter of 54.8 mm.

Mortoniceras (Submortoniceras) templetoni (Hall and Ambrose)
(Plate 60, figures 4, 4a)

Schloenbachia templetoni HALL AND AMBROSE, Nautilus, vol. 30, 1916, p. 78, (not figured) ;
 Western Pacific RR. cut between Altamont and Greenway, Alameda County, on the west
 border of the San Joaquin Valley. . . . WIEDEY, Nautilus, vol. 43, 1929, p. 25, Pl. 2, fig. 4;
 locality as given above.

The holotype of this species is in the collections of Stanford University. The following
description is taken partly from that of the authors:

The shell is flatly discoidal, compressed, having a broad umbilicus with somewhat abrupt
walls bordered by about 20 to 24 rounded, slightly elevated tubercules, from which the ribs
arise; sutures not known. According to the authors there are 45 ribs on the last whorl. They
state further that:

"some of the ribs bifurcate on the surface of the shell in nodes, without any apparent regularity of system, and from three series of costal nodes on the surface . . . not counting the
umbilical and ventral margin nodes. . . . The nodes on the ventral border are opposite each
other. The tubercules of the keel stand a little forward of the marginal nodes, in a position to
exactly meet the forward curving ribs."

With one exception, this description is acceptable; there is no evidence of nodes existing
on the keel, although it is a little distorted by rock pressure. The keel is essentially smooth,
as in other species of the genus, but with only slight accidental swellings, not nodes. There
are five rows of costal nodes on the sides, as in other species of this genus. The species is
related to *M. (Submortoniceras) gabbi* (Anderson) and should indicate the presence of
Campanian deposits near Altamont. An analogue of this species is figured by Collignon
(1932, Pl. 5) from Madagascar, as *M. (Submortoniceras) woodsi* Spath.

The holotype of the present species has the following dimensions: greater diameter, 188
mm; width of umbilicus (est.), 55 mm; height of whorl, 76 mm; breadth of whorl (est.),
24 mm.

Mortoniceras (Submortoniceras) gabbi (Anderson)

Ammonites chicoensis GABB (not Trask), Paleont. Calif., vol. 1, 1864, p. 68, Pl. 13, figs. 17,
 a, b; Pentz (Pence), Butte County.
Schloenbachia gabbi ANDERSON, Proc. Calif. Acad. Sci., 3d ser., vol. 2, 1902, p. 117, (not
 figured) ; locality as given above.

Gabb's illustration of this species is defective, and in some important respects does not
conform to his description nor to the form most frequently found at the locality from which
he obtained the type. The shell is discoidal, little inflated, and bears about 40 ribs, counted
near the periphery, all of which arise from about 14 elongated bullae on the umbilical border ;
ribs branching from the umbilical bullae, and again above the middle of the side into flattened ribs; sides of whorl flattened; ventral zone also flattened, but bearing a low, rounded,
and continuous keel; umbilicus relatively small, with abrupt walls; suture as shown by Gabb
(1864, Pl. 13, fig. 17b).

The holotype of this species appears to have been lost; a neotype (C. A. S. Type Coll.)
septate throughout, has the following measurements: greater diameter, 73 mm; width of
umbilicus, 16.1 mm; height of whorl, 31 mm; breadth of whorl, 20.6 mm. This species is
somewhat similar in size, form, and ornamentation to *M. (Submortoniceras) woodsi* Spath,
as figured by Collignon (1932, Pl. 5), but differs from the type figured by Spath (1922, Zulu-
land, Pl. 21) in being thinner, or less inflated, and more squarely truncated on the periphery;
it is also more strongly noded, the ribs branching either from umbilical nodes, or from the
median row, and the terminal row is set with their axes more nearly parallel with the
periphery.

The holotype, the neotype, and other examples, were obtained at Pentz, and were associated with *Canadoceras fraternum* (Gabb), and numerous pelecypod and gastropod species
characteristic of the Chico formation.

Fragmentary examples of the species have been found at various other points in the Great Valley, as at "Brushy Knob," and on the highway south of Altamont, and also on Garzas Creek, Stanislaus County, near the middle of the Panoche formation (middle Senonian).

Genus Butticeras Anderson n. gen.
Genotype Butticeras buttense Anderson

The group of small Upper Cretaceous (Campanian) ammonites for which the above name is here proposed is not large. That the genus belongs in Mortoniceratidae appears probable from its association with members of this family, and from the fact that in early and young stages of growth it possesses a keel, the character of which seems to conform to that of this family. At maturity this keel is lost, the periphery becomes rounded and smooth, the sides are costate, and the costae are more or less strongly noded, though only on the umbilical border, and at their outer extremity near the ventral border. From the umbilical nodes, the ribs arise in pairs, trios, or larger groups, but they exhibit no evidences of other nodes than those at their extremities.

The umbilicus is of moderate size or small, with abrupt walls, surmounted by about 15 tubercules of rounded form.

Among the most distinctive characters of the genus are its suture lines, as shown in the genotype; this line is dominated by a strong median lobe, on either side of which is a broad rounded saddle, each of which is divided by a minor lobe of small depth.

Only two species of the genus are now known, both appearing in the Chico formation, which they characterize, along with *Mortoniceras, (Submortoniceras), Grossouvreites* and other cephalopods.

Butticeras buttense Anderson n. sp.
(Plate 53, figures 3, 3a, 3b, 4)

Shell discoidal, not greatly compressed, sides slightly inflated. Surface, nearly smooth, shows only inconspicuous costae at maturity, branching from small umbilical nodes into three, four, or more diverging thread-like costae that curve forward upon approach to periphery. The umbilicus is of moderate or small size, walls vertical and smooth, set at top with small but clearly visible nodes; periphery, after losing its keel becomes at first narrowly angular, then rounded and smooth; suture lines as shown in the figure, with a large central lobe, on either side of which is a secondary lobe much reduced in size.

The holotype (C. I. T. Coll.) (Pl. 53, figs. 3, 3a, 3b) has the following dimensions: greatest diameter, 44.5 mm; width of umbilicus, 11 mm; maximum height of whorl, 18.6 mm; breadth of whorl, 11 mm. This example was found by W. P. Popenoe, at locality 1041 (C. I. T.) near the bridge on Butte Creek, at the junction of its branches, in Butte County, and in the Chico formation. Also a paratype (Pl. 53, fig. 4) from the same locality has the following dimensions: maximum diameter, 44.5 mm; breadth of whorl, approx. 10.7 mm; maximum height of whorl, 18.6 mm; width of umbilicus, approximately 11.9 mm. A similar but smaller example of the same species was found by the writer a mile west of Pentz, at locality 1125 (C. A. S.), associated with *Mortoniceras (Submortoniceras) pentzanum* n. sp., *Canadoceras* aff. *C. fraternum* (Gabb), and *"Helicoceras" vermiculare* (Gabb).

Butticeras studleyi Anderson n. sp.
(Plate 51, figures 3, 4, 4a)

In size, form, and ornamentation, this species is not unlike the preceding, but it differs from it in having a relatively larger umbilicus, well-developed ribs, and more prominent umbilical nodes, from which the ribs arise, usually in pairs, though sometimes singly, nearly straight, though curving sharply forward on approaching the ventral zone.

Two examples of this species were found by Taff, Hanna, and Cross at locality 27836 (C. A. S.) on Chico Creek, a mile below the Mickey ranch house, associated with many other species, including *Mortoniceras (Submortoniceras) randalli* n. sp., *M. (Submortoni-*

ceras) chicoense (Trask) and many pelecypods and gastropods. In general form and ornamentation, the holotype resembles *Muniericeras blandfordi* (Stoliczka), as figured by M. Collignon (1932, Pl. 4).

The shell is discoidal, compressed, with a narrow periphery, bearing in young and ephebic stages only, a low keel, which later assumes a bevelled and finally a rounded form, as in the preceding species. The suture lines is its most striking feature, consisting of a low, flattened siphonal saddle, two broad lateral saddles, and three minor saddles near the umbilical border. Holotype (C. A. S. Type Coll.) has the following dimensions: greatest diameter, 41 mm; width of umbilicus, 14 mm; height of whorl, 16 mm; breadth of whorl, 9 mm. The paratype (C. A. S. Type Coll.) is smaller, having a diameter of 34 mm; an umbilical measure of 11 mm; and a breadth of 7 mm. One example of this species was found by Popenoe at locality 1041 (C. I. T.), on Butte Creek, Butte County, in the Chico formation. The species is named in recognition of the work done in the Chico formation of Butte County by Prof. C. K. Studley of Chico. Type locality 27838 (C. A. S.) on Chico Creek, near the middle of the exposed section.

Order BELEMNOIDEA

Family BELEMNITIDAE de Blainville

Genus **Neohibolites** Stolley

Neohibolites fontinalis Anderson

(Plate 5, figure 3)

Belemnites sp. ANDERSON, Proc. Calif. Acad. Sci., 3d ser., vol. 2, 1902, p. 40, Pl. 8, figs. 169, 170; Texas Springs (Texas Flat by error), Shasta County, California.
Neohibolites fontinalis ANDERSON, Geol. Soc. Am., Special Paper, No. 16, p. 231, Pl. 81, figs. 7, 8; Texas Springs, Shasta County.

The original specimen was destroyed in the San Francisco fire. A later visit to the type locality resulted in the finding of better material, which may be described as follows:

Guard long and slender, slightly fusiform in its lower two-thirds, expanded in its alveolar portion; section of guard circular, axis central; phragmacone only slightly inserted, with an apical angle of about 26 degrees; ventral groove rather faint, not showing on the holotype; apex acuminate. The holotype No. 8977 (C. A. S. Type Coll.) measures: length, 98 mm; greatest diameter, 7 mm; diameter below alveolus, 5 mm.

The species resembles *Neohibolites ultimus* (d'Orbigny) from the Cenomanian of England, but its relation is perhaps only generic. It is longer and more slender, and has a more acuminate point. Its horizon, as shown by its associates, including *Sonneratia stantoni*, *Beudanticeras haydeni,* and *Terebratella densleonis*, is near that at Horsetown, and is regarded as uppermost Albian, and at the base of the Upper Cretaceous; it is not known to occur in the Horsetown group. It may be compared to *"Belemnites" stylus* Stoliczka, from southern India although it does not show a ventral groove, as does the Indian species.

LITERATURE CITED

ADKINS, W. S.
  1918 *The Weno and Pawpaw formations of the Texas Comanchean,* Univ. Texas Bull., no. 1856, p. 1–172.
  1928 *Handbook of Texas Cretaceous fossils,* Univ. Texas Bull., no. 2838, p. 1–385, pls. 1–137.

ANDERSON, F. M.
  1895 *Some Cretaceous beds of Rogue River Valley, Oregon,* Jour. Geol., vol. 3, p. 455–463.
  1902a *Cretaceous deposits of the Pacific Coast,* Calif. Acad. Sci., Proc. (3), vol. 2, p. 1–54.
  1902b *The physiographic features of the Klamath Mountains,* Jour. Geol., vol. 10, p. 144–159.
  1904 *Stratigraphy of the southern coast ranges of California,* Bull. Geol. Soc. Amer., vol. 15, p. 581–582 (abst.).
  1905 *A stratigraphic study in the Mount Diablo Range of California,* Proc. Calif. Acad. Sci., (3) vol. 2, p. 155–248.
  1908 *A further stratigraphic study in the Mount Diablo Range of California,* Proc. Calif. Acad. Sci., (4), vol. 3, p. 1–40.
  1938a *Faunal and chronological aspects of the Upper Cretaceous in the Great Valley of California,* Geol. Soc. Amer., Proc. 1937, p. 235.
  1938b *Lower Cretaceous deposits in California and Oregon,* Geol. Soc. Amer., Spec. Paper 16, 339 p.
  1938c *Synopsis of the Upper Cretaceous deposits [Chico Series] in California and Oregon,* Geol. Soc. Amer. Bull., vol. 49, no. 12, Pt. 2, p. 1863, (abst).

ANDERSON, F. M., AND HANNA, G. D.
  1935 *Cretaceous geology of Lower California,* Proc. Calif. Acad. Sci., (4), vol. 23, p. 1–34.

ANDERSON, R., AND PACK, R. W.
  1915 *Geology and oil resources of the west border of the San Joaquin Valley north of Coalinga, California,* U.S.G.S., Bull. 603, 220 pages.

ARNOLD, R., AND ANDERSON, R.
  1907a *Diatomaceous deposits of northern Santa Barbara County, California,* U.S.G.S., Bull. 315, p. 438–447.
  1907b *Geology and oil resources of the Santa Maria oil district, Santa Barbara County, California,* U.S.G.S., Bull. 322, 161 pages, map.
  1907c *Preliminary report on the Santa Maria oil district, Santa Barbara County, California,* U.S.G.S., Bull. 317, 60 pages, map.
  1910 *Geology and oil resources of the Coalinga district, California,* U.S.G.S., Bull. 398, 354 pages.

ARNOLD, R., AND JOHNSON, H. R.
  1910 *Preliminary report on the McKittrick-Sunset oil region, Kern and San Luis Obispo Counties, California,* U.S.G.S., Bull. 406, 225 pages, maps.

ASHLEY, G. H., et al.,
  1939 *Classification and nomenclature of rock units,* Bull Amer. Assoc. Petrol. Geol., vol. 7, no. 7, p. 1068–1098.

BECKER, G. F.
  1885 *Notes on the stratigraphy of California,* U.S.G.S., Bull. 19, 28 pages.

BECKER, G. F., AND WHITE, C. A.
  1888 *Geology of the quicksilver deposits of the Pacific slope,* U.S.G.S., Mon. 13, xix + 486 pages, atlas.

BENNISON, A. P.
  1940 *Late Cretaceous of the Diablo Range,* Read at the Meeting of the LeConte Club, Stanford University, March 2, 1940.

BÖSE, EMIL
  1903 *Informe sobre los temblores de Zanatepec a fines de septiembre de 1902, y sobre el estado actual del volcan de Tacana,* Méx. I. G., Par 1; 5–25 (1903), Méx. Sec. Fomento, B (2) 3, no. 5, IV:59–79 (1903).
  1923 *Algunas faunos cretácicas de Zacatecas, Durango y Guerrero.* Mexico, I. G., Bol. 42, pp. 1–219, Pls. 1–19.
  1927 *Cretaceous Ammonites from Texas and Northern Mexico,* Univ. Texas Bull., no. 2748, p. 143–312.

BÖSE, E., AND CAVINS, O. A.
  1927 *The Cretaceous and Tertiary of southern Texas and northern Mexico,* Univ. Texas Bull., no. 2748, p. 7–142.

Böse, E., and Wittich, E.
1913 *Informe relativo a la exploración de la región norte de la costa occidental de la Baja California*, Mex. I. G., Par 4, p. 307–529.

Boule, M., Lemoine, P., and Thevenin, A.
1906 *Paléontologie de Madagascar*. III. *Cephalopodes Crétacés de Diego Suarez*, Ann. Paléont., T. 1, fasc. 4; T. 2, fasc. 1. Paris.

Brewer, W. H.
1866 *Whitney's geology of California*, Amer. Jour. Sci. (2), vol. 41, p. 231–246, 351–368.

Burckhardt, Carlos
1900 *Traces geologiques d'un ancien continent Pacifique*, Rev. Musio de la Plata, T. 10, p. 177.
1906 *Géologie de la Sierra de Mazapil de Santa Rosa*, Guide Congr. Géol., Mexico, fasc. 26, 40 pp. maps.
1930 *Etude synthétique sur le Mésozoique*, Soc. Paleont. Suisse Mém., vol. 49, p. 1–123, 32 figs.

Camp, C. L.
1942 *California Mosasaurs*, Mem. Univ. Calif., vol. 13, no. 1, vi + 68 p., 26 figs., 6 pls.

Campbell, A. S., and Clark, B. L.
1944 *Radiolaria from the Upper Cretaceous of middle California*, Geol. Soc. Amer., Spec. Paper 57, 61 p., 8 pls., 2 figs. incl. index, geol. maps.

Chamberlain, T. C., and Salisbury, R. D.
1907 *Geology*, 3 vols., New York: Henry Holt and Co., vol. 1, *Geologic processes and their results*, xix + 684 pp. (1905); vol. 2, *Earth history; Genesis—Paleozoic*, xxvi + 692 pp. (1906); vol. 3, *Earth history; Mesozoic—Cenozoic*, xi + 624 p. (1907).

Clapp, C. H.
1911 *Geology of the Victoria and Saanich quadrangles, Vancouver Islands, B. C.* Can. Geol. Survey, Sum. Rep. 1910, p. 102–109.
1912a *Geology of the Nanaimo sheet, Nanaimo coal field, Vancouver Island, B. C.*, Can. Geol. Survey, Sum. Rep. 1911, p. 91–105, map.
1912b *Notes on the geology of the Comox and Suquash coal fields, Vancouver Island*, Can. Geol. Survey, Sum. Rep. 1911, p. 105–107.
1912c *Southern Vancouver Island*, Can. Geol. Survey, Mem. 13, 208 pages, map.

Clark, S. G.
1940 *Geology of the Covelo district, Mendocino County, California*, Univ. Calif. Publ., Bull. Dept. Geol. Sci., vol. 25, no. 2, p. 119–142, 7 figs.

Collignon, M.
1932 *Fossiles du crétáce supérieur du Menabe*, Ann. de Paléont., vol. 21, fasc. 2, p. 1–54, Pls. 1–9.
1937 *Ammonites cénomaniennes du sud-ouest de Madagascar*, Serv. des Mines, Madagascar, Ann. Geol. f. 8, p. 31–69, 11 Pls.
1938 *Ammonites campaniennes et maestrichtiennes de l'ouest et du sud de Madagascar*, Serv. des Mines, Madagascar Ann. Geol., f. 9, p. 55–115, 16 figs., 9 Pls.

Cooper, J. G.
1894 *Catalogue of Culifornian fossils* (Parts II, III, IV, V), Calif. State Min. Bur., Bull. 4, 65 pages.

Darton, N. H.
1921 *Geologic reconnaissance in Baja California*, Jour. Geol., vol. 29, no. 8, p. 720–748, 22 figs.

Diller, J. S.
1886 *Notes on the geology of northern California*, U.S.G.S., Bull. 33, p. 373–386.
1891 *Note on the Cretaceous rocks of northern California*, Amer. Jour. Sci., (3), vol. 40, p. 476–478.
1893 *Cretaceous and Early Tertiary of northern California and Oregon*, Geol. Soc. Amer. Bull., vol. 4, p. 205–244, map.
1903a *Description of the Port Orford quadrangle, Oregon*, U.S.G.S., Geol. Atlas, Port Orford Folio no. 89.
1903b *Klamath Mountain section, California*, Amer. Jour. Sci., (4), vol. 15, p. 342–362.

Diller, J. S., and Stanton, T. W.
1892 *Geology of the Taylorsville region of California*, Geol. Soc. Amer. Bull., vol. 3, p. 369–394.
1894 *The Shasta-Chico Series*, Geol. Soc. Amer. Bull., vol. 5, pp. 435–464.
1908 *Geology of the Taylorsville region, California*, U.S.G.S., Bull. 353, 128 pages, map.

Douville, R.
1906 *Sur des ammonites provenants des environs de Lima, et une nouvelle coupure de la famille des Hoplitides*, Favrella, *n. gen.*, Soc. Géol. de France, Bull. 20, xii, p. 164–166.

ELDRIDGE, G. H.
  1902   *The Petroleum industry of California,* Eng. and Mng. Jour., New York, vol. 73, p. 41.
ENGLISH, W. A.
  1926   *Geology and oil resources of the Puente Hills region, Southern California,* U.S.G.S., Bull. 768, p. 17–18.
ETHERIDGE, ROBT. JR.
  1902a *A monograph on the Cretaceous invertebrate fauna of New South Wales,* Geol. Survey, N. S. Wales, Paleont. no. 11.
  1902b *The Cretaceous Mollusca of South Australia,* Royal Soc. So. Australia, Mem., vol. 2, pt. 1, 54 pages.
FAIRBANKS, H. W.
  1893a *Geology and mineralogy of Shasta County,* [*Calif.*], Calif. State Min. Bur., 11th Rept. of Mineralogist, p. 24–53, map.
  1893b *Geology of Tehama, Colusa, Lake and Napa counties,* [*Calif.*], Calif. State Min. Bur., 11th Rept. of Mineralogist, p. 54–75.
  1893c *The validity of the so-called Wallala beds as a division of the California Cretaceous,* Am. Journ. Sci., ser. 3, vol. 45, p. 473–478.
  1894   *Geology of northern Ventura, Santa Barbara, San Luis Obispo, Monterey, and San Benito counties,* [*Calif.*], Calif. State Min. Bur., Rept. 12, p. 493–526.
  1895   *The stratigraphy at the California coast ranges,* Journ. Geol., vol. 3, p. 415–433.
  1896   *The age of the California coast ranges,* Am. Geol., vol. 18, p. 271–282.
  1898   *Geology of a portion of the southern coast ranges,* Jour. Geol., vol. 6, p. 551–576.
  1904   *Description of the San Luis quadrangle,* [*Calif.*], U.S.G.S., Atlas San Luis fol. (no. 101), 14 pages, map.
FARQUHAR, F. P. (ed.)
  1930   *Up and down California, 1860–1864,* Journal of Wm. H. Brewer, professor of agriculture in the Sheffield Scientific School from 1864 to 1903. New Haven: Yale Univ. Press, xxx + 601 pp., illustr. Preface by Russell H. Chittenden.
FRITSCHE, C. H.
  1923   *Neue Kreidefauna aus Sud Amerika (Chile, Bolivia, Peru, Colombia),* Neus Jahrb. Mineral., Geol. Paläont., Beil. Bd. 50, p. 1–56, 313–334.
GABB, W. M.
  1864   *Description of the Cretaceous fossils,* Calif. Geol. Survey, Paleont., vol. 1, p. 58–81, 102–236, pls. 9–31.
  1869   *Cretaceous and Tertiary fossils,* Calif. Geol. Survey, Paleont., vol. 2, 299 p., illustr.
GERTH, ENRIQUE
  1925   *La Fauna Neocomiana de la Cordillera Argentina, en la Parte meridional de la Provincia de Mendoza,* Acad. Nat. Cien., Cordoba, Actas, vol. 9, p. 57–130, 6 pls.
  1928   *Neue Faunen der oberden Kreide mit Hippuriten aus Nordperu,* Leidsche Geol. Med., II, 4, vol. 5, p. 231–241.
GROSSOUVRE, A. DE
  1894   *Les Ammonites de la Craie Superieure: Mém. pour Servir á l'explication de la carte,* Géol. Détailée de la France—Recherches sur la Craie Superieure.
  1901–1908   *Recherches sur la Craie Supérieure,* Fasc. 1–2.
HAUG, E.
  1900   *Les Geosynclineux et les aires continentales,* Contrib. a l'étude des transgressions marines, Soc. Géol. de France, Bull., (3), T. 28, p. 617.
HESSE, C. J., AND WELLES, S. P.
  1936   *The first record of a dinosaur from the West Coast,* Science (n.s.), vol. 84, no. 2172, p. 157–158.
HILL, R. T., AND VAUGHAN, T. W.
  1898   *The Lower Cretaceous Gryphaeas of the Texas region.* U. S. Geol. Surv. Bull., vol. 151, p. 1–139.
HUEY, A. S.
  1937   *Stratigraphy of the Tesla quadrangle, California,* Proc. Geol. Soc. Amer., 1936, p. 335, (abst.).
HULIN, C. D.
  1935   *Geologic features of the dry placers of the northern Mojave Desert,* Calif. Dept. Nat. Res., Div. Mines, State Mineralogist's Rept. 30, p. 417–426.
HYATT, A.
  1894   *Phylogeny of an acquired characteristic,* Amer. Philos. Soc. Proc., vol. 32, no. 143, p. 349–647, illustr.
  1903   *Pseudoceratites of the Cretaceous,* U.S.G.S., Mon. 44, 351 p., illustr., (T. W. Stanton, ed.).
JENKINS, OLAF P. (ed)
  1940–1943   *Geologic formations and the economic development of the oil and gas fields of*

California, State of California, Dept. Nat. Resources; Division of Mines, Bull. 118, pts. 1, 2, 3, 4.

JIMBO, K.
1894 *Beitrage zur Kenntniss der Fauna der Kreideformation von Hokkaido (Japan).* Paleont. Abh., n. f., Bd. 2 (6), Heft 3, p. 1–46, pls. 1–39.

KEW, W. S. W.
1920 *Cretaceous and Cenozoic Echinoidea of the Pacific coast of North America,* Univ. Calif. Publ., Bull. Dept. Geol., vol. 12, p. 23–236, pls. 3–42.

KILIAN, W., AND REBOUL, P.
1909 *Les Céphalopodes neocrétacés des îles Seymour et Snow Hill,* Wissensch. Ergebn. der Schwedischen Südpolar-Expedition, 1901–1903, (conducted by Otto Nordenskjold), Bd. 3, Lief. 6.

KIRBY, J. M.
1943 *Upper Cretaceous stratigraphy of the west side of Sacramento Valley, south of Willows, Glenn County, California,* Bull. Amer. Assoc. Petrol. Geol., vol. 27, no. 3, p. 279–305.

KOSSMAT, F.
1895–1898 *Untersuchungen ueber die Südindische Kreideformation,* Beitr. Paläont. und Geol. Oesterr. Ungarns u. des Orient, vol. 9, vol. 11.
1897 *The Cretaceous deposits of Pondicherri,* Rec. Geol. Survey India, vol. 30.

LAWSON, A. C.
1895 *Sketch of the geology of the San Francisco Peninsula, [Calif.],* U.S.G.S., Ann. Rept. 15, p. 399–476.
1914 *Description of the Tamalpais, San Francisco, Concord, San Mateo, and Haywards quadrangles, [Calif.],* U.S.G.S. Geol. Atlas, San Francisco Folio (no. 193), 24 p., maps.

MacKENZIE, J. D.
1916 *Geology of Graham Island, British Columbia,* Can. Dept. Mines, Mem. 88, Ottawa, Canada.

MARTIN, BRUCE
1913 *Geological section of a portion of the Coast Ranges in the eastern part of San Luis Obispo County, California,* Bull. Geol. Soc. Amer., vol. 24, p. 93, (abst.).

MARTIN, G. C.
1926 *The Mesozoic stratigraphy of Alaska,* U.S.G.S., Bull. 776, p. 286–481.

MEEK, F. B.
1876 *Descriptions and illustrations of fossils from Vancouver's and Sucia Islands and other northwestern localities,* U.S.G.S. Terr. (Hayden), Bull. 2, p. 351–374, illustr.

MERRIAM, J. C.
1897 *The geologic relations of the Martinez group of California at the typical locality.* Jour. Geol., vol. 5, p. 767–775.
1901 *A Contribution to the geology of the John Day Basin, [Ore.],* Univ. Calif. Publ., Bull. Dept. Geol. Sci., vol. 2, p. 269–314.

NAGAO, TALSUMI
1934 *Cretaceous Mollusca from the Miyako district, Honshu, Japan* (Lamellibranchiata and Gastropoda). Hokkaido Imp. Univ., Fac. Sci. (4), vol. 2, no. 3, p. 177–277, 17 pls.

NEWBERRY, J. S.
1856 *Report on the geology of the route (Williamson's survey in California and Oregon),* U. S. Pacific R. R. Expl. (U. S. 33 Congr. 2nd Sess., S. Ex. Doc. 78, 4 Ex. Doc. 91), vol. 6, Pt. 2, p 24–25.

PACK, R. W., AND ENGLISH, W. A.
1914 *Geology and oil prospects in Waltham, Priest, Bitterwater and Peachtree Valleys, California,* U.S.G.S. Bull. 581-D, p. 119–160, map.

PACKARD, E. L.
1916a *Faunal studies in the Cretaceous of the Santa Ana Mountains of southern California,* Univ. Calif. Publ., Bull. Dept. Geol., vol. 9, p. 137–159. Abstract in: Bull. Geol. Soc. Amer., vol. 27, p 174.
1916b *Mesozoic and Cenozoic Mactrinae of the Pacific coast of North America,* Univ. Calif. Publ., Bull. Dept. Geol., vol. 9, p. 261–360, illustr.
1921 *The Trigoniae from the Pacific coast of North America,* Univ. Oregon Publ., Geol., vol. 1, p. 1–58.
1922 *New species from the Cretaceous of the Santa Ana Mountains, California,* Univ. Calif. Publ., Bull. Dept. Geol. Sci., vol. 13, p. 413–462, 15 pls.

PALMER, R. H.
1928 *The rudistids of southern Mexico,* Calif. Acad. Sci., Occ. Pap. 14, p. 1–137, pls. 1–18.

PAYNE, MAX B.
  1941 *Moreno shale, Panoche Hills, Fresno County, California,* Geol. Soc. Amer. Bull., vol. 52, no. 12, pt. 2, p. 1953–1954.
PERVINQUIÈRE, L.
  1907 *Etudes de Paléontologie Tunisienne. I. Cephalopodes des terrains secondaires,* Dir. gen. des Travaux publics, Carte géol. de la Tunisie, Paris. Rudeval, ed.
  1912 *Etudes de paléontologie Tunisienne., II Gastropodes et Lamellibranches des terrains crétacés,* Dir. gen. des Travaux publics, Carte géol. de la Tunisie, Paris. Rudeval, ed.
POPENOE, W. P.
  1937 *Upper Cretaceous Mollusca from southern California,* Jour. Paleont., vol. 11, no. 5, p. 379–402, 5 pls.
  1941 *The Trabuco and Baker conglomerates of the Santa Ana Mountains, [Calif],* Jour. Geol., vol. 49, no. 7, p. 738–752, 3 figs. Abstract in: Bull. Geol. Soc. Amer., vol. 52, no. 12, pt. 2, p. 1954–1955.
  1942 *Upper Cretaceous formations and faunas of southern California,* Amer. Assoc. Petrol. Geol. Bull., vol. 26, no. 2, p. 162–187, 4 figs.
  1943 *Cretaceous: east side of Sacramento Valley, Shasta and Butte counties, California,* Bull. Amer. Assoc. Petrol. Geol., vol. 27, no. 3, p. 306–312.
REED, R. D.
  1933 *Geology of California,* Amer. Assoc. Petrol. Geolog., xxiv + 355 p., 60 figs., 1 pl.
REED, R. D., AND HOLLISTER, J. S.
  1936 *Structural evolution of Southern California, with map,* Amer. Assoc. Petrol. Geol., xix + 157 p., 57 figs., 9 pls. Bull. Amer. Assoc. Petrol. Geol., vol. 20, no. 12, 1529–1692, 57 figs., 9 pls.
REESIDE, J. B., JR.
  1924 *Upper Cretaceous and Tertiary formations of the western part of the San Juan Basin of Colorado and New Mexico,* U.S.G.S., Prof. Paper 134, p. 1–70, 5 figs., 4 pls. (incl. map).
  1926 *A Comparison of the genera* Metaplacenticeras *Spath and* Placenticeras *Meek,* U.S.G.S., Prof. Paper 147, p. 1–5, 2 pls.
  1927a *Cephalopods from the lower part of the Cody shale of Oregon Basin, Wyoming,* U.S.G.S., Prof. Paper 150A, p. 1–19, 8 pls.
  1927b *The Scaphites, an Upper Cretaceous ammonite group,* U.S.G.S., Prof. Paper 150B, p. 21–40, 3 pls.
  1927c *The cephalopods of the Eagle Sandstone and related formations in the western interior of the United States,* U.S.G.S., Prof. Paper 151, iii + 87 p., 1 fig., 45 pls.
  1938 *The western interior of North America in later Cretaceous time,* Science, n.s. vol. 87, no. 2264, p. 466, (abst).
ROMAN, FREDERIC
  1938 *Les ammonites Jurassiques et Cretacés; essai de genera,* Paris: Masson et Cie, 554 p., 53 pls., 496 figs.
RUSSELL, R. D.
  1929 *Fossil pearls from the Chico formation of Shasta County, California.* Am. Jour. Sci., ser. 5, vol. 18, p. 416–428.
SCHENCK, H. G.
  1943 *Acila princeps, a new Upper Cretaceous pelecypod from California.* Journ. Paleo., vol. 17, p. 60–68, pls. 8–9.
SCHLÜTER, C.
  1871–1872 *Cephalopoden der oberen deutschen Kreide, 1st abst.,* Palaeontographica, vol. 21, p. 1–120, pls. 1–25.
SCHUCHERT, CHARLES
  1909 *Paleogeography of North America,* Geol. Soc. Amer., Bull., vol. 20, p. 427–605, maps.
  1923 *Sites and nature of the North American geosynclines,* (Presidential Address): Geol. Soc. Amer. Bull., vol. 34, no. 2, p. 151–229, 17 figs. (paleographic maps).
  1935 *Historical geology of the Antillean—Caribbean Region,* New York, John Wiley and Sons, 811 pages.
SHUMARD, B. F.
  1858 *Descriptions of new fossils from the Tertiary formation of Oregon and Washington Territories, and the Cretaceous of Vancouver Island,* St. Louis Acad. Sci. Trans., vol. 1, p. 120–125.
SCOTT, GAYLE
  1926 *Etudes stratigraphiques et Paléontologiques sur les terrains Crétacés du Texas,* Thèse Fac. Sci. de Grenoble, 1 + 218 pages, 3 pls.

SEUNES, JEAN
   1890 *Recherches géologiques sur les terrains secondaris et l'Eocène Inférieur de la région sous-pyrénéenne du sud-ouest de la france,* Ann. Mines, (8), vol. 28, p. 209–458.
SMITH, J. P.
   1898 *Development of Lytoceras and Phylloceras,* Proc. Calif. Acad. Sci., (3) vol. 1, p. 129–160.
   1899 *The larval stages of Schloenbachia,* Jour. Morph., vol. 16, p. 237–268.
   1900 *The development and phylogeny of Placenticeras.* Proc. Calif. Acad. Sci., (3) vol. 1, p. 180–240.
SPATH, L. F.
   1921 *On Upper Cretaceous Ammonoidea from Pondoland,* Durban Mus. Ann., vol. 3.
   1922 *On the Senonian ammonite fauna of Pondoland,* Trans. Roy. Soc. South Africa, vol. 10, pt. 3, 113–147.
   1929 *Corrections of cephalopod nomenclature,* Naturalist, p. 267–271.
   1930 *Ammonoidea of the Gault,* London: Paleontographical Society, 1923–1930, vol. 1, x + 311 p., pls. 1–30.
   1933 *The evolution of Cephalopoda,* Biol. Rev. and Biol. Proc., Cambridge Philos. Soc., vol. 7, p. 418–465.
   1943 *Ammonidea of the Gault,* London: Paleontographical Society, 1931–1943, vol. 2, x + 313–787 p., pls. 31–72.
STANTON, T. W.
   1893 *The fauna of the Shasta and Chico formations,* Geol. Soc. Amer. Bull., vol 4, p. 245–256.
   1894 *The Shasta-Chico series.* Geol. Soc. Amer. Bull., vol. 5, p. 435–464.
   1895 *Contributions to the Cretaceous paleontology of the Pacific Coast; the fauna of the Knoxville beds.* U.S.G.S., Bull. 133, p. 1–132, illust.
   1896 *The faunal relations of the Eocene and Upper Cretaceous on the Pacific coast,* U.S.G.S., 17th Ann. Rept., Pt. 1, p. 1005–1060, illustr.
   1897 *On the genus Remondia Gabb, a group of Cretaceous bivalve mollusks,* U. S. Nat. Mus., Proc., vol. 19, p. 299–301.
STEINMANN, G.
   1895 *Das Alter und die Fauna der Quiriquina schichten in Chile,* Beitr. Geol. u. Paleo. von Süd Amerika. Neues Jahrb. Mineral. Paleont., Beil-Bd. 10.
STEINMANN, G., et al.
   1894 *Beitrage zur Geologie und Paleontologie von Sudamerika,* Neues Jahrb. für Mineral. und Paleont., Beil.-Bd. 10.
STEINMANN, G., AND HAUPT, O.
   1907 *Beitrage zur Fauna des Oberen Malm und der Unteren Kreide in der Argentinischen Cordillere,* Neues Jahrb. Mineral., Geol. Paläont., Beil.-Bd. 23, p. 187–236.
STEINMANN, G., AND PAULCKE, W.
   1903 *Ueber die Kreideformation in Sudamerika und ihre Beziehungen zu Anderen Gebieten,* Neues Jahrb. Mineral., Geol., Paläont., Beil.-Bd. 17, p. 252–312.
STEPHENSON, L. W.
   1915 *The Cretaceous-Eocene contact in the Atlantic and Gulf Coastal Plain,* U.S.G.S. Prof. Pap. 90, p. 155–182, maps.
   1923 *The Cretaceous formations of North Carolina; Part I, Invertebrate fossils of the Upper Cretaceous formations,* North Carolina Geol. Survey, vol. 5, pt. 1, 604 p., 102 pls. (incl. map.).
   1941 *The larger invertebrate fossils of the Navarro group of Texas,* Univ. Texas, Publ. no. 4101, 641 p., 95 pls., 6 tables, 13 figs. incl. index maps.
STEPHENSON, L. W., AND REESIDE, J. B., JR.
   1938 *Comparison of Upper Cretaceous deposits of Gulf regions and western interior region,* Bull. Amer. Assoc. Petrol. Geol., vol. 22, no. 12, p. 1629-1638, 3 figs. incl. index map.
STEWART, RALPH B.
   1926 *Gabb's California fossil type gastropods,* Proc. Acad. Nat. Sci. Phila., vol. 78, p. 287–447.
   1930 *Gabb's California Cretaceous and Tertiary type lamellibranchs,* Acad. Nat. Sci., Phila., Sp. Pub. No. 3, p. 1–314, pls. 1–17.
STOCK, CHESTER
   1941 *Duckbill dinosaur from the Moreno Cretaceous of California,* Geol. Soc. Amer., Bull., vol. 52, no. 12, p. 1956, (abst.).
STOLICZKA, F.
   1863–1866 *Cretaceous fauna of southern India,* vol. 1, p. 41–216, pls. 26–94.
   1871 *Cretaceous fauna of southern India,* vol. 3. *Pelecypoda.* parts 5–13, p. 225–537, pls. 13–50.

TAFF, J. A.
    1934 *Physical properties of petroleum in California. Problems of petroleum geology,*
          Amer. Assoc. Petrol. Geol. (Sidney Powers Mem. Vol.), p. 177–234, 1 fig., map.
    1935 *Geology of Mt. Diablo and vicinity,* Geol. Soc. Amer. Bull., vol. 46, no. 7, p. 1079–
          1100, 1 pl., geol. map, 1 fig., structural map.
TAFF, J. A., HANNA, G. D., AND CROSS, C. M.
    1940 *Type locality of the Cretaceous Chico formation, California,* Geol. Soc. Amer. Bull.,
          vol. 51, no. 9, p. 1311–1327, 2 pls., 2 figs., incl. index map.
TALIAFERRO, N. L.
    1941 *Geologic history and structure of the central coast ranges of California,* Bull. Calif.
          Div. Mines, no. 118, pt. 2, p. 119–163, 5 figs., incl. index maps, 1 pl.
    1944 *Cretaceous and Paleocene of Santa Lucia Range, California,* Bull. Amer. Assoc.
          Petrol. Geol., vol. 28, no. 4, p. 449–521.
TRASK, J. B.
    1855 *Description of Ammonites Batesi, from Shasta County, California, etc.,* Proc. Calif.
          Acad. Nat. Sci., vol. 1, p. 40.
    1856a *Report on the geology of northern and southern California,* Sacramento: 66 pages.
    1856b *Description of a new species of ammonite and baculite from the Tertiary rocks of
          Chico Creek,* [Calif.], Calif. Acad. Nat. Sci. Proc., vol. 1, p. 85–86, (2d ed. 1873,
          p. 92–93).
    1856c *Description of three species of the genus* Plagiastoma *from the Cretaceous
          Rocks of Los Angeles,* Calif. Acad. Nat. Sci. Proc., vol. 1, p. 86, (2d ed. 1873, p.
          93–94).
WARING, C. A.
    1917 *Stratigraphic and faunal relations of the Martinez to the Chico and Tejon of
          southern California,* Proc. Calif. Acad. Sci., (4), vol. 7, p. 41–124, illustr., maps.
WATTS, W. L.
    1894 *The gas and petroleum yielding formations of the Central Valley of California,*
          Calif. State Min. Bur., Bull. 3, 100 pages, maps.
    1900 *Petroleum in California,* Amer. Inst. Min. Eng., Trans., vol. 29, p. 750–756.
    1901 *Oil and gas yielding formations of California,* Calif. State Min. Bur., Bull. 19,
          236 p., maps.
WEAVER, C. E.
    1944 *Geology of the Cretaceous (Gualala group) and Teritary formations along the
          Pacific Coast between Point Arena and Fort Ross, California,* Univ. Wash. Publ.
          Geol., vol. 6, no. 1, p. 1–29, 13 pls. incl. index, geol. maps.
WHITE, C. A.
    1885a *On the Mesozoic and Cenozoic paleontology of California,* U.S.G.S., Bull. 15,
          33 pages.
    1885b *On new Cretaceous fossils from California,* U.S.G.S. Bull. 22, 25 pages, illustr.
    1889 On invertebrate fossils from the Pacific coast., U. S. Geol. Surv. Bull. 51, p. 1–102,
          illustr.
    1891 *Correlation papers, Cretaceous,* U.S.G.S. Bull. 82, 273 p., maps.
WHITEAVES, J. F.
    1876 *On some invertebrates from the coal-bearing rocks of the Queen Charlotte Islands,*
          Can. Geol. Survey, *Mesozoic Fossils,* vol. 1, pt. 1, p. 1–92, 10 pls.
    1879 *On the fossils of the Cretaceous Rocks of Vancouver and adjacent islands in the
          Strait of Georgia,* Can. Geol. Survey, *Mesozoic Fossils,* vol. 1, pt. 2, p. 93–190,
          illustr.
    1883a *On some supposed annelid tracks from the Gaspé sandstones,* Royal Soc. Can.,
          Proc., Trans., vol. 1, iv, p. 109–111, illustr.
    1883b *On the Lower Cretaceous rocks of British Columbia,* Royal Soc. Can., Proc.,
          Trans., vol. 1, iv, p. 81–86, illustr.
    1884 *On the fossils of the coal-bearing deposits of the Queen Charlotte Islands,* Can.
          Geol. Survey, *Mesozoic Fossils,* vol. 1, pt. 2, p. 191–262, illustr.
    1887 *Notes on some Mesozoic fossils from various localities on the coast of British
          Columbia,* Can. Geol. Survey, Ann. Rept., vol. 2: B, p. 108–114.
    1893 *Descriptions of two new species of* Ammonites *from the Cretaceous rocks of the
          Queen Charlotte Islands,* Can. Record. Sci., vol. 5, p. 441–446, illustr.
    1900 *On some additional or imperfectly understood fossils from the Cretaceous rocks of
          the Queen Charlotte Islands, with a revised list of the species from those rocks.*
          Can. Geol. Survey, *Mesozoic Fossils,* vol. 1, pt. 4, p. 263–307, illustr.
    1903 *On some additional fossils from the Vancouver Cretaceous, with a revised list of the
          species therefrom,* Can. Geol. Survey, *Mesozoic Fossils,* vol. 1, pt. 5, p. 309–416,
          illustr.

WHITEHOUSE, F. W.
  1926 *Cretaceous Ammonoidea of eastern Australia,* Mem. Queensland Mus., vol. 8, pt. 3,
         p. 195–242, pls. 34–41.
WHITFIELD, R. P.
  1880 *Paleontology of the Black Hills of Dakota.* In Newton, H., and Jenney, W. P., *Re-
         port on the geology and resources of the Black Hills of Dakota.* U. S. Geogr. Geol.
         Surv. Rocky Mtn. Reg. p. 325–468.
WHITNEY, J. D.
  1865 *Geological survey of California; Geology,* vol. 1. *Report of Progress and Synopsis
         of the Field Work from 1860 to 1864,* xxvii + 498 pages.
  1869 *Preface,* California geological survey. Paleontology vol. 2, p. vii–xiv.
WILLIAMS, HOWEL
  1929 *Geology of the Marysville Buttes, California,* Univ. Calif. Publ., Bull. Dept. Geol.
         Sci., vol. 18, no. 5, p. 103–220; abstract in Bull. Geol. Soc. Amer., vol. 40, no. 1,
         p. 174–175.
WOODS, HENRY
  1914 *Cretaceous faunas of the northeastern part of the South Island of New Zealand,*
         New Zealand Geol. Survey, Paleont. Bull. 4, p. 1–375, pls. 1–20.
YABE, H.
  1903 *Cretaceous Cephalopoda from Hokkaido (Japan).* Pt. I, Journ. Coll. Sci., Imperial
         Univ., vol. 18, p. 214–218.
  1904 *Cretaceous Cephalopoda from the Hokkaido, Pt. II,* Jour. Coll. Sci., Imperial Univ.,
         vol. 20, art. 2, p. 1–45, pls. 1–6.
  1927 *Cretaceous stratigraphy of the Japanese Islands,* Sci. Repts. Tohoku Imper. Univ.,
         Sendai, Japan, (2) vol. 11, p. 27–100.
YABE, H., AND SHIMIZU, S.
  1923 *A Note on the genus* Mortoniceras, Jap. Jour. Geol. and Geog., Tokyo, vol. 2, no. 2,
         p. 27–30.

EXPLANATION OF PLATES

PLATE 1.—*FOSSILS FROM THE UPPER CRETACEOUS OF CALIFORNIA AND OREGON*

Figure *Page*

1, 2. *Durania ? californica* n. sp. (1) Holotype (fragment) (C. A. S. Type Coll.). Greatest width, 75 mm; length (incomplete), 110 mm; showing fluted columns below; crowded prisms above. Locality 1346 (C. A. S.), mouth of Hulen Creek, Shasta County. (2) Partial section of paratype, enlarged, showing thick walls and enlarged prisms. 126

3, 4. *Rhynchonella densleonis* Anderson. Sketches based on original drawings by Anderson in 1902 of holotype (C. A. S. Type Coll.). Apparently lost in the fire of 1906. (3) Upper valve of holotype. (4) Front view of holotype. Length 14 mm; width, 17 mm. From near old Horsetown, Shasta County; Cenomanian, or older. 86

5. *Trigonia packardi* n. sp. Holotype (C. A. S. Type Coll.). Length, 55.6 mm; height, 40 mm; maximum convexity both valves together, 26 mm. Locality 1345 (C. A. S.), at Texas Springs, Shasta County; lower Cenomanian. 109

6. *Trigonia colusaensis* n. sp. Holotype (C. A. S. Type Coll.). Maximum length, 102 mm; height, 71 mm; greatest thickness, 48 mm. Locality 1291 (C. A. S.), 4 miles north of Sites, Colusa County; lower Cenomanian. 110

7. *Avicula gainsana* n. sp. Holotype (C. A. S. Type Coll.). Length, 57 mm; width, 26 mm; thickness, 8.6 mm. Locality 1345-C (C. A. S.), North Fork of Cottonwood Creek, half a mile above the mouth of the Hulen Creek, Shasta County; Cenomanian. 106

8. *Remondia oregonensis* n. sp. Holotype (C. A. S. Type Coll.). Length (incomplete), 80 mm; height, 41 mm; total thickness, 20 mm. Found at Locality 445-C (C. A. S.), "Dark Hollow," on old Pioneer Road, 4 miles southwest of Phoenix, Oregon; upper Albian. 131

FOSSILS FROM THE UPPER CRETACEOUS OF CALIFORNIA AND OREGON

FOSSILS FROM THE UPPER CRETACEOUS OF CALIFORNIA AND OREGON

PLATE 2.—*FOSSILS FROM THE UPPER CRETACEOUS OF CALIFORNIA AND OREGON*

Figure *Page*

1, 2. *Syncyclonema latum* n. sp. Holotype and paratype (C. A. S. Type Coll.). (1) Holotype. Height (incomplete), 45 mm; width, 45 mm; length of hinge, 13 mm. (2) Paratype. Surface showing faint radial lines near axis of umbones. Found at Locality 445-C (C. A. S.), "Dark Hollow," on old Pioneer Road, 4 miles southwest of Phoenix, Oregon; upper Albian. 117

3, 3a, 4, 4a. *Gryphaea distorta* n. sp. Holotype and paratype (C. A. S. Type Coll.). (3, 3a) Holotype. (3a) Lower valve, side view. (3) Top view. Length (incomplete), 35 mm; height (incomplete), 30 mm; depth of lower valve, 13 mm. (4, 4a) Paratype. Height (incomplete), 21 mm; Holotype and paratype from Locality 12779 (C. S. M. B.), 4 miles north of Sites, Peterson Ranch, Colusa County; Cenomanian. 107

5, 5a, 5b. *Gryphaea accipter* n. sp. Holotype (C. A. S. Type Coll.). (5a) Lower valve, side view. (5, 5b) Front and rear views. Height (incomplete), 28 mm; length, 21 mm; thickness of lower valve, 18 mm. Same locality as preceding; Cenomanian. 107

6, 6a, 6b. *Trigonarca jacksonensis* n. sp. Holotype (C. A. S. Type Coll.). (6) Right valve. Greatest length, 75 mm; height, 45 mm; thickness of single valve, 25 mm. (6a) Section of right valve. (6b) Interior view, showing ligamental area. Locality: "found on the former Sheble ranch, 2.5 miles southwest of Phoenix, Oregon." 96

7. *Trigonia perrinsmithi* n. sp. Holotype No. 2691 (Stanford Univ. Type Coll.). Greatest length, 126 mm; height, 80 mm: thickness of left valve, 25 mm. From 1 mile northeast of old Horsetown, Shasta County. 110

PLATE 3.—*FOSSILS FROM THE UPPER CRETACEOUS OF CALIFORNIA AND OREGON*

FOSSILS FROM THE UPPER CRETACEOUS OF CALIFORNIA AND OREGON

FOSSILS FROM THE UPPER CRETACEOUS OF CALIFORNIA

PLATE 4.—*FOSSILS FROM THE UPPER CRETACEOUS OF CALIFORNIA*

Figure *Page*

1, 1a. *Pervinquieria gainesana* n. sp. Plasto-holotype (C. A. S. Type Coll.). (Cast of Univ. Calif. Mus. Paleo. Type Coll. holotype No. 14940). Greater diameter, 120 mm; height of whorl, 45 mm; maximum breadth, 38 mm. (1) Side view, showing branching of the ribs, and ornamentation by three rows of nodes. (1a) Oblique front view, showing keel, and relative breadth of whorl. North fork of Cottonwood Creek, 0.6 mile above the mouth of Hulen Creek. 257

2, 3. *Pervinquieria sylvana* n. sp. Holotype (C. A. S. Type Coll.). Greater diameter, 110.5 mm; width of umbilicus, 38 mm; maximum breadth of whorl, about 46.8 mm. (2) Side view of incomplete whorls, showing ribs branching from umbilical nodes, and single ribs arising from umbilical border, and the abrupt umbilical wall. (3) Outer portion of same, slightly reduced. Locality 1346 (C. A. S.), North fork of Cottonwood Creek, 0.6 mile above the mouth of Hulen Creek. *See* also Pl. 7, fig. 2. 258

4. *Ampullina avellana* (Gabb). Hypotype (C. A. S. Type Coll.), slightly reduced. Same locality as given above. 151

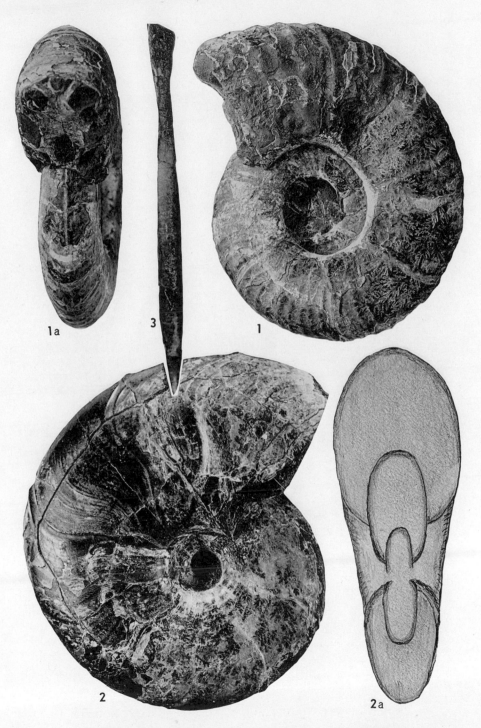

1a   3   1

2   2a

FOSSILS FROM THE UPPER CRETACEOUS OF CALIFORNIA

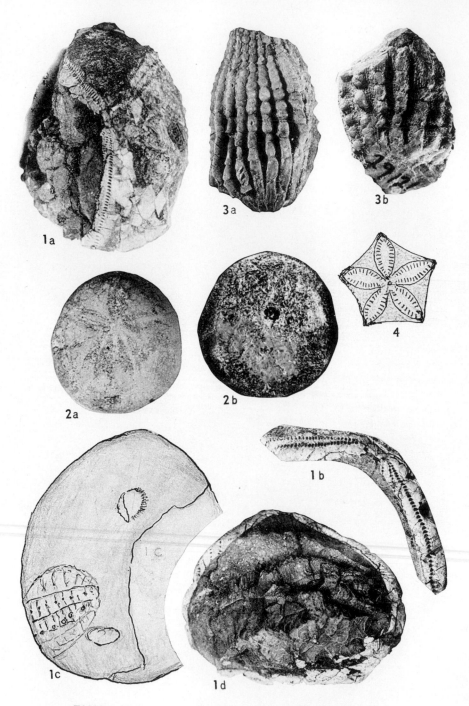

FOSSILS FROM THE UPPER CRETACEOUS OF CALIFORNIA

PLATE 6.—*FOSSILS FROM THE UPPER CRETACEOUS OF CALIFORNIA*

Figure *Page*

1a, 1b, 1c, 1d. *Echinocorys yoloensis* n. sp. Holotype (C. A. S. Type Coll.). View of exterior. (1a) Aboral surface of holotype. (1b) Detail of ambulacra. (1c) Sketch of oral surface. Holotype dimensions as sketched—length, 64 mm; breadth, about 54 mm; height, 50 mm. (1d) Side view of holotype. Locality 1343 (C. A. S.), found at the north end of Pleasant Valley, Yolo County. 85

2a, 2b. *Cassidulus mercedensis* n. sp. Holotype (C. A. S. Type Coll.). (2a) Aboral surface. (2b) Oral surface. Length, 18 mm; greatest breadth, posterior to mouth, 16 mm; height about 8 mm. Found by Allan Bennison at Locality 29106 (C. A. S.), 2000 feet south of northwest corner sec. 20, T. 8 S. R. 8 E. M. D. M., Pacheco Pass quad., Garzas Creek. 85

3a, 3b. *Pachecocrinus joaquinensis* n. sp. Holotype (C. A. S. Type Coll.). (3a) Length, 30 mm; width 19 mm; thickness, 12 mm; thickness of single arm 2 mm. Holotype from Locality 29650 (C. A. S.). (3b) Paratype from Locality 29121 (C. A. S.). 83

4. "*Pentacrinus*" *fairbanksi* n. sp. Drawing of face of columnal. 84

FOSSILS FROM THE UPPER CRETACEOUS OF CALIFORNIA

FOSSILS FROM THE UPPER CRETACEOUS OF CALIFORNIA AND OREGON

PLATE 8.—*FOSSILS FROM THE UPPER CRETACEOUS OF CALIFORNIA AND OREGON*

Figure | *Page*

1, 1a. *Beudanticeras haydenii* (Gabb). Hypotype No. 5944 (C. A. S. Type Coll.). (1) Side view. (1a) Oblique front view of same. Greatest diameter, 65 mm; width of umbilicus, 10 mm; greatest breadth of whorl, 15 mm; greatest height of last whorl approximately 37 mm. From North fork of Cottonwood Creek, 0.6 mile above the mouth of Hulen Creek, Shasta County. Upper Albian or Lower Cenomanian. 212

2. *Puzosia* (*Parapuzosia*) *hindsi* n. sp. Holotype (C. A. S. Type Coll.). Greatest diameter, 50 mm; height of whorl, 23 mm. Locality 2233 (C. A. S.); found half a mile southeast of the mouth of Hulen Creek, Shasta County. 237

3, 3a. *Lytoceras* (*Gaudryceras*) *texanum* n. sp. Holotype (C. A. S. Type Coll.). (3a) Side view. (3) Oblique front view. Greatest diameter, 25 mm; greatest breadth of whorl, 9 mm. Found at Texas Springs, Shasta County. Lower Cenomanian. 184

4, 4a. *Mantelliceras oregonense* n. sp. Hypotype (C. A. S. Type Coll.). Fragment. Length, 68 mm; height of whorl, 25 mm. Locality 445-C (C. A. S.), found at "Dark Hollow," on old Pioneer Road, 4 miles southwest of Phoenix, Oregon. Upper Albian. *See* also Pl. 14, figs. 1, 1a. 244

5, 5a. *Lyelliceras stanislausense* n. sp. Holotype (C. A. S. Type Coll.). Greater diameter, about 30 mm; breadth of whorl, 13 mm; height of whorl, 10 mm. (5) Side view. (5a) Oblique rear view, showing character of ventral zone, and spines on inner whorls. Locality 31131 (C. A. S.), found on upper branch of Garzas Creek, Stanislaus County, California. Lower part of Cenomanian. 247

6. *Pervinquieria* aff. *P. inflata* Sowerby. Hypotype (C. A. S. Type Coll.). Fragment of outer whorl. Approximate measurements are as follows: greatest diameter, 139 mm; height of whorl, 55 mm. Locality 2324 (C. A. S.), found on a north branch of Waltham Creek, 1.6 miles east of Parkfield road, Fresno County. Upper Albian. *See* also Pl. 7, fig. 3. 258

PLATE 9.—*FOSSILS FROM THE UPPER CRETACEOUS OF CALIFORNIA*

Figure *Page*

1, 2. *Beudanticeras argonauticum* n. sp. Holotype (C. A. S. Type Coll.). Locality 1346 (C. A. S.), Hulen Creek, near the north fork of Cottonwood Creek, western Shasta County. 213

3, 3a, 4. *Joaquinites fascicostatum* n. sp. Holotype (C. A. S. Type Coll.). (3) Showing usual form and ornamentation; greater diameter, 58 mm; width of umbilicus, 12 mm; height of whorl, 28 mm; breadth of whorl, 20 mm; (3a) View showing portion of whorl and umbilicus enlarged. (4) Apertural view. Locality 31593 (C. A. S.), on Joaquin Ridge, Fresno County; Maestrichtian. 219

5. *Scaphites* aff. *S. roguensis* Anderson. Hypotype (C. I. T. Type Coll.). Greater diameter 20.9 mm, lesser diameter including body whorl 18.3 mm. Locality 1010 (C. I. T.), on Salt Creek, Shasta County. 250

6, 6a. *Pervinquieria furberi* n. sp. Paratype (C. A. S. Type Coll.). (6) Side view. (6a) Profile, apertural view. *See* also Pl. 11, fig. 1. 258

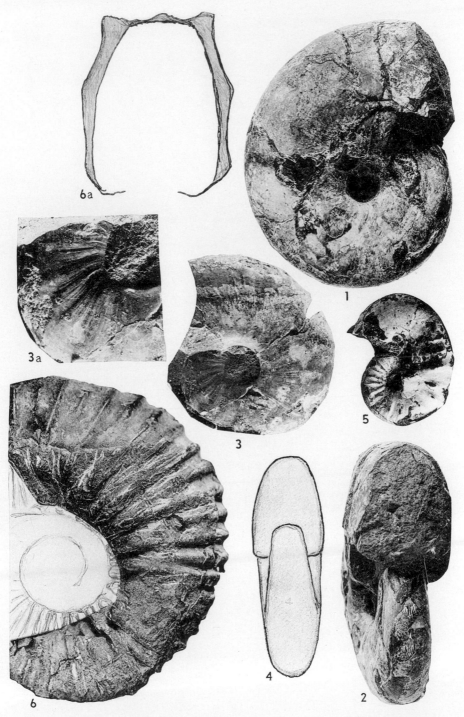

FOSSILS FROM THE UPPER CRETACEOUS OF CALIFORNIA

FOSSILS FROM THE UPPER CRETACEOUS OF CALIFORNIA AND OREGON

PLATE 10.—*FOSSILS FROM THE UPPER CRETACEOUS OF CALIFORNIA AND OREGON*

Figure *Page*

1. *Puzosia* (*Parapuzosia*) *colusaënsis* (Anderson). Hypotype (C. A. S. Type Coll.). Maximum diameter, 176 mm; width of umbilicus, 46 mm; breadth of whorl, 68 mm. Locality 1346 (C. A. S.), mouth of Hulen Creek, north fork of Cottonwood Creek, Shasta County; Cenomanian 236

2, 2a. *Lytoceras* (*Tetragonites*) *jacksonense* Anderson. Holotype No. 44 (C. A. S. Type Coll.). Natural size. New figures. (2) Side view of holotype. (2a) Front view of same, drawn from the holotype, showing section of whorl. Locality 445 (C. A. S.), "Forty-nine" mine, south of Phoenix, Oregon; Cenomanian. 186

3, 3a. *Desmoceras* (*Latidorsella*) *inane* (Stoliczka). Hypotype (C. A. S. Type Coll.). Natural size. (3) Side view, showing periodic transverse grooves, and umbilical pit. (3a) Oblique front view showing breadth of whorl. Dry Creek, northern Tehama County; lower Cenomanian. 215

4, 4a. *Beudanticeras diabloense* (Anderson). Holotype (Univ. Calif. Mus. Paleo. Type Coll.). Figures of holotype reproduced. Greatest diameter, 25 mm; breadth of whorl, 12 mm. Probably found on Curry Creek, east of Mount Diablo; Cenomanian. 214

PLATE 11.—*FOSSILS FROM THE UPPER CRETACEOUS OF CALIFORNIA AND QUEEN CHARLOTTE ISLANDS*

Figure	*Page*
1. *Pervinquieria furberi* n. sp. Holotype (C. A. S. Type Coll.). Fragment of outer whorl, and portion of an inner whorl. Dimensions of holotype: maximum diameter, approximately 180 mm; height of last whorl, 63 mm; breadth of last whorl, approximately 43 mm; width of umbilicus, 71.5 mm. Found at Locality 28180 (C. A. S.), on Dry Creek, northern Tehama County; Upper Albian. *See* also Pl. 9, figs. 6, 6a.	258
2. *Turrilites bergeri* Brongniart. Hypotype (C. A. S. Type Coll.). Fragment, consisting of two and a half whorls. Total height 43 mm; maximum width about 33 mm. Enlarged. Found at Locality 31097 (C. A. S.), about 300 feet above local base of the Upper Cretaceous, on Dry Creek, northern Tehama County.	193
3, 3a, 3b. *Anisoceras charlottense* n. sp. Holotype (C. A. S. Type Coll.). Total length, 82 mm; greatest breadth, 32 mm; greater height, 25 mm. (3) Oblique side view, showing ribbing on side. (3a) Ventral view, showing major and minor ribbing. (3b) Section of shaft at smaller end. Found near Skidegate, Queen Charlotte Islands.	209
4. *Turrilites pachecoensis* n. sp. Holotype (C. A. S. Type Coll.). Consists of portions of three whorls. Length, 75 mm; greatest width, 65 mm. Locality 27858 (C. A. S.), found on Quinto Creek, center S ½ of SE ¼ sec. 3 T. 9 S., R. 7 E. M. D. M.; Stanislaus County; lower Cenomanian.	193
5, 5a. *Cyrtochilus stylus* n. sp. Holotype (C. A. S. Type Coll.). Length, 95 mm; greater diameter, 9 mm. (5a) Cross section of holotype near buccal end. Locality 31097 (C. A. S.), Dry Creek, Tehama County, 4.6 miles west of Rosewood.	188

FOSSILS FROM THE UPPER CRETACEOUS OF CALIFORNIA AND QUEEN CHARLOTTE ISLANDS

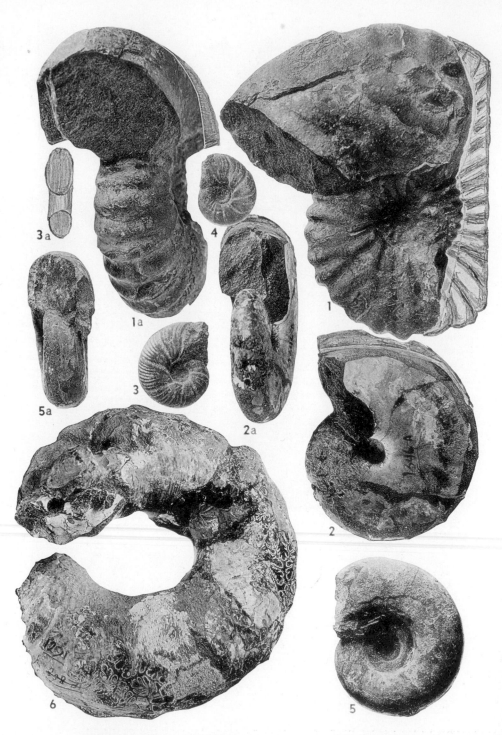

FOSSILS FROM THE UPPER CRETACEOUS OF CALIFORNIA

PLATE 12.—*FOSSILS FROM THE UPPER CRETACEOUS OF CALIFORNIA*

Figure   *Page*

1, 1a. *Stoliczkaia praecursor* n. sp. Holotype (Univ. Calif. Mus. Paleo. Type Coll.). Greater diameter, 84 mm; width of umbilicus, 20 mm; breadth of whorl, 30.5 mm. (1) Side view, showing umbilical pit. (1a) Oblique front view, showing relative breadth of whorl. Lower Cenomanian. 246

2, 2a. *Desmoceras (Latidorsella) barryae* n. sp. Holotype (C. A. S. Type Coll.). Greater diameter, 51 mm; width of umbilicus, 6.5 mm; height of whorl 26 mm; breadth of whorl, 15 mm. (2) Side view. (2a) Oblique front view. Locality 1346A (C. A. S.), 1 mile above mouth of Hulen Creek; lower Cenomanian. 214

3, 3a, 4. *Puzosia (Parapuzosia) waringi* n. name. Holotype and paratype (C. A. S. Type Coll.). (3, 3a) Holotype No. 8819. Greatest diameter, 23 mm; breadth of whorl, 9 mm. (3a) Drawing showing section of whorl. (4) Paratype No. 8820; greatest diameter 19 mm; breadth of whorl, 7 mm. Jackass Flat, Shasta County; Cenomanian. 236

5, 5a. *Lytoceras (Tetragonites) henleyense* n. sp. Holotype (C. A. S. Type Coll.). Greater diameter, 44 mm; width of umbilicus, 18 mm; breadth of whorl, 16 mm. (5) Side view, showing smooth surface and width of umbilical pit. (5a) Front view, showing breadth of whorl. Locality 444 (C. A. S.), found near Henley, Siskiyou County; Coniacian. *See* also Pl. 41, fig. 7. 185

6. *Turrilites petersoni* n. sp. Holotype (C. A. S. Type Coll.). Fragment of spiral coil. Diameter of coil, 100 mm; section of whorl, circular; greater diameter of larger end, 45.5 mm; diameter of smaller end, 35 mm. Locality 1291 (C. A. S.), found just below the Venado formation on the Peterson ranch, 4 miles north of Sites, Colusa County; Albian or Cenomanian. *See* also Pl. 75, fig. 4. 193

PLATE 13.—*FOSSILS FROM THE UPPER CRETACEOUS OF CALIFORNIA AND OREGON*

Figure *Page*

1, 1a. *Acanthoceras lecontei* n. sp. Holotype No. 32858 (Univ. Calif. Mus. Paleo. Type Coll.). Cast of holotype (C. A. S. Type Coll.). (1) Consists of a large fragment. Length 73 mm; greater height of whorl, 62 mm; greater breadth of whorl, 37 mm. (1a) Section of whorl, 37 mm. Locality A3823 (U.C.), found 1 mile southeast of Crockett, Contra Costa County; Cenomanian. 242

2, 2a. *Mantelliceras phoenixense* n. sp. Holotype (C. A. S. Type Coll.). (2) Holotype dimensions: greater diameter, 100 mm; width of umbilicus, 40 mm; height of whorl, 37 mm; breadth of whorl (est.), 33 mm. (2a) Section of whorl, showing involution, and 5 rows of tubercles. Found at the old "Forty-nine" mine, southwest of Phoenix, Oregon. 244

3. *Puzosia* (*Holcodiscoides*) *weaveri* Anderson. Holotype No. 14930 (Univ. Calif. Mus. Paleo. Type Coll.). Greater diameter, 55 mm; breadth of whorl, 20 mm; width of umbilicus, 19 mm. Found 3 miles east of Rodeo, Contra Costa County. 240

4. *Puzosia* (*Parapuzosia*) *onona* Anderson. Holotype No. 8821 (C. A. S. Type Coll.). Reproduced. Greater diameter, 30 mm; breadth of whorl, 10 mm. Locality 1345 (C. A. S.), from Jackass Flat, Shasta County; Turonian. 237

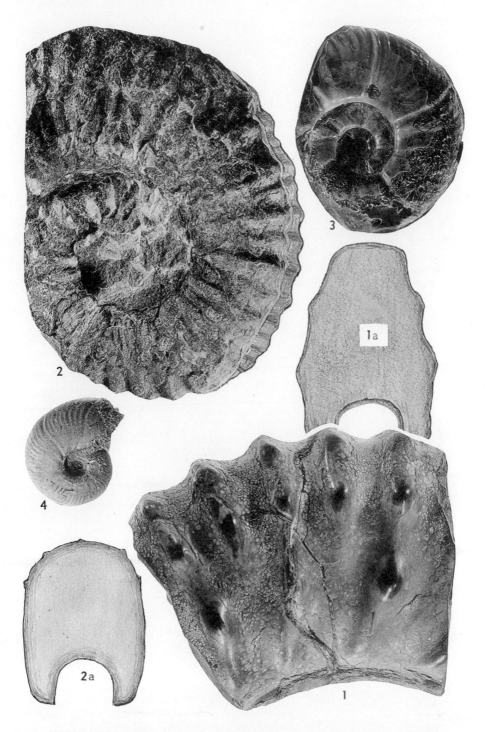

FOSSILS FROM THE UPPER CRETACEOUS OF CALIFORNIA AND OREGON

FOSSILS FROM THE UPPER CRETACEOUS OF CALIFORNIA AND OREGON

PLATE 14.—*FOSSILS FROM THE UPPER CRETACEOUS OF CALIFORNIA AND OREGON*

Figure *Page*

1, 1a. *Mantelliceras oregonense* n. sp. Holotype (C. A. S. Type Coll.), received from E. L. Packard. Greater diameter, 78 mm; breadth of whorl, 55 mm. Found at old "Forty-nine" mine, 2 miles south of Phoenix, Oregon. Upper Cenomanian. *See* also Pl. 8, figs. 4, 4a. 244

2. *Mantelliceras* aff. *M. conquistador* n. sp. Hypotype (C. A. S. Type Coll.). Fragmentary example. Length, 150 mm; height of whorl, 64 mm; breadth of whorl, 80.5 mm. Locality 31230 (C. A. S.), found on Little Cow Creek, Shasta County, near Calkins ranch house; upper Cenomanian. 245

3, 4, 4a, 5, 6. *Oregoniceras condoni* n. sp. Holotype, paratype, and two hypotypes (C. A. S. Type Coll.). (3) Holotype, 36 mm (4, 4a) Paratype. Greater diameter, 28 mm. (4) Side view, showing width of umbilicus, and single and divided ribs, arising on umbilical border from bullae. (4a) Slightly oblique front view, showing thickness of whorl. (5) Hypotype. (6) Hypotype showing ornamentation, with single and branching ribs. 265

PLATE 15.—*FOSSILS FROM THE UPPER CRETACEOUS OF CALIFORNIA AND OREGON*

Figure *Page*

1, 1a. *Cunningtoniceras roguense* n. name. Holotype (L. S. J. U. Type Coll.). Large fragment of body chamber. Length, 165 mm; width, 100 mm; height of whorl, 60 mm. (1) View of ventral surface, showing large lateral tubercles. (1a) View of left side, showing strong tuberculate ribs. Found at old "Forty-nine" mine, near Phoenix, Oregon; Cenomanian. 246

2. *Mantelliceras conquistador* n. sp. Holotype (C. A. S. Type Coll.). Consists of large fragment, one-fourth of whorl, or more; length, 185 mm; breadth, 85 mm; height on median line 75 mm. Locality 31230 (C. A. S.), found on Little Cow Creek, east of the Calkins ranch house; Cenomanian. 245

3. *Liopistha anaana* (Anderson). Holotype (Fairbank's Coll.) sketched from Pl. 7, fig. 151 in Anderson (1902). Found in Silverado Canyon, Orange County; lower Turonian. 119

4, 5. *Thyasira cretacea* Whiteaves. Hypotypes (C. A. S. Type Coll.). (4) Hypotype, right valve (incomplete). Length, 32 mm (illustrated portion). (5) Hypotype, left valve. View of top, showing ligamental area. Length, 37 mm; thickness of valve, 10 mm. Both found at Locality 1467A (C. A. S.), Enos Canyon, 7 miles northwest of Winters, Yolo County. 133

FOSSILS FROM THE UPPER CRETACEOUS OF CALIFORNIA AND OREGON

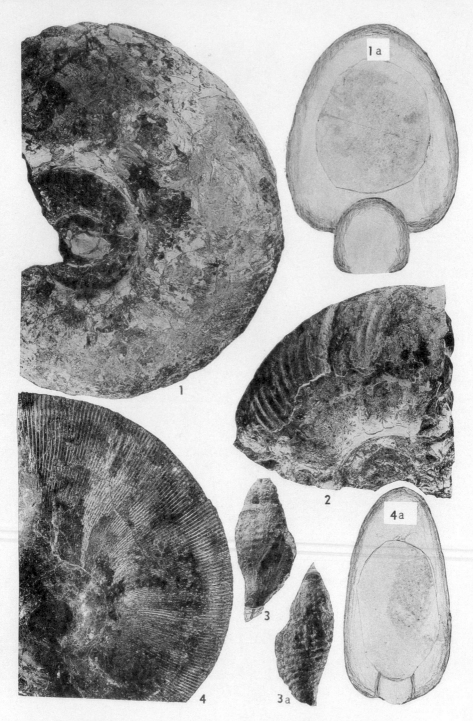

FOSSILS FROM THE UPPER CRETACEOUS OF CALIFORNIA

PLATE 16.—*FOSSILS FROM THE UPPER CRETACEOUS OF CALIFORNIA*

Figure *Page*

1, 1a, 2. *Puzosia* (*Austiniceras*) *giganteum* n. sp. Holotype and hypotype (C. A. S. Type Coll.). (1, 1a) Holotype. Greater diameter, 446 mm (17.5 inches); width of umbilicus, 146 mm; breadth of whorl, 132 mm. Locality 2245 (C. A. S.), found on Dry Creek, west of Rosewood, western Tehama County. (2) Hypotype. Found in long gulch, 1 mile north of middle fork of Cottonwood Creek, Shasta County, near horizon of *Vascoceras shastense* (Anderson); Turonian. 239

3, 3a. *Volutoderma crossi* n. sp. Holotype (C. A. S. Type Coll.). Length, 33 mm; width, 16 mm; length of aperture, 21 mm. Locality 1293D (C. A. S.), found on SW ¼ sec. 4, T. 32 N., R. 3 W., M.D.B. and M.; Frazier Corners, Shasta County; Turonian. 174

4, 4a. *Phylloceras velledae* Michelin. Hypotype (C. A. S. Type Coll.). (4) Greater diameter, 97 mm; width of umbilicus, 13 mm; breadth of shell, 25 mm. (4a) section of same. Locality 2233 (C. A. S.), found in a deep ravine about half a mile southeast of the mouth of Hulen Creek, Shasta County. 180

PLATE 17.—*FOSSILS FROM THE UPPER CRETACEOUS OF CALIFORNIA*

Figure *Page*

1, 2. *Inoceramus glennensis* n. sp. Holotype and paratype (C. A. S. Type Coll.). (1) Holotype. Length (incomplete), 67 mm; width (incomplete), approximately 33 mm; thickness, approximately 10 mm. (2) Paratype. Left valve. Length (incomplete), 66.8 mm; width, 31.5 mm; thickness, 10 mm. Found 3 miles south of Fruito, on Willow Creek, Glenn County; lower Turonian. 99

3, 4. *Inoceramus duplicostatus* n. sp. Holotype mould and plasto-holotype. (C. A. S. Type Coll.) (4) Plaster cast of holotype. (3) Holotype mould. Length, 41.4 mm; maximum width, 20.2 mm; locality 444A (C. A. S.), Rocky Gulch southwest of Hornbrook, Siskiyou County; Turonian. 100

5. *Trigonia branneri* n. sp. Holotype No. 2786 (L. S. J. U. Type Coll.). Length, 86 mm; height, 60 mm; thickness, of left valve, 17 mm. Found 1 mile south of Henley, Siskiyou County; Turonian. 112

6, 7. *Trigonia churchi* n. sp. Holotype (C. A. S. Type Coll.). Length, 80 mm; height, 58 mm. (6) Oblique side view, showing character and width of escutcheon area. (7) Side view, showing width of shell, and ribbing. Locality 1788 (C. A. S.), found on Jalama Creek, 1 mile east of mouth of Escondida Creek, Santa Barbara County. 115

FOSSILS FROM THE UPPER CRETACEOUS OF CALIFORNIA

FOSSILS FROM THE UPPER CRETACEOUS OF CALIFORNIA AND OREGON

PLATE 18.—*FOSSILS FROM THE UPPER CRETACEOUS OF CALIFORNIA AND OREGON*

Figure *Page*

1, 2. *Inoceramus klamathensis* Anderson. Syntype No. 45 (C. A. S. Type Coll.). (1) Left valve. Length, 36 mm; width, 20 mm; thickness of left valve, 13 mm. (2) Syntype No. 46. Right valve. Natural size. Figures reproduced from Anderson (1902). Found on Willow Creek, 4 miles north of Montague, Siskiyou County "(and ? at the 49 Mine in southern Oregon)." 104

3, 4. *Inoceramus contracostae* n. sp. Holotype and paratype (C. A. S. Type Coll.). (3) Holotype. Left valve. Length (incomplete), 55 mm; width (incomplete) 25 mm; convexity (1 valve), approximately 5.8 mm. (4) Paratype. Locality 29084 (C. A. S.), found in Round Valley, Contra Costa County; Middle Campanian. *See* also Pl. 55, fig. 3. 103

5, 6. *Bullina yoloensis* n. sp. Holotype and paratype (C. A. S. Type Coll.). (5) Holotype. Length, 8.5 mm; breadth, 3.5 mm. (6) Paratype. Length, 7 mm; breadth, 4 mm. Found at Locality 1467A (C. A. S.), 7 miles northwest of Winters, Yolo County; Coniacian. 177

7. *Glycymeris pacificus* (Anderson). The holotype was originally in the collection of Dr. H. N. Fairbanks. Approximately natural size. Found on Santiago Creek, Orange County; Turonian. 97

8, 9, 10. *Glycymeris shastensis* n. sp. Holotype and paratype (C. A. S. Type Coll.). (8, 9) Holotype. Length, 29.5 mm; height 28.5 mm; convexity (1 valve) 13 mm; enlarged to show the details of dentition. (10) Paratype. Length 20.2 mm; height, 20.4 mm; convexity (1 valve) 7.7 mm. Locality 27830 (C. A. S.). Found 4.5 miles east of Millville, Shasta County. 97

11, 12. *Inoceramus aduncus* Anderson. Holotype No. 43 (C. A. S. Type Coll.). Length (incomplete), 58 mm; height, 31.5 mm; thickness of valves, 22.5 mm. Locality 445 (C. A. S.), found at the "Forty-nine" mine, 2 miles south of Phoenix, Oregon; Turonian. 100

13. *Inoceramus eolobatus* n. sp. Holotype (C. A. S. Type Coll.). Length (incomplete), 78 mm; width (incomplete), 45 mm; thickness of one valve, 12 mm. Locality 1291 (C. A. S.), found on the Peterson ranch, 4 miles north of Sites, Colusa County; Cenomanian. 99

Plate 19.—*FOSSILS FROM THE UPPER CRETACEOUS OF CALIFORNIA AND OREGON*

Figure *Page*

1, 1a, 1b, 1c. *Coelopoceras hyatti* n. sp. Holotype (C. A. S. Type Coll.). (1) Reduced in size. Greater diameter (incomplete), 95 mm; width of umbilicus, 10 mm; height of whorl, 58 mm; breadth of whorl, 22 mm. (1a and 1c) Natural size. (1b) Enlarged. Drawings show side and rear views of the holotype. Locality 2245 (C. A. S.), found 15.1 miles southeast of Beegum station, on road to Rosewood, Tehama County; Turonian, or upper Cenomanian. 249

2, 2a, 2b. *Scaphites klamathensis* Anderson. Holotype and paratype (C. A. S. Type Coll.). Types lost in fire of 1906. (2, 2b) Holotype. Figures reproduced from Anderson (1902). Length, 13 mm; width of same, 9 mm. (2a) Paratype. Drawing of early whorl, enlarged. Found on north border of Shasta Valley, Siskiyou County; Turonian. 251

3, 3a. *Scaphites roguensis* Anderson. Holotype and paratype (C. A. S. Type Coll.). Types lost in fire of 1906. (3) Holotype, figures reproduced from Anderson (1902). Length, 20 mm; width, 15 mm; breadth of whorl, 6 mm. (3a) Paratype. Found at the "Forty-nine" mine, 2 miles south of Phoenix, Oregon. 250

4, 4a. *Scaphites pittensis* n. sp. Holotype. (C. A. S. Type Coll.) (4) Greatest length, 19 mm; width of shell, 16 mm; breadth of body chamber, 5 mm. (4a) Suture line of same. Locality 1293A (C. A. S.), found 1 mile north of Frazier Corners, Shasta County; Turonian. 252

5. *Nonacteonina stephensoni* n. sp. Holotype (C. A. S. Type Coll.). Length (incomplete), 24 mm; greatest breadth, 11 mm. Found in the Garzas sandstone in the Volta Quadrangle. Maestrichtian. 159

6, 6a. *Oregoniceras jillsoni* n. sp. Holotype (C. A. S. Type Coll.). Consists of a large fragment. Total diameter (est.), 90 mm; height of whorl, approximately 45 mm; breadth of whorl, 32 mm. Locality 444 (C. A. S.); material saved from fire of 1906. From "Forty-nine" mine or Clawson's Quarry, Ore. 267

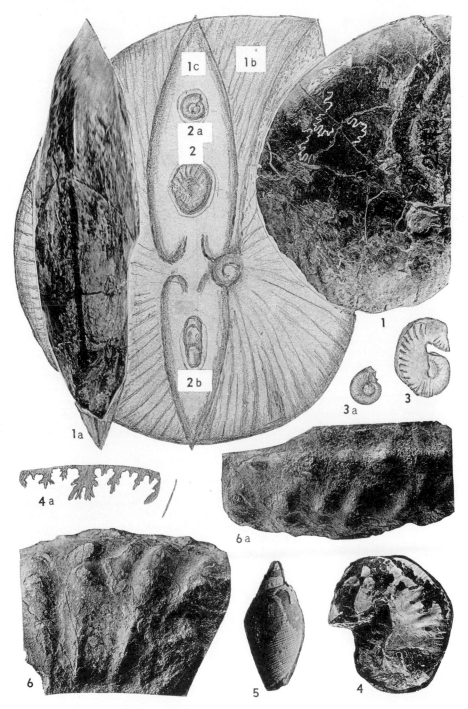

FOSSILS FROM THE UPPER CRETACEOUS OF CALIFORNIA AND OREGON

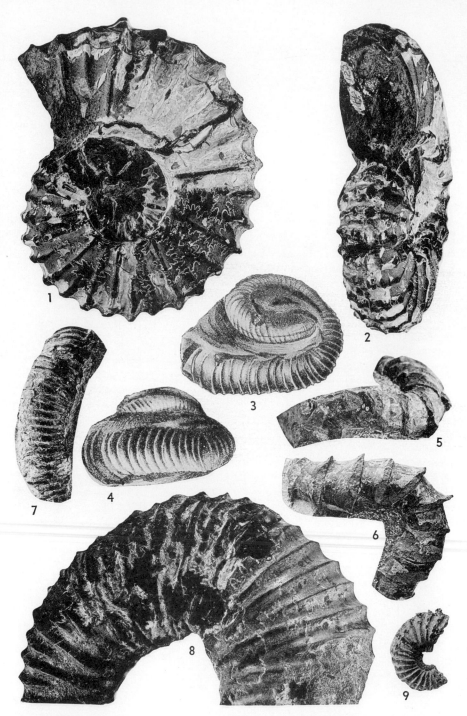

FOSSILS FROM THE UPPER CRETACEOUS OF CALIFORNIA AND OREGON

PLATE 20.—*FOSSILS FROM THE UPPER CRETACEOUS OF CALIFORNIA AND OREGON*

Figure | *Page*

1, 2. *Acanthoceras shastense* Reagan. Holotype (L. S. J. U. Type Coll.). Greater diameter, 120 mm; width of umbilicus, 43 mm; height of whorl, 45 mm; breadth of whorl, 41 mm. Found on the north fork of Cottonwood Creek, Shasta County. See Pl. 60, fig. 5. 242

3, 4, 7. *Bostrychoceras serpiens* n. name. Holotype. (C. A. S. Type Coll.). Lost in fire of 1906; figures reproduced from Anderson (1902). (3, 4) Holotype. Diameter of spiral portion, 20 mm. (7) Paratype (C. A. S. Type Coll.). Portion of uncoiled arm of another specimen. Length, 45 mm. Locality 445 (C. A. S.), near Phoenix, Oregon; Turonian. 204

5, 6. *Hyphantoceras irregulare* n. sp. Holotype (C. A. S. Type Coll.). Total length (on curve), 75 mm; breadth of whorl, 18 mm. (5) Oblique top view. (6) Side view. Locality 445 (C. A. S.), found at "Forty-nine" mine, near Phoenix, Oregon; Turonian. 210

8, 9. *Calycoceras* (*Metacalycoceras*) *auspicium* n. sp. Holotype and paratype (C. A. S. Type Coll.). Reduced. Greater diameter, 110 mm; width of umbilicus, 36 mm; height of whorl, 46 mm. Locality 445 (C. A. S.), "Forty-nine" mine, near Phoenix, Jackson Co., Oregon. (9) Paratype. Portion of young whorl of same species, natural size, showing early tubercules on the ribs. Specimens from Locality 465 (C. A. S.). 243

PLATE 21.—*FOSSILS FROM THE UPPER CRETACEOUS OF CALIFORNIA AND OREGON*

Figure *Page*

1. *Volutoderma jacksonensis* n. sp. Holotype (C. A. S. Type Coll.). Length (incomplete), 85.4 mm; width (incomplete), 32 mm. Locality 445 (C. A. S.), found at the old "Forty-nine" mine, 2 miles southwest of Phoenix, Oregon; Turonian. 174

2, 3. *Natica* (*Gyrodes*) *conradiana* (Gabb). Hypotypes (C. A. S. Type Coll.). Natural size. (2) Height (incomplete), 31 mm; greatest width, 45 mm; greatest width of umbilicus, 18 mm; (3) Height, 23 mm; greatest width, 25 mm; greatest width of umbilicus, 10 mm. Locality 1346A (C. A. S.), North fork of Cottonwood Creek, 1 mile above the mouth of Hulen Creek, Shasta County; Upper Albian. 149

4, 4a. *Cypraea argonautica* n. name. Holotype No. 42 (C. A. S. Type Coll.). Reproduced from Anderson (1902). Length, 23 mm; width, 18 mm. Locality 445A (C. A. S.), found on the Fitch ranch (formerly Smith), 3 miles west of Phoenix, Oregon; Turonian. 177

5. *Trajanella acuminata* n. sp. Holotype (C. A. S. Type Coll.). Length (incomplete), 82 mm; width, 32 mm; height of spire, 55 mm (lower portion missing). Locality 1345 (C. A. S.), Texas Springs, 2 miles east of Horsetown on road leading to Centerville; Turonian. 161

6, 7. *Gyrodes siskiyouensis* Anderson. Holotype No. 41 (C. A. S. Type Coll.). Reproduced from Anderson (1902). Height, 22 mm; width, 23 mm. Found on north slope of Siskiyou Mountains, 4 miles south of Ashland, Oregon; Turonian. 150

8, 9. *Gyrodes dowelli* White. Hypotype. (C. A. S. Type Coll.). Two views. Height, 36 mm; width, 32 mm; width of umbilical pit, 12 mm. Locality 1293A (C. A. S.), 1 mile north of Frazier Corners, Shasta County; Turonian. 149

10, 10a. *Turritella hearni* Anderson. Holotype No. 6855 (C. A. S. Type Coll.). Length, 29 mm; width, 7 mm. Found on Hagerdorn ranch, 4 miles north of Montague, Siskiyou County; (10a) Hypotype (C. A. S. Type Coll.). Length 30 mm; maximum diameter 10.7 mm; Middle Turonian. 153

11. *Turritella petersoni* Anderson. Holotype No. 6854 (C. A. S. Type Coll.). Length, 21 mm; width, 6 mm. Locality 1291 (C. A. S.), found on Peterson ranch, 4 miles north of Sites, Colusa County; lower Cenomanian. 153

12. *Haliotis lomaënsis* Anderson. Holotype No. 69 (C. A. S. Type Coll.). Length, 13 mm; width, 8.6 mm. Locality 13304 (C. S. M. B.), found at Point Loma, beneath beds with *Coralliochama orcutti* White; Campanian. 146

13, 13a. *Bullina nortonensis* n. sp. Holotype (C. A. S. Type Coll.). Shows back and side views of same. Length, 5 mm; breadth, 3 mm. Locality 1467A (C. A. S.), found at Enos Canyon, 7 miles northwest of Winters, Yolo County. 178

14. *Acteonina colusaensis* n. sp. Holotype (C. A. S. Type Coll.). Height, 35 mm; width, 22 mm. Locality 12785 (C. S. M. B.) (= C. A. S. Locality 1291), found on Peterson ranch, 4 miles north of Sites, Colusa County; Cenomanian. 158

15, 16. *Cypraea fontana* n. sp. Holotype (C. A. S. Type Coll.). Length, 23.5 mm; width, 17 mm; height of spire, 2 mm. Locality 1345 (C. A. S.), found at Texas Springs, Shasta County; Lower Cenomanian. 177

FOSSILS FROM THE UPPER CRETACEOUS OF CALIFORNIA AND OREGON

FOSSILS FROM THE UPPER CRETACEOUS OF CALIFORNIA AND BRITISH COLUMBIA

PLATE 22.—*FOSSILS FROM THE UPPER CRETACEOUS OF CALIFORNIA AND BRITISH COLUMBIA*

Figure   *Page*

1, 2, 3. *Inoceramus subundatus* Meek. Hypotypes (C. A. S. Type Coll.). (1) Left valve. Length, 65 mm; height, 56 mm; thickness of both valves, 34 mm. Found at Locality 444 (C. A. S.), near Klamath River. (2) Right valve, reduced. Length, incomplete, 56 mm; height, 66 mm; thickness of valve, 16 mm. Locality 25730A (C. A. S.), found on east flank of Rumsey Hills, Salt Creek, western Colusa County. (3) Right and left valves. Length (incomplete), 75 mm; height, 70 mm; thickness of both valves, 37 mm. Locality 444 (C. A. S.), found on south side of the Klamath River, Siskiyou County, Coniacian. *See* also Pl. 26, fig. 4. 101

4. *Inoceramus undulatoplicatus* Roemer. Hypotype (L. S. J. U. Type Coll.). Young example. Natural size. Found on Sucia Island, Strait of Georgia; Coniacian. *See* also Pl. 43, figs. 3, 4, 5. 102

5, 6. *Inoceramus meekianus* n. sp. Holotype and paratype. (C. A. S. Type Coll.). (5) Holotype. Length, incomplete, 56 mm; height, 55 mm; thickness of single valve, approximately 8.5 mm. Locality 228 (C. A. S.), found on Sucia Island, Strait of Georgia. (6) Paratype. Length, 66 mm; height, 55 mm; thickness of both valves, 27 mm. Locality 444A (C. A. S.), found on south side of Klamath River, 1 mile south of Hornbrook, Siskiyou County; Coniacian. 101

PLATE 23.—*FOSSILS FROM THE UPPER CRETACEOUS OF CALIFORNIA*

Figure   *Page*

1, 1a. *Romaniceras hesperium* n. sp. Holotype (C. I. T. Type Coll.). Greater diameter, 160 mm; width of umbilicus, 55 mm; greater breadth of whorl (between ribs), 63 mm. Locality 3727 (C. I. T.), about 150 yards S. of N. line of S½ sec. 4, T. 32 N., R. 3 W. in bed of Swede Creek, Hathaway Bros. Ranch, north of Oak Run, Shasta County; Turonian. 245

2, 3. *Oregoniceras siskiyouense* (Anderson). Hypotypes (C. I. T. Type Coll.). (2) Greater diameter, 31 mm; width of umbilicus, 8.2 mm; breadth of whorl, 11 mm; height, 14.5 mm. (3) Greater diameter, 40 mm; width of umbilicus, 11 mm; breadth of whorl, 11 mm. Locality 1042 (C. I. T.), Rancheria Creek, near Henley, Siskiyou County. *See* Pl. 24, figs. 1, 1a, 2, 3. 266

4, 5. *Calycoceras* (*Eucalycoceras*) *diabloense* n. sp. Holotype (C. A. S. Type Coll.). Greater diameter, 93 mm; width of umbilicus, 28 mm; height of whorl, 44 mm; breadth of whorl, 45 mm. Locality 25627 = 28104 (C. A. S.), found on Curry Creek, SE ¼ sec. 8, T. 1 S., R. 1 E., M. D. B. & M., Contra Costa County, at horizon of *Eucalycoceras turneri* (White); lower Cenomanian. 243

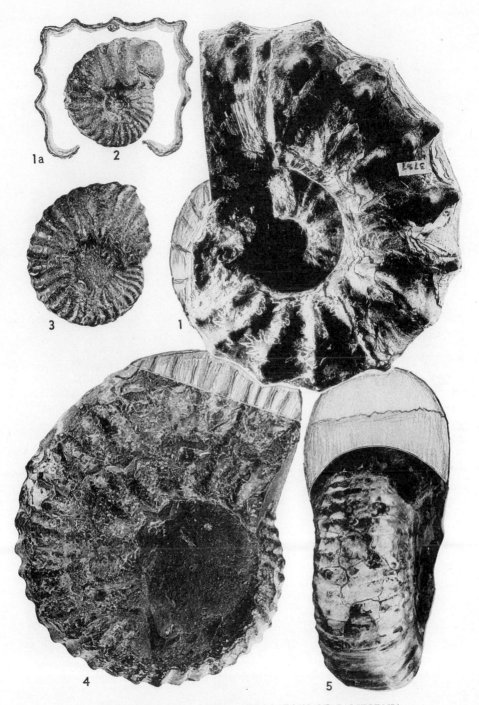

FOSSILS FROM THE UPPER CRETACEOUS OF CALIFORNIA

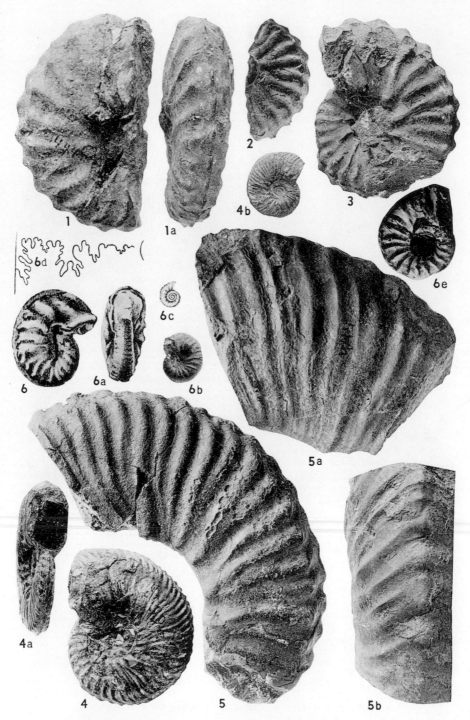

FOSSILS FROM THE UPPER CRETACEOUS OF OREGON

PLATE 24.—*FOSSILS FROM THE UPPER CRETACEOUS OF OREGON*

Figure
Page

1, 1a, 2, 3. *Oregoniceras siskiyouense* (Anderson). Hypotypes and neotype (C. A. S. Type Coll.). (1, 1a) Hypotype. Greater diameter, 58 mm.; width of umbilicus, 15 mm; height of whorl, 27 mm; maximum breadth of whorl near ventral zone, 20 mm; minimum, 12 mm. (2) Hypotype. Maximum diameter, 33 mm. (3) Neotype No. 25. Maximum diameter, 48 mm; height, 23 mm; breadth, 14.5 mm. All examples found at Locality 445 (C. A. S.), the "Forty-nine" mine, 2 miles south of Phoenix, Oregon; upper Turonian. *See* also Pl. 23, figs. 2, 3. 266

4, 4a, 4b. *Oregoniceras oregonense* (Anderson). Holotype and hypotype (C. A. S. Type Coll.). (4, 4a) Holotype No. 36. Maximum diameter, 44 mm; width of umbilicus, 10 mm; height of whorl, 17 mm; greater breadth of whorl, 10 mm. Found at "Forty-nine" mine, 2 miles south of Phoenix, Oregon. (4b) Hypotype, young example. Maximum diameter, 13.6 mm; upper Turonian. 264

5, 5a, 5b. *Oregoniceras knighteni* (Anderson). Holotype and hypotype (C. A. S. Type Coll.). (5) Portion of holotype. Maximum diameter, 97 mm; breadth, 26.6 mm; width of umbilicus, 15 mm. (5a, 5b) Large fragment of outer whorl of hypotype, slightly reduced, showing character of ribbing and ventral zone of older stages of growth. Locality 445 (C. A. S.), found at the "Forty-nine" mine, 2 miles south of Phoenix, Oregon; upper Turonian. *See* also Pl. 33, figs. 1, 1a, 2, 3. 264

6, 6a, 6b, 6c, 6d, 6e. *Scaphites condoni* Anderson. Holotype, paratype, and hypotypes (C. A. S. Type Coll.). (6, 6a) Holotype No. 34, natural size. Greater diameter, 25 mm; diameter of coil, 16 mm; breadth of body chamber, 10 mm. (6d) Original drawing of suture line, reproduced. (6b) Paratype No. 34A. Greater diameter, 13 mm. Holotype and paratype Locality 445 (C. A. S.), "Forty-nine" mine, Phoenix, Oregon. (6c) Hypotype, young coil, enlarged × 2. (6e) Hypotype. Maximum diameter, 13.8 mm; maximum breadth, 5.8 mm; from Locality 3728 (C. I. T.). 249

PLATE 25.—*FOSSILS FROM THE UPPER CRETACEOUS OF OREGON*

Figure　　　　　　　　　　　　　　　　　　　　　　　　　　　　*Page*

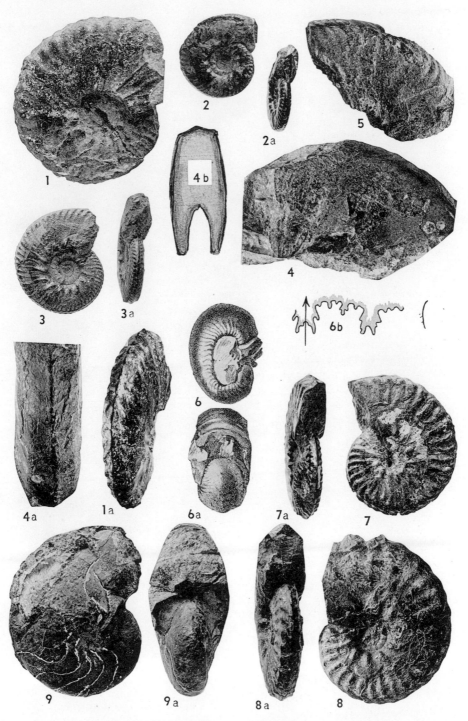

FOSSILS FROM THE UPPER CRETACEOUS OF OREGON

FOSSILS FROM THE UPPER CRETACEOUS OF CALIFORNIA

PLATE 26.—*FOSSILS FROM THE UPPER CRETACEOUS OF CALIFORNIA*

Figure *Page*

1, 2, 3. *Cucullaea* (*Idonearca*) *gravida* (Gabb). Three hypotypes (C. A. S. Type Coll.). (1) Exterior of right valve. Length 36.5 mm, height 28.5 mm. (2) Fragment of left valve showing dentition. Length 22.4 mm, height (incomplete) 19.6 mm. (3) Immature example showing dentition. Length 33 mm; height 26.9 mm. Locality 1293C (C. A. S.) Bella Vista District, Shasta County. 89

4. *Inoceramus subundatus* Meek. Hypotype. (C. A. S. Type Coll.). Length approximately 63 mm; height approximately 54 mm. From Locality 28325 (C. A. S.) south side Crow Creek, NE ¼ sec. 33, T. 6 S., R. 7 E., M.D.M., Stanislaus County. *See* also Pl. 22, figs. 1, 2, 3. 101

5, 6. *Opisoma pacifica* n. sp. Holotype (C. A. S. Type Coll.). Length, 48 mm; height, 66 mm; thickness, 28 mm. From Locality 29118 (C. A. S.), in the Moreno formation on Mustang Creek. 122

7, 7a. *Trigonia melhasei* n. sp. Holotype (C. A. S. Type Coll.). Length, 54 mm; height, 29 mm; thickness (convexity) of valve, about 13 mm. (7a) View from above showing escutcheon. Found about 1 mile east of Frazier Corners, Shasta County; Turonian. 113

8. *Trigonia bowersiana* n. sp. Holotype (C. A. S. Type Coll.). Length, 60 mm; height, 50 mm. From Locality 252 (C. A. S.), Santiago Canyon, Orange County (= Univ. of Oregon Locality 14542 according to F. M. Anderson). 116

PLATE 27.—*FOSSILS FROM THE UPPER CRETACEOUS OF CALIFORNIA AND OREGON*

Figure *Page*

1, 1a, 1b, 1c. *Scaphites inermis* Anderson. Neotype and two paratypes (C. I. T.), enlarged, × 2. (1, 1a) Neotype. Greater diameter, 14.6 mm; less diameter, 13 mm; breadth of whorl, 5 mm. (1b, 1c) Paratypes, young coils of same. Locality 1010 (C. I. T.), in the SW corner of SE ¼ sec. 34, T. 33 N., R. 3 W., M. D. M., Redding quadrangle, Shasta County; Turonian. 251

2, 2a. *Pachydiscus oregonensis* n. sp. Holotype (C. A. S. Type Coll.). Side and front views. Greater diameter, 101.4 mm; width of umbilicus, 26 mm; height of whorl, 46.7 mm; breadth of whorl near umbilicus, 33 mm. Wholly septate. Found at the "Forty-nine" mine, 2 miles south of Phoenix, Oregon; Turonian. 221

3, 3a, 4, 4a. *Pachydiscus ashlandicus* (Anderson). Holotype No. 33, Paratype No. 33a (C. A. S. Type Coll.). (3, 3a) Holotype. Greater diameter, 77 mm; width of umbilicus, 23 mm; height of whorl, 31.5 mm; breadth of whorl, 25 mm. (4, 4a) Paratype. Young shell of same. Greater diameter, 12 mm; width of umbilicus, 10 mm; breadth of whorl, 10 mm. Holotype and paratype from Locality 446 (C. A. S.), found 4 miles south of Ashland, Oregon; Turonian. 221

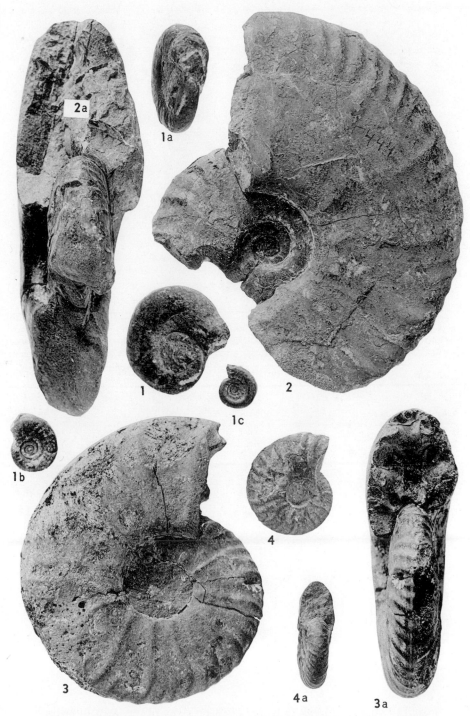

FOSSILS FROM THE UPPER CRETACEOUS OF CALIFORNIA AND OREGON

FOSSILS FROM THE UPPER CRETACEOUS OF CALIFORNIA AND OREGON

PLATE 28.—*FOSSILS FROM THE UPPER CRETACEOUS OF CALIFORNIA AND OREGON*

Figure *Page*

1, 2. *Fagesia siskiyouensis* Anderson. Holotype No. 4689 (C. A. S. Type Coll.). Greater diameter, 75 mm; width of umbilicus, 28 mm; height of whorl, 30 mm; breadth of whorl, 50 mm. Found near Henley, Siskiyou County, California; Upper Turonian. 248

3, 3a. *Fagesia klamathensis* n. sp. Holotype (C. A. S. Type Coll.). Greater diameter, 130 mm; width of umbilicus, 35 mm; height of whorl, 55 mm; breadth of whorl, 65 mm. Locality 455 (C. A. S.), found near Henley, Siskiyou County, California; Upper Turonian. 248

4, 4a, 4b. *Oregoniceras multicostum* (Anderson). Neotype No. 32 and Neoparatype 32a (C. A. S. Type Coll.). (4, 4a) Neotype No. 32. Maximum diameter, 23.6 mm; width of umbilicus, 8.5 mm; height of whorl, 9.3 mm; breadth of whorl, 5.9 mm. (4b) Neoparatype No. 32A. Maximum diameter, 18.5 mm; width of umbilicus, 5.8 mm; height of whorl, 8 mm; breadth of whorl, 5 mm. Both found at Locality 445A (C. A. S.) on the Fitch (formerly Smith) ranch, 3 miles west of Phoenix, Oregon. 265

PLATE 29.—*FOSSILS FROM THE UPPER CRETACEOUS OF CALIFORNIA*

Figure *Page*

1. *Acteonina californica* Gabb. Neotype (C. A. S. Type Coll.). Length, 72 mm; maximum width, 39 mm. Locality 31918 (C. A. S.); Thompson Creek, near Putah Creek, Glenn County. 156

2. *Acteonina bellavistana* n. sp. Holotype (C. A. S. Type Coll.). Height, 51.6 mm; width, 25 mm. Locality 1293A (C. A. S.) 1 mile north of Frazier Corners (Bella Vista), Shasta County; Turonian. 157

3. *Acteonina berryessensis* n. sp. Holotype (C. A. S. Type Coll.). Height (incomplete), 60 mm. Found on Thompson Creek, western Glenn County; Turonian. 157

4, 4a, 4b. *Acteonella packardi* n. name. Holotype (C. A. S. Type Coll.). (4) Holotype. Front view, showing aperture. (4a) Rear view of specimen shown by Packard (1922, Pl. 36, fig. 4). (4b) Illustrates plications of the columella of holotype. Locality 444A (C. A. S.), Rocky Gulch, near Hornbrook, Siskiyou County. 160

5. *Acteonella rustica* n. sp. Holotype (C. A. S. Type Coll.). Total height, 53.8 mm; maximum width, 29.3 mm. Locality 33721 (C. A. S.), found 2 miles above the Calkins home on Little Cow Creek, Shasta County. 161

6. *Acteonella oviformis* Gabb. Hypotype (C. A. S. Type Coll.). Partial restoration of Gabb's species, based on the present specimen and on his figure of the holotype (1869, pl. 28, fig. 58); Locality 27831; (C. A. S.), 3 miles north of Bellavista, along Dry Creek in road near center of the E side SE ¼ sec. 31, T. 33 N., R. 3W., M. D. M., Shasta County. 160

7, 7a. *Acteonella frazierensis* n. sp. Holotype and paratype (C. A. S. Type Coll.). (7) Holotype. Height, 43 mm; maximum width of shell (including outer lip), 24 mm; restored length, 55 mm. Locality 28103 (C. A. S.), Stinking Canyon, northeast of Redding, Shasta County. (7a) Paratype. Height, 27 mm; maximum width, 12 mm. Found at Locality 27831 (C. A. S.), 3 miles north of Bellavista, Shasta County. 161

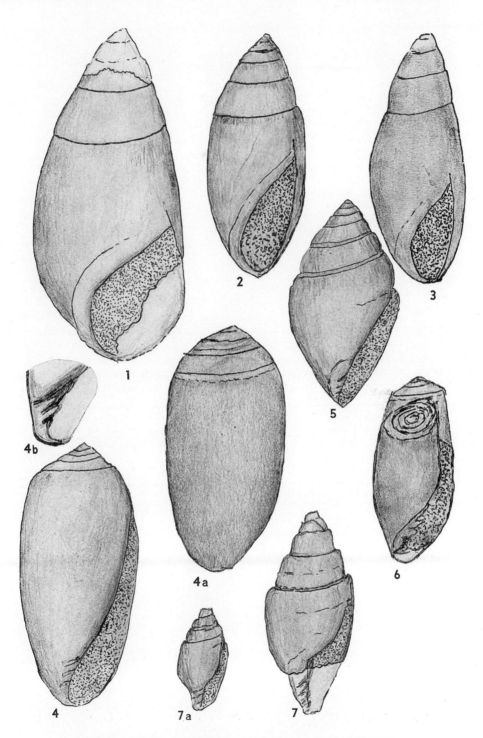

FOSSILS FROM THE UPPER CRETACEOUS OF CALIFORNIA

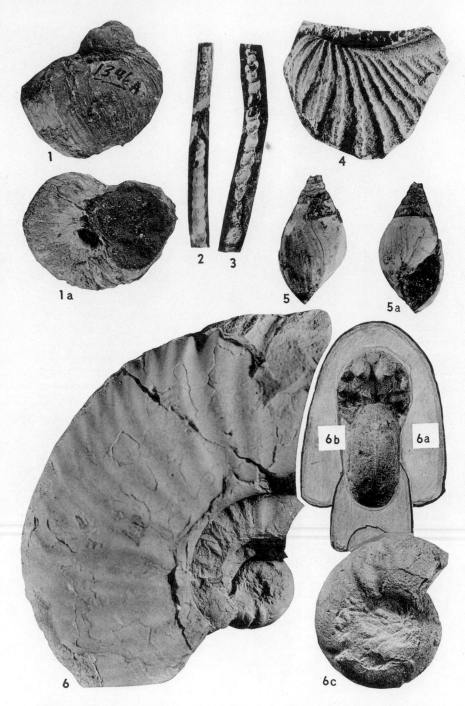

FOSSILS FROM THE UPPER CRETACEOUS OF CALIFORNIA AND OREGON

PLATE 30.—*FOSSILS FROM THE UPPER CRETACEOUS OF CALIFORNIA AND OREGON*

Figure | *Page*

1, 1a. *Polinices gainesanus* n. sp. Holotype (C. A. S. Type Coll.). Maximum height, 33 mm; maximum width of body whorl, 34 mm; height of aperture, 24 mm. Found at Locality 1346A (C. A. S.) on north fork of Cottonwood Creek, Shasta County; upper Albian. 151

2, 3. *Nerinea stewarti* n. sp. Holotype and paratype (C. A. S. Type Coll.). (2) Holotype. Total length, 52 mm; maximum breadth, 4 mm. (3) Paratype. Total length, 53 mm. Found at Hickman ranch, middle fork of Cottonwood Creek; upper Turonian. 155

4. *Trigonia klamathonia* n. sp. Holotype (a rock mold) and plaster cast of same. Length (partly estimated), 45 mm; maximum height, 27 mm; convexity of valve, 12 mm. Found about 4 miles south of Hilt, on the west border of the small Cottonwood Valley, above Hornbrook, Siskiyou County. 112

5, 5a. *Acteonina roguensis* n. sp. Holotype (C. A. S. Type Coll.). Height, 28.4 mm; maximum width, 12 mm. (5) Rear view. (5a) View showing aperture. From "Forty-nine" mine, 2 miles south of Phoenix, Oregon. 158

6, 6a, 6b, 6c. *Puzosia (Eocanodoceras) hannai* n. sp. Holotype (C. A. S. Type Coll.). Fragment in 2 sections. Inner whorls showing nature of ribbing on immature shell. Locality 2245 (C. A. S.), 15.1 miles southeast of Beegum on road to Rosewood, across Dry Creek from ranch house. Turonian. 239

PLATE 31.—*FOSSILS FROM THE UPPER CRETACEOUS OF CALIFORNIA*

Figure *Page*

1. *Pachydiscus rosewoodensis* n. sp. Holotype (C. A. S. Type Coll.). Greater diameter, 140 mm; width of umbilicus, 35 mm; height of whorl, 55 mm; breadth of whorl, 40 mm. Found at Locality 31102 (C. A. S.), near Rosewood, Tehama County; upper Turonian. 222

2. *Oxybeloceras biconstrictum* n. sp. Holotype (C. A. S. Type Coll.). A large fragment. Length, 95 mm; greater breadth, 20 mm; thickness of same, 10 mm. Found at Locality 31100 (C. A. S.), beneath the horizon with *Oregoniceras* sp., and *Prionotropis bakeri* Anderson, 1.8 miles west of Rosewood on Dry Creek, North Tehama County; upper-middle Turonian. 202

3. *Hyphantoceras laqueum* n. sp. Holotype (C. A. S. Type Coll.). Width of outer coil, 82 mm; greater diameter of whorl, 15 mm; section of whorl, subcircular. Found at Locality 31115 (C. A. S.), southwest branch of Cortina Creek, Colusa County, west of Sand Creek and of Rumsey divide; probably Turonian. 210

4, 4a. *Bostrychoceras occidentale* n. sp. Holotype and paratype (C. A. S. Type Coll.). (4) Holotype. Portions of 2 whorls. Width of larger coil, 44.6 mm; greater diameter of whorl, 21 mm. (4a) Paratype. Width of coil, 68 mm; greater diameter of whorl, 22 mm. Holotype and paratype found together at Locality 1293A (C. A. S.), 1 mile north of Frazier Corners, Shasta County; Turonian. 205

FOSSILS FROM THE UPPER CRETACEOUS OF CALIFORNIA

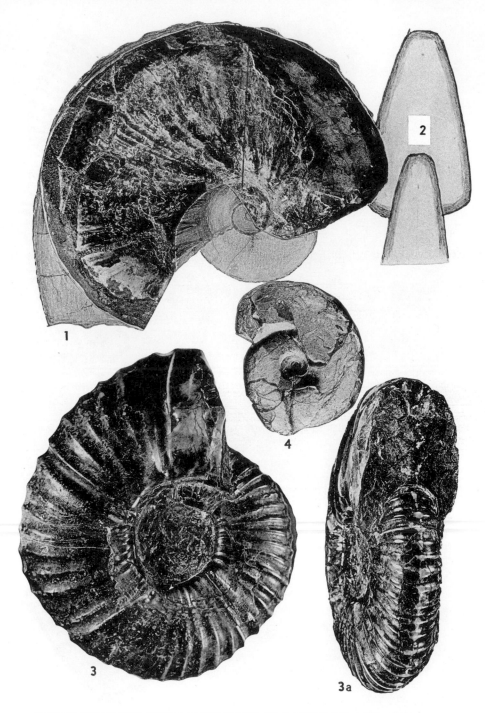

FOSSILS FROM THE UPPER CRETACEOUS OF CALIFORNIA AND SUCIA ISLAND

PLATE 32.—*FOSSILS FROM THE UPPER CRETACEOUS OF CALIFORNIA AND SUCIA ISLAND*

Figure *Page*

1, 2. *Placenticeras vancouverense* (Meek). Hypotype (C. A. S. Type Coll.). (1) Greater diameter (incomplete), 90 mm; width of umbilicus, 20 mm; breadth of whorl, 28 mm. (2) Section of whorl at maximum height of figured example. Found at Locality 228 (C. A. S.), on Sucia Island, Strait of Georgia; Coniacian. 256

3, 3a. *Canadoceras georgianum* n. sp. Plasto-holotype (C. A. S. Type Coll.). A cast of holotype (L. S. J. U. Type Coll.). Side and front views. Greater diameter, 135 mm; width of umbilicus, 41 mm, breadth of whorl, 44 mm. Found on Sucia Island, Strait of Georgia; Coniacian. 234

4. *Lytoceras* (*Tetragonites*) *kernense* n. sp. Holotype (C. A. S. Type Coll.). Maximum diameter, 34.8 mm; maximum breadth of whorl approximately 13 mm; greatest width of umbilicus 9 mm. From Locality 1552 (C. A. S.), on the south border of Antelope Valley, northern Kern County. See also Pl. 73, fig. 6. 187

PLATE 33.—*FOSSILS FROM THE UPPER CRETACEOUS OF CALIFORNIA AND OREGON*

Figure *Page*

1, 1a, 2, 3. *Oregoniceras knighteni* (Anderson). Paratype, hypotype, and an additional hypotype. (C. A. S. Type Coll.). (1, 1a) Hypotype No. 30. Greater diameter, 75 mm; breadth of umbilicus, 22 mm; height of whorl, 32 mm; thickness of whorl, 18 mm; ribs relatively heavy. (2) Additional hypotype. Natural size. (3) Paratype No. 49. Slightly reduced. Locality 445 (C. A. S.), "Forty-nine" mine, 2 miles south of Phoenix, Oregon. See also Pl. 24, figs. 5, 5a, 5b. 264

4, 4a, 4b, 4c. *Oregoniceras argonautarum* n. sp. Holotype and hypotype (C. A. S. Type Coll.). (4, 4a) Holotype (lost in the 1906 fire). Greater diameter, 40 mm; breadth of umbilicus, 10 mm; breadth of whorl, 11 mm. Figures 4, 4a, and 4c from original Figures (Anderson, 1902, Pl. 2) (4b) Hypotype (4c) Suture line of holotype. Locality: "Forty-nine" mine, Jackson County, Oregon. 268

5, 5a. *Mortoniceras* (*Submortoniceras*) *buttense* (*Anderson*). Holotype No. 12096 (Univ. Calif. Mus. Paleo. Type Coll.). (5) Figure reproduced. Greater diameter, 64 mm; width of umbilicus, 16 mm; height of whorl, 30 mm; breadth of whorl, 16 mm. 5(a) Section of whorl. Locality 1125 (C. A. S.), a mile west of Pentz, Butte County. 266

6, 6a. *Oregoniceras phoenixense* n. sp. Paratype (C. A. S. Type Coll.). (6) Side view showing nature of ribbing. (6a) Oblique front view. Locality "Forty-nine" mine, near Phoenix, Oregon. *See* also Pl. 25, figs. 7, 7a. 266

FOSSILS FROM THE UPPER CRETACEOUS OF CALIFORNIA AND OREGON

FOSSILS FROM THE UPPER CRETACEOUS OF CALIFORNIA AND OREGON

PLATE 34.—*FOSSILS FROM THE UPPER CRETACEOUS OF CALIFORNIA AND OREGON*

Figure   *Page*

1, 2, 3, 3a. *Prionotropis branneri* Anderson. Two paratypes (C. A. S. Type Coll.). (1, 2) Paratype. Side and rear views of young adult shell, showing noded ribs and keel. (3) Paratype. Young shell. Side view; all figures natural size. (3a) Suture line drawn from young shell. Figures 1-3 reproductions of original paratypes as figured. Specimens lost in fire of 1906. Locality: Fitch ranch, 3 miles west of Phoenix, Oregon. 261

4, 4a, 5, 5a. *Prionocycloceras crenulatum* (Anderson). Holotype and neotype (C. A. S. Type Coll.). (4, 4a) Drawing of lost holotype; (Original figure) approximately, 30 mm in diameter. (5, 5a) Neotype. Greater diameter, 110 mm; width of umbilicus, 41 mm; height of whorl, 38 mm; breadth of whorl, 30 mm. Found on Richardson ranch, 4 miles north of Montague, Siskiyou County; lower Senonian. 263

6. *Prionotropis casperi* n. sp. Holotype (C. A. S. Type Coll.). View of right side. Greater diameter, 93 mm; width of umbilicus, 33 mm; height of whorl, 36 mm; breadth of whorl, 26 mm. Locality 445A (C. A. S.), found on the Fitch ranch, 2 miles west of Phoenix, Oregon; lower Senonian. *See* also Pl. 39, figs. 3, 4. 262

PLATE 35.—*FOSSILS FROM THE UPPER CRETACEOUS OF CALIFORNIA*

Figure *Page*

1, 1a, 1b. *Nowakites klamathonis* n. sp. Holotype and paratype (C. A. S. Type Coll.). (1) Holotype. Large fragment of body whorl. Greater diameter, 170 mm; width of umbilicus, 61 mm; breadth of whorl, 58 mm. (1a, 1b) Paratype, showing inner coils of another example, dimensions as follows: length, 104 mm; height of whorl, 48 mm; breadth of whorl, 42 mm. (1a) After reversal. Locality: Richardson ranch, 4 miles north of Montague, Siskiyou County; Coniacian. 230

2, 2a. *Kotôceras subsugatum* n. name. Holotype (C. A. S. Type Coll.). Lost in fire of 1906. Reproduced from Anderson (1902). Side and front views. Greater diameter, 27 mm; width of umbilicus, 4 mm; breadth of whorl, 11 mm. Found on the Richardson ranch, 4 miles north of Montague, Siskiyou County; lower Senonian (Coniacian). 217

3, 3a. *Desmophyllites siskiyouensis* n. sp. Hypotype (C. A. S. Type Coll.), Natural size. Side and rear views. Greater diameter, 35 mm; maximum height of last whorl, 18.9 mm; maximum breadth of last whorl, 15 mm; found at Locality 1467A (C. A. S.), probably Enos Canyon, Yolo County, California. Coniacian. *See* also Pl. 41, figs. 1, 2, 3, 3a. 215

4. *Nowakites* (?) *puertoensis* n. sp. Holotype (C. A. S. Type Coll.). Greater diameter, 140 mm; width of umbilicus, 55 mm. Found at Locality 28323 (C. A. S.), on Puerto Creek, Stanislaus County; lower Senonian. 231

FOSSILS FROM THE UPPER CRETACEOUS OF CALIFORNIA

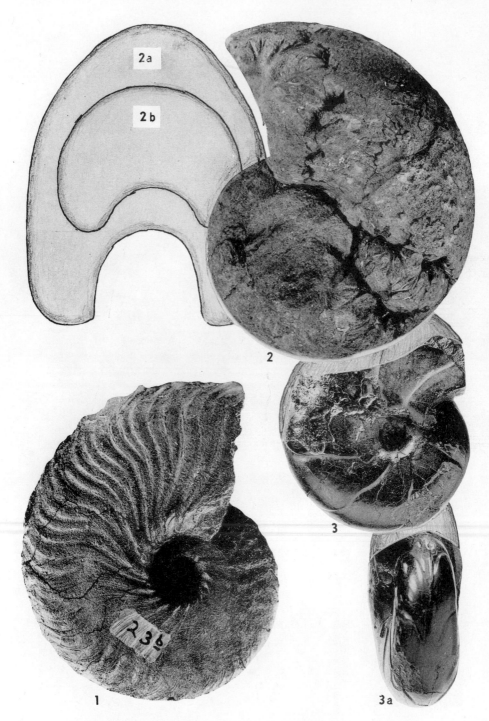

FOSSILS FROM THE UPPER CRETACEOUS OF CALIFORNIA

PLATE 36.—*FOSSILS FROM THE UPPER CRETACEOUS OF CALIFORNIA*

Figure *Page*

1. *Metaplacenticeras californicum* (Anderson). Neotype No. 23B (C. A. S. Type Coll.). Greater diameter, 86 mm; width of umbilicus, 18 mm; height of whorl, 41 mm. Locality 44 (C. A. S.), found half a mile west of Henley, Siskiyou County; Coniacian. 254

2, 2a, 2b. *Parapachydiscus henleyensis* (Anderson). Holotype No. 22 (C. A. S. Type Coll.). (2) Remnant of the holotype after the fire of 1906; left side. Maximum diameter, 90 mm; maximum breadth last whorl, approximately 53 mm. (2a, 2b) Sections of whorl at different stages of growth. (2a) Section of whorl, reduced from a diameter of 14 inches. (2b) Section of whorl, reduced from a diameter of 3.5 inches. Locality 444 (C. A. S.). 224

3, 3a. *Kotôceras richardsoni* n. sp. Holotype (C. A. S. Type Coll.). Side and front views. Greater diameter, 61 mm; width of umbilicus, 10 mm; breadth of whorl, 25 mm. Locality 455A (C. A. S.), found on the Richardson ranch, 4 miles north of Montague, Siskiyou County; Coniacian. 217

PLATE 37.—*FOSSILS FROM THE UPPER CRETACEOUS OF CALIFORNIA*

Figure   *Page*

1, 2, 3, 4, 4a. *Metaplacenticeras pacificum* (Smith). Holotype and paratype (1) Reproduction of original figure of holotype. Greater diameter, 165 mm; width of umbilicus, 42 mm; breadth of whorl, 42 mm. (2) Paratype. Reproduction of original figures. Greater diameter, 48 mm. (3) Ideal section of whorl, 56 mm; diameter; greater breadth of same, 16 mm. (4, 4a) Side and front views of early stage. (All figures after Smith, 1900). The original figures of 4, 4a (Smith, 1900, pl. 25 figs. 1, 2) were cited by Smith as *Placenticeras Californicum*. Locality: Found half a mile west of Henley, Siskiyou County. 254

5, 5a, 5b. *Kossmaticeras* (*Madrasites*) *voyanum* n. name. Holotype 12115 (Univ. Calif. Type Coll.). Cast of Holotype No. 8888 (C. A. S. Type Coll.). Greater diameter, 60 mm; width of umbilicus, 18 mm; breadth of whorl, 22 mm. (5b) Suture line of same. Locality: Found in the Cottonwood district, Shasta County; Cenomanian. 241

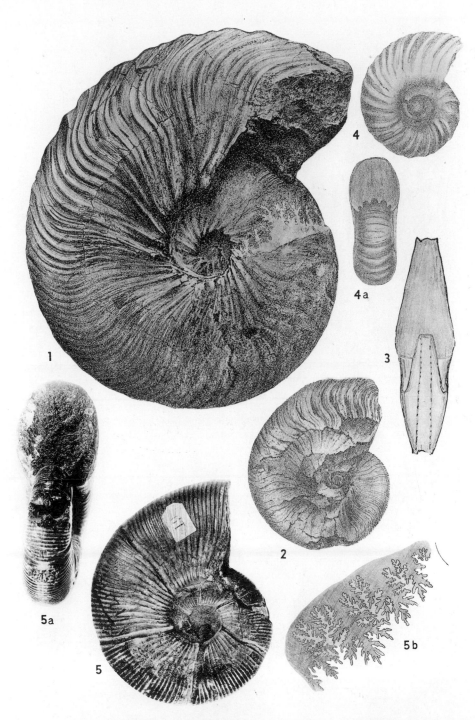

FOSSILS FROM THE UPPER CRETACEOUS OF CALIFORNIA

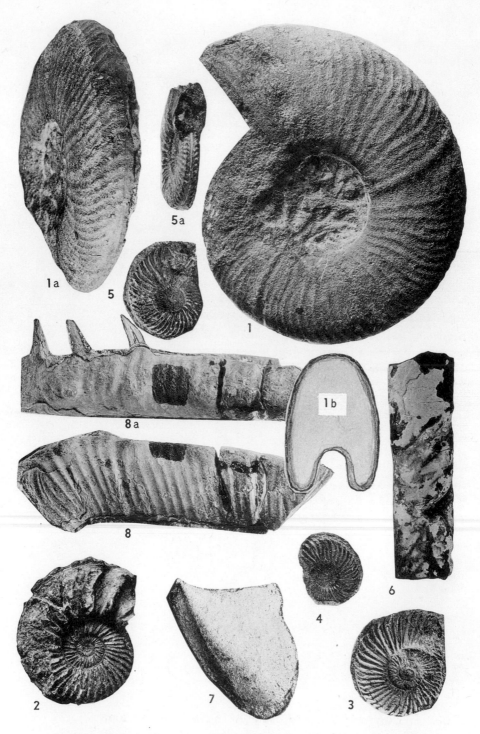

FOSSILS FROM THE UPPER CRETACEOUS OF CALIFORNIA AND OREGON

PLATE 38.—*FOSSILS FROM THE UPPER CRETACEOUS OF CALIFORNIA AND OREGON*

Figure	*Page*
1, 1a, 1b. *Puzosia (Parapuzosia) hearni* n. sp. Holotype (C. A. S. Type Coll.). (1, 1a) Side and rear views. Greater diameter, 90 mm; width of umbilicus, 27 mm; breadth of whorl, 27 mm. (1b) Section of whorl, drawn from holotype. Locality: Found on the Hagerdorn ranch, 8 miles northeast of Yreka, Siskiyou County; upper Turonian.	238
2, 3, 4, 5, 5a. *Prionotropis bakeri* (Anderson). Holotype and three hypotypes. (2, 5a) Hypotype. Greater diameter, 35.6 mm; approximate width of body whorl, 10.5 mm. (3) Holotype No. 39. Maximum diameter, 29.8 mm; height of body whorl, 10 mm; approximate width of body whorl, 6.8 mm. (4) Hypotype (smaller specimen). Greater diameter, 18.6 mm. (5) Hypotype (larger specimen). Greater diameter, 20.8 mm. Holotype from Locality 445 (C. A. S.), "Forty-nine" mine, near Phoenix, Oregon, Hypotypes from Locality 445A (C. A. S.), from the Fitch ranch, 2 miles southwest of Phoenix, Oregon.	261
6. *Cyrtochilus major* n. sp. Holotype (C. A. S. Type Coll.). Fragment of nonseptate limb, Length, 60 mm; greater diameter, 18.4 mm; lesser diameter, at larger end, 16.4 mm; greater diameter at smaller end 16.6 mm; lesser diameter at smaller end, 14.4 mm. Locality: Found on Hayes Gulch, 2 miles northwest of Gas Point, Shasta County, in lowest beds of the Upper Cretaceous; Upper Albian.	189
7. *Avicula roguensis* n. sp. Holotype (C. A. S. Type Coll.). Natural size. Length, 15 mm; greater width, 10.3 mm; inflation about 2.5 mm. Locality: Found at the "Forty-nine" mine, south of Phoenix, Oregon; Turonian.	106
8, 8a. *Anisoceras draconis* n. sp. Holotype No. 47 (C. A. S. Type Coll.). Length (incomplete), 80 mm; greater diameter, 20 mm. Locality 444 (C. A. S.), found half a mile west of Henley, Siskiyou County; Turonian.	209

PLATE 39.—*FOSSILS FROM THE UPPER CRETACEOUS OF OREGON*

Figure *Page*

1, 2, *Fagesia californica* Anderson. Paratype No. 4685 (C. A. S. Type Coll.). Greater diameter, 70 mm; width of umbilicus, 22 mm; height of whorl, 28 mm; breadth of whorl, 46 mm. Locality 445A (C. A. S.), found near Fitch ranch, 2 miles west of Phoenix, Oregon; upper Turonian 248

3, 4. *Prionotropis casperi* n. sp. Holotype and paratype (C. A. S. Type Coll.). (3) Holotype. Greater diameter, 93 mm; width of umbilicus, 33 mm; height of whorl, 36 mm; breadth of whorl, 26 mm. (4) Paratype. Young shell. Greater diameter, 40 mm; width of umbilicus, 15 mm. Holotype and paratype from Locality 445A (C. A. S.), 2 miles west of Phoenix, Oregon; upper Turonian. *See* also Pl. 34, fig. 6 262

5, 5a. *Diplomoceras ellipticum* (Anderson). Holotype No. 35. (C. A. S. Type Coll.). Reproduction of Anderson's (1902) figure. Length, 56 mm; greater diameter at larger end, 11 mm; lesser diameter at larger end, 10.5 mm. Locality 445 (C. A. S.), found at the "Forty-nine" mine, southwest of Phoenix, Oregon; upper Turonian. 198

6, 6a, 7. *Hyphantoceras ceratopse* (Anderson). Holotype No. 37. (C. A. S. Type Coll.). Reproduction of Anderson's (1902) figure. (6, 6a) Holotype. Length, on curve, 75 mm; greater diameter, 12 mm; width, 9 mm. (7) Fragment of holotype No. 37. Length, 33.3 mm. Locality 445 A (C. A. S.), found at Fitch (Smith) ranch, 2 miles west of Phoenix, Oregon; middle or upper Turonian. 209

8. *Diplomoceras phoenixense* (Anderson). Holotype (C. A. S. Type Coll.). Original figure (1902). (Slightly reduced), lost in 1906 fire. Found at the "Forty-nine" mine, near Phoenix, Oregon; Turonian. 199

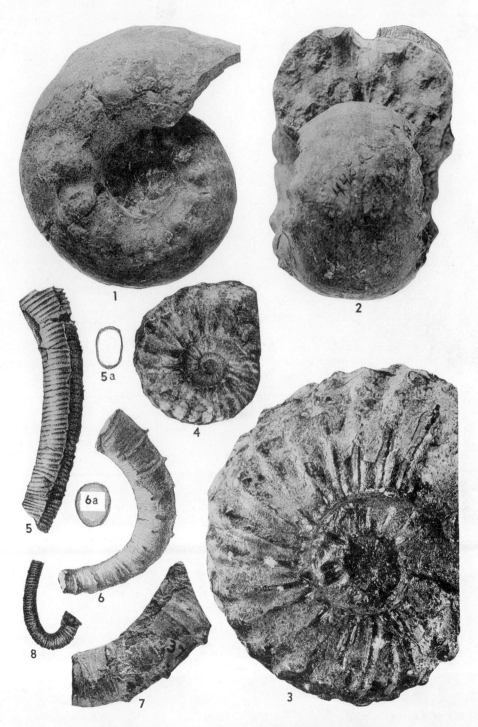

FOSSILS FROM THE UPPER CRETACEOUS OF OREGON

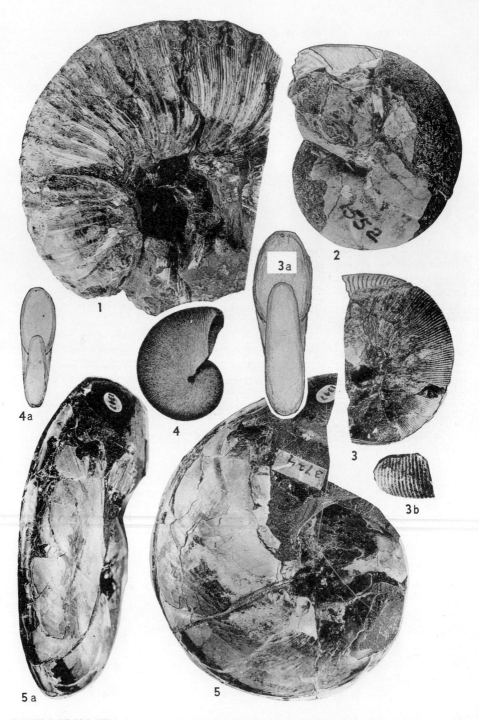

FOSSILS FROM THE UPPER CRETACEOUS OF CALIFORNIA AND VANCOUVER ISLAND

PLATE 40.—*FOSSILS FROM THE UPPER CRETACEOUS OF CALIFORNIA AND VANCOUVER ISLAND*

Figure *Page*

1. *Lytoceras* (*Gaudryceras*) aff. *L. tenuiliratum* Yabe. Hypotype (C. I. T. Type Coll.). Reduced. Greater diameter, 160 mm; width of umbilicus, 50 mm; breadth of whorl, 45 mm. Locality 1347 (C. I. T.) Found on Roaring River, a little above its mouth, about one-quarter mile downstream from old ranch house on the Drew place near middle sec. 3, T. 29 N., R. 6 W., Shasta County; upper Turonian. 183

2. *Desmophyllites selwynianus* (Whiteaves). Hypotype (C. A. S. Type Coll.). Greater diameter (incomplete), 60 mm; width of umbilicus, 5 mm; breadth of whorl, 15 mm. Locality 1552 (C. A. S.). Found on south border of Antelope Valley, Kern County; Coniacian. 215

3, 3a, 3b. *Phylloceras vaculae* n. sp. Holotype (C. I. T. Type Coll.). Greater diameter, 49 mm; width of umbilicus, 6 mm; breadth of whorl, 14 mm. (3a) Section of whorl.. (3b) Fragment of shell, showing detail of sculpture. Locality 1346 (C. I. T.). Found on Little Cow Creek, 1.5 miles east of Frazier Corners, Shasta County; lower Senonian. 181

4, 4a. *Phylloceras ramosum* Meek. Holotype, after Meek. Slightly reduced. Found at Comox, Vancouver Island, in Lower Coal Measures; Lower Senonian. 181

5, 5a. *Kotöceras frazierense,* n. sp. Holotype (C. I. T. Type Coll.). Greater diameter, 85 mm; width of umbilicus, 10 mm; breadth of whorl, 20 mm. Locality 1347 (C. I. T.). Found on Little Cow Creek, 1.5 miles east of Frazier Corners, Shasta County; lower Senonian. 217

PLATE 41.—*FOSSILS FROM THE UPPER CRETACEOUS OF CALIFORNIA*

Figure *Page*

1, 2, 3, 3a. *Desmophyllites siskiyouensis* n. sp. Holotype, paratype, and hypotype (C. A. S. Type Coll.). (1) Holotype. Greater diameter, 47 mm; width of umbilicus, 4.6 mm; breadth of whorl, 16 mm. Locality 444 (s 455) (C. A. S.). (2) Paratype. Locality 455 (C. A. S.), found at Henley, Siskiyou County. (3, 3a) Hypotype. Side and front views. Locality 1552 (C. A. S.), on south border of Antelope Valley, Kern County. All figures natural size. Coniacian. *See* also Pl. 35, figs. 3, 3a. 215

4, 4a. *Lytoceras* (*Gaudryceras*) *delvallense* n. sp. Holotype and cast (C. A. S. Type Coll.). (4) Holotype (a rock mould). Greater diameter, 112 mm; width of umbilicus, 62 mm; breadth of whorl, 37 mm. (4a) Section of whorl, drawn from holotype. Found in the aqueduct tunnel, east of Del Valle shaft, Alameda County, California; lower Senonian. 183

5, 5a. *Lytoceras* (*Gaudryceras*) *alamedense* Smith. Hypotype (C. A. S. Type Coll.). Side and front views. Greater diameter, 57 mm; width of umbilicus, 25 mm; breadth of whorl, 19 mm. Locality 1343 (C. A. S.). Found at north end of Pleasant Valley, Yolo County; lower Senonian. 182

6. *Desmophyllites yoloensis* n. sp. Holotype No. 9816 (C. A. S. Type Coll.). Greater diameter, 34 mm; width of umbilicus, 3.5 mm. Locality 1467A (C. A. S.), found at Enos Canyon, 7 miles northwest of Winters, Yolo County; Coniacian. 216

7. *Lytoceras* (*Tetragonites*) *henleyense* n. sp. Holotype (C. A. S. Type Coll.). Greater diameter, 44 mm; width of umbilicus, 18 mm; breadth of whorl, 16 mm. Locality 444 (C. A. S.). Found near Henley, Siskiyou County; Lower Coniacian. *See* also Pl. 12, figs. 5, 5a. 185

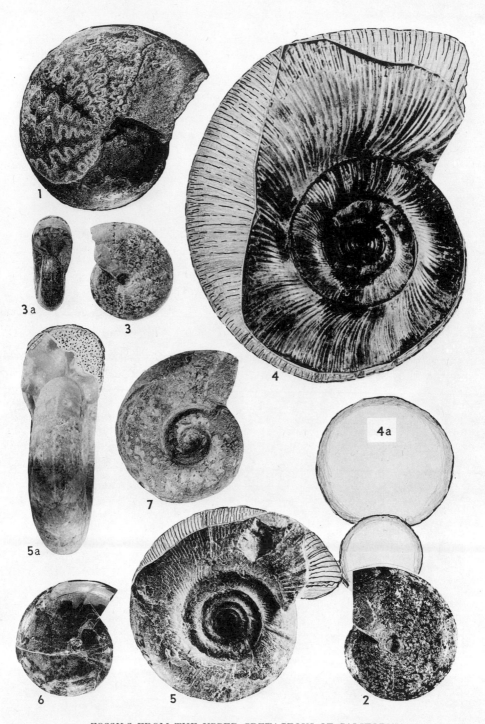

FOSSILS FROM THE UPPER CRETACEOUS OF CALIFORNIA

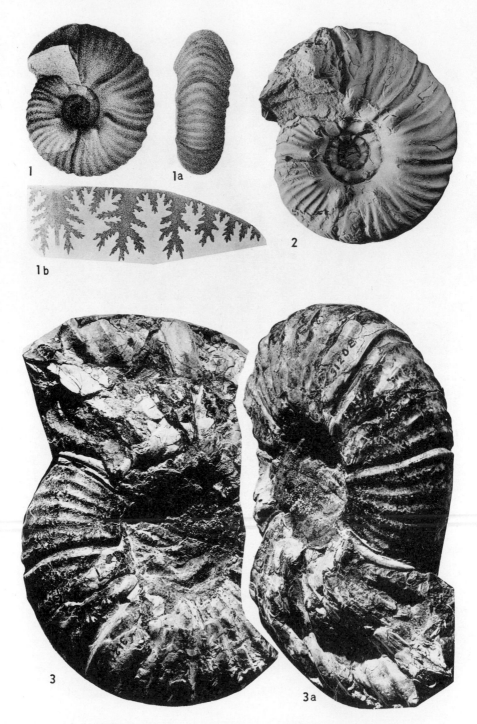

1

1a

1b

2

3

3a

FOSSILS FROM THE UPPER CRETACEOUS OF CALIFORNIA AND BRITISH COLUMBIA

PLATE 42.—*FOSSILS FROM THE UPPER CRETACEOUS OF CALIFORNIA AND BRITISH COLUMBIA*

Figure *Page*

1, 1a, 1b, 2. *Canadoceras newberryanum* (Meek). Holotype No. 12394 (U. S. Nat. Mus.) reproduced. (1, 1a) Side and rear views. (1b) Suture line drawn by Meek. (2) Plasto-holotype No. 4699 (C. A. S. Type Coll.). Cast of holotype in U. S. National Museum, Washington. Dimensions as follows: greater diameter, 58.5 mm; height of whorl, 26 mm; width of umbilicus, 18 mm; breadth of whorl, 23 mm. Found at "Komooks, Vancouver's Island", probably in the "Productive Coal Measures"; lower Senonian. 232

3, 3a. *Canadoceras celeste* n. sp. Holotype (C. A. S. Type Coll.). Side and oblique front views. Greater diameter, 108 mm; width of umbilicus, 31 mm; greatest breadth of whorl, 28 mm. Locality 31208 (C. A. S.). Found on the east border of "Nigger Heaven" basin, Yolo County; Coniacian, lower Senonian. 234

FOSSILS FROM THE UPPER CRETACEOUS OF CALIFORNIA AND OREGON

FOSSILS FROM THE UPPER CRETACEOUS OF CALIFORNIA

PLATE 44.—*FOSSILS FROM THE UPPER CRETACEOUS OF CALIFORNIA*

Figure *Page*

1, 1a. *Eupachydiscus arbucklensis* n. sp. Holotype (C. A. S. Type Coll.). Greater diameter, 132 mm; width of umbilicus, 40 mm; breadth of whorl, 43 mm. Crowded suture lines shown in the figures. Locality 25730 (C. A. S.), on Sand Creek, on the H. L. Dobbins ranch, Colusa County. *See* also Pl. 45, fig. 1; Coniacian, lower Senonian..... 223

2, 2a. *Nowakites dobbinsi* n. sp. Holotype (C. A. S. Type Coll.). Side and oblique front views. Greater diameter, 87 mm; width of umbilicus, 24 mm; breadth of whorl, 32 mm. Locality 25730 (C. A. S.), on Sand Creek, Colusa County; Coniacian, lower Senonian. 231

PLATE 45.—*FOSSILS FROM THE UPPER CRETACEOUS OF CALIFORNIA*

Figure *Page*

1. *Eupachydiscus arbucklensis* n. sp. Paratype (C. A. S. Type Coll.). Greater diameter (three-fourths costate), 200 mm; width of umbilicus, 75 mm; height of whorl, 70 mm; breadth of whorl, 60 mm. Locality 25730 (C. A. S.), on Sand Creek, Colusa County; Coniacian, lower Senonian. *See* also Pl. 44, figs. 1, 1a. 223

2, 2a. *Parapachydiscus cortinaensis* n. sp. Holotype (C. A. S. Type Coll.). Greater diameter, 131 mm; width of umbilicus, 27 mm; height of whorl, 55 mm; greatest width of whorl, 47 mm; (2a) Oblique front view of same. Locality 25730 (C. A. S.), Sand Creek, Colusa County. 226

3. *Nowakites rumseyensis* n. sp. Holotype (C. A. S. Type Coll.). Greater diameter, 75 mm; width of umbilicus, 21 mm; height of whorl, 34 mm; breadth of whorl, 30 mm. Locality 25730 (C. A. S.), on Sand Creek, southwestern Colusa County; Coniacian, lower Senonian. 231

4. *Didymoceras orestimbense* n. sp. Holotype (C. A. S. Type Coll.). Natural size. Fragment of sinistral coil. Greater diameter of coil, 45 mm; height of whorl, 25 mm; breadth of whorl section, 17 mm. Locality 27854 (C. A. S.), on SE ¼ sec. 36, T. 7 S., R. 6 E., M. D. B. and M.; from a boulder in lower Panoche conglomerate; Coniacian, lower Senonian. 197

FOSSILS FROM THE UPPER CRETACEOUS OF CALIFORNIA

FOSSILS FROM THE UPPER CRETACEOUS OF CALIFORNIA

PLATE 46.—*FOSSILS FROM THE UPPER CRETACEOUS OF CALIFORNIA*

Figure *Page*

1, 1a. *Mortoniceras* (*Submortoniceras*) *randalli*, n. sp. Hypotype 5952 (C. A. S. Type Coll.). Oblique views of ventral zone, showing keel and other features. Greater diameter, 58 mm; width of umbilicus, 28 mm; height of whorl, 28 mm; breadth of whorl, 25 mm. Locality 27838 (C. A. S.), 3 miles or more below Frank Mickey's house on Chico Creek, Butte County. *See* also Pl. 50, figs. 2, 2a, 3. 269

2. *Eupachydiscus willgreeni*, n. sp. Holotype (C. A. S. Type Coll.). Fragment. Greater diameter (est.), 186 mm; width of umbilicus, 34 mm; height of whorl, 70 mm; breadth of whorl, 56 mm. Locality 25730 (C. A. S.), on Sand Creek, southwestern Colusa County, on the ranch of Hugh L. Dobbins; Coniacian, lower Senonian. 223

3. *Puzosia* (*Holcodiscoides*) *gorrilli* n. sp. Holotype (incomplete) (C. A. S. Type Coll.). Outer whorl (est.) 204 mm; width of umbilicus, 70 mm; height of whorl, 76 mm; breadth of whorl, 62 mm. Inner whorl, greater diameter, 102 mm; width of umbilicus, 38 mm; breadth of whorl, 24 mm. Locality 25730 (C. A. S.), on Sand Creek, southwestern Colusa County; Coniacian, lower Senonian. 240

4, 4a. *Puzosia* (*Parapuzosia*) *arenaica* n. sp. Holotype (C. A. S. Type Coll.). Greater diameter, 65 mm; width of umbilicus, 22 mm; height of whorl, 23 mm; breadth of whorl, 15 mm. (4a) Section of whorl. Locality 25730 (C. A. S.), on Sand Creek, southwestern Colusa County; Coniacian; lower Senonian. 238

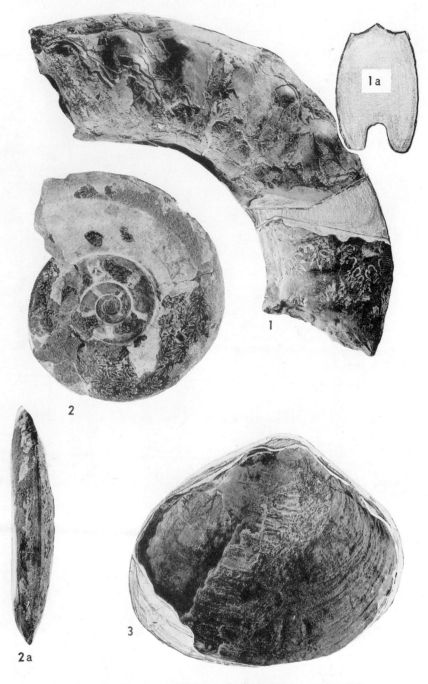

FOSSILS FROM THE UPPER CRETACEOUS OF CALIFORNIA

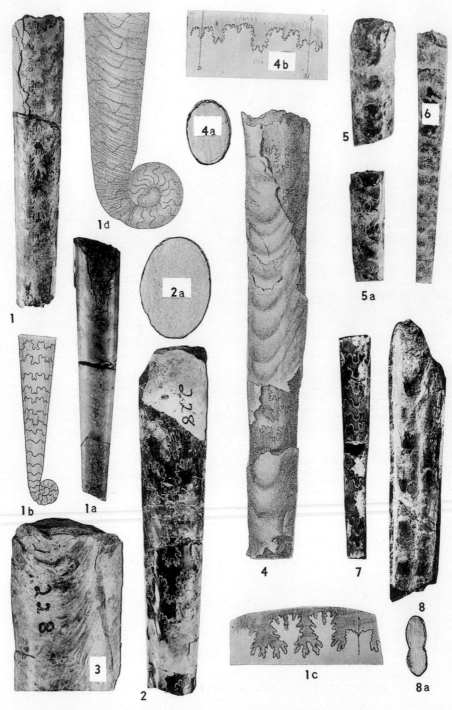

FOSSILS FROM THE UPPER CRETACEOUS OF CALIFORNIA AND SUCIA ISLAND

PLATE 48.—*FOSSILS FROM THE UPPER CRETACEOUS OF CALIFORNIA AND SUCIA ISLAND*

Figure *Page*

1, 1a, 1b, 1c, 1d. *Baculites chicoensis* Trask. Hypotype No. 5951 and another hypotype (C. A. S. Type Coll.) Fragmentary examples. (1) Hypotype No. 5951. (1a) Another hypotype. Length 75 mm; greater diameter at larger end, 13.2 mm; lesser end, 9.5 mm. (1c) Suture of adult. (1b, 1d) Drawings of early stages of development (after Smith, 1901). Locality 27837 (C. A. S.), Big Butte Creek, Butte County; Campanian. *See* also Pl. 60, figs. 3, 3a, 3b. 190

2, 2a, 3. *Baculites inornatus* Meek. Two hypotypes (C. A. S. Type Coll.). (2, 2a) Longer hypotype. Length, 102.6 mm; maximum diameter, approximately 23.5 mm; lesser diameter, 16 mm. (3) Shorter hypotype. Length, 52.8 mm; maximum diameter approximately 34.8 mm; lesser diameter, 24.6 mm. Locality 228 (C. A. S.), found on Sucia Island, Strait of Georgia (Topotypes). 190

4, 4a, 4b. *Baculites fairbanksi* Anderson. Copy of figure of holotype, after Anderson (1902). Figure slightly reduced. Length, 115 mm; greatest diameter, 15 mm; lesser diameter, 12 mm. Found at Silverado Canyon, Orange County; Turonian. *See* also Pl. 49, figs. 4, 4a. 190

5, 5a, 6. *Baculites lomaensis* n. sp. Holotype and paratype (C. A. S. Type Coll.). (5) Holotype. Approximate length, 35 mm; greater diameter, 13 mm; lesser diameter 8.6 mm. (5a) Paratype (part); approximate length, 33.4 mm; greater diameter, 10.3 mm. Locality 2361 (C. A. S.), on Joaquin Ridge, 11 miles north of Coalinga; upper part of Panoche formation; upper Campanian. (6) Paratype (C. A. S. Type Coll.). Length, 66.9 mm; greater diameter, 8.7 mm; lesser diameter, 6 mm. Found at above locality. Closely related to *Baculites vagina Forbes.* 191

7. *Baculites subcircularis* n. sp. Holotype (C. A. S. Type Coll.). Length about 36 mm; maximum diameter, 5 mm. Locality 28442 (C. A. S.), near the mouth of Briones Creek, Contra Costa County. 192

8, 8a. *Baculites* aff. *B. capensis* Woods. Hypotype (C. A. S. Type Coll.). (8a) Cross section. Slightly reduced. Locality 31289 (C. A. S.), on Cache Creek, near concrete bridge, Yolo County; lower Senonian. 192

Plate 49.—*FOSSILS FROM THE UPPER CRETACEOUS OF CALIFORNIA AND SUCIA ISLAND*

Figure *Page*

1. *Mammites rancheriae* n. sp. Holotype, a rock mould and cast (C. A. S. Type Coll.). Greatest diameter, 200 mm. Locality 455 (C. A. S.), half a mile west of Henley, Siskiyou County. 247

2. *Baculites rex* n. sp. Holotype (C. A. S. Type Coll.). Length (incomplete) 240 mm (approximately 9 7/16 inches); greater diameter, approximately 58.5 mm; lesser diameter (estimated), 48 mm. Locality 28325 (C. A. S.), on south side of Crow Creek, in NE ¼ sec. 33, T. 6 S., R. 7 W., M. D. M. 191

3. *Serrifusus joaquinensis* n. sp. Holotype (C. A. S. Type Coll.). Height, 55 mm; greater width of whorl, 45 mm. Locality 2362 (C. A. S.), Fresno County, in upper part of Panoche formation, on Los Gatos Creek; upper Campanian. 171

4, 4a. *Baculites fairbanksi* Anderson. Hypotype (C. A. S. Type Coll.). Slightly reduced. Length, 50 mm; greater diameter, 17 mm. (4a) cross section of same. Locality 228 (C. A. S.), on Sucia Island, Strait of Georgia; Coniacian. *See* also Pl. 48, figs. 4, 4a, 4b. 190

5. *Cucullaea* (*Idonearca*) *alamoensis* n. sp. Holotype (C. A. S. Type Coll.). Length, 55 mm; height, 46.3 mm. Locality 1346-C (C. A. S.), North fork of Cottonwood Creek. 88

6, 6a, 6b. *Baculites buttensis* n. sp. Holotype (C. A. S. Type Coll.). Length, 35.8 mm; greater diameter, 8.4 mm; lesser diameter, 6.4 mm. Locality 27835 (C. A. S.), Chico Creek. 191

FOSSILS FROM THE UPPER CRETACEOUS OF CALIFORNIA AND SUCIA ISLAND

FOSSILS FROM THE UPPER CRETACEOUS OF CALIFORNIA

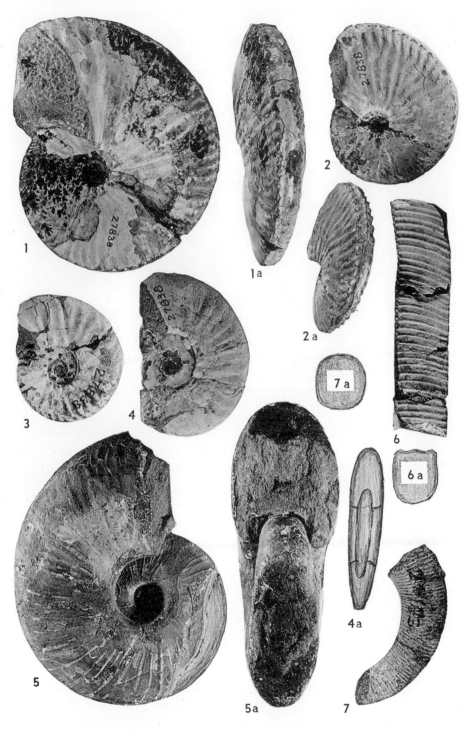

FOSSILS FROM THE UPPER CRETACEOUS OF CALIFORNIA

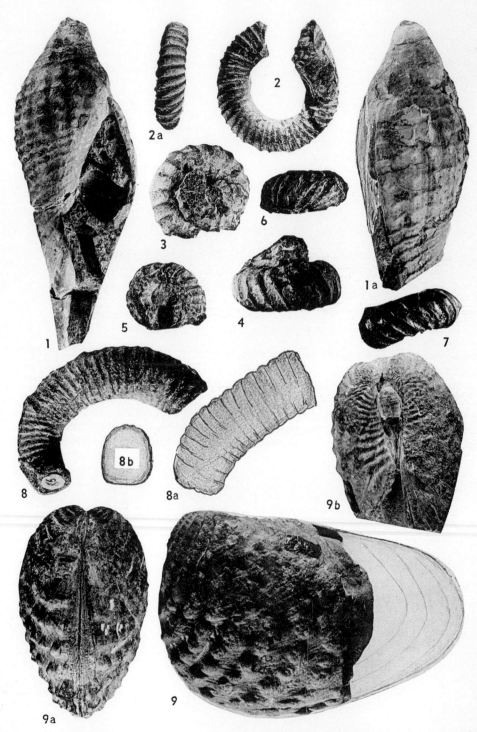

FOSSILS FROM THE UPPER CRETACEOUS OF CALIFORNIA

PLATE 52.—*FOSSILS FROM THE UPPER CRETACEOUS OF CALIFORNIA*

Figure *Page*

1, 1a. *Volutoderma californica* Dall. Hypotype (C. A. S. Type Coll.). Front and rear views. Height (incomplete), 87 mm; maximum breadth, 32 mm; length of aperture, 62 mm. Locality 1125B (C. A. S.), Tuscan Springs, 8 miles northeast of Red Bluff, Tehama County, in lower part of the Chico formation; Campanian. 173

2, 2a. *Bostrychoceras declive* (Gabb). Hypotype (C. A. S. Type Coll.). Width of coil, 29 mm; greatest diameter of whorl, 7 mm; lesser diameter, 5 mm. Locality 1125 (C. A. S.), 1 mile west of Pentz, Butte County; Campanian. 207

3, 4. *Bostrychoceras sanctaeanae* n. sp. Holotype (C. I. T. Type Coll.). Sinistral coil, natural size. Top and side views. Width of coil, 23 mm; height of whorl, 11 mm. Locality 85 (C. I. T.), Trabuco Creek, Orange County. 206

5, 6. *Bostrychoceras* aff. *B. brewerii* (Gabb). Hypotype (C. I. T. Type Coll..). Fragmentary example, showing top and side views; (5) Top, natural size. Width of coil, 18.6 mm; height of whorl, 8 mm. (6) Side view of same. Locality 85 (C. I. T.), on Trabuco Creek, Orange County; Campanian. 206

7. *Bostrychoceras brewerii* (Gabb). Fragmentary hypotype (C. A. S. Type Coll.). Natural size, 23.8 mm in length. Locality 1125 (C. A. S.), 11 miles north of Oroville, near Pentz, Butte County; Campanian. 205

8, 8a, 8b. *Bostrychoceras trabucoense,* n. sp. Holotype (C. I. T. Type Coll.). (8) Holotype. Length, 52 mm; whorl, subcircular. Greater diameter, 14 mm; lesser diameter, 12.5 mm. (8a) Drawing showing a straightened portion of the shell. Length, 40 mm. (8b) Section of the holotype at buccal end. Locality 85 (C. I. T.), on Trabuco Creek, Orange County. 206

9, 9a, 9b. *Trigonia hemphilli* n. sp. Holotype 994 (C. A. S. Type Coll.). Length (incomplete), 67 mm; height of shell, 69 mm; convexity (both valves together), 48.5 mm. (9a) Front view. (9b) Top view. Locality 12123 (C. A. S.), near Pigeon Point, San Mateo County; Campanian. 115

PLATE 53.—*FOSSILS FROM THE UPPER CRETACEOUS OF CALIFORNIA*

Figure *Page*

1, 1a. *Phylloceras pachecoense* n. sp. Holotype (C. A. S. Type Coll.). (1) Fragment of nearly a third of whorl. Peripheral length, 160 mm; height of whorl, 100 mm; breadth of whorl, 40 mm. (1a) Section of whorl of holotype. Locality 29108 (C. A. S.), in Moreno formation; Maestrichtian. 182

2. *Phylloceras gargantuum* n. sp. Holotype (C. A. S. Type Coll.). Large fragment constituting the holotype, forming about a third of the whorl. Greater length, 24 inches (609 mm); breadth of whorl, 6 inches (152 mm); height of whorl, 18 inches (457 mm). Greater diameter of whorl (estimated), not less than 29 inches (736 mm). Locality 28542 (C. A. S.), 800 feet south of center of sec. 15, T. 14 S., R. 11 E., M. D. B. M., on east flank of Panoche Hills, Fresno County. Probably in the Panoche formation; Campanian. 180

3, 3a, 3b, 4. *Butticeras buttense* n. sp. Holotype and paratype (C. I. T. Type Coll.). (3) Holotype. Greater diameter, 44.5 mm; height of whorl, 18.6 mm; width of umbilicus, 11 mm; breadth of whorl, 11 mm. (3a) Suture line of the same, enlarged. (3b) Drawing showing cross section of same. (4) Paratype. Maximum diameter, 31.4 mm; breadth of whorl, approximately 8.5 mm; maximum height of whorl, 15.5 mm; width of umbilicus, approximately 8.2 mm. Locality 1041 (C. I. T.), on Butte Creek, Butte County, 3.8 miles upstream from covered bridge over Butte Creek on Paradise Road and 10.2 miles along Chico-Centerville road from junction with Highway 99; Chico formation. Locality same for both holotype and paratype. 272

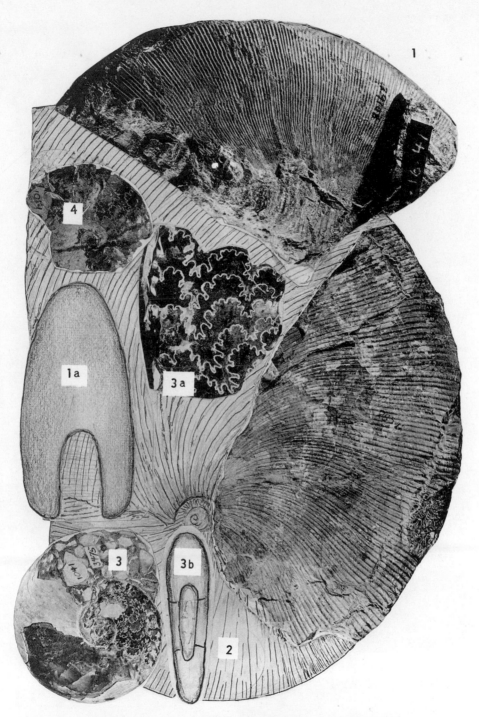

FOSSILS FROM THE UPPER CRETACEOUS OF CALIFORNIA

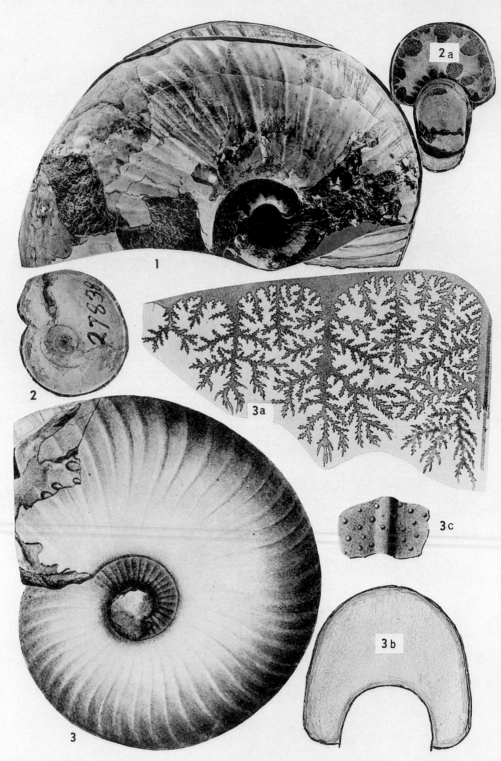

FOSSILS FROM THE UPPER CRETACEOUS OF CALIFORNIA AND VANCOUVER ISLAND

PLATE 54.—*FOSSILS FROM THE UPPER CRETACEOUS OF CALIFORNIA AND VANCOUVER ISLAND*

Figure *Page*

1. *Parapachydiscus bidwelli* n. sp. Holotype (C. A. S. Type Coll.). Greater diameter, 150 mm; width of umbilicus, 36.4; breadth of whorl, 7.8 mm. Locality 27838 (C. A. S.), on Chico Creek, 3.1 miles by road south of the bridge at the Mickey ranch, Butte County. *See* also Pl. 51, figs. 5, 5a. 228

2, 2a. *Parapachydiscus* aff. *P. gabbi,* n. name. Two hypotypes (C. A. S. Type Coll.). (2) Hypotype, young example enlarged. Greater diameter, 19.7 mm; breadth of whorl, 10.4 mm; width of umbilicus, approximately 4.5 mm. (2a) Hypotype, somewhat older example, almost natural size. Height of whorl, 17 mm; breadth of largest whorl, 18 mm. Locality 27838 (C. A. S.), on Chico Creek. 226

3, 3a, 3b, 3c. *Parapachydiscus gabbi* n. name. (3, 3a, 3b, 3c) Reproduction of Gabb's figures (1864, Pl. 27, figs. 199a, 199b, 199c; Pl. 28, figs. 199a). (3, 3a) Holotype and suture. (3b) Section of last volution. (3c) Surface magnified to show the granulation. Locality of discovery not clearly stated by Gabb; given only as Comox, Vancouver Island. 226

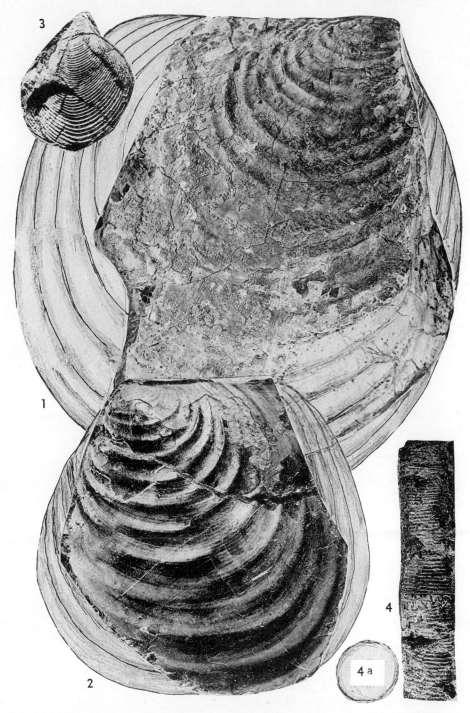

FOSSILS FROM THE UPPER CRETACEOUS OF CALIFORNIA AND OREGON

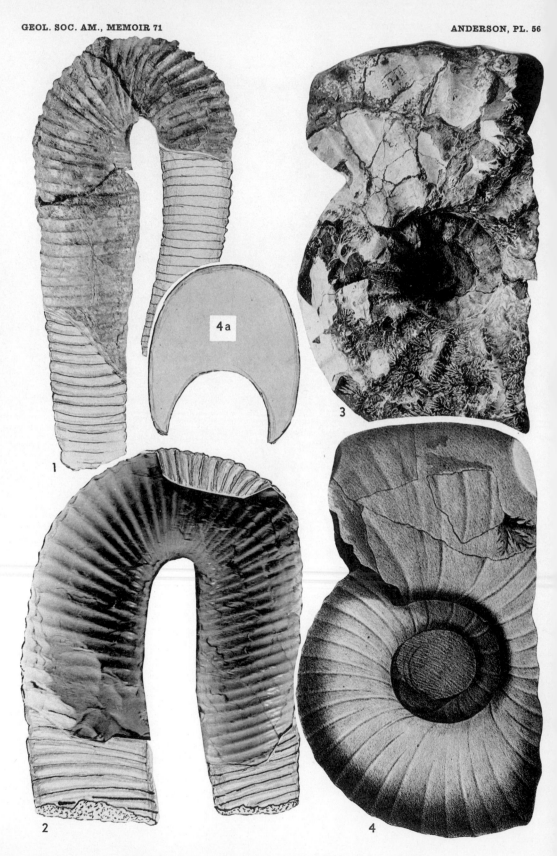

FOSSILS FROM THE UPPER CRETACEOUS OF CALIFORNIA

PLATE 56.—*FOSSILS FROM THE UPPER CRETACEOUS OF CALIFORNIA*

Figure *Page*

1. *Oxybeloceras petrolense* n. sp. Holotype (C. A. S. Type Coll.), consisting of a fragment and part of the rock mold and specimen in rock. Figure partly restored from specimen in rock. Length of fragment, 95 mm; greater breadth of buccal limb, 29 mm; width of loop, 56 mm. Locality 31364 (C. A. S.), on Petroleum Creek, east flank of Rumsey Hills, Yolo County. 203
2. *Diplomoceras o'shaughnessyi* n. sp. Holotype (C. A. S. Type Coll.), consisting of large fragment showing parts of both limbs, partly restored. Length of smaller limb, 125 mm; width of loop, 114 mm; section of limbs, subcircular. Found in aqueduct tunnel, 1.12 miles west of Tesla Portal, San Joaquin County. 201
3. *Parapachydiscus diabloensis* n. name. Holotype No. 12111, (Univ. Calif. Mus. Paleo. Type Coll.), consisting of large fragment almost wholly septate. Greater diameter, 110 mm; width of umbilicus, 31 mm; height of whorl, 40 mm. Locality of discovery not definitely stated by Gabb, but perhaps in "Round Valley," Contra Costa County. 229

4, 4a. Gabb's drawings (1869, vol. 2, Pl. 21) of above holotype. 229

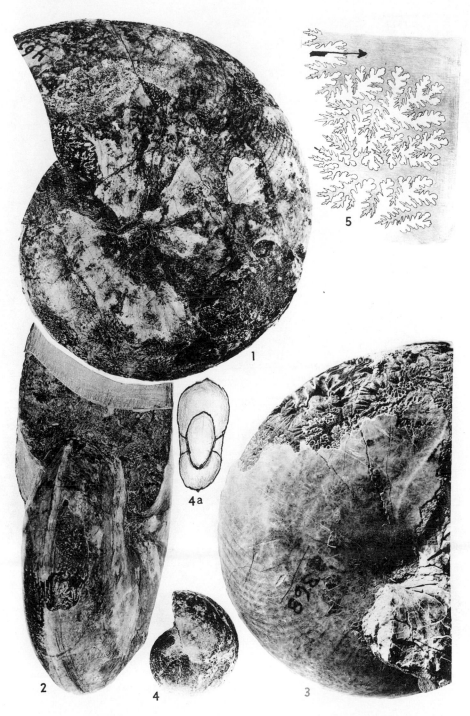

FOSSILS FROM THE UPPER CRETACEOUS OF CALIFORNIA

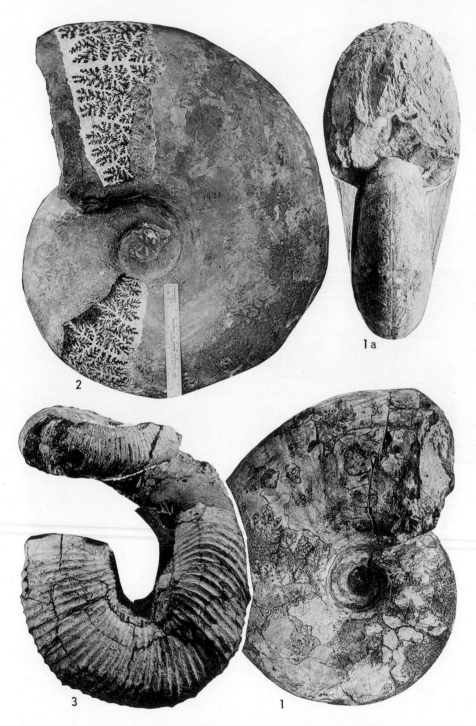

FOSSILS FROM THE UPPER CRETACEOUS OF CALIFORNIA AND LOWER CALIFORNIA

PLATE 58.—*FOSSILS FROM THE UPPER CRETACEOUS OF CALIFORNIA AND LOWER CALIFORNIA*

Figure *Page*

1, 1a. *Parapachydiscus abbotti* n. sp. Holotype (San Diego Soc. Nat. Hist.) Side and front views. Greater diameter, 520 mm; width of umbilicus, 87.3 mm; height of whorl, 220 mm; breadth of whorl, 205 mm. Found on south side of Point Loma, San Diego County; Upper Campanian. 229

2. *Parapachydiscus catarinae* Anderson and Hanna. Holotype 4245 (C. A. S. Type Coll.). Greater diameter (wholly septate), 503 mm; width of umbilicus, 74 mm; breadth of whorl, 170 mm. From Arroyo Catarina, Lower California; Upper Campanian. 224

3. *Nostoceras mexicanum* n. sp. Holotype (C. A. S. Type Coll.), consisting of one coil of the spiral, and the retroversal loop. Length of loop, 73 mm; width of loop, 85 mm; breadth of loop (interior), 21 mm; width of normal spiral, 63 mm. Found 2 miles or more above the mouth of Arroyo Santa Catarina, Lower California; Upper Campanian. 196

FOSSILS FROM THE UPPER CRETACEOUS OF CALIFORNIA

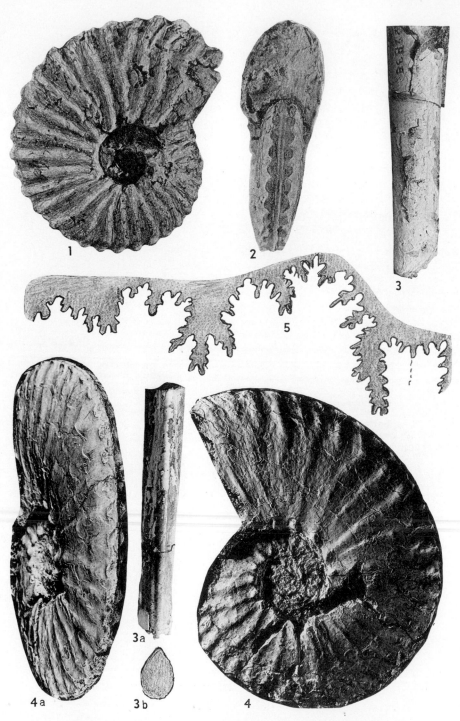

FOSSILS FROM THE UPPER CRETACEOUS OF CALIFORNIA

PLATE 60.—*FOSSILS FROM THE UPPER CRETACEOUS OF CALIFORNIA*

Figure   *Page*

1, 2. *Mortoniceras* (*Submortoniceras*) *chicoense* (Trask). Neotype 5785 (C. A. S. Type Coll.). (Neotype of *Ammonites chicoensis* Trask *in* Taff, Hanna, and Cross, 1940, p. 1320). Locality 27838 (C. A. S.), in the Chico formation, on Chico Creek, Butte County. 269

3, 3a, 3b. *Baculites chicoensis* (Trask). Neosyntypes Nos. 5786, 5787 (C. A. S. Type Coll.). (Taff, Hanna, and Cross, 1940, p. 1321). (3) Neosyntype No. 5786. Length of fragment, 78.8 mm; greatest diameter, 18 mm. (3a, 3b) Neosyntype No. 5787. Length of fragment, edge view, 77.7 mm; least diameter, 11 mm. Found with the preceding on Chico Creek. *See* also Pl. 48, figs. 1, 1a, 1b, 1c, 1d.

4, 4a. *Mortoniceras* (*Submortoniceras*) *templetoni* (Hall and Ambrose). Plasto-holotype 4240 (C. A. S. Type Coll.), a cast of holotype in L. S. J. U. Type Coll. Found in Western Pacific R.R. cut between Altamont and Greenway, Alameda County; Campanian. 271

5. Suture line of *Acanthoceras shastense* Reagan (1924). From the holotype. *See* also Pl. 20, figs. 1, 2. 242

PLATE 61.—*FOSSILS FROM THE UPPER CRETACEOUS OF CALIFORNIA AND BRITISH COLUMBIA*

Figure *Page*

1, 2. *Inoceramus turgidus* n. sp. Holotype (C. A. S. Type Coll.). Side and front views. Length, 112 mm; height, 83.8 mm; breadth, 84 mm. Locality 28171 (C. A. S.), found in the Chico formation, on Chico Creek, Butte County; Campanian. 104

3. *Cymbophora buttensis* n. sp. Holotype (C. A. S. Type Coll.). Length, 60 mm; height, 46 mm; thickness, a maximum width for a single valve, 12 mm. Locality 1125 (C. A. S.), near Pentz, Butte County, in the Chico formation; Campanian. 145

4. *Cucullaea (Idonearca) youngi* Waring. Hypotype (C. A. S. Type Coll.). Length, 43.8 mm; height, 41 mm. Locality 229 (C. A. S.), found on Waldron Island, Strait of Georgia; Senonian. 90

5, 5a, 5b. *Cucullaea (Idonearca) buttensis* n. sp. Holotype (C. A. S. Type Coll.). Length, 72 mm; height, 64 mm. Locality 28172 (C. A. S.), Chico Creek, Butte County. 92

6. *Parallelodon (Nanonavis) bremneri* n. sp. Holotype (C. A. S. Type Coll.) Length, 34 mm; height, 18 mm; breadth across both valves about 12 mm. Locality 1658 (C. A. S.), half a mile north of junction of main Honda Creek Road with that leading across hills northward to Santa Ynez Valley. The locality is in the bottom of the canyon below the road. 95

FOSSILS FROM THE UPPER CRETACEOUS OF CALIFORNIA AND BRITISH COLUMBIA

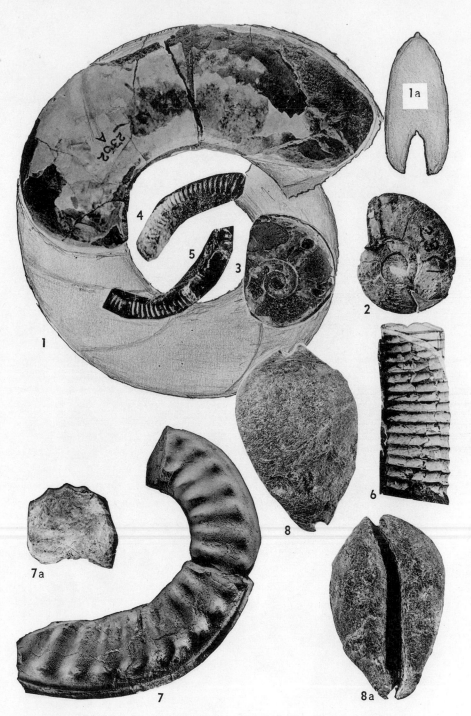

FOSSILS FROM THE UPPER CRETACEOUS OF CALIFORNIA

PLATE 62.—*FOSSILS FROM THE UPPER CRETACEOUS OF CALIFORNIA*

Figure *Page*

1, 1a. *Hauericeras* aff. *H. gardeni* (Baily). Hypotype (C. A. S. Type Coll.). (1) Fragmentary example. Peripheral length, 117 mm; maximum height of whorl, 40 mm; breadth of whorl, 16 mm. (1a) Section of whorl. Locality 2362A (C. A. S.), on Los Gatos Creek, Fresno County; upper Campanian. 220

2, 3. *Hauericeras churchi* n. sp. Holotype and paratype (C. A. S. Type Coll.). (2) Holotype. Greater diameter, 30.5 mm; breadth of whorl, 6 mm. Locality 2361 (C. A. S.), on Joaquin Ridge, northwest of "Oil City," Fresno County. (3) Paratype (natural size). Locality 28102 (C. A. S.), Basin Hollow, Clover Creek, near Millville, eastern Shasta County. 220

4, 5. *Diplomoceras vermiculare* n. sp. Holotype and paratype (C. A. S. Type Coll.). (4) Paratype. (5) Holotype. Length, 40 mm; width of whorl, 4 mm; section of whorl, nearly circular. Locality 28441 (C. A. S.), on north side of Briones Valley, on west side of NW ¼ sec. 29, T. 1 N., R. 2 E., M. D. B. and M., Contra Costa County; Campanian. 201

6. *Diplomoceras* aff. *D. recticostatum* (Seunes). Hypotype (C. A. S. Type Coll.). Fragment. Length, 40 mm; height, 18 mm. Locality 28441 (C. A. S.), on north side of Briones Valley, on west side of NW ¼ sec. 29, T. 1. N., R. 2 E., M. D. B. and M. Contra Costa County, Campanian. 200

7, 7a. *Peroniceras tehamaense* (Gabb). Holotype (Univ. Calif, Mus. Paleo. Type Coll.). Diameter across volution 139 mm; width across chamber (including nodes) at point of break (7a), 35.5 mm. "Battle Creek, Shasta County." 260

8, 8a. *Cypraea gualalaensis* n. sp. Holotype (C. A. S. Type Coll.). Upper and lower views. Length, 50 mm; breadth, 32 mm; height, 23 mm. Found at Locality 251 by S. G. Clark, near Gualala, Mendocino County; Maestrichtian. 176

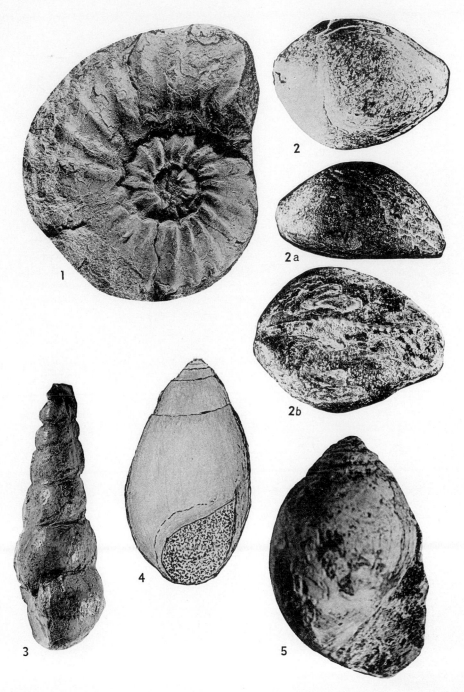

FOSSILS FROM THE UPPER CRETACEOUS OF CALIFORNIA

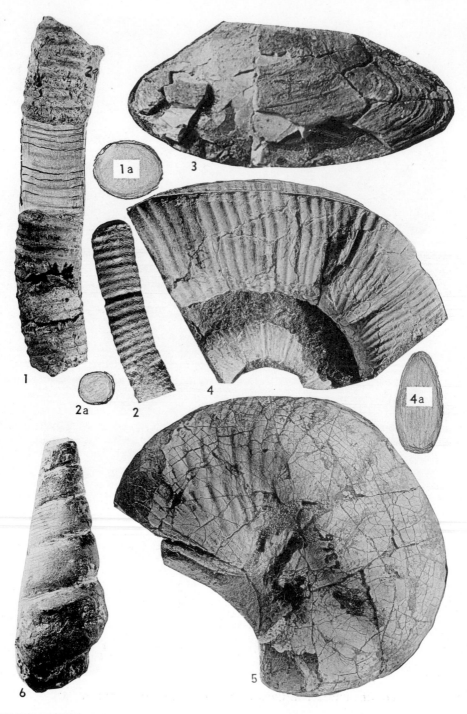

FOSSILS FROM THE UPPER CRETACEOUS OF CALIFORNIA AND LOWER CALIFORNIA

PLATE 64.—*FOSSILS FROM THE UPPER CRETACEOUS OF CALIFORNIA AND LOWER CALIFORNIA*

Figure *Page*

1, 1a. *Diplomoceras mercedense* n. sp. Holotype (C. A. S. Type Coll.). Partly restored. Slightly reduced. Length (large fragment), 50.5 mm; maximum diameter 20.8 mm; lesser diameter, 17.7 mm. Locality 29656 (C. A. S.), 1 mile south of Ortigalita Creek, on the north flank of the Panoche hills; Maestrichtian. 200

2, 2a. *Diplomoceras mercedense* n. sp. Paratype (C. A. S. Type Coll.). Fragment. Length, 46.4 mm; lesser diameter, 11 mm; greater diameter, 13.3 mm; nearly circular, bearing U. S. Nat. Mus. No. 7006, from east line of sec. 24, T. 12 S. R. 10 E., M. D. M.; Maestrichtian. 200

3. *Remondia shastensis* n. sp. Holotype (C. A. S. Type Coll.). Length of shell, 62 mm; height of shell, 28 mm. From North fork of Cottonwood Creek, 1 mile northeast of the mouth of Hulen Creek, Shasta County. 131

4, 4a. *Exicrioceras ortigalitense* n. sp. Holotype (C. A. S. Type Coll.). Length, 90 mm; height of larger whorl, 31 mm. (4a) Section of outer whorl. Locality 29656 (C. A. S.), 2500 feet north of SE. corner sec. 33 T. 11 S., R. 10 E., M. D. B. M. Charleston School quadrangle, Merced County; Maestrichtian. 208

5. *Nautilus* (*Cymatoceras*)*hermosus* n. sp. Holotype (C. A. S. Type Coll.). Shell (incomplete) showing part of surface features only. Locality 2366 (C. A. S.), W. ½ sec. 25, T. 19 S., R. 14 E., M. D. B. M., 8 miles north of Coalinga; Maestrichtian. 179

6. *Turritella peninsularis* Anderson and Hanna. Holotype 4709 (C. A. S. Type Coll.). Length, 61 mm; maximum width, 21.6 mm. Locality from Santa Catarina Landing, Lower California; Maestrichtian. 154

PLATE 65.—*FOSSILS FROM THE UPPER CRETACEOUS OF CALIFORNIA*

Figure *Page*

1, 1a, 2. *Didymoceras kernense* n. sp. Holotype (L.S.J.U. Type Coll.). Retroversal loop. Total length of larger limb, 112 mm; width of loop, 81 mm; diameter of buccal limb, 38 mm; diameter of smaller limb, 32 mm. (2) Ventral view of smaller limb showing looped pattern of ribs. Found in Buena Vista Hills, Kern County. 196

3. *Diplomoceras mustangense* n. sp. Holotype (C. A. S. Type Coll.) forming part of smaller limb. Length, 78 mm; greater breadth, 16 mm; section elliptical. Smaller diameter, 13 mm. Locality 29118 (C. A. S.), half a mile south of Mustang Gulch, sec. 33, T. 8 S., R. 8 E., M. D. B. and M. 200

4, 5. *Lytoceras* (*Tetragonites*) *epigonum* Kossmat. Two hypotypes (C. A. S. Type Coll.) (4) Maximum diameter, 34 mm. (5) Maximum diameter, 34 mm. Locality 2362 (C. A. S.), on Los Gatos Greek, 8 miles northwest of Coalinga, Fresno County, in the lower part of the Moreno formation. *See* also Pl. 67, figs. 3, 3a. 187

6, 6a. *Parapachydiscus coalingensis* n. sp. Holotype (C. A. S. Type Coll.). Greater diameter, wholly septate, 117 mm; width of umbilicus, 32 mm; breadth of whorl, approximately 37.3 mm. (6a) Section of whorls. Locality 2362 (C. A. S.), 8 miles northwest of Coalinga, Fresno County, in lower part of the Moreno formation. 227

FOSSILS FROM THE UPPER CRETACEOUS OF CALIFORNIA

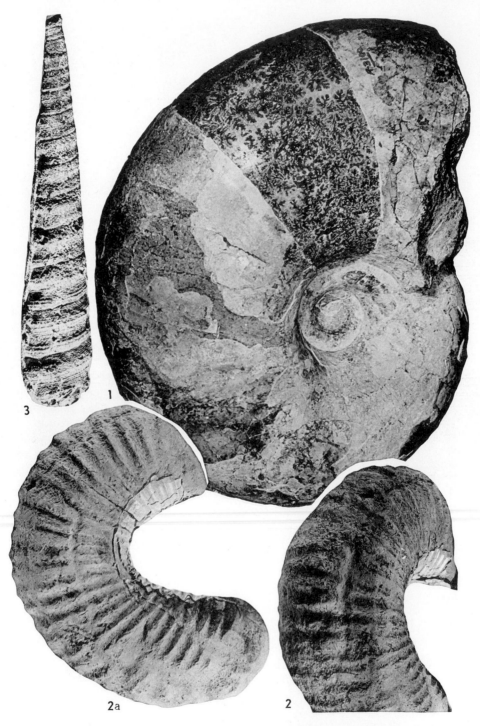

FOSSILS FROM THE UPPER CRETACEOUS OF CALIFORNIA AND LOWER CALIFORNIA

PLATE 66.—*FOSSILS FROM THE UPPER CRETACEOUS OF CALIFORNIA AND LOWER CALIFORNIA*

Figure *Page*

1. *Parapachydiscus princeps* n. sp. Holotype (Univ. Calif. Mus. Paleo. Type Coll.). Greatest diameter, 20 inches (508 mm); breadth of whorl, 233.7 mm; width of umbilicus, 96.5 mm. The whorl, wholly septate, if extended half a whorl, as a living chamber, would attain a diameter of 727 mm; with a proportional thickness, constituting one of the largest known in California. Locality A 3100 (Univ. Calif.), found near Arroyo Catarina, Lower California. 225

2, 2a. *Exiteloceras desertense* n. sp. Holotype (C. A. S. Type Coll.). Side and peripheral views. Length, 165 mm; distance between limbs, 24 mm. Locality 28303 (C. A. S.), Fresno County. 202

3. *Nerinea robertiana* n. sp. Plasto-holotype (C. A. S. Type Coll.) (Cast from original rock mould bearing U. S. Nat. Mus. No. 7009a). Length (incomplete), 90 mm; maximum diameter (incomplete), 16 mm. Found near the center of sec. 11, T. 12 S., R. 10 E., M. D. B. and M., at the head of the first arroyo south of 872-foot hill in the upper part of the Moreno formation, in the Pacheco Pass quadrangle, Fresno County. 155

PLATE 67.—*FOSSILS FROM THE UPPER CRETACEOUS OF CALIFORNIA*

Figure *Page*

1, 1a, 2. *Parapachydiscus panochensis* n. sp. Inner portion of holotype (C. A. S. Type Coll.). Shell large; holotype may have had a diameter of more than 356 mm and a breadth of 120 mm. Portion of inner whorl, length approximately 143 mm; height, 73 mm; breadth (approximately), 62.5 mm. Locality 28542 (C. A. S.), found in the Panoche Hills, 800 feet S of center sec. 15, T. 14 S., R. 11 E; M. D. B. M. 226

3, 3a. *Lytoceras* (*Tetragonites*) *epigonum* Kossmat. Hypotype (C. A. S. Type Coll.). The figures represent an example of medium size. Maximum diameter of whorl, 59 mm; breadth of whorl, 25 mm. Locality 29102 (C. A. S.), center S ½ sec. 26, T. 10 S., R. 9 E., M. D. B. and M. Volta quadrangle, Merced County; probably Maestrichtian in age. *See* also Pl. 65, figs. 4, 5. 187

4. *Bostrychoceras puertoense* n. sp. Holotype (C. A. S. Type Coll.). Holotype appears to be a fragment of a large form, 203 mm (8 inches) in length (incomplete), and with a diameter of 101.6 mm (4 inches) without the shell; said to have had a length of 12 inches when found. Locality 31125 (C. A. S.), near "Swallow Rock", Puerto Creek, NE ¼ sec. 30, T. 5 S. R. 7 E. M. D. B. M. Stanislaus County, near the horizon of *Parapachydiscus coalingensis* n. sp.; Maestrichtian. 204

5, 5a. *Parapachydiscus stanislausensis* n. sp. Inner coil of holotype (C. A. S. Type Coll.). Maximum height, 104 mm; breadth (approximately) 32 mm. Relatively thinner in form than the preceding type; ribs crossing the periphery without a pronounced forward curve. Locality 29664 (C. A. S.), found in the Moreno formation, Puerto Creek; Maestrichtian. 227

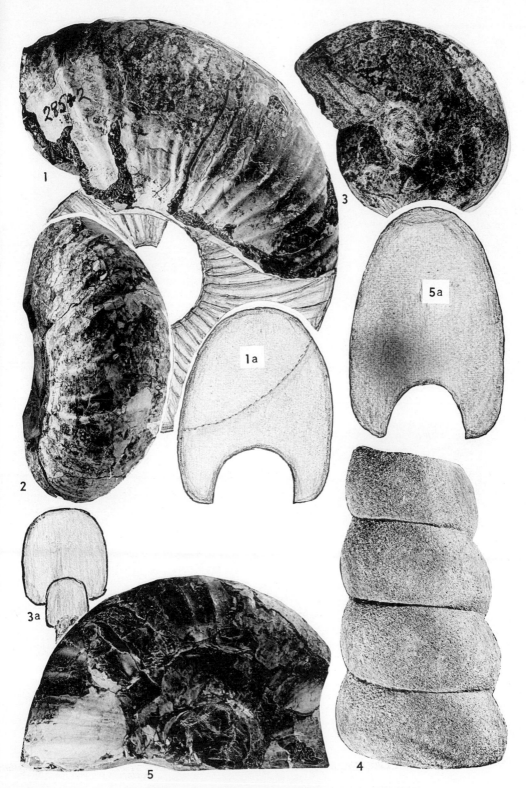

FOSSILS FROM THE UPPER CRETACEOUS OF CALIFORNIA

FOSSILS FROM THE UPPER CRETACEOUS OF CALIFORNIA

PLATE 68.—*FOSSILS FROM THE UPPER CRETACEOUS OF CALIFORNIA*

Figure *Page*

1. *Lytoceras* (*Gaudryceras*) *coalingense* n. sp. Holotype (C. A. S. Type Coll.). Diameter 71 mm. Locality 2362 (C. A. S.), on Los Gatos Creek, sec. 4, in the lower part of the Moreno formation; Maestrichtian. 184

2. *Didymoceras fresnoense* n. sp. Holotype (C. A. S. Type Coll.). Length of loop, 57 mm; width of loop, 73 mm; diameter of either arm, 28 mm. Locality 29666 (C. A. S.), Puerto Canyon, half a mile above Panoche-Moreno contact, center SW ¼ sec. 29, T. 5 S., R. 7 E., M. D. B. and M. Orestimba quadrangle; Maestrichtian. 197

3. "*Meretrix*" *marshana* n. sp. Holotype (C. A. S. Type Coll.). Length, incomplete, 63 mm; height, 44 mm. Locality 2356 (C. A. S.), on Marsh Creek, Contra Costa County. 136

4, 4a. *Lytoceras* (*Gaudryceras*) *birkhauseri* n. sp. Holotype (C. A. S. Type Coll.). Greater diameter (estimated) approximately 108 mm; width of umbilicus (estimated) 45 mm; breadth of whorl, 35 mm. Small example, partly restored, giving side view and edge view. Wholly septate examples have been found 7 inches in diameter. Locality 2361 (C. A. S.), 2 miles NW. of Oil City, Fresno County. 185

5, 5a. *Diplomoceras jimboi* n. sp. Holotype (C. A. S. Type Coll.). Maximum diameter, 24.6 mm; lesser diameter, 22.3 mm; length, 33 mm. Locality 2362A (C. A. S.), in the lower part of the Moreno formation, on Los Gatos Creek, near Coalinga, Fresno County; Maestrichtian. 199

PLATE 69.—*FOSSILS FROM THE UPPER CRETACEOUS OF CALIFORNIA AND OREGON*

Figure *Page*

1. *Pholadomya diegoensis* n. sp. Holotype (C. A. S. Type Coll.). Length, 67 mm; height, 39 mm; breadth of shell, 20 mm. Found on the south side of Point Loma, San Diego County. Upper Campanian. 132

2, 3. *Diplomoceras cascadense* n. sp. Holotype and paratype (C. A. S. Type Coll.). (2) Paratype (incomplete) length, 46.4 mm. (3) Holotype (incomplete) length, 66.9 mm; maximum diameter of whorl, 10.2 mm. Text and original label cited from Locality 445 (C. A. S.), at the old "Forty-nine" mine, in southern Oregon. Specimen marked from Locality 465 (C. A. S.), upper Turonian. *See* also Pl. 55, figs. 4, 4a. 199

4, 4a, 4b. *Prionocyclus californicus* n. sp. Holotype (C. I. T. Type Coll.). (4) Drawing of imperfect rock mold. (4a, 4b) Holotype. (4a) Oblique view showing keel and ribs. Fragment of whorl 34.9 mm long. (4b) Side view. Locality 1034 (C. I. T.), on Oak Run Creek, Shasta County; Coniacian. 262

5, 5a, 5b, 5c. *Peroniceras shastense* n. sp. Holotype (C. I. T. Type Coll.). (5) Weathered section of holotype, partially restored. (5a) Fragment of whorl, 40 mm long. External view. (5b) Section of whorl. (5c) View of periphery showing keels. Locality 1034 (C. I. T.), on Oak Run Creek, Shasta County; Coniacian. 260

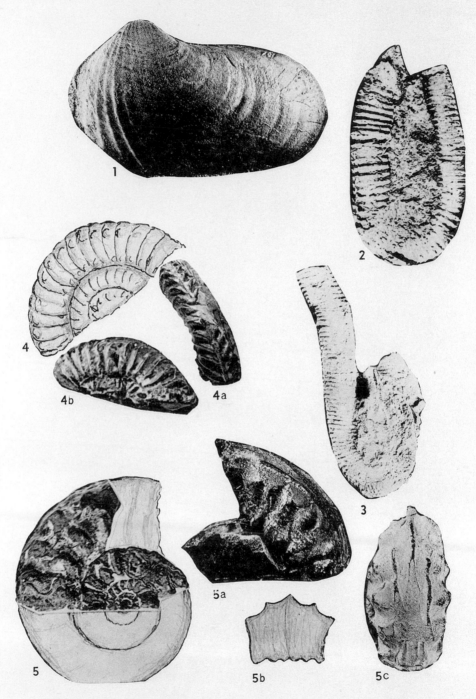

FOSSILS FROM THE UPPER CRETACEOUS OF CALIFORNIA AND OREGON

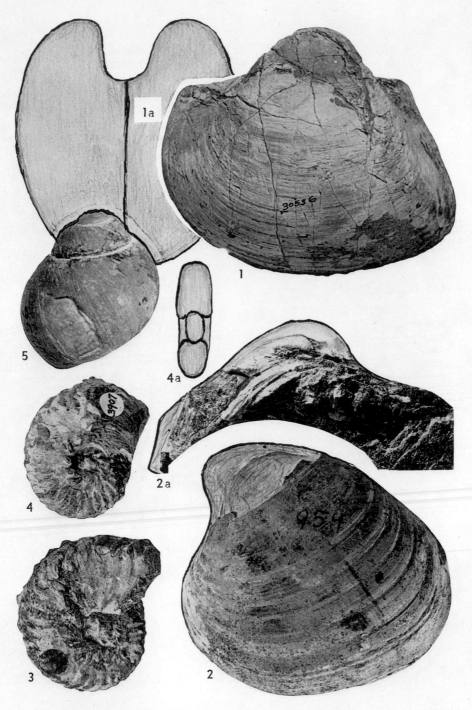

FOSSILS FROM THE UPPER CRETACEOUS OF CALIFORNIA AND LOWER CALIFORNIA

PLATE 70.—*FOSSILS FROM THE UPPER CRETACEOUS OF CALIFORNIA AND LOWER CALIFORNIA*

Figure   *Page*

1, 1a. *Cucullaea (Idonearca) calabaza* n. sp. Holotype (C. A. S. Type Coll.). Length, 102 mm; height, 90 mm. Locality 30536 (C. A. S.), found in Santa Monica Mountains, Los Angeles County, California, much above the position of the Pleasants member, with *Metaplacenticeras.*   91

2, 2a. *Trigonocallista major* (Packard). Hypotype (C. A. S. Type Coll.). Length, 88 mm; height (incomplete), 79.5 mm; convexity (1 valve), approximately 35 mm. Locality 954 (C. A. S.), on the northeast side of Punta Banda, on the southwest border of Todos Santos Bay, Lower California.   138

3, 4, 4a. *Metaplacenticeras ? bowersi* n. name. Holotype (Univ. Calif. Mus. Paleo. Type Coll.) (3) Holotype. (4, 4a) Paratype (C. I. T. Type Coll.). Maximum diameter, 35.5 mm; minimum diameter, 29.2 mm; maximum height body whorl, 15.3 mm; maximum breadth body whorl, 12 mm. Locality 1159 (C. I. T.), from Dayton Canyon, Calabasas quadrangle, Los Angeles County, Calif.   255

5. *Polinices mercedensis* n. sp. Holotype (C. A. S. Type Coll.). Natural size. Maximum height, 45 mm; maximum width, 37 mm; height of aperture, 30 mm. Locality 30556 (C. A. S.), on Los Banos Creek; Lower Maestrichtian.   151

FOSSILS FROM THE UPPER CRETACEOUS OF CALIFORNIA

FOSSILS FROM THE UPPER CRETACEOUS OF CALIFORNIA AND LOWER CALIFORNIA

PLATE 72.—*FOSSILS FROM THE UPPER CRETACEOUS OF CALIFORNIA AND LOWER CALIFORNIA*

Figure *Page*

1, 2, 3. *Exicrioceras diabloense* n. sp. Holotype and paratype (C. A. S. Type Coll.). (1, 2) Holotype. Greatest diameter of coil (loop), 39 mm. Views of obverse portions of holotype. Locality 21923 (C. A. S.), 1800 feet west and 2000 feet north of of SE corner sec. 19, T. 8 S., R. 8 E., M. D. B. M. (3) Paratype, natural size. Locality 29123 (C. A. S.), Pacheco Pass quadrangle; Moreno formation. 208

4. *Turrilites excelsus* n. sp. Holotype (C. A. S. Type Coll.). Reduced. Height, 72 mm. Locality 29123 (C. A. S.) = 28455 (C. A. S.), in the Moreno formation, three-quarters of a mile south of Garzas Creek, Stanislaus County; Moreno formation. 194

5. *Neocyrtochilus bryani* n. sp. Holotype (C. A. S. Type Coll.). Length of both limbs, 22 mm; width across both limbs, 4 mm. Locality 30553 (C. A. S.), in sec. 12, Los Banos Creek, Merced County, in the Moreno formation; Maestrichtian. 189

6. *Didymoceras californicum* n. sp. Holotype (C. A. S. Type Coll.). Entire length, 105 mm; height of spiral (incomplete), 55 mm; breadth of spiral, 57 mm. Locality 29664 (C. A. S.), NE ¼ NE ¼, sec. 30, T. 5 S., R. 7 E., M. D. B. and M., Orestimba quadrangle, on the south side of Puerto Creek, Stanislaus County, in the Moreno formation; Maestrichtian. 197

7. *Exiteloceras bennisoni* n. sp. Holotype (C. A. S. Type Coll.). Peripheral measure of the loop (approximately) 115 mm; transverse measure of loop, 75 mm. Found with the preceding, on the south side of Puerto Creek, Stanislaus County. 201

8. *Solenoceras mexicanum* n. sp. Holotype (C. A. S. Type Coll.). Length, 18.3 mm; width across both limbs approximately 8 mm. Locality 953 (C. A. S.), found about 9 miles north of Enseñada, Baja California. 211

9. *Crassatella mercedensis* n. sp. Holotype (C. A. S. Type Coll.). Length, 80 mm; height, 60 mm. Locality 29117 (C. A. S.) = 28310 (C. A. S.), on Los Banos Creek, Merced County. 129

FOSSILS FROM THE UPPER CRETACEOUS OF CALIFORNIA

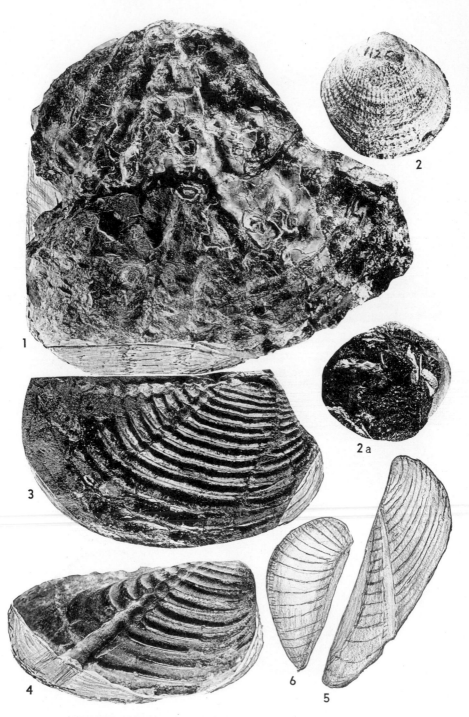

FOSSILS FROM THE UPPER CRETACEOUS OF CALIFORNIA

PLATE 75.—*FOSSILS FROM THE UPPER CRETACEOUS OF CALIFORNIA*

Figure *Page*

1, 1a. *Cucullaea* (*Idonearca*) *melhaseana* n. sp. Holotype and paratype (C. A. S. Type Coll.). (1) Paratype. Length (incomplete), 55 mm; height, 50 mm; (1a) Holotype. Length, 63 mm; height, 50 mm. Locality 27833 (C. A. S.), Shasta County; Turonian. 90

2. *Acteonina yrekensis* n. sp. Holotype (C. A. S. Type Coll.). Height, 47 mm; maximum width, 35 mm. Locality Hagerdon Ranch, 4 miles north of Montague, Siskiyou County, California; Turonian. 157

3, 3a. *Gosavia biconica* n. sp. Holotype (C. A. S. Type Coll.), (3) Holotype, slightly enlarged. Height, 43 mm; maximum breadth, 25 mm. (3a) Size × 1 1/5. Locality 1294A (C. A. S.), 4.6 miles north of bridge at Redding, Shasta County; Turonian. 175

4. *Turrilites petersoni* n. sp. Holotype (C. A. S. Type Coll.). Drawing of part of first lateral saddle of suture. Locality Peterson Ranch, 4 miles north of Sites, Colusa County, California; Cenomanian. *See* also Pl. 12, fig. 6. 193

FOSSILS FROM THE UPPER CRETACEOUS OF CALIFORNIA

INDEX